ATOLL ENVIRONMENT AND ECOLOGY

ATOLL ENVIRONMENT AND ECOLOGY

BY HEROLD J. WIENS

NEW HAVEN AND LONDON, YALE UNIVERSITY PRESS

Library of Congress catalog card number: 62-8266
International standard book number: 0-300-01044-3

*Distributed in Great Britain, Europe, and Africa by Yale University Press, Ltd.,
London; in Canada by McGill-Queen's University Press, Montreal; in Mexico
by Centro Interamericano de Libros Académicos, Mexico City; in Central and
South America by Kaiman & Polon, Inc., New York City; in Australasia by
Australia and New Zealand Book Co., Pty., Ltd., Artarmon, New South Wales; in
India by UBS Publishers' Distributors Pvt., Ltd., Delhi; in Japan by John
Weatherhill, Inc., Tokyo.*

*Published with assistance from the foundation established in memory of
Amasa Stone Mather of the Class of 1907, Yale College.*

*This volume is the result of research and field study conducted under the auspices
of the Pacific Science Board of the National Research Council under the United
States National Academy of Sciences and of the Geography Branch of the Office
of Naval Research, United States Department of the Navy. Reproduction in whole
or in part is permitted for any purpose of the United States Government.*

CONTENTS

v

LIST OF FIGURES

xi

LIST OF PLATES

(Following page 504)

All photographs not otherwise ascribed were taken by the author.

PREFACE

In 1953 I was informed by a colleague of an opportunity to join an expedition of natural scientists to make a field study the following summer of the east Caroline atoll of Kapingamarangi. Curiosity about an unfamiliar geographic realm led me to apply for the position of geographer to the expedition, and the charm of an unspoiled segment of primitive Polynesian civilization deepened the curiosity into a more serious interest. It was in this mood that I accepted the request of the Pacific Science Board in the following year to engage under its sponsorship in the long study that has culminated in the present book.

The Pacific Science Board, as a branch of the National Research Council of the National Academy of Sciences, had enlisted the interest and financial aid of the Geography Branch of the Office of Naval Research to make an effort to fill the gap in scientific knowledge about Pacific coral reefs and atolls. It had been evident that, although a great amount of field and theoretical work concerning atolls had been done, only a beginning had been made in describing the holistic ecology of the atoll. The best-studied aspect of atoll environment had been the geological one. A many-sided study of the physical and biological problems of atoll land, reef, and lagoon was needed prior to the nuclear bomb tests at Bikini and Eniwetok, to study the effects of such explosions and the accompanying radiation. This has brought rapid progress in atoll studies and the better understanding of atoll environment. The many expeditions sent out by the Pacific Science Board under the financial auspices of the Office of Naval Research of the United States Navy led to the publication in the *Atoll Research Bulletin* and other professional journals of a great number of special studies in geology and geography, oceanography, the marine and terrestrial biological sciences, and anthropology. Much scattered information of varied aspects of atoll environment and ecology appears in the writings of explorers, sea-farers, missionaries, and adventurers, but many of these data were un-assembled and uncorrelated.

The purpose of this project was to attempt to make the old data and the many new studies more readily available, understandable, related, and usable by compiling, analyzing, and synthesizing the great mass of data from the numerous sources into one volume that would be more than a hand-book and broader in scope than a research monograph. The volume was envisaged as a useful reference book for students and for administrators and naval personnel in the Pacific islands.

Some authorities on coral atolls no doubt feel, with F. R. Fosberg, that investigations in the special fields of atoll study have not been nearly thorough enough as yet to permit a comprehensive exposition of atoll ecology and that it is only possible at present to organize the available data and to formulate more clearly a great many of the outstanding problems. I agree with this position, but have tried to organize the available data, as far as my experience permitted, in an ecological framework, so as to present an approximation of the holistic view of atoll environment together with the interacting elements of its biota, including man. At times during the course of my six years of work on this study I have felt that, had I had greater knowledge of the subject of ecology initially, I might well have refused to consider the undertaking so blithely launched.

The early title of the project, "Man and Nature on Coral Atolls," although purposely broad to allow a wide latitude of approach, proved so audacious that the concept of human ecology on coral atolls was eliminated in favor of a brief last chapter devoted to that specific subject. However, man's part in atoll ecology inevitably crops up indirectly or directly in most of the rest of the book. On the other hand, a study of human ecology must involve the social sciences, which would demand a volume in itself. The present volume, thus, is largely limited to a dissection of the landscape and the physical and biological complex of the coral atoll in its tropical realm, with the view particularly to an understanding of the stage on which man operates and of his prospects in the future development of human life on atolls.

In a geographical study in which regional characteristics and distribu-tions are incompletely known, a certain bias is inevitable, because examples are likely to be drawn from the areas studied the most or the areas from which collections have been made. Many of the systematic studies have been made only recently and have emphasized a few individual atolls in the Marshalls, Carolines, Gilberts, or Tuamotus. On some atolls certain aspects have been intensively investigated; on other atolls different aspects may have received special attention. To generalize from such individual studies is rather risky; yet this must be done to a certain degree where the probability of correctness appears good, always keeping in mind that the data is highly localized. In other instances, generalizations cannot be made, but examples provide indications of probable or possible applications to other atoll areas. Owing to the high degree of uniformity of marine and atmospheric climates over much of the atoll realm valid conclusions concerning ecology may be arrived at more readily than in the more complex high-island and continental realms. But it must be kept in mind that peculiarities unique to certain atolls do occur. Obviously, considerable compromises with satisfactory procedures and data have had to be made.

The criteria used for inclusion in or exclusion from this study are in part subjective and in part set by the availability of data or of more competent analyses. Within the framework of the purpose defined, I have included what I felt I would want to know were I newly assigned to live and work on or to study and enjoy the coral atolls. A certain amount of familiar descriptive materials concerning atolls has been included, even though for some people these may be "old stuff." Since much of the material is derived from various issues of the Pacific Science Board's *Atoll Research Bulletin,* I have been liberal in quoting first-hand descriptions where direct quotation appeared more vivid than paraphrasing.

I am deeply indebted to the various specialists from whose studies and reports most of the data has been obtained and whose illustrative charts may have been copied or redrawn to serve this volume. For those who have been generous enough to communicate data personally in letters or to comment upon parts of the manuscript, I owe deep gratitude. My thanks go especially to Rhodes W. Fairbridge, Kenneth Emery, and Edwin Hamilton, who helpfully criticized certain sections on marine geology. I wish to thank F. R. Fosberg for his kindness in permitting me to use a large number of notes abstracted from miscellaneous sources by him or by M. H. Sachet.

A great many people in the U. S. Trust Territory of the Pacific Islands have been informative, helpful, and hospitable upon the three occasions of my field trips in the Marshalls and Carolines between 1954 and 1958. These include friends in the Trust Territory Administration and among the Micronesian and Polynesian residents of some twenty atolls and reef islands, as well as in the U. S. Navy. I hope that though unnamed they may understand my gratitude. I wish to acknowledge special indebtedness to Maynard Neas, the former Marshalls District Administrator, subsequently at Ponape, and his staff at Majuro, and Richard Umhoefer, formerly the District Representative at Kwajelein, and subsequently in the Ponape District Administration, and his wife Shirley.

The greatest debt of gratitude must go to the Pacific Science Board and to the Geography Branch of the United States Office of Naval Research, under whose auspices this whole project, as well as the long-term atoll research program, was conceived and financially supported. Specific thanks are due to Harold J. Coolidge and Mrs. Lenore Smith, Executive director and secretary, respectively, of the Pacific Science Board, Dr. Louis Quam and Miss Evelyn Pruitt, successively head of the Geography Branch of the Office of Naval Research, and their staffs for sympathetic support of the research and for their patience during the extended time required to complete the work.

Finally, I wish to acknowledge the debt to my wife Elizabeth, whose aid has hastened the completion of this work and who, during my absences in field work, has carried a disproportionate share of family burdens.

H. J. W.

New Haven, Conn.
June 15, 1961

CHAPTER 1

ATOLL DEFINITION AND THE ATOLL ENVIRONMENT

An atoll has been defined by Shepard (1948, p. 251) as an oval-shaped coral reef surrounding a lagoon in which there are no islands other than slightly emerged reefs or small sand cays (Plates 1 and 2). Although he was careful to preface this with the statement that the term "coral reef" has been applied to calcareous deposits in which coral may be an insignificant element or as one of many equally significant elements, the use of the adjective "oval-shaped" is misleading. Atolls may have a great variety of shapes to which the terms "oval," "ringlike," or "oblong" could by no means be applied, as will be shown in Chapter 3.

A better definition, given by Kuenen, was used by Newell and Rigby (1957, p. 21): Atolls include "all more or less continuous reefs surrounding a distinctly deeper lagoon with or without lagoon reefs . . . which rise from a sea bottom which is too deep for the growth of coral reefs. In this way we exclude reefs without a lagoon, raised coral islands which have no central depression." Moreover, as Newell and Rigby point out, atolls do not necessarily support islands, and they may be entirely submarine features, as in the case of numerous "banks" and "shoals" among the Caroline Islands.

These authors also point out that Kuenen's simple definition does not indicate all the more important characteristics common to atolls, such as the fact that the upper seaward slopes generally are much steeper than the angle of repose of loose sediments, a consequence of upward growth over a subsiding base. A simple but precise definition contains further difficulties, which concern the nature of the lagoon. Where to draw the line between the large body of water readily recognized as an atoll lagoon and the smaller ponds in a coral reef is a problem. Some atolls have more

1

than one lagoon. Some have numerous ponds or basins of various sizes separated by reefs and sand bars, so that the singular form of the term "a distinctly deeper lagoon" might appear to exclude them. Thus such atolls as Palmyra, Nanumea, Vaitupu, and Elato have two lagoons divided by a strip reef. These apparently are formed by reef growth rather than by sedimentation.

Washington Atoll has a lagoon proper on its southeast end with two

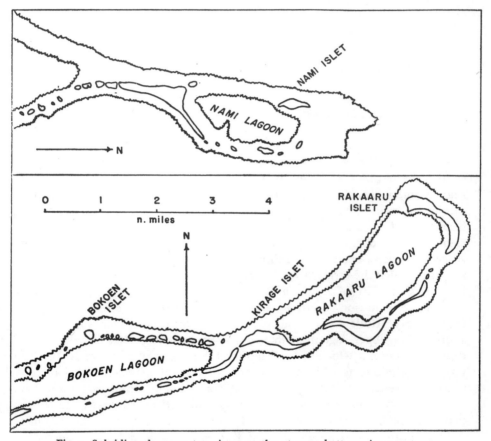

Fig. 1. Subsidiary lagoons: top, Arno northwest arm; bottom, Arno east arm.

separate depressions northeastward; these are bogs filled with sediments but once may have had deep water. Fanning Atoll has several lagoon basins and several depressions filled with sediments. An extreme case is Christmas Atoll, which has several dozen ponds or "lagoons" in various stages of filling by sediments. These ponds or lagoons may be regarded somewhat differently from the lagoons formed in the reef rim, such as the two examples each on Arno and Jaluit and the three on Mili (Figs. 1 to 3). Both types may

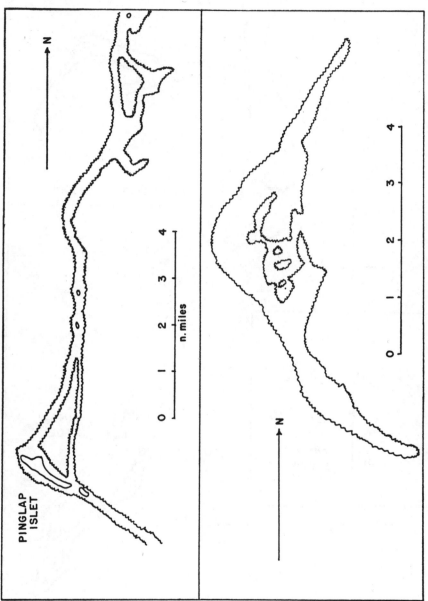

Fig. 2. Subsidiary lagoons: top, Jaluit west reef; bottom, Ngulu west reef.

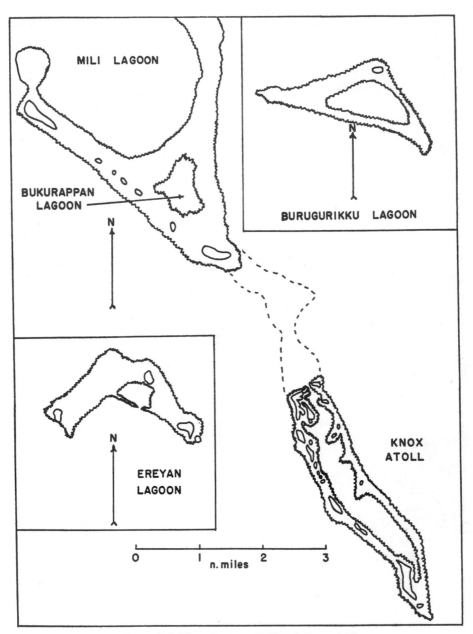

MILI LAGOON

BUKURAPPAN
LAGOON

N

BURUGURIKKU LAGOON

EREYAN
LAGOON

N

KNOX
ATOLL

0   1   2   3
n. miles

Fig. 3. Subsidiary lagoons: Mili and Knox Atolls.

be termed "secondary lagoons" (Plates 3 and 4). They are still different from what Davis (1928, p. 15) terms "lagoon atolls"—small annular reefs enclosing little lagoons within the larger lagoon.

An examination of the United States Hydrographic Office charts of secondary lagoons and comparison with small atolls show that size may not be used as a distinguishing characteristic of true atoll lagoons, inasmuch as the secondary lagoons along the rims of some reefs may be even larger than the main lagoons of other atolls. Table 1 gives the widest and longest

TABLE 1

Dimensions of Regular and Secondary Atoll Lagoons

Atolls	Regular or main lagoons	Secondary lagoons
Knox	0.5 by 3.3	
Elato:		
N lagoon	0.7 by 1.9	
S lagoon	0.5 by 1.2	
Toas	0.6 by 1.5	
Mokil:		
N lagoon	0.6 by 0.7	
S lagoon	0.3 by 1.0	
Pulusuk	0.3 by 0.4	
Mili:		
SE secondary lagoon		0.6 by 0.9
NE secondary lagoon		0.5 by 1.4
N secondary lagoon		0.3 by 0.6
Arno:		
E secondary lagoon		1.1 by 3.8
NW secondary lagoon		0.9 by 2.2
Ngulu		0.3 by 1.0
Jaluit, west reef:		
N secondary lagoon		0.6 by 1.3
S secondary lagoon		0.6 by 2.5
Nukuoro pass area:		
Secondary lagoon		70 by 100 (yards)

dimensions of some "regular" atoll lagoons and those of some secondary lagoons (see also Figs. 1 to 4). Distances are in nautical miles, except for the Nukuoro example.

Knox and Toas Atolls are not listed in Bryan's check list of atolls (1953), although the sailing directions for the Pacific Islands (U. S. Navy, 1952) designate them as separate atolls. Each has all the characteristics associated with an atoll: a calcareous reef standing by itself enclosing a lagoon, with vegetated islets scattered along the enclosing reef. However, each is close to a larger atoll—in the case of Knox (Fig. 3) a very much larger one, and Knox has been relegated to the position of an appendage of the larger Mili. Knox is less than 2.1 nautical miles from the southeast extension of Mili, to which it is connected by a submerged reef with a depth of only 20 feet. On the other hand, Knox Lagoon is much larger than the lagoon of Mokil, a small isolated atoll in the eastern Carolines (Fig. 4).

From another point of view, Knox Lagoon might well be considered a secondary lagoon of Mili Atoll, corresponding to the secondary lagoon in the southeastern corner of Mili southeast of Lukunor Islet. This lagoon, which here is named Bukurappan Lagoon, after the name of the nearest islet in that sector of Mili (Fig. 3), is wider than that of Knox, although it is only one-third as long. A similar secondary lagoon at the northeastern end of Mili is somewhat larger, and here is named Burugurikku Lagoon, after the nearest islet. Both Bukurappan and Burugurikku are completely without passage to the larger lagoon of Mili or to the ocean. In the central part of the northern reef of Mili, however, is still another enclosed body of water, Ereyan Lagoon, named after the adjacent islet.

Toas Atoll (Fig. 4) occupies the same position with respect to Elato Atoll that Knox does to Mili, except that the former two are of more equal size. Toas is only about a mile from Elato, and the two generally have been designated the Elato Islands. The maximum depth in the reef connection between the two atolls is about 70 feet. Elato itself is divided into two separate lagoons, apparently because of reef growth across the narrow channel that once connected the two lagoons.

Arno offers several interesting secondary-lagoon phenomena. These occur also at narrow extremities. In one instance, the connection with the main lagoon remains but appears to be growing closed slowly. In the other two instances, the secondary lagoons have been completely cut off by reef growth. In the extreme eastern arm of Arno is a large secondary lagoon here named Rakaaru Lagoon, after the islet at its eastern end (Fig. 1). It is 1.1 nautical miles wide and 3.8 nautical miles long, more than twice the size of the two lagoons of Mokil Atoll. Owing to the existence of Kirage Islet on the narrow reef connection between this secondary lagoon and Arno's main lagoon farther westward, and the narrowness of the solid reef here, the writer is doubtful that this was ever connected to the main lagoon by a lagoon channel. West of Kirage Islet, however, is another lagoon of slightly smaller size but with a channel ⅓ nautical mile wide leading to the main lagoon. However, the channel floor here is at least 24 feet shallower than the floor of the secondary lagoon opposite Bokoen Islet east of it and

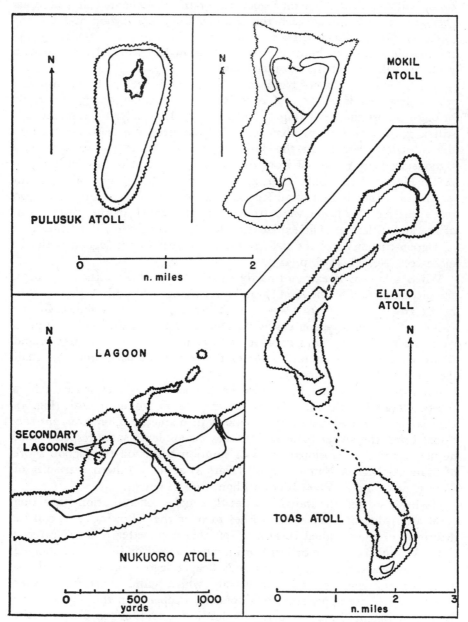

Fig. 4. A variety of small atolls and small lagoons.

even shallower than the main lagoon westward. The channel thus occupies the position of a sill between the basin of the main lagoon and the secondary basin of Bokoen Lagoon. Since this sill is only about 108 feet deep, it is within the depth limits of active reef growth. Ultimately, this growth probably will seal off the secondary lagoon.

In the western sectors of Ngulu and Jaluit Atolls are two other instances where sharp bends of the reef have led to their enclosure by reef spurs bridging across the bend (Fig. 2 and Plate 3). In the Ngulu case there is still a gap in the bridge, which forms a pass from the main lagoon into the secondary lagoon. In the Jaluit west reef, however, two secondary lagoons are fully closed off from the main lagoon east of it. The one opposite Pinglap Islet results from an outward reef bend. The other, about 5 miles to the north, near small Rua Islet, appears to have resulted from two reef spurs growing lagoonward from a straight stretch of the western rim of the atoll (Plate 3). The explanation for this may lie in the peculiarities of lagoon currents and the fusion of a patch reef in the lagoon with the main reef (Newell, 1956, p. 353).

When a lagoon is extraordinarily small compared with the land area, the picture evoked by the term "atoll" must change. Pulusuk Atoll, reported by Bryan (1953, p. 16) to be without a lagoon, actually is shown by the HO chart to have a lagoon 0.3 by 0.4 nautical miles in size (Fig. 4), but in comparison with the land area, it appears like a lake in a large island (Plate 2). Land area occupies most of the reef at Pulusuk, and the small lagoon is at the northern end.

Finally, one comes to the smaller pools enclosed by reef strips such as the two located in the reef adjacent to the pass at Nukuoro Atoll (Fig. 4). One is about 70 and the other 100 yards in diameter. They are constructional forms the writer believes, but they resemble in some respects what he has regarded as erosional forms or solution basins off the lagoon shore of Matamat Islet of Namorik Atoll (Plate 4) at the southern extremity of Taongi Atoll and off Ebon Islet on Ebon Atoll (Plate 5).

Having discussed the individualities that make generalization respecting coral atolls difficult, the writer wishes to offer the following as a concise definition of the so-called coral atoll or, to use a better term, calcareous atoll. An atoll is a more or less continuous emerged or slightly submerged calcareous reef surrounding a distinctly deeper lagoon or several such lagoons without emerged volcanic islands, which stand apart from other islands, and whose upper seaward slopes rise steeper than the repose angle of loose sediments from a generally volcanic foundation too deep for the growth of reef corals. As will be seen from the subsequent discussions, even this inclusive definition does not summarize all the distinguishing characteristics of calcareous atolls, although this probably excludes all those islands which are not considered to be atolls and includes all those that may be accepted as atolls.

Although the writer has avoided using the term *coral* in his definition of *atolls,* traditional usage has established such a strong link between the two terms that he will continue to use "coral" in this report, but with the reminder, in the words of Ekman (1953, p. 4), that "The big reefs are, however, not always mainly formed by corals. In many places, coralline algae of the genera Lithothamnion, Halimeda, and others are quantitatively as important or even more important, while the Foraminifera, too, often predominate quantitatively. Limestone reefs, where no corals at all are found, also exist. In such cases, the name 'coral reef' is misleading." [1] Possibly in the latter instance, Ekman was referring to Bahamian platforms with raised rims of lithified calcium carbonate sand dunes and beach ridges, which, nevertheless, Newell and Rigby (1957, pp. 21–2) contend are true coral atoll platforms blanketed by a thin veneer of oölitic limestone. In any event, in the Pacific atolls corals are one of the important and most colorful constituents of atoll reefs (Plates 46 to 50).

Location of coral reefs and atolls

Although reef corals are generally associated with "coral" atolls, it must not be assumed that coral reefs are conterminous with atolls. The distribution of the former is a function of marine climate, whereas the occurrence of the latter depends both on marine climate and on the geologic history and character of the ocean floor.

Coral reefs have long been associated with the tropics. Ekman (1953, p. 4) wrote that "On the whole, reefs are so characteristic of the tropics that the northern and southern extremes of their occurrence may be regarded as constituting the boundaries of the tropical zone. . . ." This is not wholly exact, however, unless the definition of the tropics is altered to conform with the geographic distribution of marine water with certain minimum temperature characteristics. Reef corals are found as far north as Nojima Cape on the Japanese coast at 35°N latitude near the mouth of Tokyo Bay, owing to the northward projection of the warm Kuroshio, or Japan Current. It is found as far south as 32°S latitude in the vicinity of Durban in the Union of South Africa, owing to the southward penetration of the

1. In a personal letter to the writer, Edwin Hamilton pointed out that Lithothamnion is incorrectly stated to be the modern abundant calcareous algae of the Pacific reefs, but that Porolithon is really the correct generic name. Lithothamnion is listed by J. H. Johnston as one of the common calcareous algae during the Eocene period but is not listed by him among the common modern reef builders. However, owing to the widespread use of the term by various writers concerning coral reefs, the present writer will not alter statements by other writers concerning Lithothamnion in the following discussion.

warm Mozambique Current. Both are subtropical rather than tropical regions. The reef corals here, although of the same species as those in the atoll realm, do not develop large formations, for these areas represent marginal conditions for their growth. Reef coral distribution in the Indo-Pacific region is shown in Fig. 75. Except for the Caribbean area, coralliferous reefs show only a limited development in the Atlantic. The Pacific ocean and its adjoining Asian seas form the principal development realm, followed by that in the Indian Ocean and its subsidiary basins, the Red Sea, the Persian Gulf, and the Bay of Bengal. A very limited development is found in the eastern Pacific fringe.

This characteristic tropical and exceptional subtropical distribution of reef corals is related to marine isotherms of the surface waters of the oceans and seas. Since the upper limit of temperature endurance of corals is rarely reached in the marine environment except on very shallow flats, where semistagnant water may warm up to between 33 and 38°C. in the sun, the chief thermal limit in their marine distribution is the lower limit of temperature. Vaughan (1917, p. 205) found that "Vigorous reefs will endure a temperature as low as 18.15°C. . . . It is not probable that a reef could withstand a continuous temperature so low as this. Wherever the depth of water is great enough to lower the bottom temperature below 18.15°C., more probably about 22°C., reef corals will not live."

Vaughan also pointed out (1917, pp. 220–1) that it is "a well-known oceanographic fact . . . that the waters along the western shores of continents are colder than those on the eastern sides . . . Reef corals are weakly developed on the Pacific side of Central America and Mexico and on the Atlantic coast of Africa . . . Pacific corals appear to grow more rapidly than those in the Gulf of Mexico and the West Indies . . . on a segment of a rich reef in the Indo-Pacific there are about twice as many, or a few more than twice as many, species as there are on a similar segment of a West Indian or Floridian reef. . . ." The lower temperatures of the eastern oceanic areas are caused by an upwelling of cold water from the oceanic depths in these regions.

The biological requirements of the reef-building organisms involve the presence of warm, relatively shallow, clear, saline water. Differences in salinity in different parts of the ocean, away from the mouths of great rivers, however, are not sufficient to affect the life of corals. A reduction of marine salinity to about 80 per cent of its present salinity apparently would not hurt corals (Vaughan, 1917, p. 206). Thus the geographical distribution of reef corals over the ocean surface is not affected by salinity factors except near great river mouths, although in the tropics the surface concentration of sea salts is somewhat greater than it is at considerable depths and somewhat greater than that at the surface in higher latitudes. [In terms of geological time, according to Vaughan, the ocean is becoming more salt, and it appears that marine organisms are now living in an environment considerably below the optimum condition for their existence (*The New York Times,* 1958a). This situation is significant in the consideration of the past geological history of reefs.]

The effect of large rivers in inhibiting coral reef growths not only results from the dilution of saline water with fresh water but also as a result of the turbidity from suspended sediments, which cut down the amount of light that penetrates into the water. Reef corals require abundant light for the photosynthesis of the symbiotic algae that live in their ectoderm and that appear to contribute to their healthy growth. The sediment settling upon the coral animals also adversely affects their growth and may kill them, either because the animals are directly harmed by asphyxiation (Vaughan, 1917, p. 205) or because light is cut off from their symbiotic algae. However, many corals have a remarkable ability to clean silt off their surfaces. Kuenen (1950, p. 419) points out that "Where corals are absent in somewhat turbid waters the cause often lies not so much in the suspended silt as in the absence of a suitable foundation on the muddy sea floor." Kuenen attributes the scarcity of coral reefs and islands in the wide expanse of the Sunda Shelf of Southeast Asia to the muddy sea floor and the inability of corals to grow up the first few meters from this poor foundation. Coral reefs that are found in this region probably gained a foothold on some topographical eminence that was swept clean of silt by submarine currents. Moreover, when reefs such as those in the Bay of Batavia began to grow, it is possible that the coastline of Java with its silty rivers had not advanced as far as its present position, so that the bottom conditions may have been less unfavorable at that time.

Since light and temperature decrease with increasing depths in the ocean, reef-building corals also require relatively shallow waters in which to grow. According to Vaughan (1917) the available evidence shows that a depth between 120 and 150 feet is the maximum at which a true coral reef will form. Emery, Tracey, and Ladd (1954, p. 134) cited Vaughan and others in concluding that while most reef building takes place in depths of 90 feet or less, some hermatypic (reef-building) corals reach depths of 50 fathoms, although recent collections at Bikini showing the vertical distribution of coral species suggest that "In some localities the lower limit for living reef-type corals may extend to as much as 85 fathoms or 510 feet, although at these depths such corals are insignificant contributors to the atoll." There are corals which are not reef builders that grow at much greater depths and even in the abyssal depths of the ocean floor. Aside from the light factor, governed by the depth and clearness of the water, it has been found (Vaughan, 1917, p. 205) that a temperature of about 22.8°C. is the boundary between reef-forming corals and deep-water corals.

Because corals form only one constituent of coral reefs and sometimes a minor one, however, we must examine also the depth limits for other important reef builders. An interesting summation of various evidences and conclusions by different scientists is given by Emery, Tracey, and Ladd (1954, pp. 134–5). Evidence from the Funafuti studies indicated that one form of coralline algae flourished on the outer slopes of Funafuti Atoll down to 1,200-foot depths, whereas Halimeda "invariably was found alive down to depths of 45 fathoms and in a single instance was found alive at a depth of 80 fathoms." Gardiner is cited as stating that "Lithothamnion [Porolithon] [Plates 42, 44, and 45] is an important builder of shoals in the tropics down to depths of 60 fathoms and that Halimeda can exist to 60 fathoms but that vigorous growth is not found below 40 fathoms."

From these and other cited records, Emery, Tracey, and Ladd concluded that "Light effectively controls the distribution of reef corals but that this control is much less effective as regards certain of the reef-type algae. Under proper conditions algae and large Foraminifera might extend the limit of reef growth downward for several hundred feet, building a foundation upon which corals could become established. This apparently has happened in Fiji where on many islands elevated coral reefs rest upon bedded rocks composed largely of algae and Foraminifera."

The limitation of deep water upon coral reef and atoll construction leads directly to the question of the nature of the submarine topography in the deep areas of the open ocean that permit atolls and reefs to develop. This requires a brief review of the geology of the central and western Pacific, where most of the Pacific atolls are situated.

Geology and submarine topography of the Pacific

According to Shepard (1948, p. 316), the origin of the Pacific and other ocean basins cannot be considered to be any more settled than is the origin of the earth. The Pacific is the world's largest body of water, covering an area of some 165,246,000 square kilometers, or about 63.8 million square miles, twice the area of the Atlantic, although it gets the drainage of only a little more than one-fourth of the land surface draining into the Atlantic. Its greatest breadth, about 17,200 kilometers, or 10,492 miles, is between Panama and Mindanao in the Philippines. The distance from the Bering Strait in the north to the shores of Antarctica in the south is some 15,500 kilometers, or 9,455 miles.

Depths in the great basins of the central Pacific commonly are greater than 5,000 meters, or 16,400 feet, but rarely exceed 7,000 meters, or about 23,000 feet. However, in the smaller elongated trenches located near and parallel to the continental coasts, depths often exceed 8,000 meters, or 26,000 feet. Soundings of over 10,000 meters, or 33,000 feet, have been made in at least three trenches—the Japan, the Mindanao, and the Mariana—in the last of which a depth of 35,400 feet, the deepest sounding to date, has been recorded.

Structurally, the Pacific may be conveniently divided into three provinces (Cumberland, 1956, pp. 4–8): (1) the narrow eastern rim, bordered by high chains of young fold mountains the length of North and South America; (2) the central Pacific proper, the largest and most stable structural unit of the earth's surface, in which there are only islands so small that they are lost in the immensity of the vast waters; and (3) the broad western margins, a complicated region in which arcs of andesitic volcanic island chains enclosing deep marine basins are bordered on their outward sides by huge, deep trenches such as the one mentioned above. Although all three provinces have volcanic chains rising from the sea floor, or from the continental rims, the andesitic (acid) and in places sedimentary rocks of the western margins are highly unstable areas tectonically. By contrast with the eastern rim, the boundary between the western margin and the central Pacific provinces is not close to the adjacent continent but runs hundreds of miles seaward. The so-called andesitic line follows southward the arcs of the Aleutian, Kurile, Bonin, Mariana, and Palau Islands, all volcanic chains, and then turns sharply southeastward to the Fiji Islands where it makes another sharp bend southwestward to include New Zealand within the andesitic realm.

The volcanic islands of the central Pacific province lack the andesitic and sedimentary rocks of the western margins, but instead derive from lava outpourings of dark basalt. Except for the Hawaiian Islands and a few isolated localities in the open spaces of the eastern south Pacific and areas near the continents, heavy earthquakes are unknown in the central Pacific province. However, although tectonic activity of the ocean floor has long been denied (Kuenen, 1950, p. 476), "Now that the great topographic irregularity of the sea bottom has been proved, it has become probable that folding and block faulting are as active on ocean floors as on the continents," and subsidence in parts of the atoll realm may reasonably be postulated.

Schott (1935, p. 74) has pointed out a number of interesting and noteworthy singularities of the island chains in the central Pacific province graphically shown in Plate III of his excellent book *Geographie des Indischen und Stillen Ozeans*. In the first place, even in the huge central and eastern ocean basins, which are little articulated by relief features, the island chains, including the Hawaiian, reproduced the alignments of the western mountain chains of North and South America. And this occurs in spite of the fact that the individual islands of each group usually are separated from each other by the great depths of 6,000 to 10,000 feet. Second, the northerly Marshall Islands and the double row of the Caroline Islands have an almost east-west orientation turning to meet the north-south line running from the Palaus and Yap to the Marianas and Bonins, which appears to represent an oceanic forerunner of the East Asiatic folds.

A third interesting singularity pointed out by Schott is that the great elbow formed by the andesitic line around the Fijis repeats the general curve of the Gulf of Panama on the distant Central American shores opposite. By these hypothetical remarks, Schott wished to indicate that the "pure" oceanic islands of the deep Pacific probably have some sort of tectonic kinship to the great continents. This, he said, must lead to the conclusion that while the deep sea floor need not belong to the sima of the earth's crust, nevertheless it does not differ basically in structure from the rocky content of the firm land mass.

Although none of the Pacific submarine ranges or folds compare in length with the Atlantic Ridge, they are major underwater topographic features. The Hawaiian Islands are the peaks of a 1,600-mile-long ridge (Hamilton, 1957, p. 1012). The Gilberts and Marshalls stand on a similar long ridge. The Fanning Ridge, on which stand such atolls as Palmyra, Fanning, Christmas, and Washington, extends from the equator almost to the middle of the Hawaiian Ridge. The Carolines run on still another ridge about a thousand miles long. In the eastern Pacific, a broad plateau connects the coast of South America with the Tuamotu Atolls. In addition to these ranges there are occasional individual eminences, such as that on which Wake Island is built, and clusters of volcanic peaks, such as that on which the Phoenix Islands are built. Deeply submerged individual sea-mounts (averaging 700 fathoms) occur in the vicinity of the northern Marshalls and throughout much of the southwestern Pacific (Hess, 1946). Many of them appear to have rather level tops at similar depths, as though some agent such as sea waves had beveled them to miniature plateaus of equal elevation.

Carson (1951, p. 70) has described the submarine mountains of the oceans as "earth's nearest approach to the eternal hills of the poets." In contrast to continental mountains, which all the forces of nature conspire to cut down and level as soon as they are thrust up, the mountains of the deep sea are beyond the reach of ordinary erosive forces. Because of this "virtual immortality," the oldest oceanic mountains must be infinitely older than any of the ranges left on land, and some may be of pre-Cambrian origin.

From the preceding descriptions of the submarine topography of the central Pacific basin, it is clear that the ocean floor is by no means a relatively smooth expanse of sediment-covered rocks, but in large tectonic terms is rough and wrinkled like the surface of continents. However, very few of the submarine mountains thrust their peaks above sea level to form "high" volcanic mountains. Many of the so-called "high islands," such as Kusae and Ponape in the Carolines, reach only one or two thousand feet above sea level. The use of the term "high islands" in this study need not signify great altitudes, but merely distinguishes those islands that rise above the level of the "low islands," which are the coral reef islands, limited to elevations generally under 15 to 20 feet, although sand dunes on a few low reef islands may rise 5 to 10 feet higher.

In this Pacific realm and within the limits of reef-building corals, most volcanic islands are fringed by coral reefs. One prominent exception, however, are the Marquesas Islands, which, although in the same general location as such coral-fringed islands as the Societies and such atolls as the Tuamotus, nevertheless have no reefs growing around them. The reason for this is not clear. Near the equator far to the east of them are the Galápagos Islands, also free of reef fringes. In the latter situation the explanation is simple, since the Galápagos lie in the zone of upwelling cold water from the abyssal depths. Indeed, in this eastern part of the Pacific, the north-south limits of the zone of reef coral growth become restricted to about one-third of the latitudinal stretch of the reef coral zone in the western Pacific. It may be that at intervals, tongues of this cold water drift as far west as the Marquesas and have prevented reef development (Schott, 1935, p. 309), although available records do not indicate the presence of cold water this far west. Then again, other factors presently unknown may inhibit coral reef growth on the rocks of the Marquesas coasts. Davis (1928, p. 204) stated that "The almost complete absence of coral reefs is ascribed to the restricted number of genera of corals living there and is therefore looked upon as having an ecological rather than a geological significance; but to this it may be added that the restriction in the number of coral genera is probably of geological significance, as a consequence of the temperature of the Post-glacial epoch."

Although high and low islands have been found to be associated with volcanic and coral reef forms, respectively, some further distinctions should be presented. Cumberland (1956, pp. 8–12) describes and illustrates six types of islands in the Pacific partly or completely associated with coral reefs (Figs. 5 and 6). The first is the high volcanic island surrounded by a fringing reef, as in the case of Rarotonga (Fig. 6). In this type there is no associated lagoon. Some high volcanic islands may be partly fringed by coral reefs, with other parts forming a barrier reef. Where volcanic islands are surrounded by a lagoon enclosed by a barrier reef some distance off shore, it is called an "almost-atoll." Truk and Uvea (Fig. 6) are examples of this type. The origin of this type of structure is related to the origin of atolls in which no volcanic islands appear in the lagoon enclosed by the coral reef.

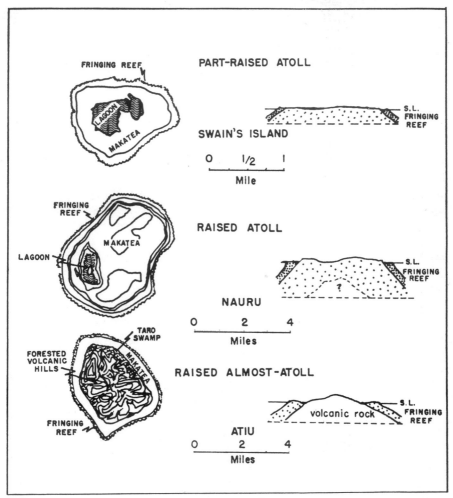

Fig. 5. Top views and cross sections of three types of atolls. [From Cumberland (1956).]

Among the raised islands, Cumberland has listed three types: (1) the partly raised atoll, as in the case of Olosenga (Swain's Island; Fig. 5), where a considerable lagoon is surrounded by a raised reef rim; (2) the raised atoll, in which the former lagoon floor is merely a depressed part of the

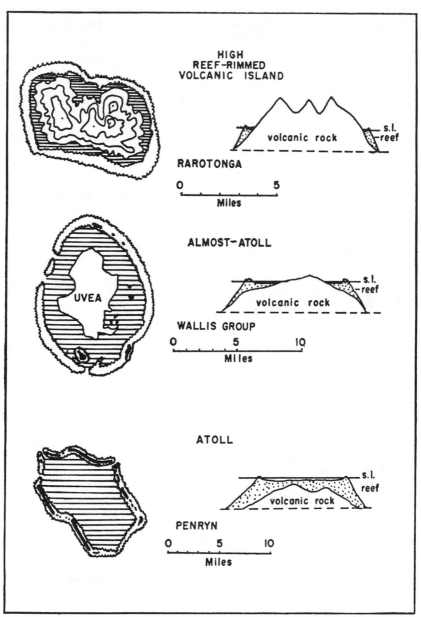

HIGH
REEF-RIMMED
VOLCANIC ISLAND

volcanic rock

s.l.
reef

RAROTONGA

0   5
Miles

ALMOST-ATOLL

UVEA

s.l.
reef

volcanic rock

WALLIS GROUP

0   5   10
Miles

ATOLL

s.l.
reef

volcanic rock

PENRYN

0   5   10
Miles

Fig. 6. Top views and cross sections of three types of atolls. [From Cumberland (1956).]

land surrounded by a high rim; and (3) the raised "almost-atoll," where a volcanic island is surrounded by a depressed fringe of sedimentary land, in turn surrounded by an elevated limestone reef. Still a seventh type of island might be added to these six—the elevated volcanic island fringed by elevated reef rock without a depressed zone of sediments between.

In all the instances of raised islands in the coral reef zone, the raised reef becomes severely eroded with long exposure because of the solubility of the limestone to the fresh water from rainfall. Their surfaces become rough, jagged, and full of pinnacles and solution holes, and the limestone becomes cavernous and porous. This land form is termed "makatea" in Polynesian; this word refers also to an island of this character in the Tuamotu group. According to Yabe and Tayama (1937, pp. 50–2), the geographical distribution of atolls in the South Seas is by no means uniform and on the contrary seems to be subject to certain external regulation, probably of tectonic origin. Thus no atoll exists in either the northern or southern Mariana groups, where elevated and terraced islands are found. Of five atolls in the Palau Islands, the southernmost is elevated and the northernmost is submerged as if the foundations of the group were tilted. Third, no elevated atolls are found in the Carolines, which has 15 sea-level and 10 submerged atolls in the west and 17 sea-level atolls in the east, thus indicating a greater apparent submersion of the land in the western part. In the Marshalls all the atolls are of the sea-level type.

Although the coral reef problem, as Davis terms it in his exhaustive study (1928), covers the origin and development of all these types of Pacific islands associated with reef growth, no attempt will be made here to review all aspects of this. The next chapter will outline briefly the present state of the theories only as they apply to atoll formation. This, nevertheless, must still touch upon associated problems of fringing reefs and barrier reefs. Interested persons are referred to Davis' study and the very extensive bibliography provided by him. For more recent additions to the literature, see the bibliography of Emery, Tracey, and Ladd (1954).

CHAPTER 2

THE GEOGRAPHY OF THE PHYSICAL
CHARACTERISTICS OF ATOLLS

In this chapter the primary purpose is to show geographical distribution patterns rather than to explain the processes and conditions that produce them. The explanations are attempted in subsequent chapters and sections. Tables 2 to 5 provide statistics on the individual atolls in the Marshalls and Carolines.

Atoll shape

In considering the physical characteristics of atolls, one of the most obvious aspects noted is the shape or outline of an atoll reef. A study of a number of atoll charts quickly dispels any notion of a uniformity of shapes. As Davis conservatively stated it, "Most atolls depart rather freely from the ideal oval or circular outline in which they have often been figured" (Davis, 1928, p. 512). Atoll shapes cannot be correlated with particular factors that allow for generalization, except to say that each has its own peculiar shape and, no doubt, reflects the individual submarine contours of its foundation.

Every imaginable shape can be found (see Fig. 7) and, with imagination, one can describe their shapes uniquely and individually. It is true, of course, that many, especially among the smaller atolls, are more or less round or oblong. Ebon in the Marshalls is shaped like a circle. Nukuoro in the Carolines is a slightly squeezed circle. Kapingamarangi is more oval (Plate 6). Nomwin is like a pear; Lukunor and Ngaruangle are ham-shaped; and Namonuito, Etal, and Namoluk rather triangular. Ujae re-

TABLE 2

Data on Reefs and Passes in the Western Carolines

Western Carolines	Reef patch in channel-mouth facing	Reef width		Pass location								Dimensions		
		Widest	Narrowest	N	E	S	W	NE	NW	SE	SW	Length	Width	Max. lagoon depth, ft.
West Fayu	SE 1	N	S									3.8	1.2	138
Lamotrek		N	SW									8	3.3	174
Elato		Bends				3						6	1.8	100 (double atoll)
Olimarao		W	S, NW			3						2.6	1.5	102
Faraulep	SW 3										3	2.3	1.2	70
Ifalik	S 1	End				1						2.1	1.6	66
Woleai		W, Bends				2				3	1	6	3.2	174
Eauripik		Bends				(Broken)						4.6	1	?
Sorol		Ends	SW								1	6.5	1.5	150
Ulithi	SW 2, NW 1	N, NW	SW, E	1		1	3		2	4	5	19	10	210
Ngulu	SW 2	Bends				2	1			1	7	18.7	11.5	252
Ngaruangle		N end										3.8	1.8	18
Kayangel		NW	SW									4	2	32
Helen	W 1	NE	W				1					14	5.5	198
Zohhoiiyoru												12	3	180
Mapia		N, W	S									8.6	3.8	?
				3	5	5	5	1	2	8	17			

TABLE 3

Data on Reefs and Passes in the Eastern Carolines

Eastern Carolines	Reef patch in channel-mouth facing	Reef width		Pass location								Dimensions		
		Widest	Narrowest	N	E	S	W	NE	NW	SE	SW	Length	Width	Max. lagoon depth, ft.
Pingelap		N, NW, S	SW									2.3	1.3	162
Mokil		S, N	W									2.3	.9	198
Ant	SE 1	W, N								1		7	4	210
Pakin		E, NE	SW								1	5	2	180
Ngatik	SE 1	NW								1		12.5	5	(492) ?
Oroluk	NW 1, SW 2	Bends				4	1		1	1	8	18	14	246
Murillo	S 1	W				1			3		2	19.2	9.5	168
							(Broken reef)							
Nomwin	SW 1	NW, SW	SE			2		1	4		3	13	11.5	148
Pulap												6	2.8	132
Puluwat		Ends, corners								1		2.6	1.2	36
Namonuito				(Everywhere around rim)								45	27	228
Kuop	SE 1, SW 2								1	1	3	11.5	3.5	174
Namoluk	?	N	SW									3.2	2	252
Losap		S	N			5				1		5.6	3.3	?
Etal		NW, E	SW									4.5	2.4	?
Satawan	N 1, SW 1	W, SW	E	1							1	17.4	7.8	216
Lukunor	S 1	W, N, NE	S			1						7.7	1.8	204
Nukuoro	SE 1	NE								1		4.2	3.2	354
Kapinga	SW 1	W, N	SW								1	7	5.5	258
				1		6	8	1	6	11	19			

TABLE 4

Data on Reefs and Passes in the Eastern Marshalls Chain

Ralik, or west chain	Reef patch in channel-mouth facing	Reef width		Pass location								Dimensions		
		Widest	Narrowest	N	E	S	W	NE	NW	SE	SW	Length	Width	Max. lagoon depth, ft.
Eniwetok	E 1	NW	SW, SE			1				1	1	22	18	228
Bikini		NW	E, S							2	6	23.5	13.8	192
Rongelap	W 1	N	S, E, W	1					1	3	4	36.5	20	204
Rongerik		Corners						1		1	1	9.2	8.5	168
Ailinginae	SW 2	Ends and bends	N								2	14.5	4.5	102
Wotho	SW 1	E	NW				2				1	11.5	5.8	?
Ujelang	SW 3	NE	SW								3	12.5	3	156
Ujae	SW 1	Ends					1				1	22.5	5.7	?
Kwajalein	SW 4, N 1	NE, bends	SE, SW	3	4				4		9	66	15	198
Lae		N, E, bends	S								1	4	2.7	216
Namu	W 3	Bends					3					31.5	6.3	144
Ailinglaplap	NW 3, SW 1	NW	E, SE						4	2	1	30	15	180
Jaluit	NE 1, SE, SW 1	NW						1		1	1	31	18	162
Namorik	W	W	N, SE									4	2.7	?
Ebon	SW 1	SW	E, SE								1	7.5	6.8	108
				4	4	1	6	2	9	10	32			

TABLE 5

Data on Reefs and Passes in the Eastern Marshalls Chain

Ratak, or eastern chain	Reef patch in channel-mouth facing	Reef width		Pass location								Dimensions		
		Widest	Narrowest	N	E	S	W	NE	NW	SE	SW	Length	Width	Max. lagoon depth, ft.
Taongi		E	W	1			1					10.2	4.2	48
Bikar	W 1	N, NE	W	1			1					6.8	3.5	72
Utirik		N, NE									1	8.7	5	162
Taka	W 1	N	W				1				2	9	8	156
Ailuk	W 1	NE, E	S, SW				3					15.5	9.2	180
Likiep	S 1, W 1	N, NW						5	5			24.8	8.7	174
Wotje	SE 2, SW 1	NE, NW, SE	SW							3	2	28	12	214
Erikub	W 3	Bends			1						3	15.6	5.5	128
Maloelap	SW 7	NE	W								7	32.1	14.5	264
Aur	NW 1	SE, S	SW, NE						4		1	16.5	10.7	288
Majuro	NE 1	W, SW	SE			1				1		22	6.3	198
Arno	NW 2, NE 3	W, NW	SE, N					2		2		23 (15)	9.7	204
Mili	NW 2, NE 3, SW 1	W, SW, SE	E			1		3	1	1	1	28	11	210
				1	2	6	6	6	10	8	17			

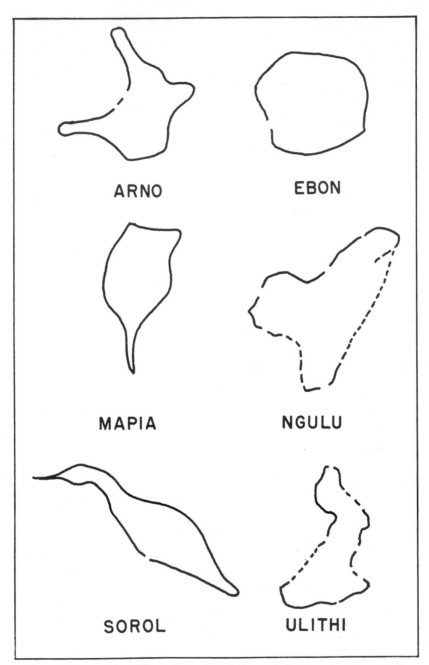

ARNO

EBON

MAPIA

NGULU

SOROL

ULITHI

Fig. 7. Six examples of the variety of atoll shapes (relative scales disregarded).

sembles a stretched-out diamond, Taongi a crescent moon, Sorol looks like the outline of a heron, and West Fayu like a headless goose without legs.

Some atolls are so irregular that their shapes are hard to describe. Many are roughly rectangular or square. Some have long reef extensions enclosing secondary lagoons, as in the case of Arno.

These extreme individualities greatly complicate the attempt to fix location and orientation in common terms in the explanation of reef features and reduce the reliability of generalizations based upon location terms for quadrant or sectors of an atoll reef rim. Were all atolls somewhat ringlike or oblong or square, it would be more meaningful to divide an atoll into four quarters by two north-south and east-west lines meeting in the approximate center. Then, when one used the term "southwestern sector," one could be reasonably sure that the reef rim there would be generally aligned northwest to southeast, and that a "northeastern sector" would be exposed to the prevailing winds and currents in large part. However, irregularity of shape often makes parts of a southwestern sector of an atoll reef partially exposed to prevailing winds and currents and may make parts of a northeastern sector completely protected from wind and current effects. In describing the occurrence of deep passes across the atoll rim, for instance, these irregularities may make an important difference, owing to exposure to or protection from wind and wave effects. A sharp bend or elbow in the otherwise exposed northeastern or southeastern sectors of a reef may mark the disappearance of the groove-and-surge erosion feature common to exposed reef edges on the windward and seaward side.

It is obvious, therefore, that while differences in shapes make for difficult generalizations in the descriptions of atoll characteristics, the shape of an atoll is highly significant as related to reef characteristics along various parts of the atoll rim.

As to the factors contributing to the shapes of atolls, perhaps the most one can say is that they are largely the result of the outer contours of the basement foundation of the atoll, whether this foundation be a single volcanic cone or a cluster of such cones whose individualities have become concealed by the calcareous caps surmounting them. Fairbridge (1950) has attributed many of the irregular shapes of atolls to submarine volcanic or calcareous sedimentary landslides, particularly where "U-shaped gashes or concave bights" interrupt the " 'normal' convex curves and circular form of the simple atoll." Unfortunately, his chief example, Bikini, for which the most detailed information is available concerning submarine topography, appears to demonstrate the opposite of his argument. He seems to have assumed a single giant volcanic cone for the foundation of Bikini Atoll, so that the concavities might appear to derive from rock slips on parts of the cone. The sonic soundings by means of which he correlated the atoll surface forms with their submarine forms reveal only the outside configurations of the basement rocks in the periphery below the calcareous cap. However, the seismic studies of Bikini (Dobrin and Perkins, 1954) and the magnetic structure studies of Bikini (Alldredge, Keller, and Dichtel, 1954) (Fig. 8) indicate that the calcareous cap conceals a complex of several volcanic cones, and that the perimeter configuration of the basement rocks of Bikini marks the outward slopes of an irregularly arranged grouping of volcanic peaks. Thus the apparent concavities of the reef result from the irregularities of the arrangement of peaks and not from landslides gouging out bights in the "normal convex curves and circular form" of the atoll. It seems likely to this writer that most of the larger and irregularly shaped atolls have this type of multiple-peak foundation. The seismic refraction study of a limited part of Kwajelein (Raitt, 1954) indicates that this atoll has a type of uneven basement foundation similar to that of Bikini. If one may assume similar internal structures for other large atolls, one would be justified in doubting Fairbridge's conclusion that "We may say that the characteristic shape of the landslide gash may be recognized in the external morphology of both oceanic volcanoes and atolls." Nor may one speak of "a definite evolution of atoll form, from the circular (convex) outline of the youthful stage to the concave patterns of maturity."

Long-axis orientation of atolls

In an examination of the charts of 162 atolls and table reefs (a term for coral reef islands without lagoons) (Tayama, 1935, pp. 268–70) in the Pacific north and south of the equator, the writer found no correlation between the prevailing winds and currents and the alignments of the long axis of atolls and table reefs. The number of atolls and table reefs with their alignments in various orientations are as follows: N–S, 43; E–W, 30; NE–SW, 23; and NW–SE, 66.

The bias in favor of the NW–SE alignments seems to result from the generally NW–SE orientation of the submarine topography underlying the Marshalls, Gilberts, and Tuamotus. It seems apparent that the long-axis alignment often coincides with and is influenced by the orientation of the submarine mountain ranges or anticlinal folds. Tectonic cracks may have produced linear arrangements of volcanoes on such folds. In other instances, alignment may be a matter of chance arrangement of volcanic clusters forming the basement foundation of the atoll concerned.

Atoll size

Largeness of atoll dimensions is significant in several different ways. One is that largeness probably indicates where at one time the higher

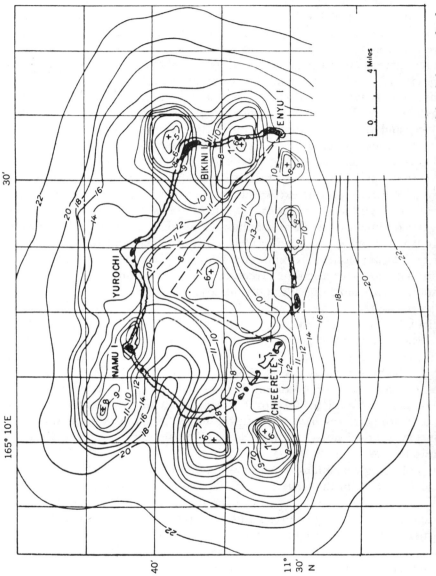

Fig. 8. Basement relief map of a model of Bikini Atoll. Contours are in thousands of feet below sea level. Low numbers indicate mountain peaks. [From Alldredge, Keller, and Dichtel (1954).]

volcanic mountains towered over the ocean or where multiple eruptions occurred within a small perimeter. At such a time as such large volcanic islands existed, they must have played an important role in the dispersal of plant and animal life in the Pacific realm. Although not necessarily a following consequence, it is probable that many of the largest such islands were also among the highest in the pre-atoll stage. Accordingly, if we may assume that the groups of atolls such as the Marshalls, Gilberts, or Tuamotus were created from a general subsidence of the same order rather than from individual isostatic island subsidence, then it is likely that many of the largest atolls today have their highest volcanic basement rocks nearer the surface, and that the calcareous cap is thinner over these basaltic peaks than over those of the small atolls in the same group.

A second significance of size relates to the other end of geologic time. Davis (1928, pp. 512–13) refers to Darwin's inference that small atolls mean atolls geologically nearing extinction through upward, inward growth with foundation subsidence. Large atolls, therefore, should have geologically longer continuance. A third significance is that generally they enclose large lagoons and zones of living reefs, both of which contribute to greater reef and lagoon fish production. A fourth significance is that large atolls often make transportation and communication from one part of the atoll to another part more difficult and time-consuming and thus lead to greater isolation, decreased social contacts if residences are scattered, and to less efficient and more poorly kept plantations and decreased copra production. The Marshalls atolls generally average the largest in the Pacific, followed by those of the Tuamotus, the Carolines, and the central Pacific. Tables 2 to 5, which list various aspects of 62 atolls of the Marshalls and the Carolines, provide figures on maximum lengths and widths for these atolls. The largest emerged atoll in the world is Kwajelein in the Marshalls, which has a maximum length of 66 nautical miles and a maximum width of about 15 nautical miles. In the Carolines Namonuito is largest, with dimensions of about 45 by 27 nautical miles.

In averaging maximum dimensions from the various atolls, the writer found that those in the western or Ralik Chain of the Marshalls are somewhat larger than those in the eastern or Ratak Chain, 21.7 nautical miles average length and 9.3 nautical miles average width, as compared with 18.4 nautical miles for length and 8.3 nautical miles for width, respectively. Wotje, Maloelap, and Mili are the largest in the eastern chain, while in the western chain are such large atolls as Kwajelein, Ailinglaplap, and Rongelap.

In the Carolines generally, atolls are much smaller than those in the Marshalls, and those in the western Carolines are the smallest, averaging 7.6 nautical miles long by 3.4 nautical miles wide, as compared with those in the eastern Carolines, which average 10.5 nautical miles long by 5.8 nautical miles wide. As in the Marshalls, the average lengths of the atolls are roughly twice the widths.

The large atolls in the eastern Carolines include Oroluk, Murillo, Nomwin, Namonuito, and Satawan. Ulithi and Ngulu are the only large atolls in the western Carolines.

Submerged atolls

Between 5 and 10°N latitude in the western Carolines there are 20 shoals or banks which most likely represent submerged atolls. Tayama (1935) asserted that 11 undoubtedly are submerged atolls. Because of the unstable tectonic zone in which they stand, their submergence may have been caused by a relatively rapid isostatic subsidence as compared with such areas as the Marshall chains. That they are not drowned atolls (that is, sunk beyond the depth of active reef-building corals and algae) is shown by the relative shallowness of the reef rims of the submerged structures. Their essentially lagoonlike structures are revealed in the relatively deeper central "lagoon" area and a much more elevated rim.

Two adjacent banks only about a mile apart but separated by a 1,200-foot-deep trench, Mogami and Gray Feather Banks, are very large, with outer reef rims 30 to 50 miles in diameter. A renewed glacial period involving a drop in sea level of about 90 feet would bring most of their rims above sea level and give them shallow lagoons of from 90 to 140 feet deep. The only significant difference between the atoll of Namonuito and these two banks 50 miles west of it is that the former has limited bits of emerged reef at the three corners of its triangular structure, most of which is submerged in depths between 40 and 50 feet. Much of the reef of Pulap Atoll is submerged also. Puluwat and Pulusuk, although described as atolls, each with very small, shallow lagoons, actually represent emergent ends of large adjacent submerged atolls known, respectively, as Uranie and Manila Banks.

McLaughlin Bank, 50 miles northwest of Mogami Bank, and Condor Reef, about the same distance west of Gray Feather Bank, also are large, submerged atoll structures. Farther west are two banks that have been charted in some detail and that reveal characteristics probably applicable also to the other submerged atolls. One is near Ulithi and is called Zohhoiiyoru. It reaches above the surface only at its northeastern corner, where it supports two islets. The rest of the rim is submerged at depths of 30 to 50 feet except at the extreme southwestern tip, where it rises to within 10 feet of the surface. Its submerged "lagoon" has maximum depths of 180 feet and its dimensions are about 3 by 12 nautical miles. A 60-foot drop in sea level would create an atoll that would have characteristics similar to those of existing atolls. These would include a submarine bench or terrace on the windward side at depths corresponding roughly with those of the windward side of Bikini (Tracey, Ladd, and Hoffmeister, 1948) and of Raroia (Newell, 1956).

The other western submerged atoll is capped in its extreme southern tip by emergent Ngaruangle Atoll, which is a small part of the 22-mile-long Velasco Reef. A 50-foot drop in sea level would make this reef a full-blown atoll, with maximum lagoon depths of about 120 feet at this level. As in the case of Zohhoiiyoru, Velasco also appears to have a terrace off its windward side but clifflike drops on the leeward reef. If it can be assumed that these may be correlated with the terraces of the Marshalls, one may argue for the existence of a greater tectonic instability and subsidence for the submerged atolls in the western Carolines.

Atoll lagoon depths

A discussion of atoll lagoon origins was presented in the preceding chapter and a description of its characteristics will be found in the next chapter. In this chapter the writer is concerned only with some statistics of lagoon-depth distribution. These relate only to the atolls of the Marshalls and Carolines, for which rather extensive soundings have been made and recorded on the HO charts. This survey was made independently of a similar survey made by B. L. Conrey (Emery, Tracey, and Ladd, 1954, p. 150) of 61 well-sounded atolls in four atoll groups. The method used by Conrey was essentially the same as that which the writer used. However, whereas Conrey used the diameter as the width between outer reef edges, the writer used the lagoon diameter between the inside reef edges. Although the use of outside reef edges matters little where atolls are large (5 to 10 miles in diameter), when they are small the reef widths sometimes exceed lagoon widths, in which case the measurements would be invalid for lagoon widths. Conrey's results, shown in Fig. 72 of the cited source, include 43 atolls in the Marshalls and Carolines, two from the Gilberts and Ellices, and 16 from the Maldives in the Indian Ocean. The writer's results are from the figures for 56 atolls in the Marshalls and Carolines.

Of the 56 atolls in the Marshalls and Carolines for which charted depths are given, 86 per cent have maximum lagoon depths of 100 to 300 feet, 59 per cent have maximum lagoon depths of 100 to 200 feet, and 28.5 per cent have maximum lagoon depths of over 200 feet. The remaining 12.5 per cent of lagoons are less than 100 feet deep. Two lagoons appear to have depths of over 300 feet, both in the Carolines. One is Nukuoro, with a maximum depth of 354 feet; the other is Ngatik, marked on the chart with a maximum depth of 492 feet. However, because HO chart 6053 for Ngatik is marked "canceled" by the Hydrographic Office, there may be inaccuracies, and in the percentage calculations and the graphs in Figs. 11 and 12 this atoll has not been included.

Of the 56 charted atolls, those having widths of 5 miles (at least along one cross line) all have lagoon depths of over 100 feet (Figs. 9 and 10).

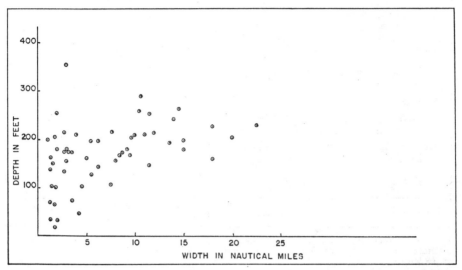

Fig. 9. Correlation of depths in atolls in the Marshall and Caroline Islands with maximum widths of atoll lagoons.

Those with widths of 10 miles (at least along one cross line) also have depths of over 150 feet. However, the deepest atolls are not the largest. Aside from Ngatik, the deepest is Nukuoro, whose dimensions are only 4.2 by 3.2 nautical miles. On the other hand, the shallowest atolls are all relatively small. Thus all the atolls with maximum lagoon depths under 100 feet also have maximum widths of less than 5 nautical miles. Of the seven in this category (all with depths of 70 feet or less), five have minimum widths of only 2 miles or less.

It may be concluded that, generally, although the lagoons of small atolls may be deep or shallow, the larger atolls all have relatively deep lagoons.

A chart showing the distribution of lagoon depths in the Marshalls and Carolines shows no correlation between maximum lagoon depths and the geographic situation of the related atolls in Micronesia. Deep lagoons and shallow lagoons both may be situated near volcanic islands or far from them. There appear to be no significant differences in lagoon depths from east to west in the Carolines or from north to south in the Marshalls, or between the Ralik and Ratak Chains of the Marshalls. In short, situation appears to have no influence upon atoll lagoon depths in Micronesia.

In summing up Conrey's results, Emery, Tracey, and Ladd wrote: "For very small atolls, less than 5 miles wide, the depth shoals rapidly from 25

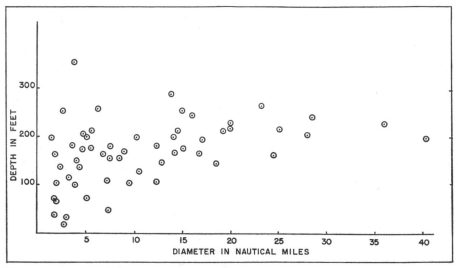

Fig. 10. Correlation of depths in atolls in the Marshall and Caroline Islands with average diameters of atoll lagoons. The average is based on one maximum length and one maximum width.

to 0 fathoms as the width decreases. For greater widths, between 15 and 30 miles, the depth appears to be fairly constant at about 45 fathoms. This relationship is attributed to relatively fast deposition of sandy debris from the reef where the radius of the atoll is less than the distance to which the sandy debris can be carried lagoonward from the reef."

Atoll passes

Of a total of 118 deep passes (navigable to ocean-going vessels) (Plate 7) noted for the various atoll groups in the northern and southern Pacific, 44 are found in the Marshalls (28 atolls), 34 in the Carolines (30 atolls), and 33 are found in the Tuamotus (72 atolls).[1] It is clear from this that the remaining groups, such as the Gilbert, Ellice, and central Pacific atolls examined, have very few deep passes.

1. Newell (1956, p. 326), using an anonymous source dated 1952, stated that "Of the 76 typical atolls of the (Tuamotu) group 47 are without a ship pass, 21 have a single pass, and 10 are each provided with two ship passes." The writer's figures for the Tuamotus were obtained from a count of atolls and passes given in the sailing directions for the Pacific Islands (U. S. Navy, 1952).

The most numerous passes proportional to atoll numbers occur in the Marshalls, followed by the Carolines. There are 1.5 passes for every atoll in the Marshalls, 1.1 for every atoll in the Carolines, and only 0.46 for every atoll in the Tuamotus. In the latter, 38 atolls are without passes of significant depth, although four or five of these may have passages permitting canoes and small boats to enter at high tide (Plate 8).

Although the Marshalls are the largest atolls among the various groups, size appears not to be a factor in pass occurrence, since the Tuamotus generally are larger than the Carolines atolls. The other atolls tend generally to be even smaller than those in the Carolines.

It long has been known that atoll passes most frequently occur on the leeward sides of atolls. The writer's statistical analysis of pass occurrences in various atoll sectors confirms this fact (Figs. 11 to 13). In an examination of charts of atolls with deep passes, the writer found that although such channels may occur in any sector, the windward sectors have the fewest. Of 118 deep passes among the various atoll groups in the northern and southern Pacific, 79 (or 62 per cent) were found in the west, southwest, and south. Their distribution is as follows: N, 15; NE, 12; E, 12; SE, 7; S, 24; SW, 21; W, 34; NW, 13.

For the Tuamotus, where the prevailing winds are southeasterly, the predominant sector for pass occurrence is west and northwest with a lesser predominance in the northeast (Fig. 11). For the northern Pacific atolls, where northeasterly winds prevail, southwest is the dominant sector for pass occurrence, with a lesser predominance in the southeast (Figs. 12 and 13), the reverse pattern from that of the southern Pacific. This fact appears to substantiate the view that pass occurrence is strongly related to prevalent wind, current, and wave directions.

The larger-scale and more-detailed charts available for the Marshalls and Carolines made possible closer examination of the pass situation in these groups. In this examination, note was made of 213 passes with depths greater than 2 fathoms, not all of which are navigable, owing to reef patches off their lagoon mouths or to other dangers. These 213 passes are situated on 48 atolls. The writer found that the largest number occur in leeward reef sectors oriented northwest to southeast. The second most numerous were found on leeward but less-protected sectors oriented northeast to southwest. Thus if one were to take a square or rectangle to represent the shape of an atoll reef and orient it so that the four corners point toward the cardinal directions, the dominant pass location would be on the southwestern side, the next dominant that on the southeastern side. The fewest would be located on the northeastern side facing the prevailing wind.

Of the 48 atolls, 34 have one or more passes in their southwestern sec-

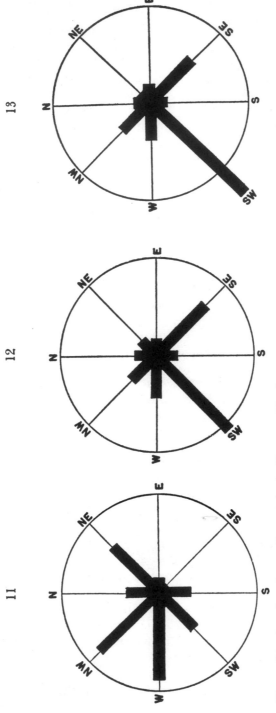

Fig. 11. Location of 45 deep atoll passes in the Tuamotu Islands.
Fig. 12. Proportion of atolls in the Marshall and Caroline Islands having one or more passes in each atoll sector.
Fig. 13. Location of 213 passes deeper than 2 fathoms in various atoll sectors in the Marshall and Caroline Islands.

tors. The corresponding figure for the southeast is 23, the west 14, the northwest 11, the south 7, the north and northeast 6 each, and the east 5. Figure 12 shows these situations graphically. Figure 13, in which the sector locations of the 213 passes in these 48 atolls are shown, emphasizes the importance of the southwestern sector for pass occurrences. It has 85 of the total number. The southeastern sector has 34, the northwest 27, the west 25, the east 12, the south 11, the north 10, and the northeast 9.

Taking the northern, northeastern, and eastern sectors as the generally exposed reef sectors, and the western, southwestern, and southern sectors as well-protected sectors, we find 31 out of the 213 on the windward sectors, and 121 in the well-protected leeward sectors.

Actually, the northwestern and southeastern sectors often are well protected also, since the prevailing wind and waves run parallel to the reef edge in these sectors. It is reasonable, therefore, to include in the leeward category passes in all sectors except the northern, northeastern, and eastern reefs of atolls north of the equator. Viewed thus, one may state that 85 per cent of atoll passes north of the equator lie on the leeward reef sectors of atolls and only 15 per cent on the exposed windward reefs. However, since the exposed windward sectors as defined above constitute one quadrant of the full circle, the bias of pass situation in favor of leeward sites is even greater than the 85 per cent stated, since this 85 per cent of the total number of passes is distributed along only 75 per cent of the 360 degrees, while the 15 per cent of the total number is distributed along 25 per cent of the full sweep of the azimuth. Hypothetically then, one may say that for each degree of the compass in the northwestern, southwestern, and southeastern quadrants on an idealized atoll north of the equator, one can expect to find a pass almost twice as often as one would find a pass in the northeastern quadrant.

Proliferation of patch reefs and reef spurs at the lagoon mouths of passes

One of the phenomena that struck the writer's attention in the examination of atoll charts and aerial photographs of atolls is the unusually prolific growth of patch reefs and the lagoonward-turning reef spurs (Plate 9) inward of the lagoon mouths of passes (Fig. 14 and Plates 10 and 11). To determine whether there were any relationship between this phenomenon and the situation and orientation of atoll passes, the writer examined the detailed HO charts for the 48 atolls in the Marshalls and Carolines having one or more passes and recorded the number of passes having or lacking such unusual growths, noting the sector in which the passes occur in each case, as well as the particular alignments of the passes as they crossed reefs. In evaluating the results shown in Table 6 and Fig. 15 several factors that

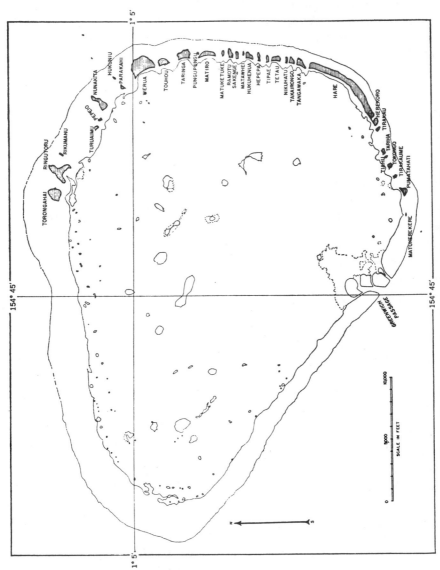

Fig. 14. Kapingamarangi, a classic type of atoll. [From Wiens (1956).]

reduce the reliability of the conclusions must be taken into consideration. The first is that a minor element of subjectivity was involved in the counting of the passes, owing to the fact that in a few instances atolls have large parts of their rim submerged to a depth below the 2 fathoms arbitrarily taken as minimum depth for the constitution of a pass. In such cases, for instance, where an entire side of an atoll or a large part of a side was submerged, the sector was ignored, because the conditions presented by such a situation would most likely be much different from

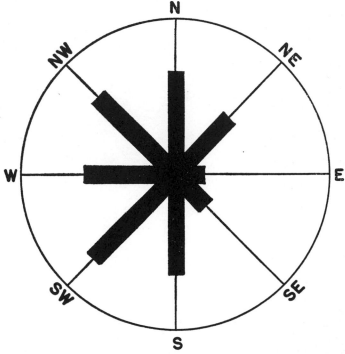

Fig. 15. Percentage of passes that have patch-reef growth off their lagoon mouths in various atoll sectors in the Marshall and Caroline Islands.

conditions associated with the origin and maintenance of a narrow pass. Moreover, it is not always clear from the charts whether the patch reef at the lagoon mouth of a pass grew there because of the situation at the lagoon mouth or whether it grew by some chance reason as do other patch reefs often scattered over an atoll lagoon. However, where a patch reef was separated by over 200 yards of deep water from the peripheral reef at the pass, the writer excluded the occurrence from the count. In considering percentages in Table 6 it is obvious that where a sector has only a few

passes with or without unusual patch reef development an error in count
or in judgment for inclusion or exclusion will cause a proportionately
large percentage change. Thus the conclusions must be viewed with caution. The characteristic pattern of development is shown in Fig. 14.

In general, the results showed that the percentage of passes having such
patch reef development is greatest in the northern, southern, and western
sectors. The phenomenon occurs least often in the eastern and southeastern
passes and but slightly more often in the northeastern-sector passes. In
Table 6 the numerator indicates the number of passes with unusual patch

TABLE 6

The Relation between Patch Reefs and Passes

Sector	Ratio: with/without patch reefs (alignments indicated)	Simple ratio disregarding alignments	Total passes with patch reefs, %
N	$\dfrac{5 \text{ N-W, 1 NW-SE}}{6 \text{ N-S}}$	$\dfrac{6}{6}$	50
NE	$\dfrac{5 \text{ NE-SW}}{8 \text{ NE-SW}}$	$\dfrac{5}{8}$	38.5
E	$\dfrac{2 \text{ E-W}}{15 \text{ E-W}}$	$\dfrac{2}{15}$	11.8
NW	$\dfrac{10 \text{ NW-SE}}{9 \text{ NW-SE}}$	$\dfrac{10}{9}$	52.7
SE	$\dfrac{3 \text{ NW-SE}}{9 \text{ NW-SE, 3 N-S, 1 E-W}}$	$\dfrac{3}{13}$	18.7
W	$\dfrac{15 \text{ E-W, 2 NE-SW}}{22 \text{ E-W}}$	$\dfrac{17}{22}$	43.6
SW	$\dfrac{39 \text{ NE-SW, 2 E-W}}{25 \text{ NE-SW, 7 N-S, 1 NW-SE}}$	$\dfrac{41}{33}$	55.5
S	$\dfrac{11 \text{ N-S, 5 NW-SE}}{18 \text{ N-S}}$	$\dfrac{16}{18}$	47.0

reef development at their lagoon mouths, and the denominator indicates
those without such development. The alignments of the axes of the passes
are indicated in each case. These ratios are given for passes at each of the
eight chief sectors of the atoll rim grouped by degree of exposure to prevailing winds, currents, and waves.

Table 6, summarized in Fig. 15, appears to indicate a real correlation
between atoll passes and the frequency of unusual patch reefs and reef
strip development off the lagoon mouths of the passes. This correlation
appears to show that passes in sectors with an easterly component are much

less likely to develop such patch reef growth and that those sectors that lie facing due east are least likely to favor such growth, as it has been shown also to be least favorable for pass development. By contrast, the southwestern sector is the most favorable to such growth, as it is for channel occurrence also.

Because of the factors contributing to unreliability of data in the above analysis, a further count was made of atolls in the Marshalls and Carolines (each having but a single pass), and it was noted whether patch reefs occurred off the lagoon mouths of these passes. In the Marshalls and Carolines 14 atolls were noted, each having a single pass. These occurred in the following reef sectors: N, o; S, 3; SE, 1; SW, 3; W, 4; E, 3; NE, o; NW, o.

It is seen that of the 14 passes, 11 have leeward positions, 79 per cent of the total. Ten of the 14, or 72 per cent, have reef patch occurrence at their lagoon mouths, but not one of the three occurring in eastern reef sectors has this phenomenon. By contrast, 91 per cent of these leeward passes on single-pass atolls are shown to have such unusual patch reef occurrence. This corroborates the results of the preceding analysis and leads to the conclusion that correlations do exist between patch reef occurrence off the lagoon mouths of atoll passes and the prevailing winds, currents, and waves of the coral realm. The theories of the origins of these patch reefs are discussed in Chapter 5.

Relation of reef width to atoll rims

A significant atoll feature apparently related in occurrence to situation with respect to the prevailing winds, currents, and waves is the width of the reef rim of an atoll. A careful examination of this has been made for the northern Marshalls atolls of Bikini, Eniwetok, and Rongelap (Emery, Tracey, and Ladd, 1954, pp. 143–4) (Fig. 16). A more incidental note of this question for Raroia south of the equator also has been made (Newell, 1956, p. 330). For the northern atolls, the widest reefs occur on the northwest and the narrowest in the south. For Raroia the reverse is true. The narrowest sector of the reef is the northwest and the widest is the south. Both are interpreted as being related to prevailing wind, wave, and current effects. Emery, Tracey, and Ladd wrote: "Although it is possible that reef widths are determined by the configurations of submerged reefs of an earlier state, during which wind and current directions may have been altogether different . . . it appears more reasonable that the present reefs are controlled by present conditions." Newell (1956) attributes the relative narrowness and height of the northwestern rim of Raroia (south of the equator) to "a result of full exposure to the most violent storms."

To check whether the situation as related to reef width might be a common one for atolls generally, the writer examined 62 atolls in the Marshalls and Carolines for which good HO charts were available and found that indeed there is such a common correlation. Figure 17 graphically depict the results of this study and indicates the most frequent location of the widest and the narrowest reef sectors. For these atolls north of the equator the widest reefs along an atoll rim are found most often in the northern and

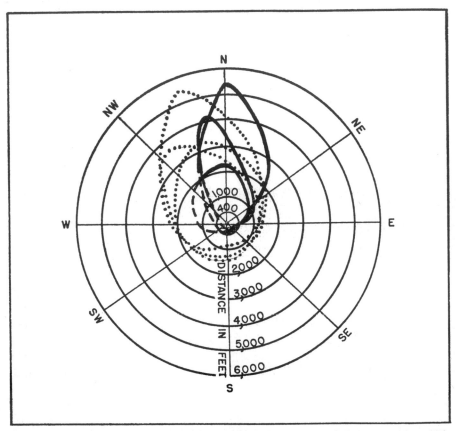

Fig. 16. Azimuthal chart of reef widths at Bikini, Rongelap, and Eniwetok. The width between islands is shown by dotted lines. The width from the reef margin to the seaward coasts of islands is shown by solid lines. Dashed lines indicate the absence of islands. [After Emery, Tracey, and Ladd (1954).]

northwestern sectors, followed by those in western and northeastern sectors. The widest reefs are least often found in the southwest, south, southeast, and east. The narrowest reefs, on the other hand, most often are found in the southwestern sector of atoll rims, followed by those on the south-southeast and eastern sectors with about equal frequency. Narrow reefs occur least often in the northwestern and northern sectors of atolls.

The situation south of the equator indicated for Raroia by Newell would logically be expected to apply as a common rule to south Pacific atolls with prevailing southeasterly winds, as the pattern of atoll passes north and south of the equator is reversed. There seems little question that the pattern of occurrence of reef widths in various atoll sectors is associated with present-day prevailing winds, currents, and waves and not those of an earlier geologic age. But there does not seem to be support from the above evidence for Kuenen's statement (1950, p. 440) that "The living reef tends to grow to windward."

Short sections of wide reefs usually occur at sharp outward bends or angles of the reef rim regardless of reef sector location (Plate 12).

Proportion of atoll reef rims occupied by land

In surveying the HO charts of Pacific atolls north and south of the equator, the writer categorized atolls according to the proportion of the length of the reef rim along which land occupied the reef, regardless of width. Of 125 atolls included in the survey north and south of the equator, 55 appeared to have less than one-third of their circumference occupied by land, while only 6 appeared to be occupied by land running around virtually the entire reef rim. These and other categories are listed as follows: land along less than one-third of rim, 55 atolls; land along more than one-third but less than one-half of rim, 34 atolls; land along one-half or more but less than two-thirds of rim, 22 atolls; land along virtually the entire circumference, 6 atolls.

From the above categorizations, it appears that on about 72 per cent of all the Pacific atolls, less than one-half of the reef circumference is occupied by land. On only about 11 per cent of these atolls does the land area occupy more than two-thirds of the reef circumference, disregarding reef widths. On less than 5 per cent of the atolls, land virtually completely encircles the lagoons.

Land on atolls

With regard to the location of land along the reef rim of atolls, charts made from data recorded on the above 125 atolls (Figs. 18 to 23) show that vegetated land areas (reef islets above high tide) occur with greatest frequency in the eastern, or windward, sectors of the reef rim. [This appears to differ from the situation in the atolls of the Indian Ocean where, according to Sewell (Kuenen, 1950, p. 437), most islets are found on the leeward reefs. However, the validity of this statement appears open to doubt, since the prevailing winds in the Indian Ocean at low latitudes reverse themselves seasonally with the monsoon changes, and what constitutes windward or leeward reefs here differ from those in the Pacific.] Prevalence of occurrence of land areas in the eastern half of the atoll rim is in marked contrast to the much diminished frequency of occurrence in the western half in the Pacific realm. This frequency in the west, northwest, and southwest is roughly only about one-half the frequency of occurrence in the east, northeast, southeast, north, and south.

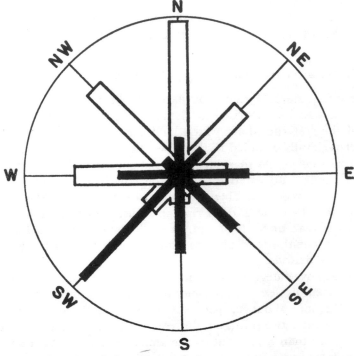

Fig. 17. Location of the widest and the narrowest reefs on atolls in the Marshall and Caroline Islands.

If the separate groups are considered, the general bias in favor of land occurrence in the eastern half of the atolls still holds true for such groups as the Marshalls, Carolines, Gilberts, Tuamotus, and the central Pacific atolls, although there are some differences as to reef sectors most favored. Thus for 19 Tuamotu atolls whose charts were examined, and for the central Pacific atolls, land areas occur most often in the northeasterly sectors; for the Carolines and Gilberts most often in the southeasterly sectors; and for the Marshalls in the easterly sectors.

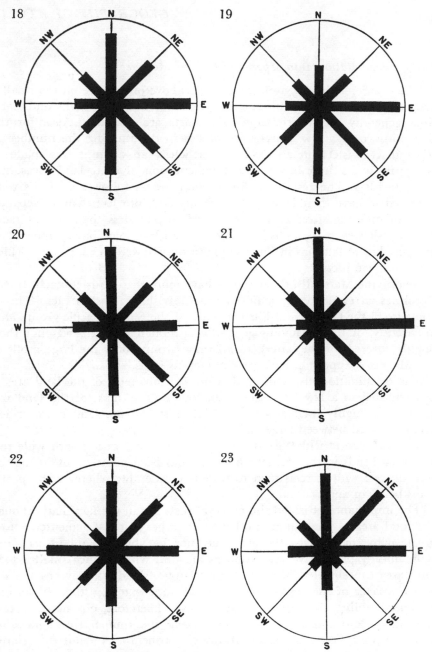

Fig. 18. Land location on atoll reef sectors of 125 atolls in the north and south Pacific.
Fig. 19. Land location of atoll reef sectors in the Marshall Islands.
Fig. 20. Land location of atoll reef sectors in the Caroline Islands.
Fig. 21. Land location of atoll reef sectors in the Gilbert Islands.
Fig. 22. Land location of atoll reef sectors in the central Pacific.
Fig. 23. Land location of atoll reef sectors in the Tuamotu Islands.

Land fragmentation into separate islets on atoll reefs

The charts for the 125 atolls mentioned above often were on too small a scale to provide accurate information, except for the Marshalls and Carolines generally, for which large-scale charts are available. Also, for the Tuamotus, only a few charts were of use in determining the number of separate reef islets on an atoll. Nevertheless, an attempt was made to categorize atolls according to the fragmentation of their land areas into separate islets. The results of this attempt are as follows: 55 atolls were observed to have their land areas each divided into less than 10 separate islets of differing sizes; 27 were observed to have less than 20 but more than 10 islets each; 43 atolls had 20 or more islets, some having more than 100 tiny bits of land [as in the case of Raroia (Newell, 1956, p. 330), which has about 280 islets].

Among the Marshalls, the majority have more than 20 islets each. In the Carolines an even greater majority have less than 10 islets each. This is true also of the Gilbert and Ellice groups, of the central Pacific group, and, apparently, of the Tuamotus generally (although the data was not thoroughly covered for the latter). In all these groups, only the large atolls of the Marshalls appear to have very numerous islets.

The examination also showed that on 65 atolls most of the land area is concentrated in a few large islets. On four or five, most of the land was found in a highly fragmented state. The rest had the land more or less evenly divided between large and small islets.

The largest and widest islets usually coincide in location with wide reef sectors at bends in the reef (Plate 12). As has been pointed out in the section on reef widths, reefs tend to widen considerably wherever sharp outward bends or angles occur.

The importance of island size on coral reefs lies in the fact that although the total area of land on an atoll may be large, if it is fragmented into a great many small islets, the area may not be able to support as much economically productive vegetation as an atoll with a much smaller total land area concentrated in a few large islands. Island size governs the size and character of the fresh-water lens to a large extent, although porosity and permeability are important factors also. Therefore, one needs to take this factor into consideration in evaluating the comparative figures for land area on different atolls and in drawing conclusions about the relative capacities for population support of different atolls.

CHAPTER 3

THE TOPOGRAPHY AND GEOLOGY OF AN
ATOLL REEF

Nomenclature and terminology

Owing to the sparseness and irregular infrequency of past studies of reef features and owing to the fact that geographical zonation on a reef or atoll structure is of significance to students in several disciplines of science, no general agreement has yet been reached on nomenclature and terminology in describing reef features. The difficulty of achieving a common classification of reef features was recognized by Stephenson (1931, p. 92):

Thinking that uniformity of nomenclature is desirable wherever it can be attained, we studied a number of accounts of reefs with the idea that some standard set of terms might be worked out, taking as a model, for instance, the classical report on Funafuti. The variation from one to another, however, is so great, that no degree of uniformity seems to be attainable. On reflection, it is proper that, at the present stage of our knowledge of reefs, this should be the case. The number of different kinds of reef in existence is considerable and the workers on each type have developed a nomenclature which was locally suitable. An attempt to apply the same terms throughout would involve the assumption that the several features named were homologous throughout the series, and at present we are not in a position to establish general homologies with any degree of security. The existing nomenclature offers serious difficulty only when a single term has been employed in widely different senses; but this can only be corrected when fuller knowledge makes a definitive classification possible.

Whether the fuller knowledge developed since this report was published justifies a definitive classification is probably debatable. The unquestionable

45

need for clarification of terminology at least brought together a committee in 1957 devoting its attention to the "vexed topic of reef terminology." The committee drew up plans for an "authoritative handbook containing the classical definitions relating to reefs, reprinted in collected form, illustrated and briefly annotated." R. W. Fairbridge, Columbia University geologist, is editor-in-chief of the project; F. R. Fosberg of the Pacific Science Board is in charge of the editorial office.

It is obvious that the reader must be cautioned to be on the alert for terms and usages herein that differ from his own terminology applying to similar reef features. This problem already has been pointed out in the first chapter, where coral atoll and lagoon are defined. Although no attempt is made in this work to present a complete list of definitions of reef terminology, the establishment of a frame of reference in the description of the various aspects of the reef inescapably requires clarification of terms. In this chapter the chief purpose is to point out the various sections, forms, and aspects of the reef that appear to have significant uniformities, singularities, and/or situations that deserve distinctive terms, and these will then provide a frame of reference for subsequent discussion.

To start with, it seems most appropriate to quote the reef-terminology-committee's definition of the scope of the word "reef."

Taking a "reef" to mean any rocky eminence of the sea-floor that causes waves to break (Webster's dictionary), and an "organic reef" one that is essentially constructed of a framework of coral, calcareous algae or other organism, it is proposed that the term also be taken loosely to include those smaller bioherms which do not cause waves to break, but nevertheless form massive organic structures (large or small) which rise appreciably above the sea-floor. The list would, therefore, embrace all forms of "coral reef," used in the broadest way, including small bioherms of non-reef-forming character built by any form or hermatypic organism, and not only the calcareous algae and anthozoan corals.

It is clear from this definition that although atoll reefs and "coral islands" are very important to the subject of reefs, they comprise only part of the picture. They are, however, the types of reefs with which we are primarily concerned in this study.

Situation with respect to prevailing wind, waves, swells, and currents, and microgeographical zonation is very marked and highly significant with regard to organic coral reefs. Owing to the irregularity and lack of uniformity of atoll shapes, pinpointing location along the rim of an atoll reef is difficult, as has been pointed out earlier.

One precaution that must be taken is to avoid giving different terms the same definition. "Eastern seaward side" and "windward seaward side," although most often they coincide, occasionally do not. Because of irregular reef projections and loops, as in the case of the eastern arm of Arno Atoll, parts of the eastern reef of an atoll may not be on the windward side, but in the lee of the wind.

Passes and channels

A closed lagoon may be defined as an atoll lagoon without navigable passes. However, the definition of a pass or passage is somewhat arbitrary. The terms "pass," "passage," and "channel" often are used interchangeably. In terms of navigation, a ship's pass, or "deep pass," would be one open to safe navigation by sea-going vessels large and small and of varying draft. A small boat or canoe pass or passage refers to a shallow pass not navigable to ocean-going vessels and generally under 1 fathom depth. Occasionally, small boat or canoe passes may be navigable to such small craft only at high tide. Such passes may be no more than a shallow "inter-islet channel" if the channel runs all the way across the reef from ocean to lagoon. Ordinarily, the inter-islet channel is merely a break in the land rim of the atoll which constitutes a part of the reef flat where the islets are relatively close together (Figs. 24 and 25). Where islets are far apart, say, more than 1,000 feet, the influence of adjacent land may be negligible, and in this case this section more properly might be termed merely a part of the inner reef flat rather than an inter-islet channel. The inter-islet channel sometimes is in the form of a re-entrant gap in the lagoon-side reef, or it may be a trough that is deeper than either the outer seaward reef flat or the lagoon reef margins.

Conspicuous atoll features

To introduce the discussion of the various prominent topographic features of an atoll, it is advantageous to examine Figs. 26 and 27 and to include here the definition and brief descriptions made of them by their authors (Tracey, Cloud, and Emery, 1955) after consultation with 17 colleagues:

The primary distinctions to be drawn [on an atoll] are between outer slope, reef, island, lagoon, and smaller reef structures within the lagoon. Channels and passes between ocean and lagoon are also of primary importance. Most of the difficulty with names, especially for those who must rely on collections and data gathered by others, lies in boundaries between the principal zones. The following terms are suggested, with purposely broad definitions:

1. *Outer slope:* the steeply descending outer slope of the reef below the dwindle point of abundant living coral and coralline algae, which is ordinarily at about 10 fathoms.

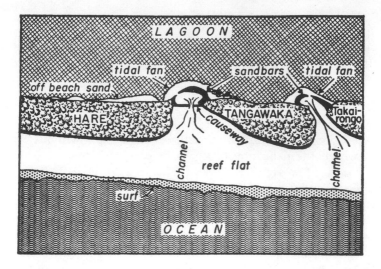

Fig. 24. Reef features near the eastern end of Hare Islet, Kapingama-rangi Atoll. [From Wiens (1956).]

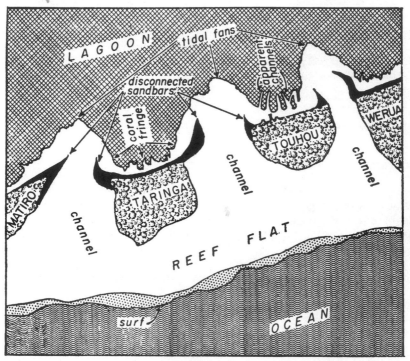

Fig. 25. Reef features near Touhou Islet, Kapingamarangi Atoll. [From Wiens (1956).]

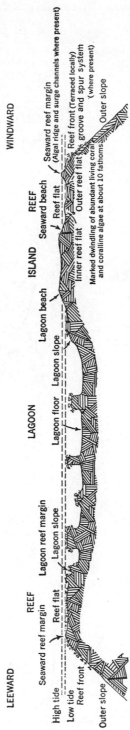

Fig. 26. Conspicuous features of an atoll and its peripheral reef shown in cross section (not to scale). [From Tracey, Cloud, and Emery (1955).]

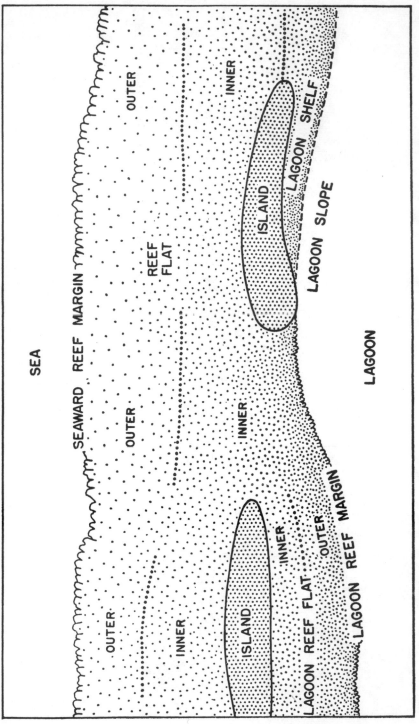

Fig. 27. Common subdivisions of an upper reef surface. [From Tracey, Cloud, and Emery (1955).]

2. *Reef front:* the upper seaward face of the reef, extending above the dwindle point of abundant living coral and coralline algae to the reef edge. This zone commonly includes a shelf, bench, or terrace that slopes to 8 to 15 fathoms [Plate 13], as well as the living, wave-breaking face of the reef. The terrace may be an eroded surface or may be veneered with organic growth. The living reef front above the terrace in some places is smooth and steep; in other places it is cut by grooves separated by ridges that together have been called groove and spur systems, forming comb-tooth patterns [Fig. 81; Plate 14]. If the terrace is broad and well defined it may be well to designate it a separate reef zone.

3. *Seaward reef margin:* the seaward edge of the reef flat, marked in places by an algal ridge and cut by surge channels, which are the land-ward extensions of the reef-front grooves. [Fosberg and MacNeil (1954) termed the drop-off from the seaward edge the *foreslope*.]

4. *Reef flat:* the upper surface of the reef, commonly exposed or awash at lowest tide. The presence of islands on the flat modifies the ecology of the reef; therefore, an important distinction should be drawn between island reef flats, or flats seaward from islands, and inter-island reef flats or flats between islands.

The reef flat is commonly divisible into outer and inner reef flats, or outer, central, and inner reef flats; but one "inner" or "outer" zone may not be the close ecologic equivalent of another "inner" or "outer" zone.

On inter-island reefs, and on seaward reef flats adjoining islands, the outer zone is toward the ocean, the inner is toward lagoon or shore. In rare instances a broad reef flat on the lagoon shore of an island [Plate 15] may be subdivided into an outer lagoon reef flat, near the island; but careful distinction should be made between its parts and those of reef flats that abut the open sea. If a reef flat is not present on the lagoon side of an island, its place may be taken by a lagoon shelf, on which detrital sediments predominate over organic growth.

5. *Seaward beach:* the seaward-facing beach of reef islands.

6. *Lagoon beach:* the lagoonward-facing beach of reef islands.

7. *Lagoon reef margin:* the lagoonward margin of the reef; unlike the seaward reef margin, it is not necessarily defined by growth. In some places, especially where islands are present, there may be no lagoon reef margin at all. If the lagoon reef margin is well defined, a lagoon reef front may be present and even a lagoon terrace, comparable to the seaward reef front and terrace. If the lagoon reef margin is poorly defined, a lagoon shelf may separate lagoon slope from reef flat or lagoon beach.

8. *Lagoon slope:* the border zone of the lagoon that slopes downward from the lagoon reef margin or lagoon beach to the lagoon floor.

9. *Lagoon floor:* the undulating to nearly level floor of the lagoon.

Minor organic prominences on lagoon floors or slopes, all broadly re-lated, range from small mounds or tall narrow pinnacles to large masses, hundreds of feet in diameter. Some prefer to use a single term for all such features, for example, coral knoll, bioherm, or patch reef. The consider-able physical and organic variety of these features is ecologically signifi-cant, however, and should be indicated in some way. In general it seems preferable to use informal names that will describe both the dominant or-ganism and the physical appearance. Examples are: algal knoll; coral-algal mound; millepore patch; *Acropora* thicket; etc.

The outer slope: terraces

Taking the preceding general classification of the atoll's structural parts as a point of departure, one may begin the discussion of these features with the *outer slope*. The detailed and careful data accumulated from Bikini and other atolls of the northern Marshalls provide the best evidences for the character of outer atoll slopes. The seaward edge of the reefs in this area is bordered by a terrace whose outer edge is at a depth of about 8 fathoms at Bikini, Eniwetok, and Rongelap Atolls and probably less at Rongerik (Emery, Tracey, and Ladd, 1954, p. 1). This terrace was found to be shallower than a lagoon terrace that was present at about 10 fathoms.

On the leeward side of the atoll the reefs are bordered by steep, locally vertical slopes that extend to a depth of 20 fathoms or more. Other parts of the leeward reefs have been made irregular by slumping and landsliding probably during severe storms from the south. The slopes around the atolls between the reef edge and 200 fathoms average about 45° and are somewhat steeper on the submarine buttresses that underlie reef projections. At greater depths the slopes become gradually gentler, until between 2,000 and 2,500 fathoms they merge with the floor of the deep sea.

How universal the 8-foot terrace is on the outer slopes of other atolls in the Pacific is not known, because few surveys of sufficient intensity and density of sounding or sonar intervals have been made of atolls to permit conclusions. However, in Chapter 2 it was indicated that evidence of such a terrace exists in the charts of two submerged atolls or banks, McLaughlin and Zohhoiiyoru, in the western Carolines region. In these instances the apparent terrace appears about 8 to 10 fathoms below the lagoon rim of the submerged atolls and may indicate tectonic instability in these regions. Figure 76 portrays the outside terrace as a 10-fathom terrace, conforming with the lagoonside 10-fathom terrace. Newell (1956, p. 341) found a similar terrace on the windward reef of Raroia "at approximately 20 meters (10 fathoms) comparable to one at Bikini . . . and the Bahamas." These data appear to support the conclusion that a terrace present at approximately 10 fathoms is a characteristic of most atolls and points to the apparent stability of the central Pacific atolls. Newell (1956, p. 334) also described an 8-meter terrace, which he equated with the grooved reef front described by Tracey, Cloud, and Emery (quoted previously). "Both terraces [at Raroia] are grooved and otherwise similar in general appearance. Probably the rim of the deeper terrace was the reef front during a Pleistocene low level of the sea."

The "8-fathom" terrace, as exemplified at Bikini, appears to be broadest and most pronounced in the northeastern, windward sector, being narrow or lacking in the leeward western side. These correlations also appear to be true at Rongelap. If, as may be supposed, this terrace is an erosional feature, these correlations appear to point to much more severe erosion on the windward side, where in parts of Bikini and Rongelap the terrace is 400 yards wide.

Beyond the terrace the bottom slopes downward very abruptly (Emery, Tracey, and Ladd, 1954, p. 68). For all profiles made, the average slope down to 200 fathoms was 37.5°. Steeper profiles occurred off the leeward slopes and less-steep slopes on the windward side, again an indicator of net erosion processes. On the average the leeward slopes were 6° steeper. Several of the steepest slopes occurred off sharp reef projections, including slopes of 67 to 68°.

Sediments

Sedimentary materials grade downward along the slopes from coarse to fine. The coarsest sediments dredged up from the slopes are those that are shallowest and nearest the reef edge. These consist chiefly of coral and Halimeda debris and are the same components that characterize the inter-mediate depths of the lagoons. The fine debris up to silt size comprised 60 per cent of the sediment at 640 fathoms and were obviously broken Hali-meda segments carried down from upper slopes. The steeper slopes are partly covered down to 500 feet with large blocks of limestone broken from the edge of the reef by waves. Most of these blocks are heavy pieces of coral. Others are cemented blocks formed of Halimeda debris, coral, Foraminifera, and sand, some of which were as solidly cemented as beach rock.

The reef front: groove-and-spur system

Above the outer 8-to-10-fathom terrace rises the living reef front, whose character varies with exposure to prevailing wind, currents, swells, and waves. This is the part of the reef front that emerges into view at the surface, rising from what Newell terms the 8-meter terrace on the windward side. This is a rather narrow terrace at best, and even on the windward side may disappear except as represented by the bottom shelves of the grooves incised in the walls of the reef front. (Emery, Tracey, and Ladd do not mention such a terrace.)

The origins and processes connected with the development of this phe-nomenon will be discussed in Chapter 5. Figure 28 shows the characteristic distribution of the groove-and-spur system of the reef front of an atoll rel-ative to prevailing forces of wind and water. Figure 29 shows an artist's

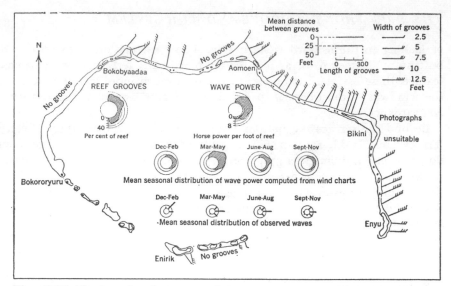

Fig. 28. Distribution of reef grooves and the wave power around the reef of Bikini Atoll. The length, width, and spacing of the grooves are proportional to the length, width, and spacing of the arrows drawn against the reef. The polar-coordinate graph at the left shows the percentage of area occupied by grooves as a function of their exposure. The polar-coordinate graph at the right shows the mean distribution of computed wave power and of observed waves. [From Munk and Sargent (1954).]

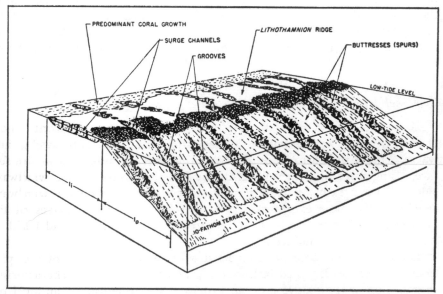

Fig. 29. The seaward face and top of a reef on the windward side of Bikini Atoll. [From Munk and Sargent (1954).]

view of the upper reef front with grooves and spurs. The surface appearances are familiar to anyone who has flown at low elevation over the windward reef of an atoll.

The diagrams in Fig. 28 show a significant correlation between the directional distribution of wave power and reef grooves. According to Munk and Sargent (1954, p. 277),

Grooves are restricted to reefs with a component of exposure to the east, the direction from which wave action is pronounced . . . No grooves were found [at Bikini] where the reef exposure has a westerly component. The distribution of grooves reveals a maximum for an east-northeast exposure, and a secondary maximum for a southeast exposure. These features are associated with the principal wave-generating areas in the trade-wind belts of the north Pacific and south Pacific, respectively. The distribution of wave power reveals the same features; except during the summer months the effect of the distant south Pacific trade winds is overshadowed by the effect of the local trade winds. For a corresponding location in southern latitudes the reverse should be true, and the distribution should be a mirror image of the one found at Bikini Atoll.

That this interpretation does not necessarily follow is indicated by Newell (1956, pp. 341-2). Raroia, which is in a corresponding location south of the equator in the Tuamotus, is surrounded by a conspicuous groove-and-spur zone. Newell stated that "The grooves of the windward outer reef are somewhat narrower and more regularly spaced than those on the leeward side. Otherwise they are about the same." Cloud (1952, p. 44) also wrote: "The grooves are ordinarily most abundantly developed on windward reefs, but they have been observed in all quarters of the wind and at places are common on leeward reefs. Their degree of prominence is believed to be controlled by strength of outflowing current, and thus surf, and by quantity of abrasive materials in transit."

The writer's observations of aerial photographs of reef fronts in the Marshalls tend to confirm Munk and Sargent's correlation between the distribution of reef grooves and directional distribution of wave power. Where they do occur on "leeward" reefs as indicated by Cloud, it probably would be found that, owing to the configuration of the reef at those locations, wave refraction brings sufficient wave power to aid the erosive forces of abrasive materials carried seaward from the lagoon across the reef or from the reef flat by the prevailing winds and surface currents (Plate 16).

Investigations of the groove-and-spur system by swimmers equipped with diving masks are dangerous, owing to the constant and powerful movement of water in the upper sea waters on the windward side, but several scientists have used this device to examine the phenomenon. Munk and Sargent (1954, p. 277) found that "The absolute depth at which the grooves commence appears to be approximately constant and to extend to the greatest depth for which wave action is appreciable." The length of the grooves, thus, is mainly a function of the degree of slope of the reef front. Most of the grooves examined by them start at a depth of 35 to 50 feet, then run up the reef slope into and through the surf zone. At the inner end they may end abruptly or be continued as *surge channels* or as tunnels with blow holes under the reef platform. "Just inside the surf zone, around the blow-holes and the heads of grooves and channels, colonies of Lithotham-nion [Porolithon] and corals rise about 2 feet above the general reef level. The upper faces of the spurs are paved with living Lithothamnion, which present an extremely rough surface [Plates 14, 42, 44, and 45]. The sides of the grooves are covered with projecting, often bracketlike colonies. The bottoms of the grooves consist of relatively smooth rock and sand" (Munk and Sargent, 1954, p. 275). In a prominently exposed windward sector the grooves were found to be spaced about 25 feet apart, were about 16 feet deep at their inner ends, and varied in width from 3 to 6 feet (Munk and Sargent, 1954, p. 26). Emery, Tracey, and Ladd (1954, p. 26) found that at fairly regular intervals along the slope there were nearly straight grooves at right angles to the reef front. These were 5 to 10 feet wide and as much as 25 feet deep at their inner ends. The floors were covered with a veneer of sand, gravel, or boulders, and the spurs separating the grooves were flattened and 25 or more feet wide.

Newell, who investigated the reef front at Raroia (1956, p. 342) found that "The deeper gorges descend precipitously to a depth of 6 or 7 meters; then, flattening gradually to a depth of about 10 to 15 meters, they debouch on the lower slope of the reef front beyond the spurs." The walls and floor of the grooves he examined

are smooth and free from all but scattered, very young colonies of corals. The rock surface is pitted, rounded, and scoured smooth, and the floor is uneven and ungraded except near the mouth where there usually is an accumulation of boulders and gravel. Here and there on the floor of the grooves are hemispherical shallow potholes of varying size more or less filled with rounded pebbles and cobbles. In some instances the potholes attain diameters of up to about 2 meters and are occupied by boulders of worn porites that could have been derived only from the outer slope.

Newell also found that many of the grooves divide near the head, producing a rough dendritic pattern of tributaries.

The groove-and-spur system appears to be invariably present on windward reefs or reefs otherwise exposed to strong, more-or-less-constant wave power. A groove-and-spur system is usually not present in leeward reef sectors, or, if it is, is weakly developed. Transitional forms occur in the weakly developed sectors. The various types of reef fronts, which result from different degrees of exposure, are described for Bikini by Emery, Tracey, and

Ladd (1954, pp. 24–6) and appear to correspond with such reef fronts in numerous other atolls the writer visited in the Marshalls or whose aerial photographs he examined. Although Wells (1951, p. 8) reported an important difference in Arno reefs from Bikini reefs—the absence of poorly developed groove-and-spur system on leeward reefs—aerial photographs contradict such a contention. In most areas where grooves are absent, there is no evidence of a terrace. The reef edge may run in a straight or smoothly scalloped line, and the seaward slope plunges very steeply to depths of 30 to 40 fathoms. The marginal zone supports a fairly rich growth of corals and algae, but these rise only a few inches above the reef flat. Growth of reef builders apparently exceeds erosion, and overhangs may develop.

In transitional zones of wave force and accompanying reef character which commonly occur on the south or southeasterly fronting reefs, the margins are very irregular in outline. In parts (Emery, Tracey, and Ladd, 1954, pp. 25–6) there are sharply irregular re-entrants in the reef margins which

are almost certainly due to erosion followed by collapse. These reentrants are 25 to 500 feet or more wide and extend into the reef for 25 to 200 feet [at Bikini]. The floor at present is covered with debris—including large blocks, the irregular outlines of which match those of the reef edge. Debris of this sort occurs to depths of at least 100 feet.

Reefs with large irregular reentrants occur on the south-southwest sides of atolls in the northern Marshall Islands. They are adapted to the weak surf of such lee shores, but the severe storm waves from the south apparently cause major damage. Even in the reentrants, however, large blocks torn from the reef edge are veneered with living corals and algae.

The seaward reef margin: the algal ridge

At the seaward edge of the windward reefs a rich growth of calcareous algae forms a gently convex rim or a cuesta-shaped structure (Emery, Tracey, and Ladd, 1954, p. 27; Newell, 1956, p. 344; Banner, 1952, p. 1). This algal or Lithothamnion (Porolithon) ridge (Plate 14), which Banner calls the coralline ridge, is reddish pink or orange-red in color and of widths from 2 to 15 meters at Raroia (Newell) and 50 to 100 feet at Onotoa (Banner). Generally it rises from 6 inches to 2 feet above the main reef flat lagoonward of it, but the cuesta type may rise to as much as $3\frac{1}{2}$ feet (Emery, Tracey, and Ladd, 1954).

Newell (1956, p. 345) stated that "In a sense the algal ridge is intertidal, but may rise locally above mean high-tide level. It is constantly bathed by breaking waves in exposed places, but it is occasionally dry on the lee side of the atoll in quiet weather during low tides." On the other hand, Emery, Tracey, and Ladd (1954, p. 27) asserted that "The upper limit of each [type of algal ridge] appears to be determined by the height to which the waves can wash at low tide, because algae of the types growing on the reef edge cannot survive even partial desiccation—they require, in fact, considerable circulation of agitated water."

Fosberg and MacNeil (1954) described it as higher and more irregular opposite islets, lower and smoother at intervals between islets. The structure is extremely strong and resistant to wave action. Commonly its surface is extremely rough. Although algal ridges generally are absent in leeward reef sectors, "On certain exceptional reefs, such as at Pokak, the leeward reef does emerge and is covered by a relatively smooth pavement of hard pink algae." In any case, the algal ridge is almost constantly moist. At low-tide stage the waves are broken against the algal ridge and only slight waves are felt in the *back-ridge trough*. With a moderately rough sea, a sheet of water pours over the ridge with each breaker, though the mean level of the leeward sea may have dropped below that of the reef flat (Newell, 1956, p. 345). When the tide is high, only a part of the wave force is expended against the algal ridge; the rest sweeps across the back-ridge trough to push over the reef flat, carrying enough energy to move coral rocks a foot or two in diameter (Banner, 1952, p. 2).

The deposition of calcium carbonate along the reef front is mainly as *in situ* skeletons of coralline algae (Porolithon), scleractinian corals, and hydroid corals. Although this is the zone of greatest productivity of the coralline algae, their skeletons rarely compose as much as 25 per cent of the solid material of the rock, between voids, and commonly they are not conspicuous in old storm blocks (Newell, 1955, p. 303):

Detrital grains of limestone and whole tests of Foraminifera have only very limited opportunity to lodge at the surface here because of exposure to vigorous wave and current action. When it is first formed, this rock consists of a rigid, open framework of sturdy, encrusting corals, overgrown and reinforced by laminar deposits of coralline algae. The reef front, at Raroia Atoll, contains primary open spaces estimated at 25% to more than 50% of the volume of the rock. For the most part they remain unfilled wherever they are exposed to vigorous turbulence. Successive generations of corals and algae bury the voids without completely sealing them. The progressive obstruction to circulation of sea water through the reef frame eventually leads to the gradual filling of the primary voids with tests of Foraminifera and fine reef detritus.

This pattern of reef porosity was found in the celebrated borings on Funafuti Atoll (Cullus, 1904, p. 403) and in the borings at Bikini and Eniwetok (Emery, Tracey, and Ladd, 1954; Fosberg and MacNeil, 1956).

Surge channels

Some of the grooves of the seaward slope continue into or through the algal ridge as *surge channels* (Plate 17), as shown in Fig. 28. Newell (1956,

p. 346) called the surge channels headward extensions of the outer grooves. These may reach lengths of 50 to 300 feet inward from the reef edge, with depths generally of 5 to 10 feet and widths from 1 to 4 feet, narrowing as they proceed inward. The channels generally are found in low areas of the reef flat and thus are excurrent areas which drain seaward much of the time (Newell, 1956, p. 346).

Pavement-forming algae cover the back slopes of the ridge and form thickened rims along the edges of the surge channels. By lateral growth they often arch over and at times may roof over channels, converting the channels into tunnels ending in blow holes which spout water with each oncoming wave and suck out water with each wave trough. According to Emery, Tracey, and Ladd, 1954, p. 27, "From some of these the water issues from geyserlike algal craters, in other areas from a series of holes along an old fissure; in still other places hundreds of holes may form a honeycomb of openings" (Plate 45).

Because of the genetic connection between the surge channels and grooves with wave power, surge channels are as generally absent from leeward reef margins as are algal ridges. "Here the margin may be a flat or irregular surface simply bevelled off into the *fore-slope* or there may be a raised area a few inches to a foot above the general reef level. There is ordinarily a conspicuous growth of living corals, often so dense as to make walking over the surface uncomfortable and hazardous. Tide pools of various sizes are common. On many atolls the leeward margin is not uncommonly uncovered at low tide" (Fosberg and MacNeil, 1954).

The reef flat

The windward seaward reef flat reaches from the algal ridge to the islet's seaward shore, if opposite an islet, otherwise to a central part of the erosional platform that extends to the lagoon margins. According to Newell (1956, p. 349),

Zonation more or less parallel to the reef margin is largely a consequence of the fact that the reef flat slopes shoreward from the crest of the algal ridge to a trough or pool some two-thirds to three-fourths of the distance from the reef edge. The trough may be as much as 40 to 50 cm. lower than the outer part of the reef flat. Because of this the outer part of the platform generally is drained before the lower inner part . . . The reef flat descends gently from the algal ridge to a low trough some 5 to 10 meters from shore. The slope is the result both of upbuilding along the reef margin and erosion near the shore . . . The excurrent areas of the reef flat vary considerably around the atoll. They are alike in being appreciably lower than adjoining reef sectors. Some of these . . . may be nearly devoid of bottom organisms, although adjoining reef sectors are well-populated.

These areas commonly are furrowed by irregular shallow grooves converging, fan-like, towards the gap in the algal ridge.

Biological zonation on the windward seaward reef flat is prominent, owing to the varying conditions of water depths and the accompanying exposure and temperature conditions. Figure 76 shows zonation for corals on such a reef. Emery, Tracey, and Ladd (1954, 27–8) described the zones inward from the algal ridge as including a *coral-algal zone,* an *outer Heliopora zone,* the *main reef flat,* and an *inner Heliopora zone.* These zones will be discussed further in Chapters 9 and 10.

Some general aspects of types of reef flats are indicated in the following description from Fosberg and MacNeil (1945):

The reef flat is evidently a plantation surface of hard, firm limestone which may probably have been formed at the present sea level by erosion of a former higher reef. Where it lies at present low tide level it is frequently a relatively smooth pavement-like surface, over which, at low tide vehicles may be driven freely. On such flats occur long cracks, either straight or curving, often hundreds of feet long, whose cause is not known. There is usually a thin layer of fine sand, often mostly living foraminifera, held by a felt-like growth of algae over most of the surface where smooth. Erosion remnants and storm-cast boulders may locally mar this surface with major irregularities [Plates 18 and 66]. Tide pools may also occur, especially in the outer zone just back of the reef margin where they may be so common as to form an almost continuous trough or moat. Elsewhere this strip may merely dip below tide level to form a shallow depression always remaining under water . . . Erosional remnants have been observed locally in this zone forming horn-like or peak-like projections extending several feet above the general surface . . . Here and there on reef flats may be found patches covered by deposits of irregularly broken limestone fragments, varying in size up to a maximum of two or three feet in diameter. These may be either loose or weakly cemented together or to the reef surface. They have been termed "rubble tracts" and consist of material torn from the edges of the reef or resulting from erosion of reef-rock of former higher surfaces.

Many investigators, including Fosberg and MacNeil, have noted that occasionally enormous blocks are torn from the reef margin and tossed upon the reef flat. Some of these are pushed by storm waves nearly to the edge of the beach. In 1956 the writer observed two such blocks each 6 by 6 by 6 feet on the southeastern reef flat of Jaluit (Plate 19) about 20 feet off the beach edge and 150 feet from the reef edge from which they were torn. Dana (1851, pp. 25–51) told of seeing a similar block 8 feet high and 15 feet in diameter on the south reef of Aratica Atoll in the Tuamotus. On Napuka in the same group, Crossland (1927) observed that the larger blocks thrown upon the reef flat were 10 by 6 by 4 feet in dimensions. On

Rose Atoll in the Samoan group, Mayor (1924, p. 75) found hundreds of blocks of limestone scattered over the flat "uniformly about 5.5 feet high" but of larger lengths and widths.

Wherever the reef flat is covered more-or-less continuously by marine water, the surface is likely to have growths of corals or coralline algae. The latter may form a relatively smooth surface, but the corals are often very sharp and rough and make walking difficult and sometimes hazardous, because of their brittleness and readiness to break or crumble under heavy weight (Plates 48 to 50). In the shallower areas especially, upward growth is limited, so that lateral growth predominates, and the forms, therefore, tend to be tabular, often ringlike, when not coalesced to form wide flats (Plates 51 and 52). These ringlike, generally massive corals are termed "microatolls," although the phrase is not an entirely happy one. Although growth is chiefly lateral and on the fringes, there is no central depression resembling a lagoon. Instead, the upper surface of these microatolls is composed of dead coral veneered with a thin mat of algae mixed with foraminiferous sand. The microatolls most often comprise Heliopora corals, porites, and sometimes the hydrozoan Millepora (Emery, Tracey, and Ladd, pp. 27–8). The more-fragile, branching Acropora colonies (Plate 46) also grow in the shallow waters of the reef flat, adding beautiful shades of pale olive-green and pale blue to the dull brownish black of the reef pavement. The dead rock surfaces of the reef flat and of the islets are generally covered by a thin film of algae, especially the blue-green algae (Newell, 1956, p. 359).

Where there are no islets, and the reef flat stretches from seaward margin to lagoon margin, there is less distinctive zonation. Such inner reefs may be divided into two broad classes. One comprises those partly occupied by eroded low platforms or other elevated reef areas covered by water during half or less than half of the tidal cycle. The rock of these groins generally is composed of boulder conglomerate and is similar in grain size and physical appearance to detrital limestone.

In some places it is similar to beach conglomerate or even to beach sandstone. Thin sections of the rock show cavities and pores mostly filled with brown, finely detrital to microgranular paste, altered here and there to finely granular calcite. Some grains are firmly cemented by acicular carbonate and some open cavities are lined with minute crystals . . . The brown paste probably represents fine material washed over the rock and filtered down through pore spaces and cavities both during and after deposition of the rock mass (Emery, Tracey, and Ladd, 1954, pp. 31–2).

These rock groins appear most often to be of sedimentary origin and of the same type as those described for Kapingamarangi by McKee (1956, pp. 5–6):

Beds of sedimentary rock rise above the reef flats along the seaward margins of all the large islands and many of the small ones, and they crop out locally within many islands. Because in most places the clastic particles of which they are formed are clearly discernible and because their stratification commonly is prominent after weathering, these rocks, for the most part, are readily distinguishable from the reef rock on which they rest. Isolated pedestals and undercut blocks formed of similar clastic rock stand on the reef flat considerable distances seaward from some islands—remnants of earlier island masses.

McKee mentioned stratified rock standing 4 to 5 feet above the present high-tide level. They appeared to be leached and partly phosphatized in some instances. He points out that rocks having a similar high-level position in many atolls of the Pacific have been recorded (David and Sweet, 1904, pp. 67–8; Ladd, Tracey, Wells, and Emery, 1950, p. 413) and that they are generally considered to represent deposits residual from a time when the sea level was higher than at present, owing to eustatic changes.

Not all such elevated island rocks are of this sedimentary type, however. Friederici (1910, pp. 103–6) found at Maria Atoll in the Tuamotus a half dozen of the smaller Tuamotuan species of *Tridacna gigas* standing in upright position with the shells open upward and grown fast at their base to the "old ledge" of the raised reef, and found similar occurrences of *Tridacna gigas in situ* on rock at Niau Atoll at elevations of 4 to 5 meters. This evidence points to the character of the rock at those places as true *reef rock,* as differentiated from *sedimentary rock.*

These types of reef surfaces on the reef flat sometimes may be eroded to a jagged surface and often occur both between islets and as the eroded seaward continuation of the rock platform underlying the islets. Their dark coloring makes them very noticeable on aerial photographs of reefs (Plate 20).

In the other class of inter-islet or inner reef flat, the flats are submerged except for a brief period during extreme low tide. The absence of islets allows the ocean water to wash entirely across the reef at most stages of tide, and in some pools or depressions there may be some circulation even at low tide. Where ecological conditions are favorable corals may be abundant. In other areas, especially on the lagoon side of the inner reef, sand flats or gravel deposits may cover wide stretches or may even emerge as sand bars at low tide.

From the marginal zone of the reef to the lagoon, rock that forms the consolidated platform of the reef flat consists of progressively greater amounts of unsorted organic remains and angular detrital material, compared with the amount of coral and algae (Emery, Tracey, and Ladd, 1954, pp. 30–1). This material appears in thin section to be cemented by a gray to brown paste or by a rind of carbonate.

Beaches

Somewhere between the land and the reef margins on each side of an islet is the area known as the beach. McCurdy (1947, p. 3) defined the beach as "the zone from the low water mark to the inland limit of the wave-deposited debris." Sverdrup, Johnson, and Fleming (1954, p. 43) stated that "The beach is defined as the zone extending from the upper and landward limit of effective wave action to low-tide level . . . The upper part of the beach is covered only during periods of high waves, particularly when storms coincide with high spring tides. The slope of the beach is largely determined by the texture of the sediments, but the extent of the beach will depend upon the range in tide."

Both definitions pose problems when applied to coral atolls and reef islands. Obviously, according to these definitions, all the part of the reef flat that dries at low tide from the landward shore outward toward the reef margin could be classified as a beach, although the wave-deposited debris may be only scattered sand, gravel, and boulders. However, scientific writers concerned with atolls do not consider the reef flat as part of the beach (Emery, Tracey, and Ladd, 1954, pp. 35–6; McKee, 1956, p. 8), although few delimit the beach precisely. It seems clear, however, that the beach is regarded as the fringing part of the islets above the level of the reef flat and that the lower limit is marked by a relatively sharp change in slope upward from the reef flat, whatever the nature of the sedimentary materials composing the beach.

The development of the reef islet beach occurs when the rush of the shallow waves across the reef flat or across the lagoon meets the sudden elevations of the islet rock, or the sand, gravel, and boulder accumulations piled up during a storm on the inner part of the flat. A beach by definition implies an accumulation of sediments on the sloping shore. Where no sediments accumulate, therefore, there is no beach. Thus we find McKee (1956, p. 8) declaring: "Beaches are relatively scarce on the seaward sides of Kapingamarangi islands; furthermore they are small and short-lived. Most of them are perched on the bevelled surfaces of stratified island rock at various distances above low-tide level." Where old elevated island rock underlies an islet and protrudes on the seaward islet margins, it may end more or less abruptly and ledgelike or it may slope (Fosberg and MacNeil, 1954).

There is usually a ramp-like slope of irregularly eroded rock, a few to many yards wide, extending down to the reef flat just above low tide level. There may be a transitional area of irregular or roughened rock slightly higher than the reef flat. The ramp-like slope may be termed the *erosion-*

ramp, as it is here that the active erosion of this elevated reef-rock [or clastic island] is taking place . . . Locally, the erosion ramp may be covered by beaches of sand, gravel, or cobbles, or the beaches may be restricted to above the edge of the protruding rock platform. The ramp itself is commonly found on the seaward side of the islets and frequently extends around along the channels between islets, but is rarely or never observed on the lagoon side. Deposits of any sort of material, sand, gravel, boulders, unsorted rubble, or even large slabs may be piled on and around the hard rock core of the islet. They may even cover it completely, in which case the islet may be mistaken for [the type formed by accumulations of loose materials].

The lagoonward beach differs generally from the seaward beaches not only in being more extensive and continuous, but it differs also in composition and color. Lagoon beaches generally are composed of finer materials, particularly where they are on the lee shore of islets where their most common constituents are foraminiferous sands of tan or orange color. Seaward beaches sometimes also have a large percentage of foraminiferous sand, but they also contain large amounts of comminuted mollusk shells and fragments of coral and coralline algae (Figs. 30 and 31). The type of beach sediment occurring depends in part upon the character of the orientation to prevailing winds and waves and to exposure to alongshore and convective currents. Seaward beaches are steeper than lagoon beaches. Wells (1951, p. 4) found that Arno Atoll had seaward beaches with slopes up to 20°, whereas lagoon beaches are wider, with slopes of 5 to 10°.

Beach rock

A very common and conspicuous feature of most atoll reefs or atoll islets are narrow elongate stratified beds of consolidated sands, gravels, and other conglomerate sediments (Plate 21), most often with a definite dip, varying from 5 to 8° (Emery, Tracey, and Ladd, 1954, p. 47) to 15 to 20° (Newell, 1956, p. 368). These are beds of beach rock derived from cementation of beach sediments. Where formed from sand beaches and well indurated, "in all respects the rock resembles beach sandstone" (Emery, Tracey, and Ladd, 1954, p. 47). McKee (1956, p. 10) stated that on Kapingamarangi Atoll the rocks varied greatly in texture and in degree of cementation, some being extremely friable, some well cemented and dense. Although he stated that much of the rock is stratified and cross-stratified and had all the characteristics normally attributed to beach rock, details of its origin still are not entirely clear.

The occurrence of beach rock may be found on all shores of an islet, but they are common only on seaward reefs and shores. Newell found them quite rare along the lagoon shore of Raroia. However, Emery, Tracey, and

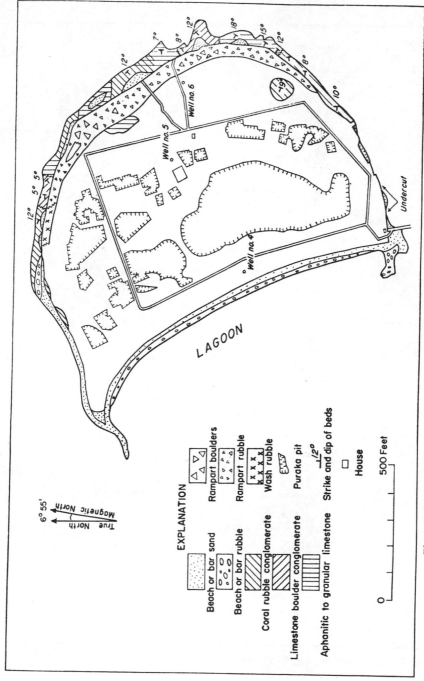

Fig. 30. Geologic map of Werua Islet, Kapingamarangi Atoll. [From McKee (1956).]

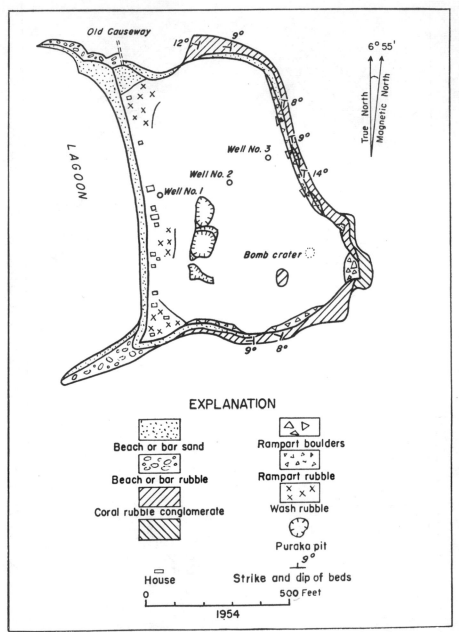

EXPLANATION

Beach or bar sand

Beach or bar rubble

Coral rubble conglomerate

Rampart boulders

Rampart rubble

Wash rubble

Puraka pit

House

Strike and dip of beds

0   500 Feet

1954

Fig. 31. Geologic map of Taringa Islet, Kapingamarangi Atoll. [From McKee (1956).]

Ladd found the rock on both shores of Aomoen Islet on Bikini. McKee and the writer found beach rock mostly on the seaward reef flats or islet shores in the inter-islet channel areas at Kapingamarangi Atoll. However, aerial photographs of various atolls in the Marshalls clearly show beach rock completely encircling islets and the areas occupied by former islets now washed away by storms. Eroded ridges of beach rock may often be seen considerable distances seaward of the present islet beaches. Newell described some that are 20 to 30 meters off the present shore, and the writer observed two lines of beach rock seaward of Torongahai Islet on Kapingamarangi Atoll that reached 100 to 200 feet seaward (Wiens, 1956, p. 38). They mark the former seaward limits of the islets lagoonward of them.

The succession of consolidated beach-rock beds may produce a 10 to 20 yard horizontal extent of rock, but usually the series is from 3 to 4 yards wide. However, the total vertical dimension of the series is not more than the distance between mean high and low tides except where such beds persist from an earlier higher sea level. In such cases they may extend 1 or 2, or even 4 feet above mean high tide, and if modern beds have been added to the series, down to low-tide level (Fosberg and MacNeil, 1954).

Beach zones

The islet beach from the reef flat to the top of the beach ridge may be subdivided topographically. The low-water line of the beach by commonly accepted usage for atolls coincides with the line where the beach slope meets the reef flat, and this may be called the "shore line" of the islet. The high-water line, of course, depends upon the tidal cycle and the periodicity of the phases of the moon and sun, and, on occasion, upon peculiarities of the weather. Between the high- and low-water lines is the plunge point, a variable zone where the waves break, whose location depends upon the height of the waves and the stage of the tide (Sverdrup, Johnson, and Fleming, 1954, p. 44). Above the high-water line the beaches rise to one or more ridges (or berms), which constitute impermanent terraces formed by deposition during calm weather and by erosion during storms. Storms may also construct depositional ridges, termed "storm beaches" by Fosberg and MacNeil, surmounting the usual berms. Where they are of coarser materials (pebble to boulder consistency) they present greater resistance to erosion by ordinary waves and may be called "beach ramparts" or may be named based upon their constituent materials, such as "pebble ramparts" or "boulder ramparts" (Plates 22 and 23).

Because their origin derives from the higher storm waves, pebble, cobble, and, especially, boulder ramparts are usually found only on the sides of the islet exposed to ocean waves. Ramparts are usually lacking on the lagoon side of islets, although where lateral exposure to storm winds occur, lagoon waves may be strong enough to erect a boulder or cobble rampart (McKee, 1956, pp. 29–30; Wiens, 1956, p. 63).

The shore may also be classified into two divisions, called "foreshore" and "backshore." The foreshore is the part of the beach seaward of the crest of the highest berm or beachridge. The backshore is the slope or terrace inland of the crest. However the term backshore may refer also to the inland-facing slope of any shore ridge or rampart.

Islets or land areas

A statistical analysis of aspects of land location and islet number on Pacific atolls has been presented in Chapter 2. The dynamics affecting land evolution and morphology will be presented in a later chapter. Here an attempt is made merely to describe the general structure of land on atolls.

Technically, land may be considered to start with the shoreline at the low-tide mark; thus it encompasses the beach, which, however, is a transition zone between marine and terrestrial areas. The land-area proper may be considered to be the part of the island that is "dry land," or the area above the level of ordinary high tides. It is to be noted, of course, that virtually no atoll land (except for that of "raised atolls") is immune to possibly complete inundation by the tsunami and typhoon waves, since the highest elevations of islets on atoll reefs generally do not exceed 15 to 20 feet. Emery, Tracey, and Ladd (1954, p. 23) stated that most of the islands of Bikini are only 8 to 12 feet above low-tide level, although the top of a dune on one islet was 23 feet above the reef flat. The maximum height of land at Raroia (Newell, 1956, p. 329) was 6 meters, or about 20 feet. At Kapingamarangi, peak elevations of islets were from 5 to 12 feet (Wiens, 1956, p. 13), although mounds built by man may rise 1 or 2 feet above this. Many islets, however, rise only 1, 2, or 3 feet above high-tide level.

The characteristic feature of islet margins are ridges, often found all around an islet, but most especially outstanding on the seaward and channel sides and somewhat more subdued and occasionally lacking on lagoon sides. Generally they are broad and rounded in profile, reaching 2 to 4 feet above the general level of the islet, often sloping down gradually to a more-or-less central depression from which there is a more gentle slope upward to the lagoonside shore ridge, usually one to several feet lower than the seaward shore ridge. Small dunes occasionally occur, commonly on lagoon shores facing the prevailing winds, i.e., west reef islets. Vegetation taking root on beaches may stop the wind-driven sand and thus lead both to the formation of dune ridges and the anchoring of them with a measure of stability. Other profiles reveal gentle downslopes from the seaward ridge all the way to the backshore trough of the lagoon beach ridge.

"The most conspicuous surface feature[s] of atoll islets," according to Fosberg and MacNeil (1954), are the enormous boulder ridges (Plate 22), often termed "boulder ramparts," which occur on some islets of most or all atolls. They are of rather random distribution, being known from coasts facing in almost all directions, and from lagoon as well as seaward sides. They are, however, far more frequent along the seaward coasts and on islets on west reefs. The texture of the material ranges up through cobble sizes to boulders, and different segments and different layers in the same ridge may be of different average size. The highest such ridge known in the northern Marshalls is on the southern coast of Lae Islet, Lae Atoll. It is about 18 feet high, with the top several feet composed of huge boulders, upward of a foot in diameter. Generally the size range is much smaller than this and the height is between 5 and 10 feet. The rocks are frequently very angular and sharp and the upper layers may have relatively little finer material in the interstices. The profile of the ridges varies from narrow with the seaward side rather steep, to broad, as much as 100 yards wide, with very gradual slopes. Where the ridge is wide there may frequently be a secondary ridge developed at its outer margin, this one much sharper and with a steep seaward slope.

"Both beach ridges and boulder ridges in some situations occur in series, with more recent ones partially superimposed on the older in a seaward or lagoonward direction from the interior of the islet. Such cases are taken to result from successive storms, each depositing a great mass of material. The vegetation on such series may be observed to be more mature on the inner ridges, and the rocks may be more blackened, also, on the inner ones" (Fosberg and MacNeil, 1954). The writer noted an example of this at Kapingamarangi Atoll (Wiens, 1956, p. 38), where on the southwestern and western sides of Torongahai Islet there appears to be a succession of three broad ridges, each probably laid by a separate typhoon. The first is just inward of the modern beach. A second appears about 40 feet inland and has a backshore slope measuring at least 30 feet. A third ridge appears up to 150 to 250 feet inland. The land here, thus, must have built outward in a westerly to southwesterly direction.

Since the backshore of these boulder and gravel ramparts may reach several hundred feet inland on the smaller and narrower islets, the seaward half or third of the islet interiors may be very bouldery and rough. Unless they rest on a more compact foundation of sand or conglomerate island rock, sea water may infiltrate through their interstices far into the islet interior, resulting in saline ground water and soil.

Where well-developed boulder ramparts are found, one also may at times discover enormous boulders and blocks of reef rock carried inland by typhoon waves. Extensive areas covered by large blocks and boulders are termed "block fields" or "boulder beds," as the case may be. McKee (1956, p. 8) uses the term "rampart wash" for the rubble or debris that is spread by storm waves as a sheet below and inland from the rampart crest. He indicated that these sheets extend inland on large islets for as much as 250 feet. On small islets at Kapingamarangi Atoll the writer has seen the entire islet surface covered by such rubble. Generally, however, the constituent materials of islets grade into finer debris and finally into the foraminiferal sand of the lagoon beach.

The interior topography may exhibit one or more depressions, and troughs occasionally appear to cut across an islet. Manmade or man-modified depressions generally take the form of taro pits, sometimes planted with taro, but in many areas abandoned to natural growth. In such depressions, the bottom surfaces usually are below the surface of the fresh-water lens and they may be under water following high-tide stage (usually with a slight lag). Sometimes they are no more than narrow trenches; at other times they may cover many acres. They are generally located in the middle parts or somewhat lagoonward of the middle parts of islets. The soil in them is mucklike, and the banks of such pits or depressions are bordered by ridges or dug-out sand and gravel, some of which rise 8 to 12 feet above the pit floors.

Where the depressions are from natural causes, the slopes are more gradual and not vertical as in the case of many taro pits. Natural depressions parallel to the long axis of the islets may result from storm-built beach ridges, which bound the peripheral of islets on all sides. Other depressions may result from storm scour. These may be irregular in shape or take the form of a saddle or transverse trench if storm-pushed ocean water has poured across an islet into the lagoon. On many atolls interior salt ponds or pools may occur because of porous substratum rock which permits marine-water infiltration, as on Jabwor and Imroj Islets of Jaluit Atoll. Sometimes these pools of salt water may have tidal inlets from the lagoon, as on Namorik Atoll and Ailinglaplap. As a result of the bombings of certain atolls in World War II many artificial depressions have been created in the form of bomb craters (Plate 84), which often have water in their bottoms, sometimes salt, other times brackish or nearly fresh, but generally foul. Only rarely are there tolerably fresh ponds on atoll islets. The depressions with salt water usually are associated with mangrove tree growth.

Islets composed entirely or with their lagoonward parts composed of successive beach ridges, have a topography of alternate ridges and furrows.

The lagoon reef flat

Reef flats on the lagoonside of islets generally are discontinuous or may be lacking altogether where sand and other sediments have obscured them. This is most apt to occur where islet shores are situated close to the lagoon reef margin. The sediments of the beach tend to continue into the sediment slopes reaching from the reef margin to the lagoon floor. In such situations no reef flat or reef margin occurs on the lagoon sides of islets. Erosional and depositional processes have caused most atoll islets to migrate inward toward the lagoon reef margins, so only rarely are extensive flats found lagoonward of islets. Examples of such lagoon reef flats occur off the narrow part of Ebon Islet on Ebon Atoll (Plate 15), where strips 100 to 400 feet wide dry at low tide to amazingly flat surfaces not unlike that found on seaward reefs (Wiens, 1957, pp. 5–6). Newell (1956, p. 352, plate 34) shows a great lagoon reef flat 700 meters wide which he believed to be built on a gravel fan. Well-defined zonation of the reef occurs less often on lagoon reefs compared to seaward reefs, but where extensive drying flats occur on the lagoon side with gradation of depth to the lagoon reef margin, zonation may be marked. In contrast to the seaward reef flat, the lagoon reef flat often has a thin to thick covering of fine silts and sand not usually found on seaward reef flats.

Lagoon reef margins

The character of the lagoon reef margin depends locally upon the movement of sediments by prevailing currents and upon the orientation and exposure. "From the reef front there is progressive increase seaward and lagoonward in the proportion of transported skeletal material and bioclastic debris, as compared to *in situ* frame material. The transition from solid reef to fragmental constituents is usually, but not invariably abrupt" (Newell, 1955, p. 305). Great accumulations of sediments along the lagoon floor near the lagoon reef margins may result in a smooth edge and more gradual lagoon slope. This probably is more apt to be true of small, shallow lagoons because they tend to fill up more quickly with sediments. However, even deep lagoons, such as that of Kapingamarangi, one of the deepest in Micronesia, appear largely to be bordered by relatively smooth-margined inclines of sediments. On the other hand, Ebon, which has an even smaller lagoon and is of shallower depth, has some very abrupt and locally vertical drops from the lagoon margin to the lagoon floor.

Differences in the lagoon reef also are related to location on exposed windward lagoon rims or on protected leeward lagoon rims. Newell (1956, p. 352) found the leeward (southeastern) shore at Raroia lacking in well-developed shore reefs but having instead innumerable coral heads (mainly massive Porites) and small patch reefs. He attributed the differences on the two sides of the atoll probably to (1) more effective delivery of oxygen and food to the windward shore, and (2) more favorable conditions of sedimentation. However, insufficient evidence is available from field studies to generalize too definitely on the reef differences between windward and leeward lagoon rims. It is certain, nevertheless, that lagoon current patterns both in horizontal and vertical water movements affect the nature of lagoon reef development. Since these patterns differ from lagoon to lagoon because of configuration peculiarities, lagoon reef character frequently changes along the rim.

Lagoon terraces

Because few sufficiently detailed depth surveys of atoll lagoons have been made, it is not known how many atoll lagoons have terraces at various depths. It has been established, however, that the northern Marshalls atolls of Bikini, Eniwetok, and Rongerik all have terraces up to 2 miles wide in parts of their lagoon rims. At Rongelap no such terrace was disclosed by the survey, but this may be because of inadequate sounding densities (Emery, Tracey, and Ladd, 1954, pp. 1, 50, 95, 104, 114). Moreover, the terrace discovered at Rongerik was on a considerably different level. In the first two atolls the depths of the lagoon terrace was between 8 and 10 fathoms, with a preponderance in the 8-fathom level. For this reason the investigators termed it the "8-fathom terrace." At Rongerik, however, the terrace ranged from 0 to 4 fathoms and averaged nearly 20 feet, or between 3 and 4 fathoms. Again, because dependence was mainly on the Japanese soundings, the inadequate density of the soundings may have resulted in the lack of indication of a deeper terrace. Aerial photographs of other lagoon reefs in the Marshalls show a mild slope from shore to a reef margin at relatively shallow depths, which may correspond to the 20-foot terrace of Rongerik. Newell (1956, p. 352) found that the "shore reefs" at Raroia "rest on a shallow terrace which may correspond to the 8-meter terrace of the sea reef."

There is little doubt that high-density sounding surveys of other atolls in the Pacific and elsewhere probably would reveal terraces at two or more depth contours in the lagoon peripheral, indicating earlier erosion levels at lower stands of the sea surface. Confirmation is presently lacking, however. A discussion of certain erosion benches or terraces in the lagoon in shallow depths as revealed by HO charts is presented in Chapter 5.

Patch reefs

One of the spectacular sights over certain atolls is the occurrence of hundreds and sometimes thousands of patch reefs that provide changing hues to the blues and greens and olive-browns of the lagoon waters (Plates 6 and 20). They provide important habitats for reef fishes and other lagoon fauna at the same time that they pose dangers to lagoon navigation. Charts and maps usually indicate only a small number of the patch reefs that exist. Frequently, the outlines of the smaller ones are shown only by a rosette-type symbol. Except for lagoons for which aerial photographs are available, even an estimate of the total number of patch reefs is not available. However, Newell (1956, p. 353) using aerial photographs estimated between 1,500 and 2,000 patch reefs at Raroia. At Bikini and Eniwetok, where the most extensive soundings have been made, there were 913 and 2,293 patch reefs, respectively. These, however, include coral knolls that are deeply submerged as well as those that reach the surface, so they do not correspond to the number that are observable from the air or surface (Emery, Tracey, and Ladd, 1954, p. 96).

The diameter of the patch reefs varies from small pinnacles a few yards wide to immense "table reefs" with diameters of over a mile. Although atoll charts are unreliable guides to patch-reef distribution, the writer's examination of charts showed no distinctive distribution patterns for lagoon patch reefs except for those associated with the mouths of passes.

Different lagoons may have concentrations in different parts of the lagoon, but no pattern of marked concentration appears. Newell found the large number at Raroia "scattered over the entire lagoon" but said they were somewhat less numerous toward the leeward (southeastern) shore than elsewhere. Emery, Tracey, and Ladd found that the chart for Eniwetok showed "no preferred side of the lagoon for either large or small coral knolls. In fact, the 20 coral knolls having diameters of more than a mile show a strikingly even spacing." On Bikini they found that "The distribution of coral knolls, like the character of the lagoon floor, appears to be controlled by the sounding density" (Emery, Tracey, and Ladd, 1954, p. 52).

However, an inspection of Newell's Plates 29 and 30 (1956) leads to the ready conviction that the patch reefs "are not entirely distributed at random." Newell points out that many are arranged in rows generally oriented downwind or more rarely transverse to the wind direction. In an air flight from Truk to Ponape in 1956 the writer was struck by a similar orientation of patch reefs in one lagoon (Oroluk) and by the fact that, as Newell noted, many of these patch reefs "show a tendency for the leeward end of the reef to taper more gradually than the windward end, streamlined in teardrop form." McKee (1956, p. 34) in his study of patch reefs at Kapingamarangi Atoll stated that "The distribution and orientation of patch reefs in the lagoon seem to reflect in large measure the trends of currents and waves . . . The many small patch reefs immediately inside the north-western and western arcs of the atoll apparently developed in response to waves of maximum fetch before the dominant winds. Likewise a general northwestward [elongation] of many reefs in the lagoon center probably reflects this dominant wave direction." From the above discussion we may be warranted in concluding that factors of wind and current directions exercise an influence in the alignment and shapes of at least many of the patch reefs within atoll lagoons, although patch reefs may appear in any part of a lagoon in the absence of unfavorable factors, such as high rates of sedimentation and sedimentary abrasion.

The lagoon floor: coral knolls

The character of the lagoon floor in general is attributable to sedimentation processes and to the constructional processes resulting in coral knolls. When the latter reach the surface or close to the surface they become patch reefs. It is obvious from the preceding discussion of the hundreds and thousands of patch reefs that occur in some lagoons that the simple picture of the lagoon floor as a more or less smooth-bottomed basin-shaped structure may be quite inaccurate. Perhaps such a picture would be justified only for relatively shallow lagoons where excessive sedimentation has killed off and buried former coral growths.

Figure 32, which shows the profiles of the lagoon floor of Eniwetok, provides a picture of a highly rough bottom topography, although the extreme vertical exaggeration makes broad mounds and plateaus appear like needles and pinnacles. The depths profiles for Kapingamarangi (Wiens, 1956), shown in Fig. 33 with an exaggeration of only about four times, looks more like the reality. In all these profiles numerous coral knolls too small to be shown by contours may give a misleading impression of the flatness of the lagoon floor, even between the knolls shown. To remedy this, Emery, Tracey, and Ladd devised what they termed the "smoothness coefficient," based upon a large number of fathogram sections of the lagoons studied. The results show that the flattest areas correspond to the areas of most abundant fine debris (1954, p. 56), "probably reflecting the mantling or smoothing effect of this deposit. The average smoothness coefficient for the entire lagoon is 4.6, meaning that only 46 per cent of the area is flat within 1 fathom." Average smoothness coefficients for the other atolls in the northern Marshalls were given as follows: Eniwetok, 43 per cent; Rongelap, 50 per cent; and Rongerik, 43 per cent.

Viewed in vertical profile, coral knolls present a great variety of shapes,

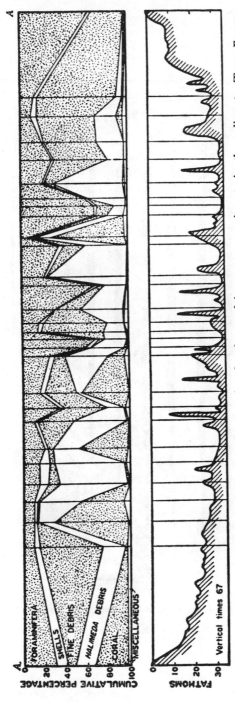

Fig. 32. Cross section across Eniwetok Lagoon showing the abundance of important constituents in the sediments. [From Emery, Tracey, and Ladd (1954).]

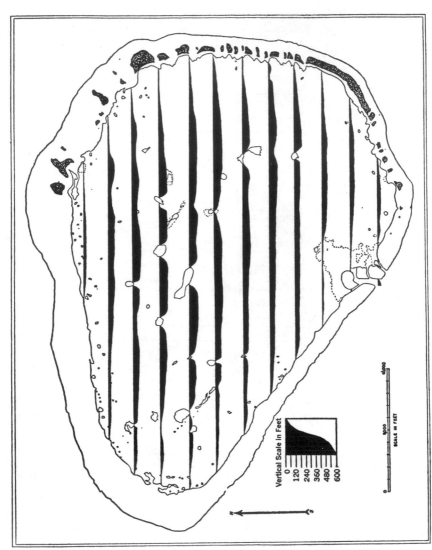

Fig. 33. Depth profiles of Kapingamarangi Lagoon. East-west cross sections are spaced about 2,300 feet apart. Vertical exaggeration, 2.95 times. [From Wiens (1956).]

as well as sizes. Many are shaped like low mounds; others grow to sharp pinnacles and are so small in diameter that they may be hit by soundings only one or two times during a traverse. Those that reach the surface have mesa-like tops because of their inability to continue upward growth and often present surfaces similar to those of the reef flats on the atoll periphery. Indeed, Newell found that the marginal and surface corals of the patch reefs on Raroia form the same associations as those of the windward shore reef. Still others may rise from broad bases supporting mushroom-shaped structures. Emery, Tracey, and Ladd (1954, p. 52) cite Dana's (1872, pp. 139–40) quotation from the journal of J. A. Whipple, who described a "coral head" standing in water 50 feet deep. Its trunk, which made up two-thirds of its height, was only 15 feet in diameter in the upper part, but it supported a tabular mass 100 feet in diameter whose top was bare at low tide. Four coral knolls surveyed on Bikini had varying shapes, viewed as patch reefs from the air. The contoured side slopes ranged up to 45°, but some other knolls examined by diving gear had vertical slopes for as much as 10 fathoms of their depth from the surface. Newell (1956, p. 353) sounded the depths around some wind-aligned elongated coral knolls and found them characteristically steeper on the windward than on the leeward ends, with intermediate slopes on the sides. He stated that the margins down to 10 to 15 meters are very steep, with a few overhanging ledges. Most of the living corals were within this depth range. At greater depths the slopes flatten to angles less than 45°. McKee and the writer made a fathometric survey of a single small coral knoll in Kapingamarangi Lagoon in 1956. Profiles of this knoll (McKee, 1956, p. 33) show that its southwestern side, in its steepest part, slopes down at about 50° within a vertical distance of 40 to 50 feet and that the northwestern side has a slope of about 40°. These were extremes, with the other sides having more gentle slopes. McKee believed this to be probably typical of the surfaced knolls at Kapingamarangi, but no data on profiles of other knolls were gathered.

Lagoon sediments

The character of lagoon sediments and sediment distribution is in part determined by whether a lagoon is with or without deep passes and by how "open" a reef is (that is, how broken the reef rim is or how much of the rim is deeply submerged). Kuenen (1947, p. 21) wrote that "Where openings or passes in an atoll reef are large, deep or numerous, the sedimentation of the lagoon floor is reduced by the sweeping action of the moving water. The reduction of sedimentation encourages the coral reef patch growth in the lagoon. Thus the more complete the encircling reef, the less likely is the lagoon to have coral knolls, pinnacles or other reef patches."

These remarks agree with the findings of Emery, Tracey, and Ladd in the northern Marshalls (1954, p. 56) and of Newell at Raroia (1956, p. 354). The former wrote: "At the greatest depths in the lagoon little of the floor is flat, suggesting that loose sediments are not able to mantle the bottom effectively because of the growth of coral knolls; this is in contrast to conditions in the peripheral areas." Newell reported that "Linear water slicks, occasionally observed between the rows of patch reefs, suggest that these are areas of convergence. The reefs then apparently lie in zones of upwelling water. Because the rows of reefs are spaced from a quarter to one-half of a kilometer apart, the convection cells must extend to the lagoon floor, effectively mixing the entire body of water and preventing accumulation of the finest sediments."

Although only five samples of bottom sediments were obtained out of forty unsuccessful hauls at Raroia lagoon, these samples indicated a general lack of mud areas in this lagoon, suggesting to Newell that the "finest detrital fractions do not accumulate but are carried out the pass in suspension." He pointed out that the adjoining atoll, Takume, which lacks a ship pass, has extensive areas of mud bottom, "as also is the case with Hikueru, Anaa, and probably other enclosed Tuamotu atolls."

As McKee pointed out for Kapingamarangi Lagoon (1956, p. 32), over-all patterns of sediment distributions on lagoon floors (Figs. 34 and 35) are much complicated by the patch reefs and by lagoon currents, which may differ from atoll to atoll. Each coral knoll has sediments on its top and sides of varieties in keeping with the general depth ranges of the coral growths—and lagoon knolls as observed at Bikini and other northern Marshall atolls are entirely or mostly composed of coral growth (Emery, Tracey, and Ladd, pp. 57 and 61). On their lower slopes are accumulated granular debris from their upper parts as well as Halimeda and Foraminifera, which grow on the lagoon floors.

The distribution of sediments for one of the four northern Marshalls atolls investigated by Emery, Tracey, and Ladd is shown in Figs. 32, 36, and 37. These investigations revealed that "The large heavy-walled Foraminifera forms, *Calcarina spengleri* and Marginopora, make up more than 25% and locally more than 50% of the beach sand. Off the beach, Foraminifera decrease in abundance to less than 10%, but in the deepest parts of the lagoon Forminifera are again abundant, comprising as much as 50% of many samples. The assemblage of Foraminifera from the deeper parts of the lagoon is, however, entirely different from that found on the beach, and includes the delicate tests of more than 150 different species." Just off the beaches fine debris comprising comminuted material from many sources, including small amounts of Lithothamnion and other coralline algae, echinoid spines, sponge spicules, and bryozoans, as well as finely fragmented bits of reef and island rock, increases lagoonward to a point several miles from shore, where values of 50 to 75 per cent are common.

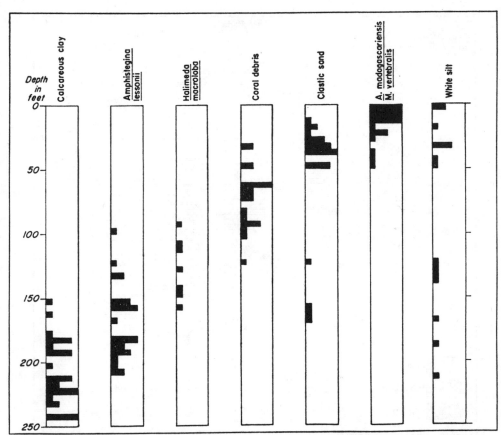

Fig. 34. Relative proportions of principal types of sediments at 5-foot depth intervals in Kapinga-marangi Lagoon. [From McKee (1956).]

Fine debris was found to be less abundant near the middle of the lagoon, where it formed less than 10 per cent of the total components. It appeared to be absent over much of the upwind periphery of the lagoon, but was widespread on the downwind periphery. In the middle and deeper parts of the lagoon, Halimeda debris made up as much as 75 to 100 per cent of each sample. Areas of abundant deep-water Foraminifera had smaller proportions of Halimeda debris.

Although Emery, Tracey, and Ladd pointed out that definitive percentages of sedimentary constituents of a lagoon are not entirely reliable for a number of reasons, there seems to be little doubt that the orders of magnitude obtained probably are about right. Percentages computed for various atolls are shown in Table 7 and show that Halimeda debris is the most

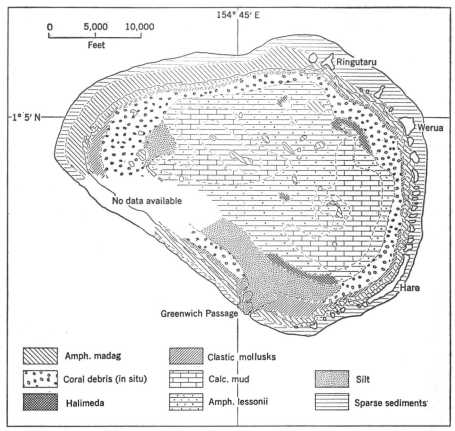

Fig. 35. Distribution of sediments in the lagoon and on reefs of Kapingamarangi Atoll. [From McKee, Chronic, and Leopold (1959).]

abundant constituent, followed by fine debris, coral, Foraminifera, mollusk shells, and miscellaneous elements.

Analysis of the few samples of sediments obtained at Raroia by Byrne (1956, p. 362) led to the conclusion that the distribution of sediments resembled that observed for the northern Marshalls atolls. The only significant difference appeared to be that at Raroia Halimeda is insignificant as a sediment producer.

The lagoons in the various atolls above have about the same range of depths. That deeper lagoons may present differing patterns of sediment distribution is shown by McKee's analysis for Kapingamarangi (1956, pp. 30–3), which has maximum depths 50 to 60 feet deeper than those for the northern Marshalls atolls and more than 100 feet deeper than that for

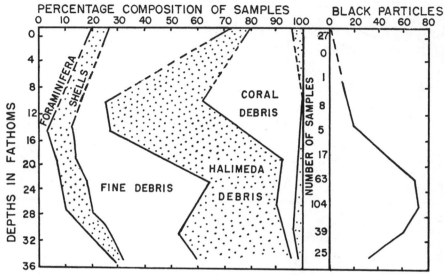

Fig. 36. Variation in composition of sediment with depth in Eniwetok Lagoon. [From Emery, Tracey, and Ladd (1954).]

Raroia. Figure 34 shows the relative proportions of the chief types of sediment in relation to lagoon depths. The "beach" Foraminifera Amphistegina and Marginopora appear to be common to those of the northern Marshalls. What McKee terms "sand," composed dominantly of clastic shell fragments, appears to correspond to the fine debris described by Emery, Tracey, and Ladd. Halimeda also appears to be important at the same depths. What distinguishes Kapingamarangi Lagoon, however, is the "cal-

TABLE 7

Sedimentary Constituents in an Atoll

Atoll	*Foraminifera*	*Fine debris*	*Halimeda debris*	*Coral*
Bikini	5	30	56	9
Rongelap	3	53	36	8
Eniwetok	9	52	26	13
Rongerik	3	36	27	34

careous mud which covers most of the lagoon bottom at depths below 34 fathoms" and which appears to be absent from the shallower floors of Raroia and the Marshalls atolls mentioned. The presence of the mud at great depths may be attributable to the absence of strong currents at these

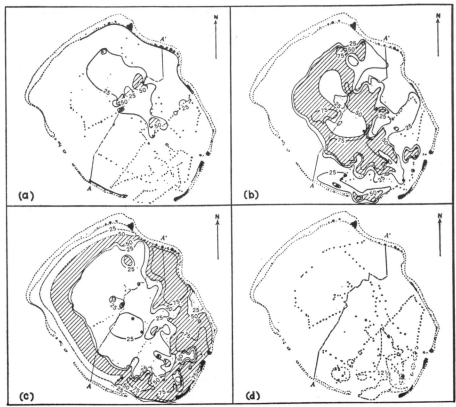

Fig. 37. Abundance of important constituents in the lagoon sediments of Eniwetok Atoll: (a) foraminifera, (b) Halimeda debris, (c) fine debris, (d) shells. Lines of equal abundance are drawn through the 25, 50, and 75 per cent values. The dashed lines indicate reef boundaries. [From Emery, Tracey, and Ladd (1954).]

depths and to the fact that the single pass breaking the southwestern reef has a much shallower depth than the deeper parts of the lagoon. In his analysis (1956) McKee stated that

The sedimentary belts within the lagoon appear to represent for the most part, the normal habitats of the various organisms involved, for a large proportion of samples show little of the mixing that would be expected if organisms had been transported by currents into pockets of accumulation. Orange foraminiferal sand of near-shore areas (belt 1) grades outward and downward into white clastic sand of belt 2. Likewise, there is gradation between the *Halimeda macroloba* sand of belt 4, and the *Amphistegina lessonii* sand of belt 5. Corals, especially branching types that cover the bottom surface mainly between depths of 30 and 90 feet, form an effective barrier in most parts of the lagoon between the sediments above and below these depths. Fragments of broken coral, many of them large, cover most of the lagoon floor between the living corals.

At the other end of the extreme are the very shallow lagoons without passes. In these, fine silts and mud are common. The dry atoll of Starbuck represents such an extreme. Arundel (1890) wrote that "At the eastern end are some large salt lagoons (most weird-looking places), where thousands of tons of the purest kind of salt are found in various forms, coarse and fine. It has evidently been a large lagoon at one time, and either from partial upheaval or by process of evaporation, has become a series of small lakes and ponds, now nearly dry . . . It is dangerous to approach very near some of them. One of my boys on one occasion went in nearly up to his shoulders, and might have gone in altogether had not assistance been at hand to drag him out." Arundel also briefly describes Enderbury and Sydney as of similar character. Sydney, about 3 miles in diameter, with "one large lagoon and several smaller ones, the latter mostly dry; the former of very salt water, quite dead, with no communication with the sea, and studded with small islets composed of shells, broken coral, sand, and a weed or fungus which comes up from the bottom every now and then, and smells horribly [*sic*], and being washed ashore dries and becomes quite hard. The water is very salt, nothing will live in it, and were it not for occasional heavy rains would in course of time evaporate."

In certain shallow lagoons the accumulation of muds may have a high guano content. Friederici (1910, pp. 101–5) asserted that he found phosphate deposits in the lagoon of Niau Atoll in the Tuamotu to be 8 meters thick and explained its accumulation from rain erosion of guano from the land rim. Waesche (1938) said that the saucer-shaped depression toward the center of Enderbury "was partially filled with soft, muddy materials which are principally bird guano."

In summary, it may be said that the character and distribution of lagoon sediments on atolls depend upon the differing character of the atoll: how deep it is, how many and how deep the passes, or whether it has any free communication with the sea. Lagoons with moderate depths having relatively deep passes and vigorous lagoon currents appear likely to have mostly coarser sediments, whereas closed, shallow lagoons in the process of drying up appear to accumulate fine sediments everywhere on the lagoon floor, with very little coral constituents in the sediments.

Organic matter is present in only extremely small quantities in sediments of the open lagoons. Total organic matter present in Bikini and Rongelap lagoon sediments amounted to only 0.60 and 0.68 per cent, respectively. Porosity of lagoonal sediments is high, far higher than normally encountered in sands, which rarely exceeds 40 per cent. Total porosities range between 53.4 and 61.3 per cent, with Halimeda debris having higher values. These high values are due to the internal grain porosities plus the very irregular grain shapes, which give rise to high intergranular porosities. The lower specific gravity of powdered Foraminifera as compared with powdered Halimeda substantiated the dominantly calcitic composition of the Foraminifera and the dominantly aragonitic composition of Halimeda (Emery, Tracey, and Ladd, 1954, pp. 64–5).

Emery, Tracey, and Ladd found that carbonates comprised 97 per cent or more of the inorganic constituents of the sediments in Bikini Lagoon. The skeletons of organisms consist chiefly of either aragonite or calcite. The calcareous red algae, as well as the Foraminifera, are of calcite, whereas the coral and Halimeda are of aragonite. The ratio of magnesium oxide to calcium oxide ranges from 0.6 to 19.7 per cent, as contrasted with the ratio of 71.9 per cent characteristic of pure dolomite. The analyses show that Halimeda has the lowest magnesium oxide content and the highest strontium oxide content. Coral appears to be similar. Foraminifera have intermediate values of magnesium oxide and the lowest strontium oxide. Calcareous red algae have the highest magnesium oxide and low strontium oxide. As the change with progressively deeper water from foraminiferal dominance to Halimeda dominance takes place, there is, therefore, a decrease in manganese oxide and an increase in calcium oxide and strontium oxide together with a transition from calcite and aragonite (Emery, Tracey, and Ladd, 1954, pp. 67–8).

CHAPTER 4

THE EVOLUTION OF CORAL ATOLLS:
EVIDENCE AND THEORY

Theories of atoll origins excited little interest before the time of Charles Darwin, although speculations on their mode of origin go back as early as 1821, when Chamisso published his observations. Summaries of the theories of and the controversies over the origin of coral reefs have been written by Cotton (1948) and by Ladd and Tracey (1949). The latter concluded then that although a considerable amount of information had been obtained from drillings and from geophysical observations, "The origin of coral reefs will probably never be settled to the satisfaction of many investigators until a great deal more is learned about the foundations of existing reefs." Fortunately, since 1949 a great deal more has been learned about these foundations.

Evidence of the nature of atoll origins

Five deep and several shallower holes have been drilled on islands in the open Pacific that have provided information on the nature of atoll and coral reef geology. The earliest was drilled in 1896 on Funafuti Atoll in the Ellice Islands and reached a depth of 114 feet (Edgeworth and Sweet, 1904). In the period 1934 to 1936 the Japanese drilled a hole on the reefs of the small island of Kita-Daito (North Borodino) to a depth of 1,416 feet (Ladd and Tracey, 1949, p. 2). In 1947 American scientists drilled six holes on Bikini Atoll of which two were very deep, 1,346 and 2,556 feet, respectively, the others being only 100 to 300 feet deep (Emery, Tracey, and Ladd, 1949, p. 74). Kuenen (1947) also reported a drilling in Maratoea Reef limestone to a depth of over 1,300 feet. This, however, was not on an oceanic atoll and Maratoea does not have a volcanic base. None of these reached through the coral reef to the basement rock. In 1951 two holes were drilled in the limestone islets on Eniwetok Atoll (Fig. 46) to depths of 4,222 and 4,610 feet, respectively, both reaching volcanic bedrock. Olivine basalt was brought up from the bottom of one of these drillings as well as by the dredging of outer slopes of Eniwetok at great depths (Fosberg and MacNeil, 1954).

This momentous achievement finally has given us information on the depths and the character of the limestone cap over the foundation of coral atolls, at least for the northern Marshalls. In addition Hess (1946, pp. 772–91) discovered a large number, possibly about 160, flat-topped submarine peaks between the Marianas and the Hawaiian Islands with tops lying 3,000 to 6,000 feet below sea level. Some 11 such peaks (termed *guyots* by Hess) were found by others in the Gulf of Alaska (Menard and Dietz, 1951) and two within 800 miles west of San Diego, California (Hamilton, 1956, pp. 2–3). All the information thus obtained has provided a much better basis than was available hitherto for evaluating the theories on the origin of coral atolls.

The character of the data gathered from the borings in different areas, the studies of dredgings of outer slopes, and other evidence needs to be included here before we consider the theories of atoll formation. Davis (1928, p. 514) stated that "The most significant result gained from the boring (at Funafuti) was that the fossils found in the core were characteristic of shallow water only; while the living organisms dredged from the external slope of the atoll at depths similar to those reached by the boring were in part such as lived at those depths and in part such as, living at lesser depths, sank to deeper water when dead." As noted by Shepard, the chief report on the boring at Funafuti (Hinde, 1904, p. 15) described the top of the section (from 0 to 150 feet) as corals growing in place and surrounded by Foraminifera and other organisms. From 150 to 748 feet it was made up largely of fragmentary material with a small percentage of coral and consisted mostly of Foraminifera and organic debris. The lower part, from 748 to 1,112 feet, was similar to the top 150 feet but it was dolomitized.

Davis (1928, p. 515) also found great significance in the determination of local gravity made by Matsuyama at Jaluit and published in 1918. This determination indicated that the thickness of the limestone capping on the volcanic foundation there that gave "the best agreement between observed and expected gravity values was between 243 and 1,000 meters" (or 800 to 3,300 feet).

On Bikini the entire reef thickness down to the bottom of the 2,556-foot-deep hole comprises material believed to have accumulated in a lagoonal environment in water mostly less than 30 fathoms in depth (Emery, Tracey, and Ladd, 1954, p. 2). No rocks encountered were older than Oligocene (40 to 30 million years ago) or possibly late Eocene (60 to 40 million years ago). "The section consisted entirely of coarse to fine detrital organic limestone of almost pure calcium carbonate, moderately consolidated at irregular intervals in the top several hundred feet, but completely unconsolidated below 725 feet except for a 24-foot unit at 1,127 to 1,151 feet. The stratigraphic section is: 0 to 850 feet, Recent and Plio-Pleistocene; 850 to 2,070 feet, Miocene; 2,070 to 2,556 feet, Oligocene (?)." In interpreting the core material from the drillings, the authors of the above have the following to say:

Recrystallization of aragonite shells and skeletons to calcite is limited to the irregularly consolidated intervals, and is believed to be due to emergence of the rocks above sea level. Accumulation of the limestone was interrupted by one early period of emergence. A 24-foot zone of recrystallized rock at 1,127 feet, of early Miocene age, is overlain by unconsolidated lower Miocene rock containing unaltered shells and skeletons. One or more possible Pleistocene emergences may have resulted in the moderate to complete recrystallization of rocks at 294 to 450 feet. Three rock units above 294 feet, characterized by distinctive Foraminifera, seem to be related to present physiographic features of the atoll, and are believed to represent three late stages of growth, probably separated by two emergences due to late Pleistocene shifts in sea level. The first stage resulted in the formation of the present lagoon bottom; the second in the broad terraces at depths of 8 to 12 fathoms; and the last in the formation of the present reefs at the surface.

All the material encountered in the two drillings to basement basalt on Eniwetok is limestone. The top layers are largely aragonite, with lower layers chiefly calcite, while the deepest parts are dolomitic in character. About 70 per cent of the sections in the two deeper holes and a much higher percentage of the shallower borings were unconsolidated, suggesting that the atoll structure was a hollow cone of hard limestone filled with loose sediments. The cavernous nature of the internal structure is shown by the fact that the drills hit numerous cavities, one of which was 55 feet in vertical diameter, and by the fact that there is no observed lag in the tidal fluctuations in these drill holes as compared with the considerable lag in the ground water of shallow wells on atoll islets (Fosberg and MacNeil, 1954).

Other pertinent data elucidating the history and evolution of coral atolls is derived from studies of the outside submarine topography and biogeology of the atoll. Emery, Tracey, and Ladd (1954) found that

The seaward edge of the reef, particularly in indentations on the windward side, is bordered by a terrace whose outer edge is at a depth of about 8 fathoms at Bikini, Eniwetok, and Rongelap Atolls and probably less at Rongerik. Thus, the seaward terrace is slightly shallower than the lagoon terrace. On the leeward side the reefs are bordered by steep, locally vertical slopes that extend to a depth of 20 fathoms or more . . . The slopes around the atolls between the reef edge and 200 fathoms average about 45° and are somewhat steeper on the submarine buttresses that underlie reef projections. At greater depths the slopes become gradually gentler, until between 2,000 and 2,500 fathoms they merge with the floor of the deep sea. . . .

Sediments of the outer slope consist mostly of coarse coral fragments and Halimeda debris near the surface. At greater depth the sediment gradually changes to fine sand and even to silt. Imbedded in these sediments are blocks of reef rock possibly weighing as much as a ton. At even greater depth, beyond the easy reach of abundant fine debris from the coral reef, the sediment is somewhat coarser, composed almost exclusively of the tests of pelagic Foraminifera, chiefly Globigerina. This Globigerina sand occurs low on the flanks of the atolls and on the tops of the *guyots* [flat-topped submerged mountains]. At depths of about 2,400 fathoms, the Globigerina sediments grade into red clay.

The areas of slow deposition of sediments on the lower slopes of the atoll and the edge of the guyot contain outcrops of basalt covered by manganese oxide. Samples of the basalt constitute the first physical proof that volcanoes are the bases of the atolls of the central Pacific. The basalt is scoriaceous and associated with it are tuff and volcanic glass. These facts are interpreted as indicating that basaltic eruptions took place near the water surface in post-Paleozoic time. Later truncation by wave action is indicated by the flat surface of the guyots and by the presence of rounded pebbles of basalt. On similar guyots [Fig. 38] east of the Marshall Islands reef corals and other fossils of Cretaceous age [69 to 72 million years ago] were discovered. The existing atolls apparently were formed atop some of the guyots or atop incompletely truncated volcanoes in post-Cretaceous time.

In considering the origins of coral atolls, one also should be acquainted with the nature of the reef builders and the reef building. At this point these will be discussed only to the extent needed to lay the foundation for the examination of the theories of atoll origins. In a later chapter marine reef ecology will be examined more closely. Yonge (1940, p. 354) stated that:

Biologically considered, coral reefs may be defined as marine communities found only in shallow tropical waters, the dominant organisms being Madreporaria containing zoozanthellae (i.e., "reef building corals") together with certain Hydrocorallinae and Alcyonareae which also form stout calcareous skeletons and contain zoozanthellae.

Owing to the exceptional powers of skeleton formation possessed by the majority of these organisms, massive reefs have been constructed which provide surface and shelter for a varied assemblage of other organisms. Some of these, notably Foraminifera and Mollusca amongst animals, and

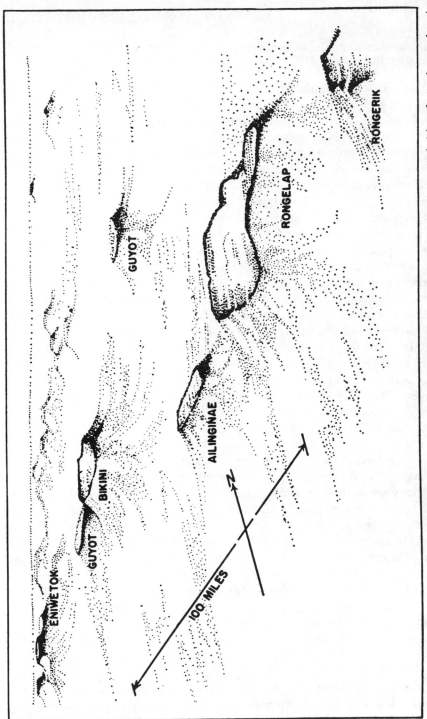

Fig. 38. Rongelap and Bikini Atolls and their surroundings as they might appear if the water were removed (view from the southeast). [From Von Arx (1954).]

nullipores among plants, assist materially in the formation and consolidation of the reefs.

Reef corals are colonial animals and their reef-building derives from their ability to precipitate calcium carbonate (lime) and to grow upon the skeletons of their predecessors. As they grow, the feeding heads on the outer edges of the colony do most of the feeding. As the lowest members gradually get smothered by sediments and other growths, the animals themselves die, leaving only the bare skeleton (MacGinitie and MacGinitie, 1949, pp. 135–6). Succeeding generations of larvae, finding suitable foundations on the limestone thus created, continually add additional layers, thus building upward and outward toward the peripheries.

There also are inanimate agencies in the shallow reef areas of coral atolls that can precipitate calcium carbonate, although the volume that they add to the reefs is not very important (Emery, personal communication, 1958). In these tropical parts of the ocean the sea water holds as much calcium carbonate in solution as it can hold. A rise in the water temperature on shallow reef flats reduces the ability of the water to hold the mineral and will cause some of it to be precipitated. Moreover, if there is too little carbon dioxide in the air, the agitation of the heated saturated sea water will hasten the process of precipitation (Vaughan, 1917).

As pointed out by Kuenen (1950, p. 420), "The rate of growth of corals and especially of reefs as a whole is a matter of particular importance to theories of atoll and barrier formation." Different ways of investigating coral growth by various scientists and the different rates of growth of different coral species have made it difficult to assess average rates of reef building. Branching forms of coral grow faster than massive forms. Kuenen believes that as a general average of all measurements it can be assumed that coral colonies grow at the rate of $2\frac{1}{2}$ centimeters per year, or a meter in 40 years, under favorable conditions and for part of their lives, but that reefs as a whole grow much more slowly. Among the reasons for this is the damage caused by storms; the inhibition of coral growths by algal mantles over dead coral; the empty spaces in branching-coral types, which require consolidation through infiltration of sediment; and patches of sand and sediment, which inhibit quick coral cover. Measurements of depths over a period of years to determine growth rates are not reliable, owing to the relatively large errors in soundings and in averaging depths. Kuenen concludes that while some reefs at present are almost stationary, others are growing upward at the rate of $\frac{1}{2}$ to 2 meters per century. On the other hand, in particular situations growth may be very rapid, as Yonge has pointed out (1940, pp. 372–3). He stated that Sewell reported a channel in the Andaman Islands, shown to have a depth of 6 fathoms in a chart prepared in 1887, which had a depth of about a foot 37 years later. This gives an annual growth of almost 1 foot a year, or 100 feet a century. It has been made apparent by the studies of various scholars that reef organisms grow at different rates under different conditions of situation and exposure to prevailing winds, waves, and currents. Few data are available on growth rates of large sections of reefs or of an entire atoll reef.

Since exposure to air and the desiccation of emergence from the sea water for other than brief periods quickly kill the major reef-building organisms, including corals, it is obvious that the upward limit of growth is near the mean tide level.

Although corals appear to flourish in the zone of agitated water not far from the surface of the ocean, the more-fragile branching types of coral generally are found only in the quiet of deeper water inside the lagoon or on the outer atoll slopes. Near the surface and especially on the windward seaward side of reefs, only massive forms can withstand the destructive force of the constantly pounding waves. In this zone the brunt of the wave shock is born by the calcareous algae. On the reef as a whole, moreover, the corals by themselves would not be able to make the stable structure of which they are a part. According to Fosberg and MacNeil (1954):

The function of binding and cementing these corals together into massive rock is performed largely by certain calcareous algae and by certain colonial animals related to corals which grow with no fixed habitat or definite form but which make a shapeless hard crust over the surfaces of the other animals, smothering them, filling in the holes and spaces between them, and presenting a smoother and more resistant surface to the force of the waves. These binding organisms, especially the plants (Lithothamnion), thrive best in the roughest, most thoroughly aerated water. For this reason the firmest structure of the atolls are on the windward slopes where the swells break continuously. Growth of reef-building organisms, generally, is faster on the outer edges of the reefs where waves break.

Theorizing on atoll origins

With the foregoing discussion of some of the characteristics and processes of the coral reef in mind, we may proceed to examine and speculate on the origins of coral atolls.

The great thickness of reef limestone revealed in the drill cores of Funafuti, Bikini, and Eniwetok allow several differing interpretations of atoll origins. The reefs were built up to the present sea level from relatively stable foundations from a time when sea level was several hundreds or several thousands of feet lower than that of today, or the reefs were built up from submerging or subsiding foundations that have sunk several thousand feet since the reefs began, or they may have been built up as a result of a combination of these processes. In any case, it is clear that events necessitated a rate of reef growth that kept up with the rate of rising sea level or with the rate of subsiding foundations, so as to maintain the reef within the depth limits of reef growth.

Even before drillings had revealed the great thicknesses of reefs, Charles Darwin had developed an ingenious theory whereby atolls originated through the growth of reefs upon subsiding volcanic islands. During the century or more since he proposed his theory, much attention has been directed to the question and many opposing theories have been proposed. Summaries and discussions of these conflicting views have been made by a number of different atoll students, especially carefully by Davis (1928), Gardiner (1931), and, more recently, by Shepard (1948), Keunen (1947, 1950), and MacNeil (1954).

Probably most students concerned with the coral reef problem now accept the main premise of Darwin's subsidence theory, especially since the recent borings at Bikini (1946) and Eniwetok (1951) confirmed the earlier (1896) boring studies at Funafuti, which showed the great thickness of shallow-water coral and algal lime structures.

At Funafuti, shallow-water coral and coraliferous algal deposits were found to a depth of over 1,100 feet (Shepard, 1948), while at Bikini they were found down to 2,556 feet (Dobrin, 1954) and at Eniwetok down to basalt at 4,222 and 4,610 feet in two drill holes. Since reef-building corals will not grow significantly at a depth deeper than about 150 feet (Vaughan, 1917, p. 205), the inference is that these deep cores once stood less than 200 feet from the surface of the sea, and that only subsidence could explain their present position relative to sea level. Ekman (1953) thought that isostatic depression of the earth's crust could occur over a period of less than one or two million years from the weight of limestone produced in such a group of coral islands as the Maldives. However, since reefs do not develop from depths greater than 50 to 85 fathoms, a layer of limestone developed from these depths up to the surface probably would be insufficient to initiate subsidence or overcome crustal resistance to downwarping. Therefore, subsidence must be explained without consideration of the reef limestone cap, although, with subsidence, the increasing thickness and weight of limestone may continue or accelerate the subsidence. Emiliani (1954, p. 854) wrote that "All that is known about the Pacific basin indicates that most of it is an area of great stability and has been such for a long time. Therefore, [geologically recent] subsidence on a regional scale, such as would be needed here, can be excluded with confidence." Thus, he concluded, "All cases of subsidence in the Pacific basin appear to be strictly local phenomena connected with volcanic intrusions and extrusions and subsequent isostatic adjustments."

However, many geologists contend that there has been a broad down-warping of the ocean basins. In discussing the origin of the northern Marshalls guyots or flat-topped seamounts, Hamilton (1956, pp. 3–4) wrote that Emery, Tracey, and Ladd (1954) postulated some regional subsidence and individual sinking of the volcanic masses to explain submergence. Hamilton (1956, pp. 47–8) stated that

Most writers, in considering the increase in ocean volume in geologic time, hold that the ocean basins sank as the volume of oceanic waters increased [because of release of waters from the interior of the earth]. Thus, the present position of the sunken islands [and the atoll foundations] must be partially due to isostatic adjustments under the volcanic ridge but also to a general sinking of the ocean floor. . . . [However] inasmuch as appreciable increase in ocean volume, sedimentation, compacting of soft sediments, and isostatic adjustments have been discontinued as major factors which could completely explain the submergence of the guyots, probably only tectonic activity or crustal movement, together with the preceding factors, would have caused deep subsidence of the area of the Mid-Pacific Mountains. Both Schuchert (1932, pp. 537–61) and Kuenen (1950, p. 549) postulate crustal movements to explain great eustatic changes. There is little large-scale faulting in the Mid-Pacific Mountains.

Hamilton (1956, pp. 47–8) found several writers favoring the explanation of Griggs (1939) and Vening Meinesz (1944; 1948) who proposed that deep subcrustal convection currents caused significant subsiding movements of the crust. Agreeing with this view, Hamilton stated that in his opinion, "Isostatic adjustment, sedimentation, compaction, and rise of sea level are not adequate to account for the great depths to which the Mid-Pacific Mountains and their guyots have been submerged." However, he felt that if one is prepared to accept the ideas of Vening Meinesz and Gunn "that the great loads on the Pacific crust are borne partly by the elastic strength of the downbowing crust and partly by hydrostatic pressure of the underlying lithosphere, then the idea should be carried to its ultimate conclusions: under an excessively great load a point might be reached beyond which the strong crust would reach its elastic limit and the mass previously supported in part by the crust would founder and seek its isostatic level . . ." In any case, he wrote: "It appears proven that a subsidence of the Pacific Basin of several hundreds of fathoms did take place in the area of the Mid-Pacific Mountains."

Newell (1956, pp. 324–5) felt that subsidence is not invariably involved in the origin of atolls and thought that Hoffmeister and Ladd (1944) had "satisfactorily demonstrated that some atolls of the Fiji and Tonga Islands have been formed over platforms not subject to extensive and long continued down-warping." With favorable ecologic factors of reef coral growth, including a foundation whose top was within the depth zone of reef growth, a coral reef will grow to the surface regardless of still-stand or submergence (granted slow subsidence or submergence) (Hamilton, 1956, p. 50).

Atolls, thus, might be built up from volcanic cones eroded down to a level of 160 or more feet below sea level to form suitable platforms for the reef builders. This essentially summarizes the so-called "antecedent platform theory" of atoll formation proposed by Wharton (1897) and elaborated upon by Hoffmeister and Ladd, although the original idea also must be credited to Darwin (Hamilton, 1956, p. 49).

Shepard (1948, p. 273) pointed out that borings on the Queensland reef and Caribbean reefs showed that they developed on sediment-covered shelves, and that this evidence was sufficient support to make the antecedent platform idea at least an important item in the history of reefs. Kuenen (1950, pp. 454–5), however, felt that the proved great thicknesses of reef limestone appear to make this theory unsound. This probably is at least true for most of the central Pacific or "oceanic" atolls. Drill cores from Eniwetok apparently have revealed no such veneer of noncoralliferous lime sediment over the basaltic foundations of that atoll.

According to the glacial control theory developed by Daly from an earlier suggestion of Albrecht Penck (Shepard, 1948, p. 268), during glacial epochs the sea level was lowered so as to truncate, by means of wave abrasion, presently submerged seamounts and provide platforms accessible to reef-building corals.

Some islands supposedly were entirely truncated during an extended period of glacial low sea level. Colder water and increased turbidity were supposed to have killed the bulk of the reef-forming corals. When the near-surface waters warmed at the end of the glacial period and the sea level rose, the surviving corals supposedly gained new hold on the edges of the wave-cut platform and built outward upon their own talus. This growth at the edge left the lagoon floor on the inside as platforms covered with a veneer of sediments, which explains the relative flatness and more or less uniform maximum depths of the lagoons. Both Shepard and Kuenen point out many unsatisfactory aspects of Daly's theory, although the glacial control theory did help to explain some things not explained satisfactorily by Darwin's theory of subsidence.

Hess's fathometric survey in the Pacific indicated the existence in the area of his survey of at least 160 flat-topped truncated and beveled cones, which he called "guyots," ranging in depth from 3,000 to 6,000 feet (Hess, 1946). If the ocean level had indeed dropped to such an extent, Daly's theory might provide a better over-all explanation for such phenomena as coral reefs and islands, the Great Barrier Reef, and the numerous submarine canyons at great depths on the continental shelves.

However, seismic refraction studies at Bikini (Dobrin, 1954) indicated a minimum depth to the igneous base of the atoll of 3,000 feet but a possible maximum of 13,000 feet, and Dobrin asserted that "if, as seems logical," the identity of the 11,000-feet-per-second refraction layer under the surface of the atoll consists of calcareous material like that now being deposited "then the atoll must have formed somewhat in the manner Darwin proposed, with a total subsidence of more than two miles." Shepard (1948, p. 268) also concluded that "There is no denying that the major tests have indicated that submergence on a large scale has taken place."

This idea of a general subsidence was noted by Zeuner (1945, p. 164), who argued that in view of the evidence for the climate of the interglacials, glacial eustacy alone did not satisfactorily explain "one of the queer facts of Pleistocene stratigraphy" which "is that the interglacial sea levels were successively lower." He wrote that it seems possible that the sea level sank by several hundred meters during the Tertiary and Pleistocene. "This is the theory of eustatism, and the most probable cause of the phenomena interpreted by it is a sinking of the bottom of the sea."

Flint (1957, p. 261) described various factors capable of causing sea-level change and wrote that "We must admit that we know little as yet concerning the glacial control of sea level. All we can discern at present is that the inferred fluctuations of sea level seem to fit the pattern of the more recent fluctuations of glaciers and to promise closer comparisons as future study adds to our knowledge."

An interesting correlation has been drawn by Emiliani (1955, p. 561) between high-carbonate stages in deep-sea sediments and low general temperatures of the sea water. This appears to provide a method for ascertaining past climatic changes. From variations in carbonate content and variations in relative abundances of cold- and warm-water pelagic Foraminifera, as indicated by their tests in ocean sediments, it has been found (Emiliani, 1954, pp. 854–5) that "A temperature decrease of some 8°C from the Middle Oligocene to the end of the Pliocene in the deep waters of the Equatorial Pacific reflects and emphasizes the general temperature trend during the Tertiary which resulted in the ice age."

Moreover, in studying the deep-sea cores Emiliani (1955, p. 567) found that the demonstrated correlation of at least five core stages (in low latitudes) with glacial and interglacial events in high latitudes "strongly indicates that the climatic pattern in high latitudes, and the wet and dry phases in equatorial and tropical regions, correlate with glacial and interglacial ages. Also, contemporaneity of colder and warmer ages the world over is indicated." He said further (p. 569) that "General agreement between ages of insolation minima and the even core stages [studied by Emiliani] supports the conclusion that summer insolation at high northern latitudes and Pleistocene temperatures may be related . . . A time correspondence seems to exist between temperature and insolation, but correspondence in amplitude is not exact. A causal connection is suggested but not proved."

It is clear that whatever the cause or causes, relatively rapid changes of sea levels have taken place during Pleistocene times. Since both subsidence and glacial-sea-level changes appear well established in the atoll evolution processes, Kuenen (1947) proposed a combination of the subsidence theory with the glacial control theory. He termed this the theory of glacially controlled subsidence. This phrase is not entirely apt, since glaciation is not taken to have influenced the subsidence of atoll foundations but merely the change in sea levels that operated in the molding of atoll superstructures. Use of this term is intended to indicate that subsidence did occur and that it explains the great thicknesses of reef limestone, the steepness of outer atoll slopes, the subsided central islands, and the barrier reefs, but that the morphology of the superstructure that gives the atoll its surface form resulted from reef-building and erosion processes which in turn derived from glacially controlled rises and falls of sea levels.

Whereas Daly contended that most reef corals were killed by the cold water of glacial periods, Kuenen assumed that there were as many coral structures before the ice age as there are at present, and he ascribed the destruction of emerged limestone during glacial low levels to chemical marine erosion and denudation. The uniformity of lagoon depths was promoted by this degradation of shallow emerged lagoon floors while aggradation of deep lagoons could continue through sedimentation. He also was inclined to assume that all emerged Tertiary reef rock was nearly or completely leveled during glacial low levels, but mostly by solution and not by mechanical truncation caused by wave action.

The main objection raised against the subsidence theory is the absence of deep lagoons and deep passes through the atoll and barrier rims. Unless pass development is a very recent phenomenon of atolls and barrier reefs, subsidence over long geologic periods might have produced many extremely deep passes. But no such passes have been found and only a few reach below normal lagoon depths. The explanation offered by Kuenen (1950, p. 467) is that there was a difference in the rates of subsidence between preglacial and postglacial times. In the earlier time that rate was so slow that reef growth kept up with rising sea levels, so that no passes developed in preglacial atolls and barriers. The postglacial subsidence, however, has been so rapid at times that weaker parts of the reef were unable to keep up with rising sea levels and these parts became drowned, thus developing numerous gaps or passes in present-day atolls and barrier reefs.

MacNeil (1954) proposed a theory interpreting atolls as subaerial erosion features modified by subsequent organic growth. Although this theory recognizes the importance of organic growth during periods of submergence, it places at least equal importance on the role of subaerial erosion during periods of emergence in the fashioning of lagoonal depressions and annular rims. The development of passes of irregular depths from weathering limestone terrain requires no special explanation in view of existing solution forms, according to MacNeil. This idea, he said, was advanced by both Yabe (1942) and Asano (1942) as a result of observations in the South Seas, and drew support from MacNeil's own observations of limestone features on Okinawa and from the laboratory experiments by Hoffmeister and Ladd [illustrations shown in MacNeil's article (1954)].

The theory of subsidence calls for instability. The latest knowledge concerning the topography of the ocean floor indicates that movements have been as active on ocean floors as on continents, and that even in the central Pacific province stability is merely a relative quality and tectonic movements do occur (see, for example, Menard, 1955). Hamilton (1957, 1022–3) and others have concluded from studied evidences that elastic yielding of the earth's crust is to be expected with oceanic islands of volcanic origin. However, Kuenen (1950, p. 475) contends that the two opposing views above can be reconciled if it is admitted that these tectonic and epeirogenic movements are very slow compared to eustatic changes of sea level derived from glacial processes. The former seldom appear to exceed 0.5 millimeter per annum and generally is much less. Rise of sea level during the melting of the Pleistocene glaciers averaged 2 to 3 millimeters and at times may have reached 10 millimeters per annum. Indeed, Flint (1957) stated that the near uniformity of rates from point to point suggests that rise of sea level rather than subsidence of the land is the chief if not sole cause of submergence.

The borings at Bikini showed that most of the material is of Tertiary age (Emery, Tracey, and Ladd, 1954, p. 2) and was not built up from the foundations during the Pleistocene. It is clear, therefore, that the present-day atolls existed as coral reefs in pre-Pleistocene times. Thus the subsidence that occurred, whether it was a general phenomenon of the ocean bed or whether it was isostatic for individual atoll foundations, was very slow. Contrasted with the slowness of subsidence, therefore, glacial movements of sea level are so fast as to have made coral reef foundations appear stable.

There may be other than glacial causes for rapid Pleistocene changes of sea level, however. Fairbridge (1958) contended that "From multiple sources of evidence there seems general support for Zeuner's theory (1952) of a non-glacially controlled eustatic drop of sea level which lowered the relative world ocean several hundred feet during the course of the Pleistocene. Any climatically controlled hypothesis must allow this additional factor."

In reviewing the various theories and arguments, the writer feels that much of what Kuenen argues is sound, although it does not appear necessary to presume truncation of exposed limestone structures during glacial low levels. Nor does it appear essential to presume a level platform for atoll foundations. In fact, the data available point to uneven foundations. The following paragraphs elaborate on these two problems and discuss further the origin of coral atolls and the flat-topped submarine guyots.

In referring to examples of reefs in the Maldives and the Indonesian regions that have been drowned by too rapid subsidence of their foundations, Shepard (1948, p. 268) suggested that many of the guyots may prove to be submerged atolls in which the lagoons have been filled. He also stated (p. 273) that it would not be surprising to learn that the reefs in the Marshalls were first formed on some of the beveled guyot surfaces and have grown up slowly from these surfaces as the guyots were submerged.

According to Kuenen (1950, p. 477), Hess, who discovered the existence of numerous guyots in the southwestern Pacific, explained their origin as volcanic cones quickly planed off by waves after extinction. "The relative rise in sea level due to oceanic sedimentation then carries the beheaded cone gradually downwards. The guyots would be the pre-Cambrian representatives from periods when no lime-secreting organisms existed to build up the cone, while cones erected later were capped by organic lime, finally by reef corals. In this manner he explains the curious absence of guyots with depths less than about 1000 m." Kuenen felt that this theory was unsatisfactory because the rate of subsidence would have to have been excessively small.

Hess, of course, suffered in his theorizing from lack of dredgings of the guyots. Since these seamounts came to his attention, dredgings from Hess and Cape Johnson guyots have brought up corals belonging to the order Scleractinia, or stony hexacorals, and include six reef-building (hermatypic) and one nonreefbuilding genera. Four of the seven genera are living on present-day reefs; three (Microsolena, Cyathophora, and Brachyseris) became extinct in the Cretaceous (Hamilton, 1956, p. 23).

That the substrata of the Marshalls atolls need not be and probably are not entirely truncated flat-topped guyots is indicated by the seismic refraction and magnetic studies of Bikini. Raitt (1954, p. 524) wrote that the considerable differences in relief of the basaltic foundation underlying Bikini is on the order of 1.5 kilometers. Magnetic studies (Alldredge, Keller, and Dichtel, 1954), moreover, point to the probable existence of eight volcanic peaks, comprising the basement material, together with two volcanic craters of great depth. The difference between the highest of these peaks and the deepest crater amounts to as much as 7,000 feet. Emery, Tracey, and Ladd (1954, p. vii) wrote: "The irregularity of the old volcanic surfaces suggests that these cones may have been islands and that they were not truncated by wave erosion during the early stages of growth of the atolls." Also (p. 131) they stated: "It seems probable that similar relations exist at Eniwetok and that the surfaces of the two deep terrace-like guyots adjoining that atoll probably continue laterally to form a single guyot whose center is located beneath the existing atoll [although] the volcanics of the terrace-like guyots and those directly beneath the present atoll may have been erupted from separate centers." In a personal communication to the writer, Hamilton wrote that the above expressed his own beliefs at that date (Jan. 9, 1958). However, in view of Hess's definition of guyots as "flat-topped," Hamilton doubted that he now would call the foundations of Bikini a guyot.

Assuming these interpretations to be substantially correct, this means that if the corals started building upward from approximately the level of the guyot surface (that is, about 4,200 feet deep), layers of coral, algal, and other calcareous sediments several thousand feet deep have filled in the former craters and also have filled in the valleys and gaps between the peaks. Thus the reef structure of today in its outward horizontal contours appears to bear little relation to that of the original volcanic foundations (which would not have been a single volcanic cone), although several of the reef bends may be associated with certain eminences (for example, lava outpourings). The central part of the lagoon, where it normally might be expected to have its maximum depths, actually has the site of one of the highest peaks of the basement rock (Fig. 8).

A number of added facts need to be considered before one should draw conclusions on the early history and formation of guyots and atolls. One is that the Mid-Pacific Mountains do not have accordant tops. This is not surprising considering that they are volcanic. "A volcanic cone could have been eroded to a flat top and have subsided (with the whole structure) before another emerged and was eroded. These two tops would not then be on the same level . . . The Mid-Pacific Mountains and their guyots are fossil landforms from the Cretaceous [and] . . . are now altered only by the slow rain of pelagic sediments from above" (Hamilton, 1956, p. 44). Moreover, he points out (p. 38), "Evidence that sharp, uneroded peaks are nearer the surface of the sea than are the flat tops of the guyots may indicate that the volcanic activity did not cease in the area of the Mid-Pacific Mountains after the flat tops of some seamounts had been truncated and part or all of the range had subsided."

Hamilton also pointed out (p. 39) that several authors (Kuenen; Emery, Tracey, and Ladd) stressed side slopes when comparing atolls with volcanoes. Kuenen concluded that practically all atolls are partly surrounded by slopes of more than 45° down to 200 meters and that these may reach down to 600 meters. By contrast, andesitic volcano slopes may be more than 35° in a few sections, but usually are no more than 25° down to 500 meters. In the northern Marshalls Emery, Tracey, and Ladd (1954, p. 128) found that atoll slopes averaged 32° for the first 250 fathoms but that the slopes of the guyots averaged only 14° in the same portion. Cinder cones slope away from the craters at about 26 to 30° (Lobeck, 1939, p. 664), whereas lava domes rarely exceed 5 to 10° on the upper slopes. Hamilton (1956, p. 40) concluded that a pre-Pleistocene atoll formed on a still-standing platform need not have the steep uppermost slopes of a modern atoll (largely owing to fast upgrowth during post-Pleistocene time) and that one should not attach too much meaning to conclusions based on a comparison of present-day atoll slopes and the slopes of Cretaceous guyots.

At the same time, Hamilton followed Emery, Tracey, and Ladd (1954, p. 128) in seeing it "extremely unlikely that the flat tops of guyots are sediment-filled craters. No known craters are large enough to give their volcanoes a flat-topped appearance in profile (such as on the guyots) should they be filled to rim level." However, Hamilton (1956, p. 42) believes the guyots are most likely wave-truncated submerged volcanoes.

No final answer can be given to these problems. The simplest hypothesis is that peaks of the main ridge of the Mid-Pacific Mountains appeared above the surface of the sea during late Mesozoic, that they were composite cones of lava and pyroclastic material, or entirely pyroclastic, and so were rapidly eroded to flat banks with the sediments of erosion inhibiting coral growth (as on Falcon Island in 1928), that about the Middle Cretaceous (Aptian to Cenomanian) coral became lodged on these flat banks and was soon killed by rapid submergence prior to the end of the Cenomanian.

At the time of the drowning of these early "almost-atolls," other islands with much higher volcanic peaks fringed about with reefs and barriers may have subsided just as rapidly for a similar time, but before they were submerged like the existing atolls, a change to a slower rate of subsidence permitted the reef organisms to maintain as rapid a growth as the rate of subsidence and allowed them in turn to develop into the present-day atolls. This hypothesis would explain why islands such as Bikini, Eniwetok, and Kwajelein, apparently with untruncated basaltic foundations of varying relief, developed into atolls from the approximate depths of the guyots adjoining them, which did not develop into present-day atolls.

If this interpretation is correct, then at one time in the ancient geologic past there were in the southwestern Pacific many times the present number of islands dotting the expanses of the ocean, while the present-day atolls stood aloft among them as numerous steep-sided, reef-fringed, and barrier-encircled volcanic islands. Such early island "stepping stones" would have offered "intermediate stops for shallow-water animals advancing across great expanses of ocean. This is especially true of the best possibility for migration—transportation by currents of animals in larval stage" (Hamilton,

1956, p. 51). This would help explain many of the faunal similarities now found on widely separated coral atolls in the Pacific. Many of these early islands have since become drowned, leaving today's atoll pattern.

The origin of lagoons and passes with a more or less uniform lower depth limit and the existence of present-day lagoons without great depths, such as might be inferred to follow the deep subsidences indicated by atoll foundations, require further explanation. During the stage of development of the present-day atolls from almost-atolls, the height of their barrier-reef-fringed volcanic islands differed. This is a probability that hardly requires proof. Assuming the almost-certain premise that the untruncated volcanic mountains of the various islands were of differing elevations, the lagoons of the atolls would have greatly varying depths at the stage when the volcanic islands all had disappeared underwater, because the atolls that sank first would have the deeper lagoons, at least as compared with other atolls of about the same size. Moreover, the depths of some lagoons at this stage may have been exceedingly deep.

Following this period of greatly varying depths may have come a glacial period during which sea level may have been lowered many hundreds of feet. By this time sediment probably had filled in the deeper lagoons, so that the great lowering of sea level exposed the bottoms of all atoll lagoons or brought them very near sea level. During such a period the elevated lagoon bottoms as well as the peripheral reefs killed by emergence would have been subject to fresh-water solution and other erosion processes, including stream erosion. Kuenen (1947, pp. 11–32) pointed out that chemical attack on elevated limestone by weathering cannot be doubted. He also felt that "The humic acid, developing under the dense tropical forest, played an important part in dissolving the lime." The latter is not an essential part of the process, however, and could only be applied to wet areas. In the case of dry atolls, the scanty desert-type vegetation would have produced little humic acid, although the atoll forms are not different from those in the wet zone.

Owing to the existing basin form of an emergent island, drainage would have been largely toward the central depression, where solution must have operated most strongly in the denudation process. The process must have been of sufficient duration so that solution and other forms of erosion brought the central depression down to or about to the level of the existing sea surface. The rims, owing to their greater solidity and higher initial elevation above the lagoon floor, probably continued to stand considerably higher, although they, too, were severely denuded. This differential probably has always existed. The writer is inclined toward Newell's feeling (1956, p. 324) that only the smallest limestone islands were truncated during Pleistocene lows. Kuenen's belief (1950, p. 452) that atolls and barrier reefs "not improbably were entirely beheaded at sea level" does

not, in Newell's words, "have compelling evidence" to support it. If limestone island truncation had been as extensive as Kuenen believed, tectonically elevated atolls or reef islands such as Makatea would seemingly have
been leveled. However, their raised cliffs date back to Tertiary times
(Agassiz, 1903, p. 58).

During the next stage of development, a rising sea level accompanying
an interglacial stage led to the upbuilding of the atoll rim, while the lagoons now became aggraded through sedimentation. Except in those parts
of the lagoon where pinnacles or prominences permitted coral reefs to
grow, the lagoon built upward largely through sedimentation, as in the
present stage. Those lagoons that had not been completely degraded down
to sea level continued the denudation process until rising sea levels brought
them also to the sedimentary aggradational stage of the others. From this
time on, at least, there would have been a considerable degree of uniformity in the maximum depths to which lagoons reached.

Subsequent glacial and interglacial processes must have repeated parts
or all of this cycle, depending upon the extent of lowering of sea levels.
The present maximum depths of most lagoons are between 100 and 300
feet, although there are individual exceptions in areas of tectonic instability.
These depths most probably are related to the most recent Pleistocene
glacial low level of the sea.

The extent of recent sea-level changes is uncertain, and scientists have
come to different conclusions. Antevs (1928) stated that if glaciation cli-
maxes in both hemispheres were reached simultaneously, the sea level was
lowered by some 305 feet. If the contemporaneity was only partial, the
sea level may at most have been lowered 290 feet. The topography of the
shallow Sunda Sea suggests that it has been partly carved out during epochs
in which the sea level stood at least 240 feet lower than at present. Kuenen
(1947) referred to Daly's estimate of a 75-meter lowering of sea level during
the last (Würm) glaciation, stating that this figure is borne out as a minimum
by the depth of the Hudson Channel and by the Sunda River system between Sumatra and Borneo. To this amount, he said, must be added 5
meters for the recent worldwide sinking of ocean level, thus making a total
of 80 meters, or 260 feet, in the rise since low level.

Flint (1947, p. 428) stated that "It is now believed that at the time of
the most extensive glaciation the sea level was reduced 350 to 400 feet, that
in the 4th glacial age it was reduced 230 to 330 feet and that if all the
existing glaciers were to melt, the sea level would be raised 65 to 165 feet
above its present position." In his more recent book (1957) he is doubtful
of the value of the estimates on ice volumes of past glaciations, owing to
the inadequacies of data on thicknesses of the large ice sheets. He wrote
that "Published values for the position of sea level at glacial maxima rela-

tive to existing sea level, deduced from assumed glacier volumes, range from −85 meters to −120 meters. The best that can be said for them is that they are of the same order of magnitude as the values inferred from geologic data, which have greater validity."

Flint went on to state that "The post-Tyrrhenian regression of sea level is therefore tentatively established at a minimum of −90 meters (295 feet), though it may have been lower . . . This implies that in Boreal time, 7,500 to 8,500 years before the present, sea level was at least 36 meters lower than now, with respect to the land."

Russell (1957) claimed that in the last 18,000 years ocean levels have risen about 430 feet and that during the past half century the rise has amounted to 2½ inches. He quoted Ahlman's estimate that the melting of all the world's present glaciers would bring a total sea-level rise of 200 feet.

From the above discussion it is evident that maximum lagoon depths are consistent with the more generally accepted last glacial minimum of sea level, although not with Russell's 430-foot level.

Sediments that fill lagoons will fill them up in the long run, as in the case of Christmas Atoll. However, during glacial periods the accumulated lagoon sediments were partly denuded mechanically and partly chemically dissolved and carried away, and many of the lagoon bottoms were probably brought to the lowest stage of sea level at Pleistocene glacial maximum. In addition, lagoons fill up with sediments at different rates, owing to their different sizes and to differences in size, number, and depth of deep passes that might carry sediments into the open ocean. Thus differing lagoons may have different depths, except that there is a maximum depth beyond which they do not go unless there is instability which causes local subsidence at rapid rates.

From the preceding discussion it can be seen that answers to the origins and evolution of coral reefs and atolls still are inconclusive in many respects. Kuenen (1953) quoted Hoffmeister and Ladd (1935) to sum up his view: "Probably no single reef theory will explain all reefs. Certainly, recognition of the complexity of the problem is essential to its solution. It does not belong within the realm of any one subject, but requires the attention of scientists of many fields, each contributing his share."

Hamilton (1956, p. 50) supported the same view. Citing Stearns (1946, p. 262) he concluded: "It is theoretically possible to get all the various kinds of reefs with and without submergence. No theory is all-embracing, and attempts to explain all reefs with one theory are destined to failure. The happy conclusion here is that almost everyone is right at some time and in some place."

CHAPTER 5

THE DYNAMICS OF ATOLL MORPHOLOGY [1]

It is obvious that the prime aspect of coral reef dynamics is the growth of skeleton deposits of the reef-building organisms. In a previous chapter the ability of coral reefs to keep up with the rate of submergence both from subsidence and from sea-level changes was pointed out. An accurate assessment of the potential growth of a reef as a whole, however, is difficult to achieve because of the complexity of factors and differences of situation involved.

Reef growth rates

Yonge (1940, pp. 372–3) cited the work of various writers who had observed growth rate first-hand. Mayor (1924) arrived at a figure of 81 feet in 1,000 years as a result of work at Samoa. Wood-Jones (1912) established the fact that corals do not always grow, and that they may grow at varying rates in different periods. Vaughan (1911; 1913; 1915; 1916), who made extensive observations in the West Indies, found that the growth rate of *Orbicella annularis,* the chief reef builder there, is from 5 to 7 millimeters annually. This would produce a reef 150 feet thick in 7,620 years. *Acropora palmata,* which grows faster, would form a similar thickness of reef in only 1,800 years. Moreover, Yonge pointed out that coral growth at the northern extremities of coral distribution is less rapid than that in the mid-tropical

1. Parts of this chapter, rewritten as an article, originally appeared in the March 1959 issue of the *Annals of the Association of American Geographers.* All the figures used in that article also appear in this book, with the permission of the editor of the Annals.

Indo-Pacific. Emery, Tracey, and Ladd (1954, p. 140) wrote that data from Sargent and Austin (1949) obtained at Rongelap indicated an increase of reef coral amounting to 3.8×10^4 grams per square meter per year. On a pore-free basis, they calculated that this would correspond to a maximum possible growth of the reef of 14 millimeters per year, if no solution by water and organisms or removal by storm occurred. They concluded that although this might hold true for reef zones in which there is a prolific growth of corals, it certainly was excessive for the reef as a whole. More-over, the method used by Sargent and Austin could not be used for cal-culating the Halimeda increase, which comprises a large percentage of the lagoon sediments. On a different basis of calculation, Odum and Odum (1955, p. 317) estimated a reef increment of 1.6 centimeters annually with erosional removal at about the same rate.

· In summing up their study of growth rates, Emery, Tracey, and Ladd (1954, p. 141) wrote:

The rates of growth or deposition obtained for the top of the atolls are as follows: (1) coral growth on reef less than 14 mm per year, (2) postgla-cial growth of reef surface—0.91 to 1.33 mm per year, (3) organic produc-tion—14 mm per year, and (4) carbon isotope [in measurement of lagoon sediment deposition]—greater than 3.8 mm per year. Although each method is open to one or more objections it is believed that at least the correct order of magnitude is indicated. In contrast, the most probable rate of dep-osition of red clay and Globigerina ooze in the vicinity is only 0.002 and 0.007 mm per year, respectively. Thus, it appears that the shallow sedi-ments are deposited atop the atoll about 1,000 times as fast as those of the surrounding deep water. It is interesting to note that the rate of deposition of the atoll sediments is probably greater than the present rate of rise of sea level due to addition of glacier melt water, 0.6 mm per year.

Sea-level changes

A variety of forces in addition to coral reef growth operate in the mold-ing of atoll topography. The ones most commonly thought of are wind, waves, currents, and rainfall. Less often does one think of the more obscure elements, which include temperature influences, chemical processes, and the biomechanical and biochemical processes brought about by organisms. All these forces, moreover, may be modified by tectonic forces, resulting in upheaval or subsidence, or by eustatic changes in sea level, resulting in emergence or submergence. If we assume that atoll structures are sub-stantially cut down during a glacial period, then the superstructure of present-day atolls may be taken to be related only to the last Pleistocene glaciation (Würm Ice Age). Although there still is not complete agreement on the extent to which the sea level was lowered during the Pleistocene glacial periods, the right order of magnitude appears to place it at approximately 300 feet. However, an important question, which is the crux of the problem of atoll land formation, is whether there has been a sea level during the Recent epoch higher than that of the present.

Shepard and Suess (1956, pp. 1082–3) estimated that 11,000 years ago sea level stood about a hundred feet lower than at present and that, except for a possible temporary halt some 7,000 or 8,000 years ago, sea level has continued to rise, although recently at a slower rate, without "any indication of a post-glacial sea level higher than that of the present." This statement seems to represent a change from Shepard's view in 1948, when he referred to wave-cut benches standing at uniform height around some coral islands. He then pointed out that "Investigations of the islands of Oceania by P. H. Kuenen, C. K. Wentworth, H. S. Palmer, H. T. Stearns, G. A. MacDonald, H. S. Ladd, J. E. Hoffmeister, and many others have shown that these terraces occur with amazing regularity. These terraces have been recognized also in the Atlantic and Indian Oceans. Probably one stand of the sea was about 25 feet above the present. A well-developed bench at about 5 feet is also recognized and has great regularity around the Hawaiian Islands. Obviously," he concluded, "a sea-level change could alone account for these benches." Emery, Tracey, and Ladd (1954, p. 141) appeared to accept this view: "During the climatic optimum estimated to have occurred 4 to 6 thousand years ago the ocean level stood 6 feet above the present level."

Fairbridge (1952) cited support for a higher Recent stand of the sea than that of the present from coastal terraces observed in western Australia.

Cloud (1952, p. 47) claimed that "the recent world-wide 6-foot fall of sea level" may be amply documented, and he cited as one example the remnants of an elevated *Heliopora* reef flat on Onotoa Atoll occurring up to 2½ feet above the inner edge of the present reef flat, as well as what he terms "elevated cobble stripes" 6 to 7 feet above the present reef flat. McKee (1956, p. 11) found on Kapingamarangi Atoll "high-level remnants of stratified rock considered to antedate the latest fall in sea level." Couthouy (1843–4, pp. 140–1) wrote: "At almost every Paumotu (atoll) visited, I found the shore of the lagoon raised from 18 to 30 inches, containing imbedded shells and corals standing as they grew." Couthouy specifically mentions Clermont Tonnerre, Raraka, and Kink's Island (Taiarao) Atolls as having such reef rock with shells *in situ*. Friederici (1910) found marine shells *in situ* elevated 1 or 2 meters on Niau and Maria Atolls, thus indicating an emergence or a former higher-sea-level stand, but he did not attempt to date the emergence.

After his field study of Raroia, Newell's opinion on recent changes (1956, p. 351) was that "The evidence of the erosion of the reef flat taken in conjunction with the general sterile appearance over great areas suggests an appreciable very recent uplift or drop in sea level of perhaps 15 or 20 cm." He was unable to find evidence on the atolls he visited of a terrace 5 or 6 feet above the present level.

Flint (1957, p. 263) apparently did not accept these interpretations of the evidence when he stated that certain "Very scattered data [which he cited] suggest that the theory of a Hypsithermal [Climatic Optimum] sea-level higher than the present one is improbable, and that emerged unde-formed strandlines which have been correlated with the Hypsithermal may be in fact very much older." Newell also pointed out that H. N. Fisk, Rufus Le Blanc, and Hugh Bernard have marshaled an impressive body of evidence from the Gulf Coast region of North America that casts doubt on an appreciably higher sea level during the Recent than that of the present.

However, in a study summing up an array of data establishing tentative correlation of postglacial radiocarbon dates and sea-level changes, Fair-bridge (1957, personal communication) demonstrated convincingly to the writer that there must have been several stands of sea level during the last 5,000 years higher than that of the present (see Fig. 39). He showed a 10-foot-higher level during the middle of the Climatic Optimum, at about 3600 years before the present (the so-called Peron Emergence). During the so-called Abrolhos Emergence, about 2300 before the present, he indicated a level 5 feet higher than that of the present, and he also showed a 2-foot-higher level (the Rottnest Emergence) at 1200 A.D.

Not all geologists are ready to accept these conclusions. During a talk given February 28, 1958, by Fairbridge before the Yale University Geology Club, Richard Flint and Karl Turekian challenged the adequacy of his data for these interpretations.

During travels among the Marshall atolls in 1956 the writer found ele-vated remnants of what appeared to be island rock resting on the lagoon reef flat of Ebon Atoll (Wiens, 1956, p. 6). These rose 5 to 6 feet above the reef flat at intervals in a line stretching over half a mile long. Individually, these "pedestals" were 30 to 40 feet long and 10 to 20 feet wide (Plate 24). At one end of the line one of the large blocks of rock was connected with the rock underlying the main islet of Ebon. Others were isolated 100 to 300 feet from the islet, with the intervening island soil or rock apparently scoured away by storm or other means of erosion. Some supported a growth of halophytic *Pemphis acidula*. Although it was not ascertained whether they were of reef rock or conglomerate in composition, it appeared that they must have originated when the sea level was higher than it is at present. Their surfaces appeared to conform to a 5-or-6-foot terrace above present mean sea level, although the heights were only estimated.

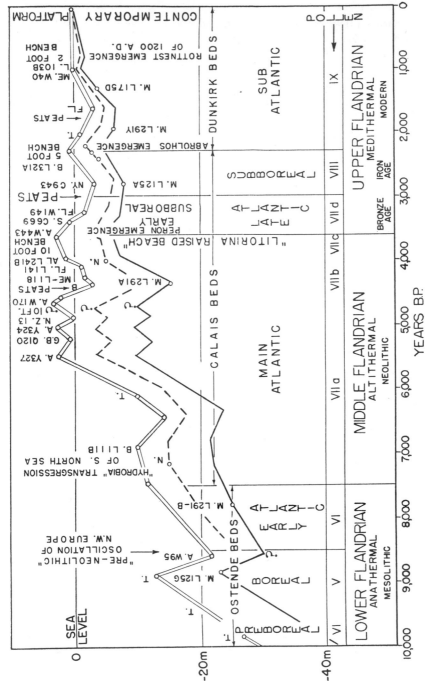

Fig. 39. Eustatic sea-level changes. [Courtesy R. W. Fairbridge.]

Controversy continues over the question whether such "terraces" are of recent or of an earlier era. Newell (1960, pp. 144–5) suggested that "Elevated terraces of Pacific islands, frequently cited (with insufficient evidence) as effects of recent high sea level, should be critically re-examined. It seems likely that they also are of Pleistocene age."

Lowering of sea level was undoubtedly an important factor in producing the atoll islands. "Gardiner expressed the opinion that all habitable atolls are the result of this shift. Some writers have suggested that the emerged atolls have resulted from the piling up of coral debris by the waves, but it seems more likely that most of them have been exposed by the lowered sea level. It has been recognized by most students that the atoll islands show abundant evidence of having emerged" (Shepard, 1948, p. 274).

Newell (1956, p. 332) nevertheless asserted that the conglomerate rock platform which underlay the loose sediments on the islets of Raroia and rose to between 0.5 and 1.0 meters above average high water was composed entirely of bioclastic material, which could have been formed near the present sea level. He found no *in situ* reef material and did not consider it an elevated platform but rather a depositional surface of cemented coral rubble. He thought it improbable (p. 346) that "atoll islets invariably rest on a pre-existing reef flat," and that islets may be formed on reefs by hurricanes without the necessity of sea-level subsidence.

The writer's observations on coral reefs in the Marshalls and eastern Carolines have been that in reef sectors where corals and coralline algae have just reached the water surface at low tide, there appears to be little sand, gravel, and boulder accumulation, and islets do not occur. Their formation appears to occur invariably in the middle and highest parts of the dead reef. The reef here has died and become planed flat in large part by erosion because the once-live corals and algae have been killed by a lowered sea level (Newell, 1956, p. 341). It is precisely at these elevated parts that sediments are heaped by hurricanes to form or to enlarge islets. Since, owing to local conditions, different reefs may grow at different rates, in some areas elevated reef remnants may form the base of islets. At other places on a reef the islets may have resulted from depositional activities of storms. The latter occurrences need not invalidate the contention supported by Kuenen (1950, p. 447) that "practically no cays and ramparts could have been formed but for the preceding emergence" of the reef. "Elevated islands" or reef islets that rise on most reef flats may be of sand or debris or of solid rock.

Kuenen (1950, pp. 452–3) took the view that erosion of exposed reef rock through chemical solution resulting from rainwater (Plate 25) is so rapid that the "pre-existing atoll and barrier rims must have suffered severe attack during the retreat of the Pleistocene oceans, and not improbably were entirely beheaded at sea-level." While he concedes that this conclusion is still highly speculative, he asserts that the amount of destruction gives an indication of the right order of magnitude. Thus, Kuenen and others who believe this with him were convinced that the present emerged reef rock could not have remained from a period before the last Pleistocene glaciation, as Flint's interpretation placed it, but that it has formed since the last glaciation. This would be particularly true where marine shells persist *in situ*.

Suggested cycle of atoll reef morphology

The writer is persuaded that the weight of evidence favors the view of Recent levels of the sea higher than the present and that the present-day land areas may be largely attributed to the exposure of reefs following the fall of the sea to near the present level. With the assumption of these premises, the writer suggests the cycle of atoll reef, lagoon, and land morphology illustrated in Fig. 40. The lowest reef profile in the figure represents the hypothetical stage at the end of glacial low level. At this level the emerged reef, once standing about 300 feet higher, had been dissolved and eroded so that only remnants of the reef peripheral (A) and small lagoon promontories (D) stood much above the level of the sea. Because of degradation, the lagoon bottom (C) at this stage had reached approximate sea level, with some depressions possibly slightly below sea level. Seaward subaerial erosion and wave abrasion had eaten far into the old raised reef to produce a fringing reef flat (B) with an outer algal ridge and a live reef front, the submarine parts of which have been eroded on the windward side to a bench representing the base level of wave force. A groove-and-spur system possibly prevailed on the windward reef margin, as at present; on the leeward reef the drop-off was steep.

Assuming this picture of the eroded emerged atoll (at this stage represented as a raised limestone island in some cases) at the end of glacial low level, the deglaciation following rising world atmospheric temperatures brought a rising sea level and with it an upward growth of the reef along the entire fringing reef flat as well as an outward growth at the reef margins. As water rose in the lagoon, sedimentation began to fill the lagoon basin. If there were gaps in the surrounding old reef, as there quite likely might have been, the tidal influx of marine water brought the recolonization of the lagoon promontories with reef corals. These started their upward and lateral expansion with the rise in the water level, shedding sediments around their base to add to those washed down from the surrounding reefs. However, the lagoon slopes would not have provided much sedimentary material until the rise of sea level and the growth on the

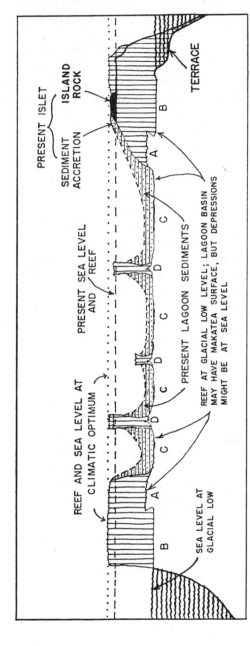

Fig. 40. Hypothetical diagram of atoll evolution. A, undercut "raised" reef remnant; B, old reef flat; C, old lagoon bottoms; D, coral patches, knolls, or pinnacles. [From Wiens (1959).]

fringing reefs had reached the surface level of the old reef, allowing tidal waters to pour across the island rock and through gaps down over the lagoon slopes.

At this stage reef growth would have begun on the rock of the old reef, covering it with new growth, while foraminiferal sand and other debris now would have begun to wash over the old reef to form sedimentary deposits on the lagoon slopes. Islets of a temporary type might have formed as storm-debris deposits, smothering portions of the reef and slowing growth at such places. They would have tended to be erased easily from the reef, since the sea level continued to rise.

Because of the great width of the reef at this period, there would have been a differential in the degree with which corals and corallines flourished in the different zones from seaward to lagoon side, especially on the windward reef. The seaward parts probably would have grown at a faster rate than the lagoon side. This would have been accentuated on the windward reef because of the smothering action of foraminiferal sands and other sediments and debris. In time, this would most likely have tended to form a slightly upward slope of the reef from the lagoon side to the seaward side. With rising water levels, this also would have meant an enlargement of the lagoon and possibly a decrease in the width of the reef at sea level on the windward side.

On the leeward reef, a slope upward toward the outer rim might not be so likely to develop because there would be more of a two-way tidal movement over the reef there than on the windward side, where the movement of the water is largely one-directional—with the wind. The growth on the leeward reef in some situations might be feeble and result in gaps or in parts of the reef lagging below the surface.

When sea levels had reached their maximum (such as might have occurred during the Hypsithermal or Climatic Optimum) and then fell below the maximum, the exposed reef died and erosion set in, both because of solution of the water-soluble lime and abrasion and subaerial denudation. Sediments washed toward the lagoon as well as downslope toward the sea. Debris tossed on the exposed reef by storm waves formed beaches and ramparts. A long standstill of sea level or fluctuations of the sea above and below this dead reef and the accumulations of sand and debris resulted in the cementation of the sediments into beach rock and island conglomerate or reef rock.

Simultaneously, wave abrasion and subaerial erosion began to plane a new reef flat, eating into the consolidated reef rock, island conglomerate, and the unconsolidated heaps of rubble and sand. If the drop were sufficient, the accumulation of sediments would have permitted a fresh-water lens to develop, making place for plant life to take hold and producing a a habitat for man, as in the present stage of atoll development.

In the lagoon, a drop in sea level resulted in the planing of protruding coral knolls to sea level. The knolls then formed patch reefs with flat, partially dead top surfaces, while the lagoon floor received increasing sediment accumulations. This again would have restricted increasingly the dimensions of the lagoon. As more of the lagoon slopes emerged with increasing glaciation, the lagoon would have shrunk inward and become increasingly shallow. The seaward reef flat would have changed to a fringing reef flat if the drop were rapid enough. In the end, if a sufficiently long low-level standstill took place, a state of the reef similar to the former low-level state would prevail, with the difference that the atoll base below the surface now might be wider than at the preceding low level, owing to sediment accumulation on the outer atoll slopes throughout the time involved and regardless of whether sea level were rising or falling. When renewed reef building took place with a new glaciation, the reef would start out with a broader base than before. Thus the expansion of the outer dimensions of the atoll depends partly upon the number of major changes of sea levels that have occurred since reef building first began. It is an ever-expanding base.

The above-described process is hypothetical, to be sure. In general, however, this may be about the way the over-all morphology of atolls takes place. Such a picture at least may serve as a frame of reference for the examination of some of the details of the morphological process.

Reef-width uniformity

More than a hundred years ago, Beechey (1831, pp. 186–93) noted in writing about the 32 atolls observed by him: "The width of the plain or strip of dead coral (reef) in the islands which fell under our observations in no instance exceeded half a mile from the usual wash of the sea to the edge of the lagoon, and in general was only about three or four hundred yards." The general uniformity of the ranges of reef widths that occur among atolls requires a theoretical examination. According to Kuenen (1947, pp. 11–32), Daly pointed out that the variation in reef widths is surprisingly small, widths of 300 to 500 meters predominating. This uniformity is taken to show support for the theory of glacial control. Kuenen stated that the exceptions, such as the reefs in the Moluccas, which attain average widths of 2,000 to 2,500 meters, were due to the absence on them of Lithothamnion veneers, which in the open Pacific, for instance, may greatly retard the growth of reefs (Gardiner, 1931).

The explanation for this uniformity in reef width seems to be related to the explanation for lagoon origin discussed earlier. Atolls start with a lagoon in which the rim is restricted in its inward growth by abundant sedimentation. Thus, the vast bulk of the expansion by live reef builders proceeds upward and outward, initially from the margins and in subsequent cycles from the existing reef flat and margins. Outward building proceeds slowly both because of the rapidly increasing depths to the surface of outer slopes and because, once the reef has reached a level near the surface, especially on the windward side, erosion by wave power may be as rapid or more rapid than new reef building, while sedimentation from the reef margin tends to smother some upward building below the lower reach of wave force.

The widths of initial fringing and barrier reefs also depend upon the slope of the island fringed. If the slope is mild the reefs logically should be wider, because reefs can take hold in relatively shallow water for a greater distance out from shore. But since most volcanic mountains have more-or-less similarly inclined slopes, the initial widths would be apt to be similar, although this would not apply in the event a reef developed on an antecedent platform within the depth limits for reef formation.

Again, the widths of atoll reefs in part depend upon the degree of erosion of emerged reefs during glacial low level. The rebuilding process starts from the outside edge and covers the surface of the reef flat, growing upward and outward. Growth lagoonward after the surface of the old island rock is reached is retarded by sedimentation in this zone as well as by the decrease of nutrients reaching this zone from the seaward side. Since all atoll reefs start this rebuilding at the same time, the final widths reached at any stage of sea level do not vary unduly, although local conditions bring about differences in widths. The maximum surface reef widths are governed by the length of time since glaciation in which reefs can be built outward and by the number of emergences and submergences.

Since the active reef builders only operate within about 150 feet of the surface of the sea, the steep outer atoll slope requires that the outward reef building must result eventually in an overhanging cliff if it is to continue or if it is not eroded currently (as it is on the windward side) by wave fracture and abrasion. But after a certain measure of overhang is achieved (such as occurs on leeward reef margins), the margin reaches a critical point of weakness relative to storm waves, so that weaker parts are broken off and fall down onto the atoll slopes or, occasionally, are tossed up onto the reef flat. Thus a point of equilibrium may be reached beyond which reefs get wider only extremely slowly as the subterranean slope builds up to provide additional foundation. On the reef margin erosion processes currently appear to be faster than construction (Newell, 1956, pp. 342, 344), and thus reefs actually may be getting narrower. Emery, Tracey, and Ladd (1954, p. 26), however, believed marginal zones of windward reefs at Bikini to be growing seaward.

It appears to be a common occurrence that reef widths are greatest on atolls at sharp bends and angles (Dana, 1851, pp. 25–51) (Plate 12). The reason for this probably is that at such bends the movement of ocean and lagoon currents causes rapid accumulation of sediments at these points, thus enlarging the foundations for upward and outward reef building.

Reef erosion and destruction

The importance of destructive forces tearing and wearing down atoll reefs and land hardly needs to be emphasized. However, much controversy continues as to the manner in which the various parts of the atoll structure are denuded and demolished. Few data are available on the rates at which various processes denude and destroy the parts of an atoll they attack, so that the roles of various erosion agents are difficult to evaluate.

The writer agrees with Kuenen (1950, p. 465) and numerous other atoll students that mechanical denudation is not a satisfactory explanation for glacial low-level beveling of the raised reef (if in fact there was such beveling) but that the destruction of the exposed limestone is largely accomplished through chemical solution by rain water. The highly eroded and honey-combed, so-called *makatea* surfaces of raised atolls give ample evidence of this process (Plate 25). On the other hand, "There is no compelling evidence for extensive planation during the short duration of the low levels as Kuenen would have us believe" (Newell, 1956, p. 324). Newell pointed out that Pleistocene low-level terraces in the Bahamas are rarely more than half a mile wide, and he felt that only the smallest limestone islands were truncated during Pleistocene lows.

In regard to subaerial and intertidal reef reduction, there is less agreement on the role of solution versus mechanical erosion. In their brief review of the problem of coral reefs, Ladd and Tracey (1949) cited the observations of Murray and Gardiner in an earlier day and of Kuenen, Umbgrove, Fairbridge, and Teichert more recently concerning the importance of the geological evidence of widespread solution limited to the intertidal zone and particularly effective at low-tide level. They pointed out that water on reef flats varies considerably in its composition from that of normal sea water, as shown by biochemists on the Great Barrier Reef and at Bikini, concluding that "The possibility of solution on a large scale as a result of this variation must be considered." Fairbridge (1948, p. 87; 1952, pp. 1–2) contended that horizontal platforming such as that which produces a coral reef flat is not the result of mechanical erosion operating at wave base but of subaerial cutting in the intertidal belt (Plate 26). Newell and Imbrie (1955, p. 10) concluded from studies of Bimini in the Bahamas and Raroia in the Pacific that marine planation is not being accomplished mainly at the intertidal level.

Emery (1946, pp. 209–28) argued that the increase in carbon dioxide in solution in tide pools during the night increased the amount of calcium ions that could be held in solution and that this led to the dissolving of the rock walls of the basin. During the day calcium carbonate, by a reverse process, is deposited as a fine precipitate to be flushed out by high-tide waves, thus leading to a gradual erosion of the reef flat. Revelle and Emery (1957, p. 705) came to the conclusion that some process of intertidal solution is much faster than solution below the intertidal zone, as shown by the fairly level surface of the reef flat at a depth less than 30 centimeters below normal low tide.

Kuenen (1950, p. 436) asserted that "The testimony of geological observations appears to establish beyond doubt the solvent action of tropical *surface* waters on reef limestone." Kuenen's arguments were endorsed by Fairbridge (1952) and Emery, Tracey, and Ladd (1954, pp. 26–30). While accepting the thesis of the solvent power of tropical surface water on limestone, Newell (1956, p. 358) alluded to the fact that Robert N. Ginsburg (1953), Gilbert Ranson (1955) as well as Newell (1951) had concluded that biomechanical and biochemical activities are adequate to produce most of the distinctive erosion forms of the intertidal zone on certain limestone coasts, and that solution by sea water is not the dominant process. Emery himself had shown that intertidal gastropods probably play an important role in the erosion, and in his study of Johnston Island (1956, p. 1513) he wrote that "The myriads of fishes that scrape and break off bits of coral and coralline algae during their feeding result in the production and transportation of sediments in quantities that may rival the amounts produced and transported by waves and currents."

If it be assumed that the growth of blue-green algae on and below the surface initiates erosion by biochemical action and penetration of algal filaments into the rock [as found by Doty, Newhouse, Miller, and Wilson (1954)], "it may be safely concluded that the rasping of the softened surface rock by gastropod radulae accelerates the process of limestone removal" (Newell, 1956, p. 360).

Estimates of rock removal through marine solution were made by Emery (1946, p. 227) in a study of tide pools that averaged 5 centimeters in depth. He calculated that it probably required 200 years to excavate the pools to this depth. The process thus appears to be relatively slow. Nevertheless, in a more recent study (Revelle and Emery, 1957, pp. 703–6) he expressed the belief that "Geologic evidence suggests that some process of solution is of great importance in removing limestone in the intertidal zone. This process is faster than solution by rain water as indicated by the existence of intertidal nips in water sheltered from wave action."

Newell and Imbrie (1955, p. 10) found their "attempts to record diurnal fluctuations of the carbonate content of surface sea water by means of systematic analyses for 'hardness' (total dissolved calcium and magnesium bicarbonates) were negative. Undoubtedly," they wrote, "calcium carbonate is precipitated more rapidly in the daytime than at night, and possibly, but not probably, calcium carbonate is redissolved at night. Our chemical tests did not reveal any significant fluctuations in the carbonate concentrations."

By contrast, Revelle and Emery (1957, pp. 705–6) found that the diurnal changes in alkalinity/chlorinity ratios strongly indicated that intertidal solution of calcium carbonate does in fact take place,

probably at such a rapid rate that it is an important factor in reducing islands and raised reefs to the monotonously uniform level of the reef flat . . . The presence of vertical gradients [of salinity] suggests that solution may occur under special local conditions. It may take place within the rock surface of the basin floors by organic acids liberated by boring algae, or by carbon dioxide produced in respiration beneath the algal mats that cover some of the floors . . . But the uniform solution of the intertidal limestone suggests that something other than localized processes is involved.

In their study of the Bimini area of the Great Bahama Bank, Newell and Imbrie (1955, p. 10) related the above processes to the biomechanical processes of erosion. During their investigation, they found "abundant evidence that blue-green algae, forming an ubiquitous cover in the intertidal and spray zones, soften and permeate the rock surfaces to a depth of perhaps one millimeter." They believed that this penetration by algal fibers was accomplished by contact leaching. Shore animals in hordes feed on this algal cover and in doing so scrape away the rock softened by the algae. A single traverse by a large gastropod was found to produce furrows 1 millimeter wide and ½ millimeter deep. With the work of vast numbers of these animals constantly going on, they believed that "This mechanical rasping is a potent means of erosion, concentrated precisely in the intertidal and spray zone where many of the mollusks do all of their grazing." These authors also concluded that rock-boring worms and the boring barnacle Lithotrya account for the removal of up to half of the rock substance eroded in the intertidal nick and that the burrows of these animals vastly increase the surface area of attack by other agencies.

Newell and Imbrie thus support in part the conclusions of Gardiner (1903) and Otter (1940), who found rock burrowers of great importance in the destruction of coral reefs. Gardiner gave the following order of their attack on coral rock: boring algae, Porifera, Polychaeta (especially Eunicidae), sipunculids, and Lithophaga. The rock is eventually broken up into fragments and then into sand, which in turn by the action of sand-triturating animals is converted into mud. The burrows of many of these organisms greatly increase the rock area, offering clean rock surfaces for further attack by other borers and for the direct solution of the rock by sea water "if this can still be considered an important factor in the destruction of calcareous rocks" (Otter, 1940, pp. 349–51).

From the preceding discussion, it is evident that as yet there is not complete agreement on the dominant processes of erosion. Fairbridge and Kuenen appear to emphasize marine solution as dominant. Newell (1956, p. 360) admitted that direct solution by sea water may be a factor and that algal penetration of the rock is significant, but he denied that they are the dominant current factors. He emphasized, and the writer believes correctly, the importance of mechanical and biomechanical abrasion as the tools for the current erosion of the reef and in the cutting back of the islets.

In a personal comment to the writer, however, Emery dissented from this view and pointed out that mechanical erosion should cut deeper than the low-tide level, which appears to be the lowest level to which reefs are truncated. Fairbridge, Revelle, and Emery all emphasized the fact that deep intertidal undercutting of raised limestone occurs in many protected inlets where wave abrasion does not operate effectively (Plate 26).

Some of the general disagreement over the dominant process possibly arises from the differences in the particular zones or areas of the atoll considered. The erosion in the grooves of the margin differs from that of the reef flat, and both differ from that of the island rock and of the loosely consolidated island sediments. The fracturing and breaking off of reef blocks along the windward reef margins and at the leeward reef cliffs are of still a different order. In considering the dominant process of erosion of atoll reef and land, all the multiple processes must be considered as a whole and an evaluation made of the bulk contribution of each process.

Unfortunately, data are lacking for evaluation on a quantitative basis. Although no data have been gathered for quantitative evaluation of the role of mechanical abrasion of the reef front, reef surfaces, and island rock by wave fracture and transport and gravel and sand scour, some observable evidence of its importance can be presented. The excellent observations of Emery, Tracey, and Ladd in the northern Marshalls and of Newell at Raroia provide direct evidence to which the writer would like to add his own. This evidence, in the main, corroborates theirs. It must be recognized, of course, that mechanical abrasion is accelerated by disintegrative forces such as algal undermining of rock and by boring worms, urchins, gastropods, and other organisms.

An aerial photograph examined by the writer showing the lagoon reef off Aineman Islet of Jaluit Atoll illustrates a type of exfoliation of the lagoon reef flat which produces a slight terrace and which could be affected by the hydraulic pressure of storm waves in a process of undermining of reef-rock layers (Plate 27). This type of erosion, through which layers of consolidated rock separated by a thin layer of sand are hydraulically lifted, might occur where a "sheet" of Heliopora expands laterally upon a previous lagoon reef flat following a rise in sea level. On the lagoon reef flat at Ebon Atoll the writer observed and photographed an area of several thousand square yards covered by a continuous "sheet" of this coral only a few inches thick and stopped in its upward growth after reaching the sea surface but spreading laterally from the periphery. The sheet comprised the coalescence of numerous separate colonies (Plate 52). Because of the foraminiferous veneer underlying it, it would appear to require no great violence of wave power to hydraulically scale off parts of such a rock layer.

More impressive are the examples of seaward wave erosion. The results of this are represented by the huge blocks broken off the reef front and tossed onto the reef flat. At Bikini (Emery, Tracey, and Ladd, 1954) they were normally 5 to 10 feet in cubic dimensions, but some blocks were 20 to 30 feet long and more than 10 feet thick. Many of these blocks have been washed 100 to 300 feet shoreward by hurricane waves. Newell (1956) furnished a photograph of one such enormous block thrown up on the reef flat at Rarioa. Its comparatively old age is shown by the intertidal undercutting that has taken place. Fosberg and MacNeil (1954) asserted that occasionally they are aggregated into large block fields, areas of the reefs completely covered by enormous fragments. While sailing by the leeward side of Lugagi Islet of Namu Atoll in 1956, the writer saw a large area of the reef flat several hundred feet across mantled with boulders from 3 to 5 feet in diameter. On the reef adjacent to the ship's pass there stood a block the dimensions of which were estimated by the writer to be 10 by 20 by 7 feet. Two blocks, each about 6 by 6 feet, were seen at Jaluit washed 150 feet from the reef margin to the beach edge (Plate 19). The relative recency of this breakage was shown by the lack of intertidal erosion such as that shown in Newell's photo from Raroia (his Plate 41). An aerial photograph of the reef at Namorick shows numerous such boulders, which appeared to be between 10 and 20 feet wide and long by 5 to 10 feet thick. Although relatively few of the larger blocks are tossed up onto the reef flat, these few undoubtedly represent only a small fraction of those which are broken off and sink down onto the atoll slopes. At Bikini slumped sections of the reef as much as 40 feet long lie on the shallow terrace that fringes the seaward edge (Emery, Tracey, and Ladd, 1954, p. 32). At the margin (p. 30) collapsed sections of the reef, which rest on submarine terraces, are indicated by matching re-entrants up to 500 feet wide and extending 25 to 200 feet into the reef. The attrition by this mechanical and hydraulic erosion of the reef must be enormous, even though much of it may require rare storm waves to be accomplished (Plate 13).

Raised reef-rock remnants or pedestals on the seaward sides of islets and in the inter-islet channels on coral atolls show the most marked effects of erosion on the fringes rather than on their upper surfaces. Moreover, former large patches of reef rock have been cut across from sea to lagoonside often in ribbonlike strips corresponding to the orientation of tidal flow lines (Plate 28). If chemical solution be conceded as the chief agent of their erosion, it would seem that the upper surfaces should erode just as rapidly as marginal erosion on their fringes, and that no ribbonlike channels would result such as might conceivably form from the abrasive scour of sediments carried with the rush of water along the inter-islet channels with the tides.

At Raroia, Newell spoke of angular clefts or notches in the reef which he terms incomplete channels. He said that these "clearly are being lengthened headward as storm waters cross the islets towards the lagoon." Several aerial photographs clearly indicate the mechanical nature of the erosion. Many examples of this type of erosion were observed by the writer in 1958 on Jaluit, where a typhoon in January had caused immense topographical changes through water scour (Blumenstock, 1958, pp. 1267–9) (Plate 29). Plates 20 and 30 show such storm erosion on the atoll of Taongi. In the latter the triangular notches on the lagoon reef edge are cut into the lagoon side of large vegetated islets and large gravel and boulder fans extend into the lagoon. They could be accounted for by headward erosion caused by storm waters running across islets earlier. Subsequently, storm-washed gravels and sands again closed the gaps and reconstituted the vegetated land. Newell concluded from his observations that the shallow channels between islets all are of very recent origin, although the deep ship passage probably is inherited from an earlier gap in the rim.

Growth versus erosion in the development of reef-front serrations

Although such incipient shallow channels appear to be rare, their advanced stages, cutting across the islet (Plates 28, 31, and 32) and forming numerous small slivers of islets, are familiar occurrences on most atolls.

According to Newell (1956, p. 328), "Topographic forms of the islands, including conspicuous flow lines in the coarse coral rubble, generally at right angles to the atoll rim, strongly suggest that the land has been inundated many times, indeed built up in places, by translation waves that sweep across the atoll rim to the lagoon." These flow lines obviously are the result of wave transport of sediments scoured loose by mechanical erosion.

The flow lines are associated with another erosional feature mentioned by Newell but not mentioned in the Bikini study (Emery, Tracey, and Ladd, 1954). On Raroia the excurrent areas of the reef flat (Newell, 1956, p. 350) commonly were found to be furrowed by irregular shallow grooves converging, fanlike, toward the gaps in the algal ridge. The grooves are discontinuous and erratic. Their floors are scoured clean by gravel and sand but are very uneven and interrupted here and there by gravel-filled pot holes. Newell regarded these grooves as incipient surge channels and said that like such channels they led to outer grooves. Because of their shallowness, these grooves on the reef flat are not always obvious to the ground observer. They did not come to the writer's attention during the traverse of long stretches of reef flats on both lagoon and seaward sides on numerous atolls. However, prior to reading Newell's monograph on Rarioa, and during the course of the examination of aerial photographs, the writer had noticed the occurrence of these shallow grooves on the seaward sides of certain reef stretches and had come to the same conclusion as Newell in relating them to developing surge channels (Plate 17). Nevertheless, they are not conspicuous for most reef flats even on aerial photographs, or for all or most sections of those atoll reefs on which the writer found them to occur.

The flow lines showing the excurrent movement of gravels along these shallow troughs furnish support for the contention that the development of surge channels and of the outer groove-and-spur system of windward reefs is chiefly the result of mechanical scour. The origin of the groove-and-spur system and the role of erosion in their formation have been points of controversy. The importance of this outer front of the atoll reef has long been known. Darwin (1889, p. 86) wrote that "Should the outer and living margin perish, of any one of the many low coral islands, round which a line of great breakers is incessantly foaming, the whole, it is scarcely possible to doubt, would be washed away and destroyed in less than half a century." Although the writer joins with Newell in regarding the groove-and-spur system as the result primarily of erosion, it appears, paradoxically, that the grooves dissipate the enormous energy of ocean waves and "play a vital part in the function of the coral reef as a breakwater. Near their outer ends, which extend to the maximum depth of appreciable wave action . . . they interfere with the normal orbital water motion associated with waves on a sloping bottom by 'taking the bottom out from under the waves'; at the inner end they pursue a 'divide and conquer' policy. The resulting effect upon waves is remarkable" (Munk and Sargent, 1954, p. 276).

In their study at Bikini, Munk and Sargent found that the distribution of the grooves can be correlated with the distribution of wave power around the atoll, being most developed where wave power is greatest (Fig. 28). They wrote that

Most of the grooves begin at a depth of 35 to 50 feet, then run up the reef slope into and through the surf zone. At the inner end they may end abruptly or be continued as surge channels, or as tunnels with blowholes under the reef platform. Just inside the surf zone, around the blowholes and the heads of grooves and channels, colonies of Lithothamnion [Porolithon] and corals rise about 2 feet above the general reef level. The upper faces of the spurs are paved with living Lithothamnion which present an extremely rough surface. The sides of the grooves are covered with projecting, often bracket-like colonies. The bottoms of the grooves consist of relatively smooth rock and sand.

It was found at Bikini that between Bikini and Aomoen Islets the grooves are spaced about 25 feet apart, are about 16 feet deep at their inner ends, and vary in width from 3 to 6 feet. Newell (1956) described the groove-and-spur zone at Raroia as very like the one at Bikini.

In explaining this phenomenon Kuenen (1950, p. 431) wrote: "At first the trenches might be explained as erosional forms, scoured by the waves in the rock of the reef. Several observations show, however," he claimed, "that they have been formed by growth. The covering with live nullipores, the formation of tunnels, the transverse connections at right angles to the rush of the waters, and finally the absence of sand or other erosion tools around the blow holes all testify to the absence of mechanical wear." Emery, Tracey, and Ladd (1954, p. 26) appear to agree with Kuenen in stating: "Probably there is mechanical abrasion during periods of exceptionally heavy weather, but this does not seem adequate to explain the grooves as erosional features." With Kuenen, they took the position that the phenomenon represents a constructional form developed by outward growth of Lithothamnion (Porolithon). But, as Newell pointed out, "It is not at all clear just how processes of organic accretion could produce the serrate reef front." In fact, Kuenen's statement has certain weaknesses that defeat its argument.

In the first place, if these features resulted chiefly from growth, the grooves would all terminate at the reef front instead of transgressing the reef edge to continue inward as surge channels or as tunnels trenched in the reef flat. The surge channels sunk in the reef flat (Plate 42) certainly could not be regarded as constructional features. Second, the covering with live nullipores is over the ridges or buttresses between grooves and along their sides, not along the bottom of the grooves, where active erosional tools in the form of gravels and sands operate. Moreover, Kuenen himself stated (1950, p. 422) that "Despite the strengthening influence of encrusting Lithothamnion on the reef structure in the breaker zone, there can be little doubt that, for the reef mass as a whole, growth is greatly retarded by the presence of *these almost stationary veneers*" [italics supplied]. Since the live nullipores prevent the growth of coral, the only significant growth agency is the nullipores, which Kuenen said constituted almost stationary agents. In an earlier day Agassiz (1903, pp. 96–7) noted that "We find the same digitating channels [Plates 13 and 16] *worn into* the sea face of the reef platform *cutting the outer edge* into knolls which are gradually *undermined* at the sea face of the reef platform, and finally are broken off in large masses; these are *thrown up* on the ledge flat and *broken up* little by little according to their size and their more or less exposed position on the platform" [italics supplied].

The formation of tunnels may be caused by algal growth covering the troughs (Plates 44 and 45), but the trough itself must have been scoured out by erosion, possibly during an emergent period. If such were the case, solution erosion by fresh-water runoff must be postulated to account for the furrows. The troughs are roofed over only where they are narrow and the roof of algae is but a small part of the space that results from erosion. The absence of sand or other erosional agents around blow holes most likely may be attributed to inadequate or inopportune observation, since this observation generally is only possible at low-tide stage, when the force of the surge might not carry sands and gravels from the bottom of the grooves through the blow holes. During high tide, when the deeper water movement might bring sand out of the blow holes, such sediments would be removed from their vicinity by the tidal currents. Moreover, it is likely that most of the abrasion is accomplished in the downward and outward transport of sediments from the reef flat rather than in upward heaving of materials, although this also must occur. In both events, the movement represents a back-and-forth surge of abrasive materials with the waves. Emery, Tracey, and Ladd (1954, pp. 25–6) stated that "There is no evidence that the algae are roofing over or otherwise filling the grooves . . . The waves remove much material from the reef in small pieces which are transported down the grooves and down the terrace." Such a movement undoubtedly would rasp out troughs across the reef flat that would lead to the development of surge channels and grooves, as was pointed out earlier. The writer also has seen sands and gravels in surge channels and pools that were connected by tunnels with the grooves on the windward reef opposite Uliga Islet on Majuro Atoll. Newell (1956, p. 346) wrote that "The surge channels [at Raroia] are headward extensions of the outer grooves, and they are being cut and deepened by gravel scour. All the Raroia examples contain potholes filled with rounded cobbles and pebbles. Many extend within 15 meters of shore." He stated that while the channels are lined at the rim by small corals and blisters of *Porolithon onkodes* (Lithothamnion), "The lower walls and floor, however, are scoured by sand and gravel as are those of the outer grooves . . . The coralline algae are not . . . very active in the gloomy recesses of the caverns where erosion clearly is dominant and accretion is at a minimum."

Another interesting bit of evidence refuting the idea of growth as the causal factor in the development of the groove system is the fact that, according to Munk and Sargent (1954), the surge channels at Bikini are "properly tuned to the average wave characteristics. An average depth of 15 to 20 feet and a length of about 200 feet between the outer end of the platform (Lithothamnion ridge) and the inner ends of the channels correspond to a fundamental period of oscillation of 8 seconds, which is also the prevailing period of the waves of the trade winds." It would be odd indeed for a growth agent such as Porolithon to adjust its growth to such a point of correlation. On the other hand, it is entirely conceivable for a mechanical erosion process to develop on a sea-level reef flat until it reaches a point of adjustment with average wave oscillation periods. Although Munk and Sargent declared an inability to clarify the reef-molding process, they asserted that

It is a clear in general that the reef form represents some kind of equilibrium between the erosive or destructive power of the waves and the growth potential of the reef-building organisms. It is generally apparent that in areas where the wave action and hence presumably destructive power is greatest, growth of reef builders is also most rapid (Yonge, 1940, pp. 355, 374). Hence windward reef faces may be nearly in equilibrium under conditions of rapid growth and erosion, leeward ones under slow growth and erosion.

The arguments against this conclusion may be seen from the following comments.

The grooves are not all the same length. Newell (1956, pp. 342–3) stated that

Where dissection is incomplete, not all the grooves extend to the outer edge of the [8-meter] terrace. This and the fact that the terrace has a very regular outer margin suggest that the form of both spurs and grooves is the effect of erosion rather than construction. There is very little roofing of the grooves by algal deposits on Raroia. On the other hand, the spurs are quite unequal in breadth. If they were simply buttresses of algal deposits being extended seaward against the surf, they would probably advance at unequal rates, and this would produce a lobate or irregular margin.

As a matter of fact, this is the character of the leeward reefs, which have little Porolithon and which usually develop no surge channels and grooves.

One final interesting phenomenon pointed out by Emery, Tracey, and Ladd (1954, pp. 26, 29–30) seemingly provides a clue to the importance of mechanical erosion versus Porolithon upbuilding. At Bikini, Eniwetok, Rongerik, and Rongelap in the northern Marshalls on the windward reefs (where Porolithon is most vigorous and important) a shallow terrace "slopes gently seaward, from a depth of 15 to 25 feet at the reef edge to a depth of about 50 feet at the outer edge. Where well developed, the terrace is rather flat for a distance of several hundred yards from the reef edge; in other places its slope is 10 to 15 degrees. The living reef rises from this terrace." By contrast, "The most striking feature of the western reef is the steepness of its seaward slope . . . The visible part of the seaward slope is indeed a steep submarine cliff . . . From a depth of 100 feet to an undetermined depth, greater than 180 feet, the cliff is vertical. . . ." They go on to point out that on the western side of the atoll the reef flat is wider than to windward. Newell (1956, p. 334) points out a similar terrace at Raroia and also in the Bahamas (Newell and Rigby, 1957, p. 24).

It is generally agreed by students of coral reefs that the windward sides of coral atolls provide the best conditions for coral growth. Thus, lacking destruction by wave power and abrasion, one would expect the reef wall on the windward sides to be clifflike rather than a gentler slope supporting sediments brought down from reef surface erosion. Such terraces appear to be most explicable as a result of erosion of the windward side by mechanical scour, leading to a gradual retreat of the reef edge through headward erosion in the surge channels (Newell, 1956, p. 346) and the breakage of the spur projections during heavy storms. Recent studies in the Bimini area of the Great Bahama Bank (Newell and Rigby, 1954, p. 68) "are suggestive that the 3-fathom depth may correspond rather closely with the base level of marine planation for the present sea level." Emery, Tracey, and Ladd (1954, p. 30) also concluded that the Bikini terrace probably is erosional but thought that it might antedate the present reef. In a study of submarine terraces off the California coast Emery (1958, pp. 39–60) found five terraces deeper than these atoll terraces, which he viewed as having been eroded by successively lesser eustatic lowerings of sea level during the Wisconsin subage.

The definition of a lower limit of wave abrasion has been rather confused in the literature. Barrell (1917, pp. 779–80) estimated the lower limit of wave abrasion of hard rock at 50 fathoms, and Umgrove (1947, p. 104) placed it at 40 fathoms. Dietz and Menard (1951) made a careful and extensive study of this question and demonstrated the unsatisfactory nature of the definition of a wave base. They stated that observations show that breakers normally form when the depth to the bottom is about 1.1 to 1.5 times the height of the wave, depending somewhat on the wave period and local wind, current, and bottom conditions. "The maximum depth at which breakers form can be termed the base of vigorous abrasion. It is probably this base and not the so-called 'wave-base' that determines the depth of a plane of marine abrasion." Although wave base thus differs from area to area, Dietz and Menard thought a typical depth of the base of vigorous abrasion around the Pacific to be 4 fathoms, even less in most parts of the world.

The foregoing account and the evidence provided by aerial photographs of the Marshalls and other atolls make clear the vast importance of mechanical erosion through the abrasive power of sands and gravels and the power of waves. Although no quantitative values can be given for its role as compared with marine solution and biomechanical erosion, the writer is persuaded that mechanical scour occupies one of the dominant roles in the destruction of atoll land and reef, particularly the reef margins.

Development of passes across reefs

In Chapter 3 the writer discussed the situation and distribution of atoll passes and related their occurrences to the wind orientations. Darwin (1889, p. 135) sought to explain pass origins in terms of the destructive effects upon corals of fresh water and sediments drained from volcanic mountains during the barrier reef stage of atoll development. Since the prevailing winds are from the east, the general flow of water in the lagoon within the barrier reef is westward. Hence the windward eastern rim is most free of the harmful effects of fresh water and sediments as compared with the leeward sectors, where parts of the reef are killed by them. This argument was used to explain the prevalence of passes at leeward sites.

This explanation is not satisfactory, because the superstructures of present-day atolls were not developed during the barrier reef stage and have nothing to do with the original atoll development. Fresh water and sediments draining from volcanic mountain streams thus do not come into the picture for modern atolls, whose morphology appears to be a result of post-Pleistocene developments.

Kuenen's explanation, recounted in the last chapter, provides a more acceptable theory. This theory is that since the last glaciation there have been periods when the rate of rise in sea level must have been faster than the rates of reef growth in weaker sectors of the reef, so that parts of the reef became drowned. In a personal communication to the writer (March 5, 1956) Newell wrote that "It does seem well established that reef growth is inhibited, for some reason or other, on the leeward side of coral atolls and I have no doubt that the occurrence of ship passes into the lagoons mainly on the leeward reef is a direct result of somewhat reduced reef growth. I am afraid that we are still in the guessing stage with respect to the relative importance of the various suggested factors." Newell stated that he had always been impressed by Yonge's argument that the windward side is characterized by relatively clear water, whereas the leeward side is somewhat more turbid. Newell also thought that although there is no record of observations, it is likely that there is appreciable upwelling on the leeward shore. This, if present, would presumably depress temperatures significantly on the leeward side, resulting in less favorable conditions for reef development. Emery, Tracey, and Ladd (1954, pp. 144, 149–50) discussed the leeward occurrence of passes but did not give an explanation of their origin beyond the statement that on the leeward side of the atoll the interglacial reef did not completely enclose the original platform, and the gaps remained unfilled and therefore became the present passes. Whatever the mode of origin, those passes that are of great depth probably have extremely slow rates of coral growth, owing to lack of light and possibly also to sedimentation. However, growth may be gradually closing the shallower passes (Yonge, 1940, pp. 372–3).

The distribution characteristics of reef widths were also discussed in Chapter 3. Emery, Tracey, and Ladd (1954, p. 145) wrote of the northern Marshalls that "Although it is possible that reef widths are determined by the configurations of submerged reefs of an earlier stage, during which wind and current directions may have been altogether different, or in part by landslides, it appears more reasonable that the present reefs are controlled by present conditions." In Chapter 3 it was demonstrated that on most atoll reefs north of the equator the widest sectors are in the north and northwest rather than in the east, as one might expect. This is in agreement with what Emery, Tracey, and Ladd found in the northern Marshalls. Thus although windward seaward (eastern and northern) sectors show the most flourishing growth, where the reefs are unbroken the net gain in reef widths appear to be greater in the somewhat protected northwestern sectors. This may partly be explained by the fact, found in the northern Marshalls, that the lagoon reef margins show the most flourishing growth in the west and north, while sedimentation was greatest in the west. Both these factors would tend to widen the reef here.

It was shown in Chapter 3 that reef sections adjoining passes on the southwestern and western sides often build inward into the lagoon and expand their surfaces. Large patch reefs are especially prevalent just inside the mouths of channels and passes. Whether these phenomena are related to differences in the nutritional situation is still debatable. Sargent and Austin (1954, pp. 293–300) believed that the corals derive their organic matter directly from their zooxanthellae, but Yonge (1940, p. 365) did not think this was so. If Sargent and Austin were correct, there should be no advantage for corals at the mouths or adjacent to passes on the western sides of atolls, since sunlight and clarity of water would be the important factors. Odum and Odum (1955, p. 305) stated that since ample light for photosynthesis penetrates the water of both front and back reefs, decreased current must be a major factor in the decrease of coral coverage. On the other hand, they also appear to accept the argument that coral polyps are in part carnivorous and that they catch zooplankton, especially at night. Johnson (1954, p. 301) asserted that the average concentration of plankton per cubic meter in the lagoon is about four times that outside the southern and western outflow. He found that while most of the plankton remain in the deeper waters and currents of the lagoon, many of them migrate at night into the faster, westward-moving surface waters. The development of large patch reefs just within and adjoining western and leeward passes and channels would appear to indicate that current movements and possibly the plankton carried by them may be related to the growth of such reefs.

On the other hand, there appear to be adverse factors which prevent coral growth within the channel bottoms, for although patch reefs and inward reef extensions may run into the lagoon for hundreds of yards bordering the channels (often bifurcated) (Plates 9 and 11), the growth apparently is very slow from the sides toward the mid-channels, and channel sides often are vertical submarine cliffs (Plate 8). It appears probable that sediments carried out of the pass may have a smothering or an abrasive effect or both, thereby inhibiting coral growth on channel bottoms. Darwin believed that sediment deposition rather than fresh water was the deterrent to coral growth in passes, although he was primarily describing barrier passes on reefs around volcanic islands. He wrote (1889, p. 89): "The sediment brought down from the land would only prevent the growth of the coral in the line of its deposition, but would not check it on the side, so that the reefs might increase till they overhung the bed of the channel . . . They probably are kept open in the same manner as those into the lagoon of an atoll, namely, by the force of the currents and the drifting outwards of fine sediment." That such sediments do in fact drift out through the channels was demonstrated by the lack of fine bottom sediments in the lagoons of the northern Marshalls sampled by Emery, Tracey, and Ladd (see McKee, 1959, p. 509).

MacNeil (1954) tried to explain the derivation of both passes and patch-reef features from subaerial erosion during the emergent stages of the reef. He suggested that the passes are the sites of former streams resulting from a coalescence of lines of sinkholes draining an emergent reef. He thought that the linear patch reefs bordering the channels, whether simple or forked, re-sulted from organic growth on exposure-hardened ridges or limestone walls bordering such streams. However, this explanation is not satisfactory, for two reasons. Many of them do not extend as linear walls into the lagoon but terminate abruptly not far from the mouth of the lagoon pass. Thus they have little resemblance to former stream banks, which would be expected to extend far toward the lagoon center. More important, the theory proposed does not explain why there should be an absence or great rarity of patch reefs at the lagoon mouths of passes on the eastern reef aligned with the easterly direction of prevailing wind and waves.

A more satisfactory explanation is that patch reefs at these locations on the leeward reefs are the result of sedimentary processes. In a study of lagoon sedimentation at Kapingamarangi Atoll, McKee found that the southern pass affected sedimentation significantly. Inward-moving tidal currents built a tongue of calcium carbonate silt lagoonward from the forked channels for about a mile. The resulting pattern resembles a river delta with distributary channels leading into the lagoon (Plate 11). Patch-reef development near the passes is facilitated by the shoaling sediments. A large proportion of such a patch reef may be composed of sediments, with a smaller proportion made up of coral and coralline material, especially in the upper parts. That is, as a sedimentary patch develops, decreased sediment near the water surface encourages the formation of an organic reef veneer. However, multiple channels through such patches may be maintained by the rush of tidal water through the channels just as in the case of delta distributaries, with the abrasive effect of sediments inhibiting or slowing down coral and algal growth on channel bottoms. Vertical channel walls often result from organic growth here, however.

Delta-like deposits are seldom present on the ocean side of reef passes because this side drops off steeply to depths of thousands of feet and because the ebbing tidal current through the pass on the leeward sides is very swift. By contrast, the inward-moving current of the rising tide is relatively slow. The sediments carried toward the pass by the ebbing tide are halted and dropped near the pass when the tide reverses. When the ebb tide is again flowing strongly, sediments that have been deposited on the channel bot-toms are probably again swept out into the deep ocean.

Owing to storm action, however, certain channels may in time become blocked with sediment. This apparently occurred at Southeast Pass, Jaluit Atoll, southern Marshalls, as a result of the January 1958 typhoon. Accord-ing to the Island Development Officer at Majuro (1958), "The pass into the lagoon was altered on the southeast end of the island [Enybor Island, Plate 9] where a sand bar extends out approximately two or three hundred feet."

The rarity of occurrence of patch reefs near the lagoon mouths of eastern windward reef sectors, particularly where the channels are aligned with the prevailing wind and wave direction, may be explained by the almost entirely one-way tidal current into the lagoon, even at ebb tide, owing to the push of the wind.

Formation of beach rock

Once land is formed, whether by reef emergence or subsequent deposition of storm debris, its preservation is greatly aided by the growth of terrestrial vegetation and the development of beach rock. The roots of vegetation help to hold the loose debris together. Marine birds roosting in bushes and trees drop guano, which in time may cause phosphatic cementation of underlying loose sediments, thus further consolidating the land.

Beach rock (Plate 21) originates from sand and gravel laid down in successive layers mostly on the lagoon sides of islets. It generally has a lagoonward-dipping character at such sites and shows stratification which indicates the nature of its origin. Consolidation of beaches into rock by means of cementation provides a protective armor for the loose sediments of atoll land, slows down wave abrasion, and reduces danger of storm scour of islet soils.

Beach rock is abundant around islets of atolls and relatively rare around high islands of moderately great rainfall, such as Guam (Emery and Cox, 1956, p. 399). In discussing the origin of beach rock, Emery and Cox summarized several theories currently held. One is that beach rock develops where the interstitial water of beaches is sea water, which is already saturated with calcium carbonate, and that it should be absent where the interstices are occupied by ground water that has passed only through volcanic rocks and is presumably not saturated with calcium carbonate. Water left by falling tide or rising through capillary action evaporates near the sand surface, precipitating salts that serve as a cement. Readily soluble salts, such as sodium chloride, are removed by the next high tide, but salts such as calcium carbonate may remain to form a more-permanent cement.

Emery, Tracey, and Ladd (1954, pp. 45–6) suggested that sun heating of the beach during the day reduces the solubility of carbon dioxide in the interstitial water close to the surface, so that its pH rises. If the water is initially near saturation, calcium carbonate is precipitated. However, Emery and Cox's study of beach rock in the Hawaiian Islands (1956) revealed no unequivocal correlation of beach rock with beaches having interstitial water composed of sea water, ground water from limestone plains, or ground water from volcanic rocks (p. 401). They also rejected a suggestion by Cloud that the cementing might result from the biochemical activity of blue-green algae.

Since these algae are probably restricted to the topmost fraction of an inch, their activities could not explain cementation of individual layers 2 feet or more thick. Nesteroff and Ranson have both suggested that bacterial action caused the deposition of amorphous calcium carbonate, but because of the insufficient amount of organic material in the sand, this does not appear to be a satisfactory explanation. Emery and Cox also found that stable beaches (Merrin, 1955) were not essential for beach-rock formation. In short, their conclusion was that although beach rock is abundant in many places, we do not know how it forms (p. 402). It is known, however, that the cementing material that binds sand into beach rock consists of calcite with some aragonite (Ginsburg, 1953; Emery, Tracey, and Ladd, 1954; Illing, 1954; Ranson, 1955) or of calcite without aragonite (Emery and Cox, 1956, p. 383).

Although many examples of old beach rock occur on atolls, not all has been formed over a long period of time. Kuenen (1950, p. 434) asserted that cases have been known in which beach sandstone has formed in 1 year. That the cementing action is rapid on reef flats is clear. In 1954 the writer saw shell cases from World War II cemented firmly and partially embedded in the reef surface. In 1956 the writer found an example of dipping, well-stratified, and partially consolidated beach rock on the seaward and windward side of an islet on Kwajelein. This undoubtedly showed beach rock in the formative process, since pieces could be kicked off by foot or broken off by hand, although the sand was firmly enough welded together to preserve the shape of the pieces broken off.

Much of the beach rock observed by the writer in the Marshalls and Carolines atolls was old. McKee (1956, p. 11) wrote that the relatively old age of the beach rock observed at Kapingamarangi Atoll is suggested by the presence of typical beds preserved as relic deposits standing above present high-tide level on several islands, by the beveled remnants of typical beach rock extending seaward a few hundred feet across the reef flat from the present island shores, and by evidence of replacement of calcium carbonate by apatite in strata both in the interiors and on the shores of several islands. He found little evidence of beach rock forming currently, although evidence of cementation of loose debris on the seaward side of reefs was abundant. Beach rock presently observed around islets on atoll reefs thus appeared to be mostly of earlier origin.

Emery and Cox (1956, p. 389) found that in the Hawaiian Islands the beach rock appeared to extend about the same distance above high tide as the wash of the waves, but in several places it extends as much as 3 feet below low tide. Thus the position and attitude of most beach rock there is closely accordant with present beaches. Some beach rock was found discordant with present beaches, owing to retreat of beaches or to coastal elevation or submergence after the beach rock was formed (p. 390). Emery suggested that at Johnston Island beach rock as deep as 20 feet below the surface probably was downwarped (personal communication, 1958).

Both beach rock presently located on current shores of islets and relic beach rock off the seaward shores of present islets serve the important role of protecting the accumulations of loose sediments on islets from storm scour and erosion. The relic bands of beach rock often found some distance from seaward shores of atoll islets act as a breakwater, a second line of defense after the reef margin and algal ridge.

Sedimentary accretion in land building on reefs

Another important role of beach-rock remnants relative to atoll land is the trapping of sand and other sediments carried lagoonward toward their lee sides by high-tide or storm waves from the ocean side. Man can copy from nature in creating land artificially by application of the same principle. This was done at Kapingamarangi by the building of a wall of large boulders gathered from the reef in the middle and higher portions of the reef, probably on a remnant of beach rock or island rock awash at high tide (Wiens, 1956). Pepeio Islet (which had 0.7 acre of planted coconut land in 1954) was asserted to have been built up in this fashion since 1919. Tipae Islet on the same atoll was aided earlier to develop to its present 1.6-acre area. Causeways built between islets have led to similar land accretions. Such sediment accumulation can be relatively rapid. On Ringutoru Islet of Kapingamarangi the lagoonward land building during the last 40 years or so has been at the rate of about 1 foot per year. The writer observed a similar movement of land lagoonward (although at a somewhat slower rate) at Likiep Village in the northern Marshalls. There the edge of an old wharf is now 20 to 30 feet from the deep water it once bordered.

The nature of the building of atoll land deserves brief mention. Those who have examined atoll islets often have found their topography to exhibit interior depressions which lead to higher rims. These simply have resulted from the formation of surrounding beach ramparts and ridges. On the seaward side and the exposed channel sides the stronger ocean waves throw up ramparts of coarse boulders and gravels that generally form the highest natural parts of the land surface. Two or more parallel or concentric ramparts may occur. The writer has seen the ramparts described by McKee (1956, pp. 8–9) for Kapingamarangi Atoll, which contain blocks up to 36 inches in diameter, and has seen similar ramparts at Ebon and Utirik. Hedley (1896, pp. 14–15) refers to an island in the Gilberts formed of successive parallel ramparts 30 to 50 feet across, described by the missionary, Whitmee, who ascribed each rampart to the result of a single storm. Hedley uses this example to bolster his argument, based upon the more decomposed state of the rubble in the interior of the islet, that islets grow peripherally seaward as well as lagoonward.

Hedley's argument as applied to relatively permanent atoll islets during the current stage of atoll land morphology does not appear to be correct. There is no indication that the ramparts were not piled onto an already existing land surface. In fact, seaward parts of the existing land may have been scoured away and added to storm debris piled in ramparts farther inland. Newell (1954, p. 16) and McKee (1956, pp. 6–8) provide carefully gathered evidence that the seaward sides of the islets on Raroia and Kapingamarangi have been wearing away rather than building seaward. However, in a personal letter to the writer, Newell emphasized his belief in the importance of storms in the atoll land-building process, and he expressed the view that most of the island building at Raroia during the last 800 years had been accomplished by hurricanes. However, he does not suggest seaward extension of land building. He thought, moreover, that this cycle was initiated by a slight drop in sea level. Hedley's thesis would conform with conditions during a period of falling sea levels but not with the recent stage of rising sea level. Aerial views of a number of widely scattered reefs provide convincing evidence of the net erosion on the seaward sides of islets.

Although the retreat of the seaward shore line may be a geologically rapid process, the retreat is relatively slow compared with the current land building lagoonward. Landowners on Kapingamarangi informed the writer that they had not observed any notable retreat of the seaward shore because of erosion during the last several decades, and no informants with whom the writer talked in the Marshalls had observed such a retreat. This does not apply to the washing away of soil and vegetation and the destruction of some individual islets by occasional hurricanes, however. Vast amounts of land can be destroyed within a few hours by a hurricane. Friederici (1910, p. 139) described the washing away of 1-to-2-meter-thick layers of sedimentary land on the principal inhabited islet of Anaa Atoll in the Tuamotus in 1906, together with all the houses, the stone church, and 85 inhabitants.

Prior to 1858 Matukerekere on Kapingamarangi was said to have had an area of about 0.7 acre, most of which was lost in a storm that year. The storm of 1905 on Arno (Stone, 1951) washed away large parts of Namej and Ine Islets, and the storm of 1918 washed away a part of Arno Islet. Nevertheless, Stone observed that examination of the areas once destroyed indicated the rapidity of rebuilding. A typhoon (presumably the 1951 storm) blowing across the lagoon at Utirik in the northern Marshalls destroyed a once-vegetated land area which the writer estimated to be a mile long narrowing to a point from a base 500 feet wide. Here a high sand ridge subsequently developed over a line of beach rock on the lagoon shore facing the wind. This appears to have prevented the sand deposits from re-covering the interior of the area, which in 1956 appeared like a desert waste. A line of beach rock bordered this on the seaward side.

The very extensive morphological changes made by the 1958 typhoon on the eastern half of Jaluit were described by Blumenstock, whose account is quoted in Chapter 6.

Most of the recent land additions observed by the writer in the Marshalls and Carolines were constructed of foraminiferous sands and small-sized gravels added along lagoon shore lines. Moderately strong wind-driven currents and waves are able to accumulate and pile up such sediments. The dozens of concentric sand ridges that have pushed lagoonward on some islets show this type of land building without major storms, and land building has been going on steadily at Kapingamarangi in the absence of typhoons. During storms such as the one at Jaluit in 1958, however, coarse gravels up to boulder size (6 to 10 inches and more in diameter) were washed into 8-foot-high bars on the reef flat or spread over the land area.

Fate of atoll land with rising sea levels

The writer has not seen mentioned elsewhere the fact that, on a long-term basis, a continuing rise of sea level also creates gradually rising beach ridges on the lagoon side as the land pushes outward toward the lagoon. The general average of beach ridges on this side of an islet, therefore, should be higher in their more recent occurrences and lower as one approaches the older ridges nearer the center. Thus the succession of beach-ridge additions on the lagoon side results ultimately in a gradual slope of the land from the top of the present lagoon beach ridge toward the central depression. During a period of dropping sea levels, these ridges conversely should produce a topography that slopes from the beach ridge, marking the downswing of sea level toward the lagoon shore line. In practice, however, storms are not equal in intensity and thus produce no such conformity to theory, although on some islets in the present stage the general slopes inland from the lagoonside beach ridges appear to run downward toward a depression.

With a topography that falls inward from the rims to a central depression, most islets of sufficient size during a period of rising sea levels would ultimately develop swampy interiors. On some of the atolls this has occurred already, as on Taringa Islet on Kapingamarangi Atoll. On others, man has, in order to grow swamp taro, hastened the process by excavating pits in low areas to reach the fresh-water lens.

In looking at the past record of fluctuating sea levels, one can see Pleistocene levels as much as 100 feet above the level of present atoll land surfaces (Flint, 1957, p. 270). As recently as 3,600 years ago a 10-foot-higher sea level (Fairbridge, 1957) (Fig. 39) would probably have submerged most present-day atoll land surfaces. We may still be in the midst of an inter-glacial period that has had a long-time trend toward a warmer earth (Carson, 1954, p. 144), or we may have reached a plateau in climatic fluctuations and thus have little change in sea level for many centuries. Looking toward the future climate, Emiliani (1955, p. 571) thought that a prophetic glimpse might be had by extending toward the future the insolation curve he obtained in his study of Pleistocene temperatures: "If its trend during the last 10,000 years continues, an insolation minimum may be expected to occur in about 10,000 years, when the northern lands will have completed their isostatic recovery. Conditions will then be favorable for the inception of a new ice age."

Projecting these facts and speculations in terms of the future of atoll land, the writer finds man's habitat on Pacific atolls facing an uncertain and probably gloomy short-term prospect but a much enlarged and perhaps improved long term prospect. In the next 5,000 to 6,000 years it is possible that periods of rising sea levels may inundate most present land on atolls and possibly destroy most present reef islets. During the first half of this century the rise in sea level has amounted to 2 to 3 inches (Russell, 1957). Were the earth's temperatures to increase and the sea level to rise at the same rate, most atoll islets would be awash or at least largely comprised of saline swamps within a thousand years. Although the rate of land building lagoonward temporarily exceeds the rate of land erosion on the seaward shore, the migration of the land area lagoonward that is taking place "will probably end with their being pushed back across the reef into the depths of the lagoon" (Kuenen, 1950, p. 447).

On the other hand, with the definite onset of continually decreasing temperatures, as forecast by Emiliani for the long-term future, the renewed glaciation in the boreal regions will result in ever-emerging land area and a much enlarged and safer habitat for man and other terrestrial life in the tropical Pacific islands that are now atolls. Enlargement will result from the availability of the entire present reef flat and much of the lagoon slopes of atolls for vegetation growth, although a "makatea" surface may render parts of it productively unusable. Greater safety will result for man and other terrestrial animal and plant life because the increasing elevation above sea level will make such land less susceptible to destruction by typhoons and tidal waves. Moreover, land now fragmented and isolated will become more-or-less continuous around the central lagoons, which will become progressively smaller. Passes into lagoons will become shallower and most lagoon bottoms eventually may also emerge to become dry land. Except for atolls and reefs now submerged or drowned, which may then emerge and add to the land area, present atolls will cease to exist (by definition) and will become "high" limestone islands. This, of course, is merely the projection of a hypothetically recurring stage in the evolution of atoll topography.

CHAPTER 6

WEATHER AND THE CLIMATE IN
THE PACIFIC ATOLL REALM

Studies of weather and climate in the Pacific atoll area suffer from the deficiency of data incidental to a vast area of water in much of which there is no land available for weather stations. Where atolls and volcanic islands do exist, the extreme isolation of many islands and the lack of reliable and technically trained weather observers further restrict the collection of data. For much of the great expanse of ocean, therefore, interpretations of weather and climate have depended upon occasional individual observations from ships and aircraft. As these generally follow certain restricted routes, data may be completely absent for many large areas.

Prior to World War I systematic data on the weather and climate of the Marshalls and Carolines were restricted largely to those collected by the Germans and after them by the Japanese. Most of the data for the Marshalls up to 1913 came from a station at Jaluit in the southern Marshalls and from a station at Ujelang in the northern Marshalls (U. S. Navy, 1944, p. 1). Data for the Japanese period (1914 to 1945) are not generally available, and the writer has not had access to these.

Weather data in the South Pacific were also rather sketchy before 1940. Thereafter, because of the developing Japanese threat in the Pacific, weather service in the southwestern Pacific was expanded greatly, and in some areas military operations resulted in the establishment of a very dense network of weather stations as well as the receipt of numerous weather reports from aircraft (Hutchings, 1953).

Prior to the beginning of tests of atomic and nuclear bombs first by the

United States in the Marshalls and later by the British on Christmas Atoll, the requirements for reliable weather data resulted in the establishment of temporary weather stations on many islands in the central and South Pacific. Others were established during the 1958 Geophysical Year, but not all the data collected is yet readily available or published. As late as 1955 the United States Weather Bureau's annual summary of climatological data for the Pacific Ocean area included records only for such atolls as Eniwetok, Ulithi (Falalop), Johnston Island, Kwajalein, Majuro, Midway, Canton, French Frigate Shoal, Palmyra, and Wake Island (Fig. 41). Other stations were situated on volcanic islands—Palau, Truk, Ponape, and Guam.

A good network of weather stations is found in the Gilbert, Ellice, Phoenix, Line, and other island groups (Figs. 42 and 43). Thus, exclusive of the Tuamotu, there were about 44 stations operating in these areas in 1945 and 4 or 5 more were added in 1951 (Hutchings, 1953, p. 41). At least 7 of these were in the Gilberts and Ellice atolls and 3 in the Phoenix atolls. The majority, however, were situated on the high islands in the Fiji, Samoa, Tokelau, Tonga, and Cook groups (Fig. 42).

Generalized monthly weather conditions for the Pacific have been summarized in chart form in the U. S. Weather Bureau's *Climatic Atlas of the Pacific, 1938* and, more recently, for the North Pacific in the United States Navy's *Marine Atlas of the World, Vol. II, North Pacific, 1956.* The Weather Bureau's publications give generalized weather data for each square of area bounded by 5 degrees of longitude and 5 degrees of latitude. The Navy's volume appears to have station analyses for only five places in Micronesia, only two of which are on atolls, Wake and Kwajelein. Outside and east of Micronesia, Johnston Island and Christmas Island are the only atolls from which station weather analyses are included in the coral reef zone north of the equator. All stations listed in the Navy atlas are at about 13 feet above mean sea level or lower. Each station has recorded data for 7 to 11 years. Radiosonde stations have been operated since 1949 on all of these except Christmas. The limited number of stations involved has resulted in the use of the data for each station to interpret the generalized weather and climate for areas of from 28,000 to 38,000 square miles in extent.

Other useful sources include the U. S. Navy reports (1943 and 1944; and the annual typhoon reports especially for 1953) and the mimeographed meteorological notes covering the Line, Tokelau, and Cook Island groups of the New Zealand Meteorological Service at Wellington.

General characteristics of tropical oceanic weather and climates

The climate of the Pacific atoll realm is marine and tropical in character. The range in air temperature is about 2°F. annually, with a slightly greater

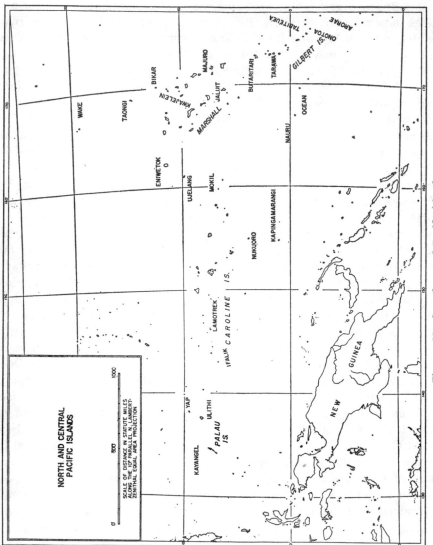

Fig. 41. North and central Pacific islands.

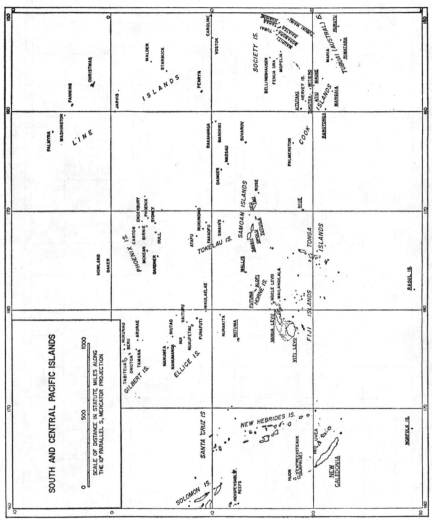

Fig. 42. South and central Pacific islands. Names of volcanic islands are underlined.

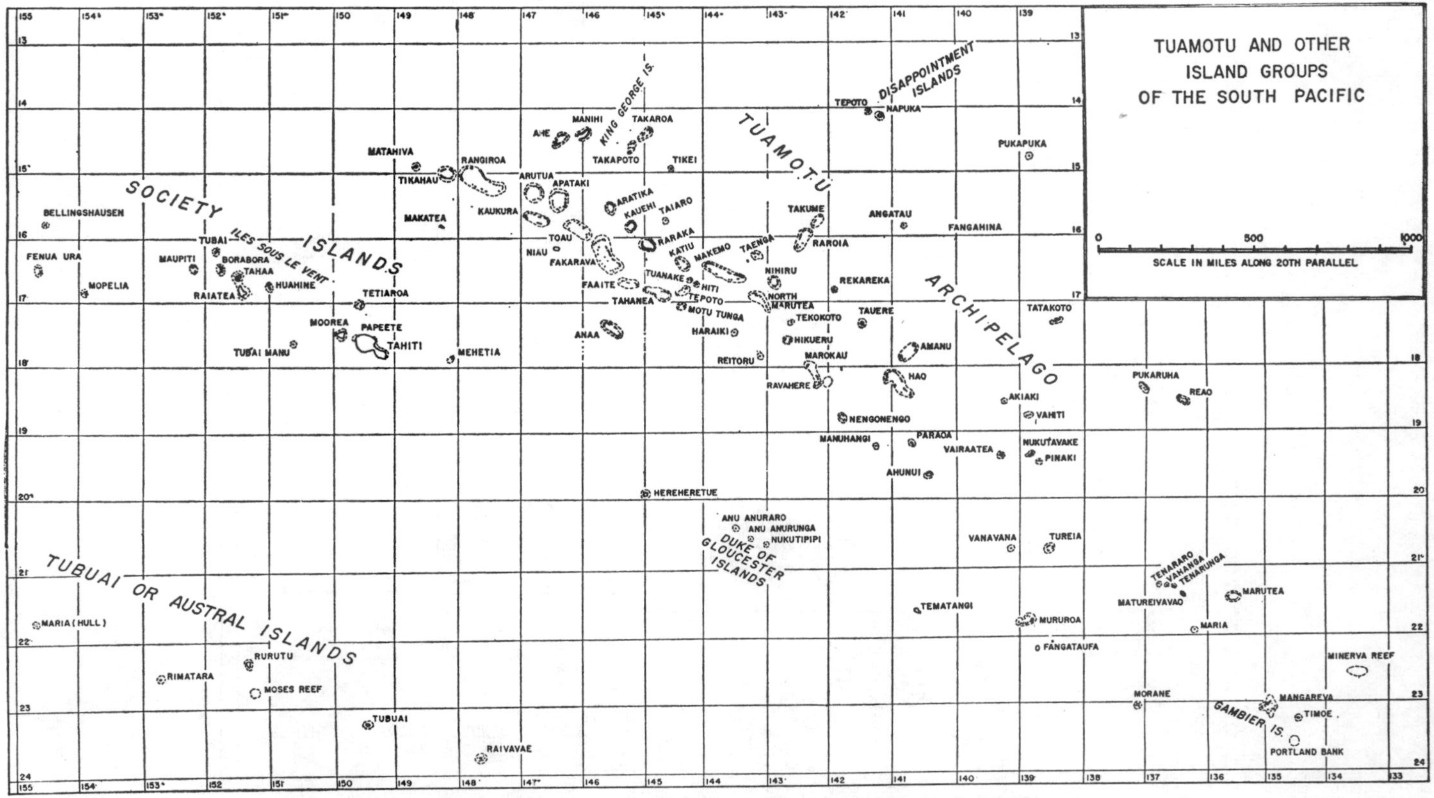

Fig. 43. Tuamotu and other island groups in the south Pacific.

range as one approaches 15 to 20°N and S latitudes. Winds are mostly those of the trades and associated cyclonic depressions. In the western extremities of the realm, the Asiatic and Australian continental air masses are a factor also. Average relative humidity is high, but sensible temperatures are moderated by the cooling breezes generally present on atolls. Atoll weather seldom seems oppressive where there is exposure to the prevailing winds.

There are considerable variations in rainfall between and among the different atoll groups. The old concept of an equatorial "doldrum belt" characterized by heavy rains appears not to have validity. Instead, "Small (about 3 miles in diameter) vertical convection cells occur in conjunction with the unstable portions of huge horizontal eddies but not in a circumglobal belt of doldrums around the heat equator" (Oliver, 1954, pp. 353–60). It seems probable (Hutchings, 1953, pp. 38–9) that there is "a continuous spectrum of tropical disturbances whose maximum intensities vary continuously from barely detectable disturbances with winds from five to ten knots, to the most intense tropical cyclones with winds exceeding 100 knots." One peculiar result of the convection and converging currents in the equatorial Pacific seems to be that while weather from the surface to an altitude of 1,000 feet may be good, flying conditions from there to 25,000 feet may be exceptionally bad (U. S. Navy, 1943, p. 5).

Areal and seasonal distribution of surface winds

The windroses in Figs. 44 and 45 show the dominant direction of winds during the months of the year in each 5 square degrees of longitude and latitude for Micronesia and Polynesia and adjoining areas of Melanesia. Each unit of length on these windroses represents a month in which the prevailing or dominant wind is in the direction indicated.

The dominance of the northeasterly and southeasterly trade winds is clearly shown in both charts. North of the equator the northeasterly trades are dominant in Micronesia. However, during several months of the year southeasterly winds prevail in the latitudes between the equator and 5°N and S over the ocean east of the 145th longitude east. For 1 to 3 months of the year there may be southeasterly winds in this area between 5 and 15°N, probably as a result of the northern shift of the thermal equator.

In westernmost Micronesia and in the northern parts of Melanesia, the influence of the seasonal Asiatic and Australian air masses appears to show up in the windroses. Winds with northwesterly and southwesterly components become prominent in the areas of the western Carolines and Palaus. Near eastern New Guinea and New Ireland, northwest and southeast winds are about equally prevalent, but northeast and southwest winds appear to be rare.

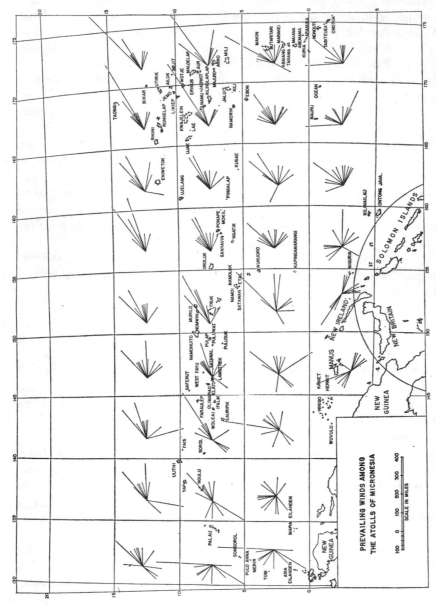

Fig. 44. Prevailing winds among the atolls of Micronesia. Each unit of line length represents 1 month during which the prevailing wind was in the direction indicated for the 5° square. [Derived from the *Atlas of Climatic Charts of the Oceans, 1938*.]

PREVAILING WINDS AMONG
THE ATOLLS OF MICRONESIA

SCALE IN MILES

100   0   100 200 300 400

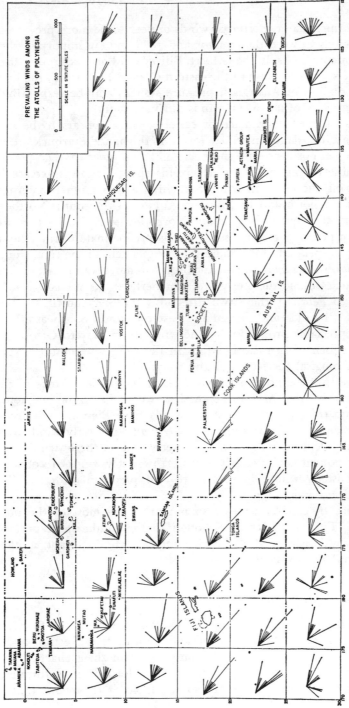

Fig. 45. Prevailing winds among the atolls of Polynesia. Each unit of line length represents one month during which the prevailing wind was in the direction indicated for the 5° square. [Derived from the *Atlas of Climatic Charts of the Oceans, 1938*.]

South of the equator, northeast winds appear to be more prevalent than southeast winds between the equator and 10°S and are important throughout the Tuamotu atolls. In the Gilbert, Ellice, and Phoenix groups, the wind patterns are similar to those in the eastern Carolines, although the influence of the Asiatic and/or Australian pressure systems may be responsible here for the dominance of northwest winds during 1 month.

The most marked dominance of easterly winds appears to be in those areas of the Line Islands in which Jarvis, Malden, and Starbuck are found. Winds between northeast and southeast make up more than 90 per cent of the total observations. Southeasterly winds show a steady increase in frequency during the southern winter, reaching a maximum from August to October in the north and in July and August in the south. Northeasterly winds are most frequent from about November to April. Farther west in the Tokelau group (Fig. 42) easterly winds predominate during the day at all times of the year and blow more than 60 per cent of the time from June to September. As the thermal equator begins to move southward in October, the frequencies of northeasterly and northerly winds increase, and from November to February these two directions together constitute about 40 per cent of all winds and exceed the easterly winds. Southeasterly winds form an appreciable proportion of the winds from May to October, being only less frequent than easterly winds in most of these months (New Zealand Meteorological Service, 1956 and 1957).

In the atolls of the northern Cook Islands the predominance of easterly winds is greatest from May to September, when they blow on more than half the days (Fig. 45). Southeasterly winds have their highest frequency during the same months and are next frequent to easterly winds over this period. From October to April northeasterly and northerly winds are comparatively frequent, and westerly and northwesterly winds are occasionally observed. Easterly winds, however, are still predominant (New Zealand Meteorological Service, 1955).

Dominance by easterly winds also is marked for most of the northern and central Tuamotu Islands, although in the southeastern part of the Tuamotus southeasterly winds become increasingly dominant, as they are in the Austral Islands, farther west.

Seasonal characteristics of wind force

Monthly charts that were compiled by the U. S. Navy (1946) cover the coral atoll zone of the North Pacific and indicate the direction and force of surface winds. Appendix A was compiled from these charts. The percentage frequency of winds of each Beaufort force from 2 through 9 is listed for each station included. From the table, it is obvious that winds among the atolls seldom rise above a fresh breeze and rarely reach gale strength. Seasonal differences are noticeable throughout the area. Fall, winter, and spring have the strongest winds. The lightest winds occur during the period from late spring through early fall.

Regional differences also are noticeable. Christmas Atoll (near the equator) rarely has winds as high as Beaufort 6. Such winds are much more common at all the other stations listed, especially at the Johnston Island station. The greatest frequency of the strongest winds north of the equator are found to occur in the western Carolines and east of Luzon in the Philippines. This is consistent with the observation that cyclonic storms tend to intensify as they move westward in this part of the Pacific.

In the Line Islands gales are infrequent. In the northern part of the scattered group they occur less than once a year, in the southern part about twice a year on the average. Tropical storms are unknown in the north and almost unknown in the south. One was reported to have affected Caroline Atoll in 1878. It is likely that the cooler tropical water in this part of the ocean has a dampening effect on the formation of cyclonic storms. Gales are rather rare in the Tokelau group also. They occur there only from November to March, the period during which the thermal equator is farthest south, and all that have been reported have been in association with tropical cyclones (which may occur once or twice in a decade) (New Zealand Meteorological Service, 1957).

In the northern Cook Islands the mean wind speed is a little greater from May to September than during the remaining half of the year. Fresh or strong winds are much more frequent in July and August than in any other month. On individual atolls, local effects produce diurnal variations in the direction and speed of the wind. On Pukapuka (Danger) Atoll, for instance, the afternoon winds are on the average lighter than the morning winds. Gales are more numerous than in the preceding two groups. However, only four gales have been reported during 12 years at Penrhyn Atoll. Farther south, gales average three or four per year, but the variation from year to year is great. Thus in 1931 some 23 gales were reported at Pukapuka, mostly from the east, although westerly and northerly gales also occur. Tropical depressions sometimes form in the northern Cook Islands and later develop into destructive typhoons. Once every few years during the months December to March, the wind and sea associated with such typhoons have caused serious damage on the atolls of the group. It is only on the southern atoll of Suwarrow (Suvarov) that wind speeds exceeding gale force have been reported. In 1942 a well-developed typhoon passed close to the atoll, blew down the trees, and sent mountainous seas over the land. Winds stronger than those of gale force also damaged the atoll in December 1940 and March 1944 (New Zealand Meteorological Service, 1955).

Winds accompanied by rain

The charts in the Navy atlas (1946) also show the percentage proportions of winds from each direction that were accompanied by precipitation at various stations in the tropical north Pacific. Graphs constructed for each station (Figs. 46 and 47) show the percentage of all wind directions accompanied by rain and the months in which the greatest percentage of winds from the indicated directions were accompanied by rain. Table 8 is a summary of these charts and graphs.

TABLE 8

Winds with Rain

Station	Maximum wind with rain for the longest period
Johnston Island	SE for 7 months; E, NE, and S for 2 months
Palmyra Atoll	NE for 8 months; E for 6 months
Christmas Atoll	NE for 8 months; SE for 4 months
Wake Island	N for 6 months; SW for 3 months; N for 2 months
Kwajelein Atoll	SE for 5 months; S for 3 months; E for 2 months; NW, SW for 1 month
Oroluk Atoll vicinity	NE for 7 months; E for 5 months; W, SW, S, and SE for 1 month
Namonuito Atoll vicinity	NE for 7 months; E, SE for 2 months; S, SW for 1 month
Ocean area east of Philippines	E for 4 months; SE for 3 months; N for 2 months; NE, 8, SW for 1 month

One may conclude from the table that in the northern part of the atoll realm in the Wake Island region, the largest percentage of winds most often accompanied by rain are northern winds. In the next zone to the south, running from Johnston to Kwajelein, southeast winds carry rain more often than other winds. For the atolls nearer the equator, such as Palmyra, Christmas, and the Caroline Islands, northeast winds appear most important for rain, in the Palau-Philippine region, east and southeast winds. Owing to the scantiness of station records covering such vast expanses of sea, however, not too much reliance should be placed upon these generalizations with the exception of the data for atolls that have data stations and for the atolls adjacent to them.

In analyzing the monthly percentage of all wind directions accompanied by rain, one sees no uniformity for seasonal peaks in the graphs (Figs. 46

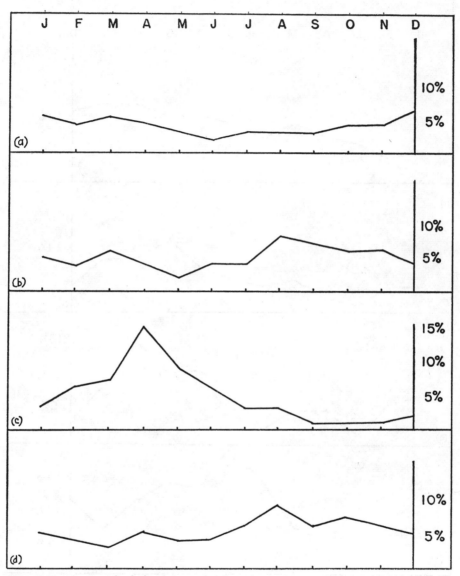

Fig. 46. Percentage of winds accompanied by rain on four Pacific atolls: (a) Johnston,
(b) Palmyra, (c) Christmas, (d) Wake.

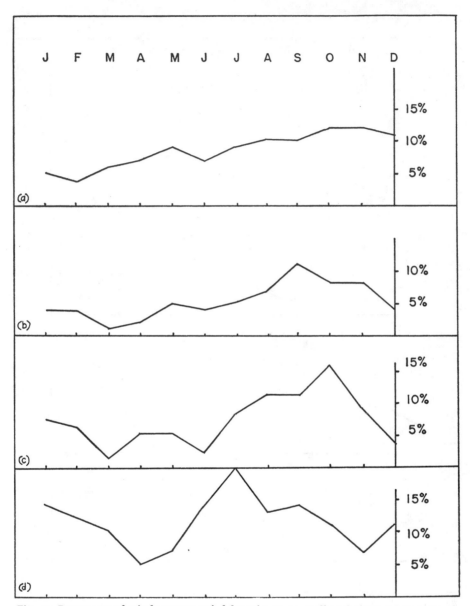

Fig. 47. Percentage of winds accompanied by rain on an atoll and three other areas of the Pacific: (a) Kwajelein Atoll, (b) Oroluk area, (c) Namonuito area, (d) sea area east of the Philippines.

and 47). Nor does there appear to be a rational regional pattern. Thus the graph for Wake resembles that for Palmyra, but that for Johnston Island is quite different. The graph for Christmas is entirely different from that of all the others: the largest percentage of winds bringing rain occurs in April, and the lowest percentage of winds bringing rain comes during fall and winter. The graphs for the Oroluk and the Namonuito vicinities, however, do appear to show general similarities, which leads to the tentative conclusion that at least in the central Carolines, the largest percentage of winds bringing rain occurs in September and October and that March is the month with the least likelihood of rain accompanying winds. The graphs show that there is, apparently, no regional uniformity (Figs. 48 and 49). Each atoll seems to have its own pattern, and no generalization can be made for a larger region.

These observations appear to indicate that rain on any particular atoll most often is associated with local convection rather than with general disturbances covering large areas of the tropical ocean. Moreover, the frequency of rains accompanying winds does not appear related to the total monthly rainfall amounts. Months with rains most often accompanying winds may have only light rainfall compared with months that have less frequent but much heavier rains.

Rainfall on atolls

Because of the lack of an adequate number of recording stations, rainfall patterns in the Pacific atoll realm are not very clear. The Weather Bureau's climatic charts (1938) not only are highly generalized but do not give amounts of rainfall, merely frequency of rains by 3-month periods. Data from different atoll groups have been compiled in Appendix B, but the lengths of time of record are very uneven, as some of the stations were established only recently.

Figures 50 and 51 are interpretive generalizations of the oceanic isohyets among the Pacific atolls. Some of the more recent data for the south Pacific are not included. Many of the isohyets are hypothetical projections. Thus the lines between Wotje (78 inches of rainfall) and Wake Island (24 inches of rainfall) probably should not have been divided so evenly, because, as interpreted from the vegetation on the atolls, Taongi is ranked with Wake in dryness and Bikar is ranked drier than Eniwetok by Fosberg (1956, pp. 186–8). Therefore, the isohyet of 50 inches of rainfall probably should run roughly east and west to the south of Bikar. The charts are highly tentative and are presented merely to suggest possible and probable patterns.

In general, the heaviest rainfall north of the equator occurs in a belt that lies between 1°38′ and 8°30′ (according to the U. S. Department of State,

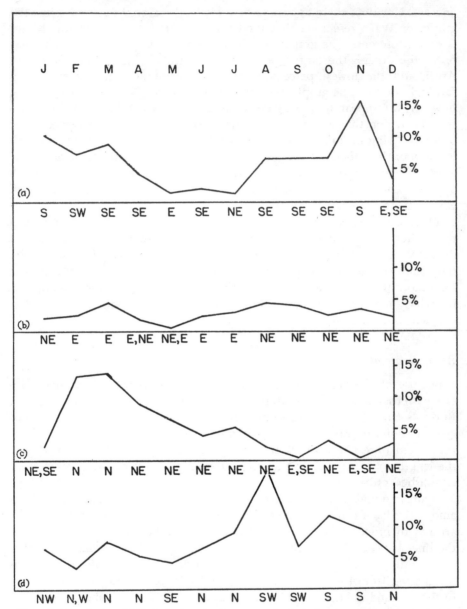

Fig. 48. Months in which the greatest percentage of winds from various directions were accompanied by rain on four Pacific atolls: (a) Johnston, (b) Palmyra, (c) Christmas, (d) Wake.

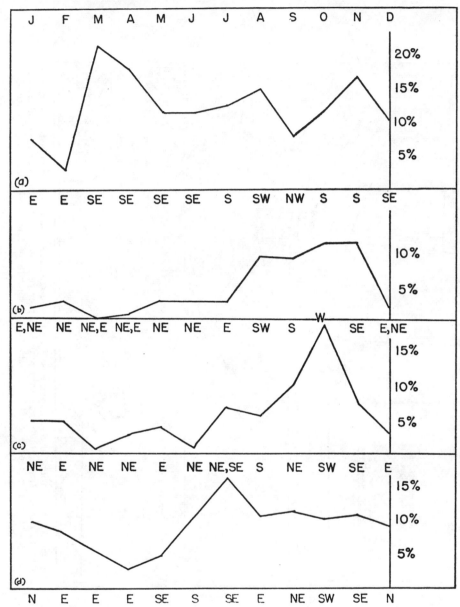

Fig. 49. Months in which the greatest percentage of winds from various directions were accompanied by rain on an atoll and three other areas of the Pacific: (a) Kwajelein Atoll, (b) Oroluk area, (c) Namonuito area, (d) sea area east of the Philippines.

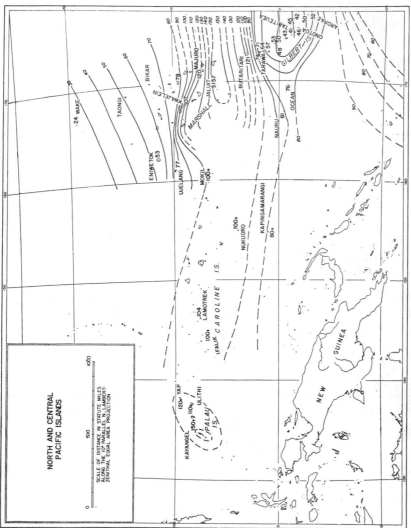

Fig. 50. Approximations of oceanic isohyets of north and central Pacific islands compiled from scattered low-island records. Large numbers refer to records of average annual rainfall (in inches). Numbers with plus signs after them represent subjective estimates of students of low-island conditions. Dashed lines indicate the more-speculative constructions.

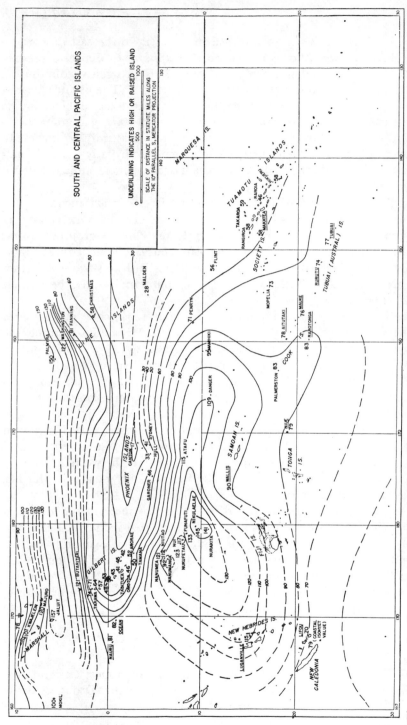

Fig. 51. Approximations of oceanic isohyets of south and central Pacific islands compiled from scattered low-island records. Large numbers refer to records of average annual rainfall (in inches). Dashed lines indicate the more-speculative constructions. Underlining indicates a high or raised island.

1955, p. 1). This belt is said to stretch from Palmyra in the east (Fig. 51) to Kayangel in the west (Fig. 50). The rainfall appears to diminish progressively to the north and south of this zone. This progressive diminution extends southward across the equator to about 3°S. The islands nearest the equator have low rainfall. Christmas in the east has only about 58 inches as compared with the 150 inches on Palmyra some 300 miles northwest of Christmas. Malden, southeast of Christmas, has only 28 inches. In the same latitude as Malden but to its west are the virtually desert islands of Canton, Howland, and Baker (Canton has an average annual rainfall of only 17 inches).

The rainfall at Butaritari in the northern Gilberts is 121 inches a year. The rainfall drops progressively southward from here to only 41 and 42 inches annually at Tabiteuea and Nikunau. In the Phoenix group the driest atolls are the northernmost, Canton and Enderbury. The next three, Phoenix, Birnie, and McKean, are somewhat wetter. Hull and Sydney, farther south, are wetter still, while Gardner, the southernmost, is the wettest (Maude, 1952, p. 70).

In the Ellice group the rainfall averages about 120 inches, much wetter than the Gilberts to their north. The southern Marshalls continue the wet zone of the northern Gilberts, but progressively show a diminution northward, from 157 inches at Jaluit to 107 at Kwajelein to 53 at Eniwetok. East of these atolls the high rainfall of 150 inches at Palmyra compares with the low 33 inches at Johnston Island, about 655 miles northwest.

Furthermore, the driest islands are in the eastern equatorial sectors, and in the zone near the equator there appears to be a progressive increase in rainfall westward. From 58 and 17 inches, respectively, at Christmas and Canton in the east the rainfall increases westward to between 41 and 57 inches generally in the central Gilberts. Kapingamarangi, 1,000 miles farther west, has an estimated 80 to 100 inches.

The eastern parts of the Pacific farther south also show this tendency to be drier. The rainfall diminishes eastward from 117.6 inches at Pukapuka (Danger) to 71 at Penrhyn and 56 at Flint. Still farther east but south of Flint and in the Tuamotu group, Raroia has only 46.4 inches (one year's record). The Tuamotus are among the drier atolls of the Pacific. Manihiki and Palmerston, a thousand miles west of the Tuamotus, have 95 and 83 inches of rain annually, respectively.

Variability of rainfall seasonally

Variability of rainfall amounts from year to year are almost as significant to human welfare as the general average rainfall amounts. Droughts occur even on the wettest atolls. The range of variation is great. At Onotoa the wettest year recorded up to 1952 was 1946 (85 inches); the driest was 1950 (6.6 inches) (Cloud, 1952). The highest annual rainfall recorded at Fanning was 207.8 inches in 1905, but in 1950 the record dropped to the all-time low of 27.8 inches. At Malden, farther south, the highest recorded rainfall was 95.6 inches in 1919, and the lowest was 4 inches in 1908. There is a marked seasonal variation in the Line group which is somewhat similar throughout the group. January to June is the wettest season, with the maximum in April and May. The driest months in the northern part are September to November, and in the south from September to December (New Zealand Meteorological Service, 1956).

In the Tokelau atolls, where the rainfall is uniformly high, there is also an appreciable seasonal variation: the drier months, April to September, coincide with the predominance of easterly winds. The average number of wet days is quite high. Considerable variations do occur in both monthly and annual totals, however (New Zealand Meteorological Service, 1957).

In the northern Cook Islands the rainfall increases rather rapidly as one goes southwestward. The variations in annual amounts are illustrated by Penrhyn and Pukapuka (Danger) (Fig. 51). Over a 10-year period the wettest year at Penrhyn was 1941 (over 150 inches), the driest 1938, 36 inches (Johnston, 1953). At Pukapuka there were 155 inches of rain in 1931 but only 85.46 inches in 1938 (Sachet, 1954). Pukapuka and Manihiki both have many more rainy days than Penrhyn. The summer half of the year, October to March, is considerably wetter than the remainder of the year. Here, too, variability of rainfall is high, with the greatest degree of variability in the northeast and the least in the southwest (New Zealand Meteorological Service, 1955).

In commenting upon variability of rainfall in the south Pacific, Seelye (1950, p. 12) wrote that the annual rainfall is most variable along the western tongue of the equatorial dry zone, where the north-south rainfall gradient is steep. Thus comparatively small disturbances of the controlling atmospheric circulation from normal would be expected to produce spectacular changes there. Variability is still higher in the Penrhyn-Tahiti region, where dry conditions associated with a permanent south Pacific anticyclone to the east may prevail, or where a wetter type of weather may persist when the quasi-stationary trough line, usually lying to the southeast from the southern Cook group, assumes a more easterly position. Seelye also found comparatively high variability in New Caledonia. He thought that irregularity of the southeastern penetration of the northwest monsoon into this region is probably an important factor, although he pointed out that the orographical control of rainfall is strong there, making it sensitive to small fluctuations in the direction of the prevailing wind.

He contrasted this with the comparative constancy of conditions found in the Santa Cruz–Rotuma region (about 12°S), where a high and consistent rainfall is recorded and pointed to its rather similar counterpart in the other hemisphere, north of Jaluit. Steinbach (1894) and Seidel (1902) both offered evidence that substantiates this, but they both include Jaluit, and Steinbach also includes Namrik and Ebon with the reliable zone of rainfall (Fig. 44). Seidel wrote that rain here is distributed throughout the entire year. In Jaluit he found that it rained almost daily at various hours of the day. A month that may show a lesser degree of rain in 1 year proved highest in the following year. The greatest amount of rain was observed in the beginning and toward the end of the northeast trade winds when rain squalls, as frequent as several a day, were particularly heavy. A somewhat drier season could be expected in some years in the months of January and February.

Seelye (1950, pp. 12–24) stated that "From the equator (west of the 180th meridian) where January is the wettest month, there is a progression through February to March for Noumea, Fiji, Tonga, and Rarotonga. In these islands the principal regular rains come from the northwest monsoon, and the spasmodic downpours with the occasional tropical cyclone come in the same season; hence the time of greatest wetness closely follows the advance of the northwesterlies over the region."

Seelye found that from a line from Samoa to south of Tahiti (along which January is the wettest month), proceeding southwestward, maximum rainfall occurs in February and March successively. Northeastward toward Malden Atoll a similar sequence continues into April and, farther north, even into May. He felt it reasonable to suppose that the pattern might continue farther eastward from May directly into June and July, the appropriate months for Pitcairn and Easter Islands, thus closely linking the dry zone with the region under the immediate influence of the great stationary anticyclone. He found that the area of the January maximum appears to widen to the north to include a narrow strip where December marks the meeting of the two regimes. This extends from Funafuti perhaps beyond Kusaie, "where December is only a secondary maximum, to Ponape, where the December rainfall peak is greater than the May one. Proceeding northward there is thus a discontinuity in the region of the Marshall Islands where April, May, or June is the wettest month, and apparently another must be passed before Ujelang is reached, for there October and September are wettest. Traces of the April maximum extend across the former boundary as evidenced by a secondary peak in the Tarawa and Kavieng [New Ireland] records. The time of occurrence of the driest month . . . is within the range, February to November, successively later in the year in progression southwards over the western section of the region" (Seelye, 1950, p. 13).

To the east, the dry zone shows its own distinctive pattern, Seelye found.

The month of minimum rainfall is experienced progressively earlier in a southward direction from Malden to Niue during the months from November to June. However, October is the driest month for the western tongue of the equatorial dry zone. At Nauru October becomes secondary to May as the dry month. He concluded that the role of these two months at Nauru is the reverse of that at Ocean Island and also at Kavieng. "Apart from the last mentioned exception, the dominance of the dry zone air mass conditions appears to cease between Ocean and Nauru Islands. It will be noted that whereas May is Nauru's driest month, it is the wettest somewhat to the north at Kusaie and Jaluit."

Seelye classed only 10 per cent or less of all months as wet months at Ponape, Jaluit, and Funafuti. However, in the equatorial dry zone east of Nauru Island the frequency of dry months was found to be over 40 per cent, the greatest single percentage being 52 at Malden Island. There the rainfall is usually meager, although the occurrence of a few exceptionally wet months accounted for most of the rainfall aggregate. Noteworthy was the rapid transition from the Malden value (via Penrhyn Atoll) of 28 per cent; to Manihiki, 19 per cent; to Danger Island, 12 per cent. He found another contrast of 44 per cent at Ocean as against 7 at Jaluit. In general, the dry months were found to outnumber the wet, with most of the exceptions being found in the wet zones of both hemispheres. Thus, for the southern summer, the frequency of the occurrence of dry months was found to be 40 per cent or more for the sector opening eastward from the Gilbert Islands, 68 per cent at Malden. In conclusion, Seelye noted that "The persistence of abnormal rainfall over several months is not uncommon, and some indication of this characteristic can be derived . . . Malden, Ocean, and, to a lesser extent, Fanning Island show the largest persistence under these stringent conditions, while the more southerly stations selected do not differ markedly from one another."

In the Tuamotu group there appear to be two clearly distinguishable seasons, one relatively rainy and associated with predominantly northeasterly winds lasting from November to April, and one relatively dry period with predominantly southeasterly winds from May to October (Danielsson, 1955, pp. 23–4).

Extended droughts

Droughts may be periodic and extended on the drier atolls and even on some of the wetter ones. The annual report for 1928 from the British Colonial Office stated that "The 14 Gilbert Islands lying between 2° North and 3° South Latitude are visited by periodical droughts, of which the cycle appears to be five to seven years. Butaritari and Little Maken, about

3° north of the Equator, are unaffected by this condition . . . During
the droughts on central and southern Gilbert Islands, it [average yearly rain-
fall] is sometimes as low as 3 inches" (Sachet, 1957). In 1917–1919 there
was a 2-year drought in the Gilberts, and in 1937–1939 there was a 3-year
drought. Another drought lasting a year and a half occurred in 1949–1951
(Catala, 1957, p. 3). Earlier droughts recorded for the same areas were
noted by the missionary Whitmee (1871, pp. 33–5) who wrote that during
his visit to Niutao in the Ellice Islands and Onotoa in the Gilberts these
atolls had been suffering a long drought and were short of food.

Farther west, Kapingamarangi, near the equator, suffered a 2-year drought
in 1916 and 1917, when 80 to 90 people reportedly starved to death (Wiens,
1956, p. 20).

Drought conditions in the Line Islands are by no means infrequent
even on Fanning and are prevalent most of the time on Malden. For the
latter, over a period of 33 years there were 14 periods each of more than
200 days with less than 0.01 inch of rain a day. The two longest periods
completely without rain were 125 and 76 days, respectively (New Zealand
Meteorological Service, 1956).

Thunderstorms over atolls

Land is so low and so small in area in the Pacific atolls that convection
arising from the presence of the atoll land is at a minimum, although the
narrow strips of land heat up to high surface temperatures. Some convectional influence might arise from the presence of relatively warm shallow
lagoon water surrounded by the cooler deep ocean water. According to
one source (U. S. Navy, 1943, pp. 8–9), thunderstorms are more likely to
occur by night than by day in tropical seas. However, another source (U. S.
Navy, 1944) lists observations indicating that thunderstorms are distributed
about equally during the day and night in the Marshalls area or occur
somewhat more often during the day. It states that of 119 such storms
occurring between December 1891 and December 1895, 18 per cent of the
total occurred between midnight and 6 A.M., 27 per cent between 6 A.M. and
noon, 24 per cent between noon and 6 P.M., and 31 per cent between 6 P.M.
and midnight.

The former source states that in the sea area surrounding Ujelang in the
northern Marshalls, thunder is recorded only for the period October to
January, the greatest frequency being in October. At Jaluit in the rainy
southern Marshalls, 17 thunderstorms are reported to occur per year on
the average, 2 each monthly at the most from June to September, and
about 2 annually for the entire winter period.

The U. S. Navy's sailing directions (1952) states that in the Kapingamarangi area near the equator and in the eastern Carolines, thunderstorms occur on an average of 2 days per month from May through November and once a month for the rest of the year. However, during the writer's 2-month stay in July and August 1954 on this atoll no thunder was heard, although heavy showers occurred occasionally.

Thunderstorms are few in the dry southern atolls of the Line Islands and increase southward toward the northern Cook Islands. At Fanning thunder is heard only about once a year on the average. From July to December it is virtually unknown. In 10 years of observation it was reported on one occasion in October. In the south at Penrhyn, thunder is heard on about 10 days a year and at Pukapuka and Manihiki about 20 times a year, being greatest during the "typhoon season," from November to April. At Atafu in the Tokelau group farther west, thunder is heard on an average of 36 days a year and is somewhat more frequent during the wetter months of the year, October to March, than in the other months (New Zealand Meteorological Service, 1955, 1956, 1957).

Effects of atoll topography upon rainfall

The land area of an atoll is too low to produce orographical rainfall and too small to affect appreciably the time of rainfall. Rain occurs mostly · during the time of maximum atmospheric instability, in the afternoon or during early morning hours (U. S. Navy, 1944, p. 4).

In the southern Gilberts are five reef islands and five atolls-with-lagoon formations more-or-less intermixed in location. The fact that the two groups show no significant differences in average annual rainfall that would set reef islands apart from atolls would seem to discredit the notion that lagoons exercise important effects upon rainfall.

Relative humidity on atolls

"The humidity is rather high among all the islands [of the Marshalls] as might be expected, and in all months, but in most localities it responds with a slight to moderate rise to the arrival of the wetter season. It is higher by night and in the early morning than by day." At Ujelang the relative humidity at 7 A.M. is 84 per cent and at 2 P.M. 74 per cent on the annual average. September and October have means in the morning and afternoon hours of 87 and 80 per cent, and February and March have means of 82 and 76 per cent, respectively (U. S. Navy, 1943, p. 13).

In the Line Islands Fanning and the northern atolls have higher relative humidity than Malden, the driest in the group. "The average value of 58 per cent in the afternoon at Malden is in fact rather a low relative humidity for a tropical island station" (U. S. Navy, 1943). Even the average morning value of 66 per cent is not high. These values compare with the 75 per cent humidity for the morning on Fanning and the values of 80 per cent on the average at Penrhyn and Manihiki during the day. In the west, at Atafu Atoll, it is even higher, averaging approximately 83 per cent. However, afternoon readings are appreciably lower at most of these stations, although the difference at Penrhyn only amounts to 2 per cent, while at the others the difference amounts to 7 or 8 per cent (New Zealand Meteorological Service, 1955, 1956, 1957).

Temperatures on atolls

In the Marshalls "Mean temperatures over the whole area average 83°F. from May through October. Mean maximum temperatures of 88° to 90°F. can be expected in September and October. Temperatures over 100°F. have been recorded at Jaluit, August–October, but 95°F. (October) is the highest on record for Ujelang [in 1944]. During this period, mean minimum temperatures of 76°F. occur in the islands, usually in the morning between 0500 and 0600. The daily variation in the temperature of 6.6 to 7.9°F. is much greater than the annual range, which seldom is more than 1°F." (U. S. Navy, 1944).

The atolls farther removed from the equator in the Northern Hemisphere have a slightly lower average annual temperature and greater seasonal variation than those within 5 to 10 degrees of the equator. Average annual temperature in 1955 for Johnston and Wake were 78.2°F. and 79.4°F., respectively, while for Kwajelein and Canton they were 81.2°F. and 82°F., respectively (U. S. Weather Bureau, 1955, p. 200). The seasonal difference at Johnston is indicated by the highest average monthly temperature of 80.2°F. in August and September and the lowest average monthly temperature of 75.3°F. in February and March of 1955, a seasonal difference of 4.9°F. At Wake the corresponding warmest month figure is 82.7°F. in August, and the coolest month is March with 76.2°F., or a seasonal difference of 6.5°F.

Farther south at Kwajelein, September, the warmest month in 1955, had an average temperature of 82.3°F., while the coolest month, March, had an average temperature of 80.1°F. The seasonal difference here is only 1.2°F. At Canton Atoll, a dry area, January, the coolest month in 1955, averaged 81.3°F. and July, the warmest month, averaged 82.5°F., also a seasonal difference of 1.2°F. At Majuro a very wet atoll, the seasonal differences proved very small in 1955 and did not follow the expected pattern. The coolest month was October. with an average of 79.8°F., although August was almost as cool, with 79.9°F. The warmest month proved to be February with 80.6°F., or with only 0.7°F. annual range.

Although both Fanning and Malden experience mean daily temperatures of 82 to 83°F. with only slight variation from month to month, Fanning has a lower daily range than Malden because of Fanning's greater rainfall and greater cloudiness. The difference is most noticeable in the wetter months, January to May. The coral surface heats up rather easily and temperatures often exceed 90°F. On an average, 95°F. is reached about once a year, and equally seldom the temperature drops to 65°F. Manihiki and Penrhyn both are farther south, away from the equator, but do not have as great a temperature range. The temperature seldom falls below 70°F. and rarely below 73°F. Mean temperatures show no appreciable seasonal variation, but maximum temperatures are lowest in July (New Zealand Meteorological Service, 1955, 1956, 1957).

Temperature extremes appear to show less variation for maxima than for minima between atolls farther from and nearer to the equator. This is shown in Table 9. Johnston and Wake, the two atolls farthest north,

TABLE 9

Minimum and Maximum Temperatures *

Atoll	Period	Maximum, °F.	Minimum, °F.
Johnston	1955	88	67
Wake	1955	90	65
Eniwetok	1955	89	71
Kwajelein	1955	92	72
Canton	1955	90	73
Palmyra	1955	89	65
Fanning	1955–1957	100	67
Malden	1955–1957	99	65
Penrhyn	1955–1957	94	72
Atafu	1955–1957	95	65

* Data for the first six atolls from U. S. Weather Bureau (1955); data for the last four atolls from the New Zealand Meteorological Service (1955–56).

have minima lower than that for Eniwetok and Kwajelein. But this is not always the case, for Palmyra, Fanning, and Malden, closer to the equator than these, had a minimum of 65°F., as low as that for Wake. These low temperatures probably are related to the cooler ocean waters to the east of them.

During a 2-month stay in 1954 at Kapingamarangi, the writer recorded the lowest temperature in July at 74°F. and the highest temperature in the shade at 94°F. The average minimum temperature for the month was 82.5°F. and the average maximum was 89.1°F. (Wiens, 1956, p. 20).

Tropical cyclones and typhoons

Until the mid-1940's the concepts of the polar-front theories as applied to the formation of tropical cyclones had gained wide acceptance. Increased data from meteorological observations and greater study of tropical weather have led to new lines of thinking on the origin of tropical disturbances and to the terminology applied. There has been such a remarkable divergence of opinion concerning the nature, structure, and life cycle of the tropical disturbances that Riehl (1954, p. 238) felt that we must reject the terms "front" and "convergence zone" in reference to the equatorial low pressure zone and use only the phrase "equatorial trough." Although convergence does occur in this zone, often there is none. Moreover, Riehl believes with Palmer (1952) that "We must dismiss the whole body of theoretical explanations developed by the air mass school in the tropics, but at the same time we must incorporate their empirical findings." The reasons for this conclusion are as follows (U. S. Navy, 1953):

1. There is no evidence of a density discontinuity in the equatorial trough region; though it could have a variety of slopes when the density contrast was extremely minute. Theoretically a front could not exist. Even if cold air were over warm, the motion would have to be strictly geostrophic. Hence, such a front becomes physically impossible. Geostrophic motion does not exist in the tropics, otherwise winds would approach infinity. The intertropical front might exist under controlled laboratory conditions if turbulence and vertical motions could be zero and all accelerations were removed. Actually, such conditions do not exist in nature.

2. The intertropical front does not move as a true front. Air flows right through the front, i.e., the wind velocities at the front are not zero. If a density discontinuity had existed, no matter how minute, the requirement of a stationary front would immediately be destroyed.

3. Aircraft reconnaissance does not frequently find a continuous line of bad weather in positions where the ITC should be located. Sometimes it exists. Sometimes there is a distance of several hundred to a thousand miles between significant bad weather. Hence, observations do not indicate the existence of a continuous line of bad weather as this front should have.

4. The climatological view of winds with a northerly component on the north side of the intertropical front and winds with a southerly component on the south side has little application in practice. Bad weather is observed located in regions where there is no apparent wind shift.

5. Typhoons do not always form on the intertropical front. There are many observations of storm development in regions where such a front could not possibly have been located. This makes it obvious, even in the case of cyclones forming along a boundary such as the intertropical front, that the potential energy available for release from the solenoid source

for the kinetic energy of cyclones is insufficient or nil and has no influence in causing cyclone formation in the tropics. As a result, the intertropical front can find no place in the theory of cyclone formation in the tropics.

In line with these opinions, the authors of the U. S. Navy's 1953 typhoon report advocated a theory of cyclone formation in the tropics that is independent of polar-front concepts and for which they believed there were ample data in support. Earlier studies had indicated a connection between typhoon formation and a "wave disturbance" in the easterly waves. Conclusions of a 1949 U. S. Air Force study of easterly waves indicated that "Pressure and pressure tendencies seem to be entirely independent of easterly waves—even with diurnal variations removed, easterly waves seem to occur about as frequently with rising pressure tendencies as with falling, at maxima as at minima [pressure]" (U. S. Navy, 1953, pp. 19–20). Easterly waves are difficult to analyze, moreover. According to the U. S. Navy (1953),

Cloud and precipitation patterns vary widely from (polar) front to (polar) front and from easterly wave to easterly wave. The area of increased cloudiness and showers may precede, straddle, or follow the windshift . . . Easterly waves offer nothing comparable to the air density discontinuity expected across a front. Visibility, surface and upper air temperatures, and dew points offer no help in the easterly wave analysis . . . The wind veers with passage of an easterly wave . . . The vagueness and indecision of this wind pattern is . . . distressing because . . . easterly waves exhibit fewer indices for recognition than do fronts.

The nature of the origin of the easterly wave has been the least understood part of the hypothesis regarding easterly waves. According to Riehl (1954, p. 211), both tropical easterlies and polar westerlies oscillate in a wavelike manner. The wave length may be between 15 and 20 degrees of longitude on the average from ridge to ridge. These waves are associated with shear zones such as wind discontinuities and jet streams, and with the development of vortices. Thus convergences in the equatorial trough, easterly waves, and cyclones are all interrelated manifestations of a circulation pattern or perturbation characteristic of the region between 10°N and 10°S, and are not separate synoptic entities (U. S. Navy, 1953).

In describing the character of the easterly wave and associated developments, Riehl (1954, pp. 213–25) wrote that a pressure wave accompanies the wave in the wind field. Temperature and pressure variations are associated with strong waves as far up as the tropopause. The temperature and pressure are nearly in phase at the surface, which is usually the zone of the most active weather. Preceding the trough of this wave is a zone of low-level divergence and of descent. Following it is a zone of low-level convergence and ascent. However, Riehl asserted that in order for the waves to exist, the depth of the easterly current must be at least 20,000 to 25,000 feet.

The passage of a wave brings changes in the weather. The thickness of the moist layer is controlled by the field of motion. Thus about 200 miles ahead of the wave trough, the top of the layer reaches a minimum often as low as 5,000 feet, and fine weather prevails. It rises quickly near the trough line and reaches a maximum over 20,000 feet in the zone of most intense convergence. Here, according to Riehl, large squall lines and rows of cumulonimbi are found. In the eastern fringes of the trough the moist layer descends again and the regular trade-wind weather is resumed.

At times during the broad-scale zonal flow of the easterlies, the waves slow up a little and their amplitudes increase as they reach the same meridian. Wave troughs during such periods are likely to be "captured" and become stationary or even retrograde. "Fracture" may occur after a time and the waves then continue in their earlier paths. The superposition intensifies the disturbance, but this usually weakens after fracture. "An exception occurs when a closed cyclonic circulation forms in the wave trough in the easterlies. It may not fill but instead may become a hurricane after the two perturbations separate" (Riehl, 1954, p. 225). A sign that a wave trough is increasing its amplitude is when bad weather spreads to both sides of the trough line and an altostratus deck with steady rain develops.

Hutchings (1953, p. 42) regarded the easterly wave as a distinct process in the formation of tropical cyclones and the tropical convergence as a separate process in their formation. He wrote: "These cyclonic disturbances tend to form in two distinct and characteristic ways, the first being connected with the intertropical convergence zone and the second being connected, especially during the winter months, with a wave-like deformation of the normal undisturbed easterly flow." He furnishes two sets of synoptic charts analyzing a typical case of each type of cyclone origin as he defines them. They are reproduced here together with his analyses:

As an example of that type of cyclogenesis which is connected with the intertropical convergence zone, reference should be made to [Fig. 52], which [shows] the development of the weather situation from 0001 hours GMT on 14 March 1944 to 0001 hours GMT on 19 March 1944. The analysis is presented by means of streamlines which attempt to depict the distribution of wind direction observed just above the layer of surface friction. . . .

In [Fig. 52(a)] the most important feature of the situation is the well marked line of convergence extending from east to west between latitudes ten and eleven degrees south. There appears to be a zone of convergence between air from the southern hemisphere (the southeast trades) and northern-hemisphere air which has crossed the equator as a northeast flow and then gradually turned into a flow from the north and northwest (the deflected northeast trades). This pattern has, however, been established only recently, and it seems likely that, although northern-hemisphere air may exist in the northern part of the area, the convergence line is more properly considered as one formed in a fairly homogeneous mass of air. Nevertheless, this convergence line would be traditionally described as the intertropical convergence zone. A singular point of convergence appears on this line just south of the Tokelau Islands. The main interest of this study lies in the convergence line and its associated singular point of convergence. . . .

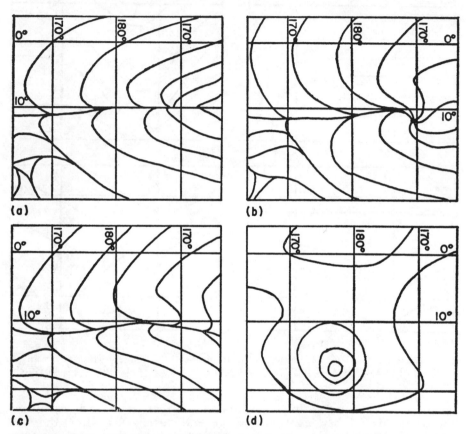

Fig. 52. Streamline and isobaric analyses of south Pacific tropical-cyclonic-cell formation, March 1944: (a) 1 A.M., March 14; (b) 6 A.M., March 14; (c) 6 P.M., March 14; (d) 1 A.M., March 19. (a), (b), and (c) are streamline analyses; (d) is an isobaric analysis. [From Hutchings (1953).]

[Figure 52(b) and (c)] show the gradual development of the centre of convergence and its slow movement toward the south. Up to this point the disturbance has hardly been perceptible in the pressure field, as may be seen from the plotted reports, but from now on a definite centre of low pressure can be observed. [Figure 52(d)] shows an isobaric analysis of the situation at 0001 GMT on 19 March. It will be seen that a strong vortex has been developed in which, later, winds attain a reported velocity of Beaufort Scale number 9.

The other type of cyclogenesis, that connected with a wave-like deformation of a general zonal current from the east, is illustrated in [Fig. 53]. [Figure 53(a)] represents an isobaric analysis of the weather situation at

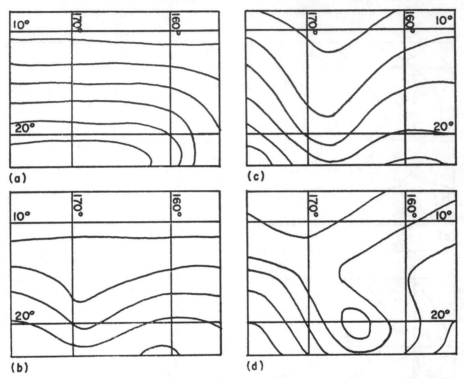

(a)   (c)

(b)   (d)

Fig. 53. Isobaric analyses of south Pacific tropical-cyclonic-cell formation, July 1951: (a) 6 A.M., July 15; (b) 6 A.M., July 17; (c) 12 noon, July 17; (d) 6 P.M., July 17. [From Hutchings (1953).]

0600 hours GMT on 15 July 1951, and shows that, at lower levels, above the friction layer, there exists a broad general current of air from the east. Although there is little information at higher levels the general temperature distribution makes it probable that this current is relatively shallow and that it becomes a westerly air flow before an altitude of 10,000 feet is reached. The current is thus characterized by a fairly high value of positive shear with height. During the next day a very slight wave-like deformation of the pressure field occurs between 165 and 170 degrees west. This deformation gradually increases in amplitude until by 0600 hours GMT on 17 July a fairly rapid development along longitude 170 degrees west is in progress [Fig. 53 (b)]. This is still more evident at 1200 hours GMT [Fig. 53(c)], and by 1800 hours GMT [Fig. 53(d)] a closed center of low pressure has formed which later deepens into an extensive and intense vortex . . . There are, then, two essentially different ways in which the tropical disturbances of this region may originate.·

Hutchings (1953, p. 48) also appears to imply that the rare Southern Hemisphere winter typhoons are formed differently from the summer ones—the winter typhoons originate from easterly wave disturbances, summer ones from intertropical convergence.

In contrast to Hutchings' idea of two separate processes, the 1953 typhoon report appears to view the origin of tropical cyclones and the origin of easterly waves as part and parcel of the same processes, deriving from the convergence in the equatorial trough. The authors of this report (U.S. Navy, 1953) considered that disturbances arise from acceleration forces acting on a current of air. The acceleration occurs when winds converge at the meteorological (thermal) equator because of the decreasing pressure. With the meteorological equator north of the geographical equator (Fig. 54)

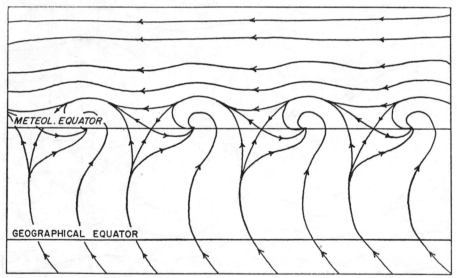

Fig. 54. Theoretical vortex train derived from zonal wind fields in the equatorial region. [From U. S. Navy (1953).]

this acceleration of an easterly wind north of the meteorological equator is related to a cyclonic tendency—a movement toward the equator (leftward). Easterly winds south of the meteorological equator and moving northward toward it (away from the geographical equator) have an initial anticyclonic tendency because of the Coriolis effect and may move in a northward or even eastward direction, depending upon the direction of minimum pressure. However, the accelerating convergence here causes a loss of anticyclonic vorticity; the current then acquires a cyclonic tendency.

"Now consider that the currents north and south of the meteorological equator are opposing one another. As the two currents approach one another, strong streamline convergence occurs and both currents develop strong cyclonic tendencies. At the meteorological equator, the southern current turns west and the northern current east" (U. S. Navy, 1953, p. 31). Theoretically, the wind at the line of lowest pressure in the convergence has two directions; thus the wind speed at the line must be an absolute minimum or zero. The resultant of the two converging streams of opposite direction on a rotating earth is a system of vortices alternating with neutral sectors and a pressure field which is composed of a series of waves whose troughs and ridges need not be perpendicular to the parallels of latitude, but which must be parallel to each other (Figs. 54 and 55). The

GEOGRAPHICAL AND METEOROLOGICAL EQUATORS

Fig. 55. Theoretical vortex train with superadjacent equators. [From U. S. Navy (1953).]

waves will have maximum amplitude at the meteorological equator and decrease in amplitude to the north and south. "The waves that form in the pressure fields and the vortices, seeking equilibrium, must continuously change longitude . . . Experience tells us that the motion of the vortices and the waves in the pressure field is westward" (U. S. Navy, 1953).

Thus the final visualization in this set of hypotheses is a train of cyclones, each separated by a neutral point, along the meteorological equator (Fig. 54). Of course, in synoptic application, one finds influences that will tend to reduce the symmetry of the train of vortices and create regions in which the atmosphere will not be in an equilibrium state of motion. The most important of these is the distortions produced by continental heterogeneity and seasonal continental pressure changes in the two hemispheres. Other influences include those from individual anticyclones resulting from the breaking up of the subtropical high-pressure belt, from the fact that these anticyclones are moving, that they vary in intensity, and that the anticyclones in the two hemispheres are independent of and out of phase with each other. "In effect, these factors will tend to destroy some cyclones and amplify others" (U. S. Navy, 1953).

The authors of the 1953 typhoon report pointed out that during the summer and fall, when the meteorological equator is located at latitudes near weather stations in the Pacific, an unending train of vortices are observed to move across the map from the Marshall Islands to the East Asian coasts (Fig. 56).

To further support their theory, the authors stated that were their reasoning correct, one should expect to find the counterpart of the atmospheric vortices in the wind-driven ocean currents. In fact, they found that there was such a counterpart in the Pacific in July when a train of vortices extended from Panama to the Philippines.

Some light is thrown upon the points of origin of North Pacific tropical cyclones and upon their paths by the following paragraph in a Navy typhoon report (1953, p. 37):

The tropical cyclones observed in the Pacific vary in structure with time as well as space. This comes about primarily as a result of a pronounced meridional component to the orientation of the meteorological equator. The acceleration influences on an air trajectory to one point on this equator will, of course, differ considerably from those approaching another point on the equator. In fact, east of the longitude of the Marshall Islands, the meteorological equator is frequently found south of the geographical equator during the northern hemisphere summer. Farther west, the equator is found as far north as the heat low of China during mid-summer. Thus, the meteorological equator sometimes has considerable angular orientation to the latitude lines [Fig. 56]. Over a distance of 60 degrees of longitude this line may be displaced northward as much as 30 degress latitude from east to west. With the meteorological equator frequently south of the geographical equator during the Northern Hemisphere summer many of those wave disturbances in the north-central Pacific are actually caused by influences of vortices in the Southern Hemisphere. During the summer near the longitude of the Marshall Islands, the meteorological equator tilts northward across the geographical equator. This is the nor-

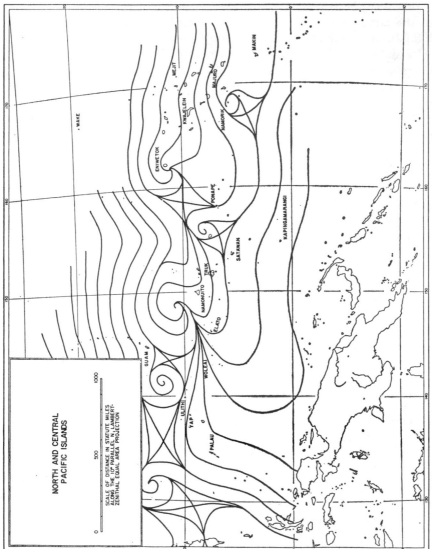

Fig. 56. Streamline surface chart of north and central Pacific islands, September 12, 1945. [From U. S. Navy (1953).]

mal region for the dissipation of the westward moving vortices in the Southern Hemisphere. This point also constitutes the primary longitude in the Pacific for the initial convergence that leads to the formation of the Northern Hemisphere tropical cyclones.

However, that easterly wave orogenesis of typhoons is not confined to the "off season" for typhoon formation is shown by the statement in the 1953 typhoon report that "Except for Viola, all of the 1953 typhoons developed from easterly waves or vortices," most of them during the summer half of the year, although one occurred in mid-February, the first detected in February in 8 years.

Typhoon frequency

Although typhoon frequency in the tropical Pacific was uncertain earlier because of the lack of recording stations in large areas of the open ocean through which storms may pass undetected, recent aerial reconnaissance practices as well as the increase of stations on scattered islands have provided more adequate data. Visher (1925, p. 26) listed the following number by regions of the Pacific: western north Pacific 23.8, eastern north Pacific 2.2, middle north Pacific 3.0, total 29.0; eastern Australia and coast 15.0, western south Pacific 12.0, eastern south Pacific ?, total 27.0.

Hutchings (1953, p. 48) felt that Visher's figures for the earliest records were too small for the western south Pacific, but that Visher's "subjective evaluation" for twelve (including those unreported in the open Pacific) appears to be a considerable overestimate. Hutchings found that the average annual number of reported storms, 3.7 (between the years 1874 and 1924), given by Visher, corresponded closely although fortuitously with his own average of 3.6 annually for storms with force of Beaufort 9 for the same area between 1940 and 1951.

The U. S. Navy typhoon reports do not distinguish the Pacific north of the equator by regions but show the paths of all typhoons reaching 64 knots or higher wind velocity detected from at least as far east as the Marshall Islands. There were 17 such storms listed in 1953, 15 in 1954, 19 in 1955, 20 in 1956, and 18 in 1957. Few of these were close to or had severe effects upon the low islands of the Marshalls or Carolines. Although many of them were detected as cyclonic storms in their movements past or through the Caroline or Marshall Islands, most of them did not attain typhoon-velocity wind speeds until much farther northwest (Fig. 57).

Visher (1925, p. 27) wrote that the annual frequency of "severe tropical cyclones" in the Fiji, Tonga, New Hebrides, and Norfolk Islands groups was two, that in New Caledonia three, in Samoa two to three, in the Tuamotus and Cook Islands 0.5, and in Tahiti and the Solomons 0.2. The

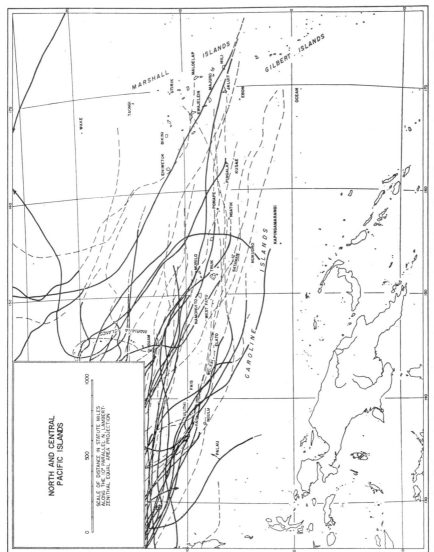

Fig. 57. Paths of 62 tropical cyclones detected from 1953 through 1957 through north and central Pacific islands. Dashed lines indicate pre-typhoon intensity. Solid lines indicate typhoon intensity (wind speeds of 64 knots or greater).

infrequency of reports of severe storms in the low islands of the Marshalls and Carolines during the last decade appears to indicate that the annual frequency here is probably not more than between 0.2 and 0.5, although Visher thought that probably about three tropical cyclones a year on the average develop in the middle section of the north Pacific. Perhaps more than three develop in the area he includes (longitude 140°N to 170°E), but they do not have high wind speeds until they have left the vicinity of the atolls. Very destructive typhoons reported for the Marshalls since the turn of the century include only those of 1905, 1951, and 1958. At Ifalik Atoll in the western Carolines middle-aged men could remember only six in their lifetime. Thus individual atolls may experience a destructive storm only at long intervals. For example, Jaluit, which was severely damaged by inundation in the 1905 typhoon, did not meet such a storm again until 1958. The tropical south Pacific appears to have considerably fewer typhoons than those in a comparable area of the north Pacific (Hutchings, 1925, p. 49).

One typhoon, however, frequently affects several islands in its path. This is especially true of such a group as the Tuamotus, where large numbers of atolls are crowded closely together. In the typhoon of 1903, for instance, more than ten atolls were severely damaged and a total of 517 people reported killed and drowned. Moreover, although the average annual number of destructive typhoons affecting an area may be low, sometimes long periods elapse without storms, while at other periods there may be one a year for several years.

Seasonal distribution of typhoons in the Pacific

Although tropical typhoons occur somewhere in the Pacific during every month of the year, there is a seasonal concentration which is different for each hemisphere. Visher's analysis (1925, p. 24) indicates that

The four months July to October inclusive, have nearly two-thirds of the tropical cyclones of the western North Pacific, and four-fifths of those of the eastern North Pacific. In the Southern Hemisphere the four months, December to March inclusive, have between two-thirds and three-fourths of these storms. On the average, September is the stormiest month in the northern Tropics and January in the southern. August and October are the next stormiest months in the Northern Hemisphere and March or February in the Southern Hemisphere. Storms are rarest in February in the western North Pacific, are unrecorded in the eastern North Pacific in March, April, and May, and are very rare in the Southern Hemisphere in August.

In his analysis of the seasonal distribution of typhoon-intensity tropical storms between longitude 150°E and 150°W in the Southern Hemisphere between 1940 and 1951, Hutchings (1925, p. 48) confirmed that there is a well-marked concentration in the period from December to March in-clusive, while typhoons were extremely rare in other months of the year. The U. S. Navy typhoon reports for 1953 to 1955 (Table 10) give the seasonal

TABLE 10

Storms of Typhoon Intensity, Northern Pacific

	1953	*1954*	*1955*
Jan.	0	0	1
Feb.	1	0	0
March	0	0	1
April	0	0	1
May	1	1	0
June	1	0	1
July	1	1	5
Aug.	5	3	2
Sept.	2	4	3
Oct.	4	2	3
Nov.	1	3	0
Dec.	1	1	1

From U. S. Navy (1953; 1954; 1955).

distribution of storms with typhoon intensities in the western north Pacific. In 1954 storms of typhoon intensity occurred on 62 days, in 1955, on 66 days.

The marked concentration of intense typhoon developments during the late summer and fall may be related to the maximum accumulation of heat at the latter part of the summer half-year in each hemisphere. This should lead to a higher rate of evaporation and higher moisture content in the atmosphere. A greater amount of moisture is then available for condensation in the convectional currents in the equatorial trough. Hence, there should be greater energy releases with convectional movements, lead-ing to the increased turbulence that develops into cyclones.

Area of typhoon origin

Visher (1925, pp. 22–3) found that one-half of the storms in the western north Pacific appear to start in 10 to 15° latitudes, about one-third in 15 to 20° latitudes, and about one-sixth in latitudes below 10°. However, he pointed out that many of the storms are not encountered and thus not re-ported until they are much farther north than their region of origin. The more intensive meteorological work done in the post–World War II period has resulted in the location of incipient typhoons nearer their areas of origin. The paths shown in Fig. 57 for instance, although only from 5 years' records, appear to show that the lower latitudes (between 5 and 10°) in the north Pacific are the most important regions of tropical cyclone orogenesis. Figure 58, which covers the western south Pacific, does not, for the most part, provide enough information to indicate whether the storms on the paths shown were of pre-typhoon or typhoon intensities. The 1953 typhoon report also describes the occurrences of cyclones as characteristic of the region between 10°N and 10°S and Riehl (1954, p. 229) pointed out that "when we glance at time sections of wind, pressure, and weather, not only in the Marshalls but also further east at Palmyra (6°N., 162°W.) and Christmas (2°N., 157°W.), disturbances are quite apparent." The first typhoon of 1956 in its formative stage was located within 120 miles of the equator (U. S. Navy, 1956).

If the theory of typhoon origin proposed in the 1953 typhoon report is right, tropical cyclones may develop anywhere along the equatorial trough. Their intensification to typhoon wind speeds only or chiefly in the western sectors of the tropical oceans may be related to the cold currents in the eastern ocean sectors caused by upwellings, which carry cool water far westward.

Typhoon paths

There appear to be some differences in the behavior of the typhoon paths in the north as compared with those of the south Pacific. Hutchings (1953, p. 54) stated that while in most areas where tropical cyclones are frequent they most often initially move westward and only later in their life history (after recurvature) move toward the east, this is not so true in the southwestern Pacific. Here, tropical cyclones "very frequently move toward the east and in most cases continue this motion until they leave the area of the chart" (that is, to higher latitudes than 30°). As compared with the North Atlantic, where Tannehill found only 10 per cent of the tropical cyclones moving east initially and another 5 per cent moving north initially, in the southwestern Pacific Hutchings found 44 per cent of 43 cyclones examined moving eastward initially. This appears to point to much more nearly equal frequencies of initial eastward and westward movements.

In the western north Pacific the paths are almost invariably westward and northwestward (Fig. 57). Most of the 1953 and 1954 typhoons, for instance, were first detected in the Marshalls area as easterly waves moving westward. Reconnaissance-plane fixes made it possible to plot their courses relatively accurately (Fig. 59). Most of them recurve northward and then northeastward in their westward progression. However, "Seven of the 17 typhoons of

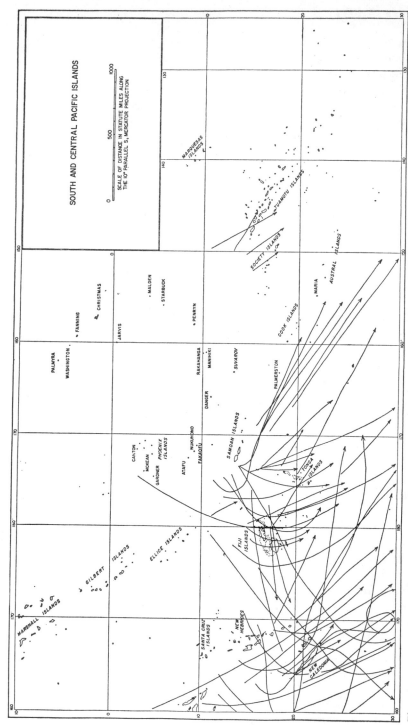

Fig. 58. Representative cyclone paths (approximate) through south and central Pacific islands compiled from data recorded prior to 1923. [After Visher (1925).]

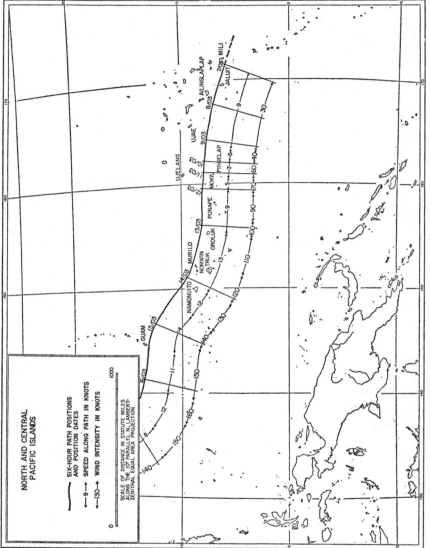

Fig. 59. Path of Typhoon Lola through north and central Pacific islands, November 7 through 20, 1957. [From U. S. Navy (1957).]

1953 here failed to recurve. The others recurved within a wide area between Marcus Island and the coast of China and maintained their intensity until they became extra-tropical. The movement appeared to be controlled by the position of the sub-tropical anti-cyclone (the Pacific High) and the migratory anti-cyclones of the middle latitudes."

The typhoon patterns in the north and south Pacific differ in some characteristics. Whereas typhoons in the north Pacific are uncommon in the westerly drift of the tradewind belt until about a thousand miles west of the Marshalls, in the south Pacific typhoon paths are especially numerous in the 600 to 700 mile stretch eastward of the longitudes of the Marshalls.

The north Pacific typhoons funnel into a much more restricted zone in their progression away from the equator. That is, the typhoon paths in the northwest Pacific for the most part move northward near the Japan Current in a swath about 700 miles wide, whereas in the south Pacific this movement away from the equator is spread over almost 3,000 miles. The correspondence with the oceanic current patterns in the two areas is remarkable.

Another noteworthy correlation is the fact that the northwest to southeast alignment of the monsoonal airflow between Eastern Asia and Australia corresponds to the zonal lines enclosing the greatest densities of typhoon paths north and south of the equator. These correlations lead one to the inference that there may be some connection between the conflict of monsoonal airflow and the trade winds in the oceanic regions east of Southeast Asia and east of Australia.

Additional support for this supposition is that both north and south of the equator, the period of most frequent typhoon occurrence is during the "summer and fall" period for the respective hemispheres. In the northern Pacific they are most frequent between July and November. In the southern Pacific they are most frequent during December to March. In these seasons in the respective hemispheres, larger volumes of well-saturated warm and unstable equatorial air masses are brought to higher latitudes in the west Pacific by the monsoonal airflow than in the regions of more steady trade winds farther east. Such airmasses provide ideal conditions for energizing weak cyclones. Also, the prevailing direction of the monsoons during the respective typhoon seasons tends to drive the cyclonic storms away from the equator and accelerate their recurvature.

Ultimately, it would seem that the position of the Australian continent, considerably eastward of the longitude of Asia, might be considered a significant influence in the position of the maximum density paths of south Pacific tropical typhoons. An important difference in the paths of typhoons north and south of the equator is that those in the south leave the tropical latitudes much more quickly than those in the north, which are found in tropical climates a thousand miles farther west. This fact correlates markedly well with the movements of the dominant ocean currents in their respective areas of recurvature or initial paths.

The chart of the 62 tropical cyclones shown in Fig. 57 appears to exhibit two interesting channels, each from 200 to 300 miles wide, along one or the other of which a large number of the cyclones attaining typhoon intensities move. The two channels have a common origin in the cyclonic paths in the eastern Carolines between about 2 and 12°N and appear to diverge between Truk and West Fayu Atolls. The group of cyclones in the northern of the two channels reach typhoon intensity some 500 miles farther east than the group in the southern channel. This may in some way be related to their quicker movement to higher latitudes. The typhoons in the southern channel tend to move south of the central Carolines but in a northwesterly direction, so that most of them travel between Ngulu and Fais or Ulithi Atolls. The western Carolines feel the brunt of their destruction, with Yap in the center of their paths. The northern channel starts between the vicinities of Ponape Island and Satawan Atoll in the east and runs northwestward, most of the typhoons passing in the west between Guam and the area within 200 miles south of Guam. In the direct path of this channel are such atolls as Murilo, Nomwin, East Fayu, and Namonuito. Faraulep and uninhabited Gaferut appear to lie in the 250- by 500-mile oblong area that is relatively free of direct typhoon paths.

The writer would like to suggest a possible explanation of this curious bifurcation in the Carolines typhoon paths as described in the first findings of the New York University Engineering Research Division hurricane project. This project, directed by Edwin L. Fisher, in a study of 16 hurricanes between 1953 and 1955 revealed "distinct although not conclusive" proof that hurricanes form over warm ocean areas, follow tracks of warm water, and fizzle out when they move over colder water (*The New York Times,* 1956). Hurricanes in their early stages traveling less than 10 miles per hour were found to swerve away from cold ocean areas, as in the cases of hurricanes Edna in 1954 and Connie in 1955 in the west Atlantic–Carribean area. Hurricane Dolly in 1953 on the fourth day suddenly lost force without apparent cause. However, a cause does appear to have existed—the cold water off Bermuda over which the storm passed that day, which produced a damping effect on the storm.

After having studied the paths of 62 tropical cyclones in the western Pacific north of the equator (Fig. 57) between 1953 and 1957 the writer believes that there may be certain similar causes for the bifurcation of typhoon paths which merit further investigation. The region apparently bypassed by typhoon paths lies northeast of the Yap-Woleai storm channel. An examination of the ocean currents in the region (Fig. 60) seems to reveal that during the summer and fall, when typhoons are most prevalent, the equa-

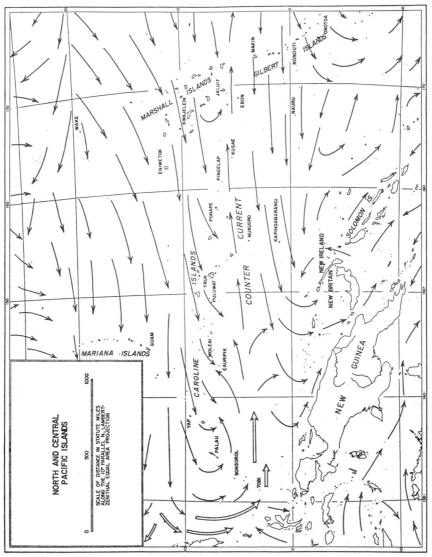

Fig. 60. Ocean-surface currents in north and central Pacific islands during February and March. [After Sverdrup (1942).]

torial currents in the western Carolines appear to nearly coincide with the Yap-Woleai storm channel. Moreover, the westernmost Carolines lie in the ocean area of confused turbulence where the westward drift has just made its turn to the east. It seems possible that the zone bordering the north side of the equatorial countercurrent would lie in the typhoon-free region between West Fayu and Fais. If Sverdrup (1942, pp. 193–5) is right in stating that there is upwelling at the northern boundary of the countercurrent, the cold water upwelled and the confused eddies in this area of the eastward reversal of the equatorial drift may act as a damper and exercise a deflective influence upon the hurricanes moving toward the cooler water surface. Thus the cyclones may be deflected either to the north or to the south, creating the two major typhoon channels noted, and leaving a region between them relatively free of typhoons.

On the other hand, Cromwell's assertion (1953, p. 201) that evidence was still lacking for such upwellings makes additional oceanographic data in this area necessary to evaluate the proposed explanation offered above.

In the southwestern south Pacific the paths of tropical cyclonic storms are not as well known as those in the north Pacific. Figure 58 shows generalized paths of tropical cyclones in the former area (so far as is known) for the period prior to 1923. The intensities of the cyclones along the paths indicated probably reached or approached typhoon intensity along most of the courses indicated (Hutchings, 1925, p. 51). However, the pattern shown indicates that most of the storms move south or southwest while within 20° of the equator, and south-southeast in higher latitudes, in general exhibiting a pattern similar to that of the north Pacific shown in Fig. 58. According to Visher (1925, p. 74), however, "A detailed study of the tracks crossing Fiji and New Caledonia shows that a large percentage of the storms moved westward or eastward across these representative island groups [so that] the straightness and simplicity of most of the published tracks of South Pacific hurricanes probably reflects inadequate information."

Many of the storm tracks of the western south Pacific, as far as the records reveal, have no well-defined point of recurve, being nearly straight or else parabolic. The position of recurvature appears to progressively increase in latitude from December to March (Visher, 1925, pp. 75–6) with a total latitudinal change from about 16 to 20° latitude. This apparently marks the southward progression of the Meteorological Equator at this period.

Although plotted paths such as those in Figs. 57 and 58 show the estimated routes of the typhoon centers, they do not indicate the swaths of destruction. Among the factors accounting for the destructiveness of typhoons are the intensities of wind speeds and the dimensions of the area within which destructive winds are felt. Thus, in 1956 the smallest storm was Typhoon Gilda, which circulated in an area only 30 to 50 miles in diameter. Although there were destructive winds of 130 knots near the center, winds of only 10 to 20 knots were reported 70 miles away from the center. By contrast, one of the most destructive storms was Typhoon Wanda, whose radius of winds (estimated in excess of 100 knots) extended 180 to 200 miles from the center (U. S. Navy, 1956). A storm such as this may inflict severe destruction along a path 400 miles wide. In November 1957 the center of Typhoon Lola (Fig. 59) passed by Pingelap Atoll about 120 miles to its north, but the 60 to 70 knot winds blew down or snapped off many breadfruit trees and coconut trees. The year's copra output was cut by an estimated 50 per cent, the taro was ruined by salt water, and 25 per cent of the houses and canoes were damaged (personal communication from H. M. Hedges, Ponape District Administrator, Feb. 27, 1958).

The great altitude to which such a disturbance may extend is indicated by Typhoon Lola, which when passing 25 miles south of Guam had a well-developed closed eye extending vertically to 52,000 feet (U. S. Navy, 1957).

Effects of typhoons and severe storms

An old song among the people of Ifalik Atoll recorded by Burrows and Spiro (1953, p. 25) pictures the consequences of a typhoon on their island:

> Men are taking wing;
> Flying in all directions
> to islands where there is food,
> and trees standing.
>
> . . .
>
> Let them go, we will stay on;
> At least we will have rain to drink;
>
> . . .
>
> Not many are staying;
> The others can't stand it without shade.
> Never mind, the rain will pour down on us,
> And we will find some shade
> Under the little trees that are left.
> Purak bushes will spring up on the beaches.
>
> . . .
>
> But the food is nearly gone;
> We watch each other eat.
> Look up and there are no trees,
> Here, where it used to be so fine.

This chant tells with poignancy the tragedy that can come to an atoll with the typhoon and the melancholy and fatalistic yet courageous acceptance of the calamity that has enabled the Pacific atoll dwellers to survive and flourish in their precarious environment.

Destruction by storm winds and waves is reflected in the manifold aspects of the atoll environment. The shallow-water areas of both seaward reef margins and lagoon slopes and the land of the islets suffer morphological change. The vegetation is variously damaged by wind or marine inundation, as are man and his structures, and the fauna on the land. The greatest destruction occurs when marine water pours across the land under the drive of the typhoon winds and washes away entire islets.

The effects of different storms vary according to the differing conditions, of course. Some of these differences may be noted in Appendix C. However, characteristic effects on atoll environment and ecology have been well summed up by the preliminary account (Blumenstock, 1958) of the first intensive field investigation of the physical and biological effects of a typhoon upon an atoll undertaken a short period after the storm. Because of its relevance the entire account is quoted.

On January 7, 1958, a small, very intense typhoon passed directly over Jaluit Atoll in the Marshall Islands (5½°N., 169½°E.) [compare Plates 33 and 34]. The first reports thereafter indicated that the typhoon had wrought many profound changes, especially in its effects upon the morphology of several of the islets and upon the vegetation and soils. Accordingly, the Pacific Science Board of the U. S. National Academy of Sciences, acting together with the Office of Naval Research and the U. S. Trust Territory of the Pacific, sponsored the formation of a party of seven scientists to conduct a brief, but intensive, field study at Jaluit. In addition to myself, the field party included Dr. A. H. Banner, director of the Marine Biological Laboratory, University of Hawaii; Dr. F. R. Fosberg, Pacific Vegetation Project, U. S. Geological Survey; Dr. J. Linsley Gressitt, chairman, Entomology Department, Bishop Museum; Dr. Edwin D. McKee, geologist, U. S. Geological Survey; Dr. Herold J. Wiens, professor of geography, Yale University; and Mr. J. B. Mackenzie, who has been director of the Agricultural Experiment Station maintained at Jaluit by the U. S. Trust Territory of the Pacific during the past several years. It is the purpose of this article to report very briefly and in a preliminary sense on the principal findings of this field party, which studied conditions on several different islets of Jaluit during April 24–May 2.

The typhoon. Because of the paucity of weather observations over the ocean to eastward, the storm that struck Jaluit was not known to be of typhoon intensity before it struck. It was, however, being carried as a storm that had appeared at Palmyra Island (5°53′N., 162°5′W.) and was approaching Jaluit from the east. After striking Jaluit, the storm moved on a west-north-west heading through the Marshall and Caroline Islands and into the Philippine Sea, where it died out. Among the islands seriously afflicted by the storm were Ponape, Truk, and the Hall Islands, all in the Caroline Islands. When the typhoon intensity of the storm was first established it was named "Ophelia"; and that name will be used here.

At Jaluit, judging from eye-witness accounts and from the field evidence, "Ophelia" produced winds with sustained speeds of at least 125 knots and brought ahead of it and with it pronounced storm tides on which large

wind waves were superimposed. Strong winds came initially from the
north-east quadrant, then backed through west to south. There was at
least one distinct lull, indicating that the eye of the storm crossed the
atoll. There was initially a series of wave surges from the east, and
these inundated several of the islets along the eastern reef, in one
instance to a depth of 6 ft. above the ground in a locality that is more than
8 ft. above mean sea level. These first inundations occurred between late
morning and mid-afternoon (180th meridian time) and were quite promptly
followed by much lesser inundations upon the islets along the western
rim, the wave having been renewed within the lagoon, which is about 15
miles wide (from east to west) and 30 miles long (from north-north-west to
south-southeast). Later, in the afternoon or early evening, there was further,
but only partial, inundation from waves moving eastward in the lagoon
and waves moving south-eastward over the ocean to the west of the atoll.
By dawn on January 8 the storm had subsided and the wind had become
easterly, the normal tradewind direction.

Geomorphic changes. The observations of McKee and Wiens in particular, but also those of the other members of the party, led to the identification
of several new geomorphic features, especially on those islets that suffered
major inundations. These include depositional and erosional forms.

The chief depositional forms produced by the storm were locally prominent gravel ridges upon the reef flat on the ocean side of some of the eastern
islets [Plate 35]; new or augmented beach ridges of gravel; gravel sheets,
often tongue-shaped, extending across two-thirds of the islets in many places;
and outwash features on the lagoon-side of the eastern islets. These lagoon-
side sediments were strewn upon the reef and beyond into deeper water
[Plate 36], as was shown by bottom samples obtained by Banner and McKee.
They also may have helped form the gravel bars observed in some locations
on the lagoon-side, both on the reef flat and beyond, though these bars also
contain sediments derived from the floor of the open lagoon itself.

The most prominent erosion feature was the channels scoured out by the
water. The best-developed ones originated at a break in the old beach ridge
on the ocean-side of the eastern islets and extended several hundred yards
across to the lagoon-side, where they gave rise to pronounced outwash
features. Minor erosion features include plunge holes and scour pits.

Soils. On those eastern islets that were awash, the soils existing prior to
the storm were either buried or scoured out over wide areas. On the islet
of Mejatto, for example, more than half of the pre-existing soil now lies
beneath a sheet of coral rubble that is from 5–6 in. to 2½ ft. thick [Plates
37 and 38]. Severe scouring has sluiced off about one-fourth of the soil. The
remaining 15–25 per cent is either partially eroded or else persists with little
or no change, except, perhaps, in salinity.

A discovery made by McKee and Fosberg may prove to be of special
interest. In a well cross-section, at a depth of about 3 ft., they found an
undisturbed soil profile overlain by coral rubble to provide a disconformity
that is precisely analogous to that produced by "Ophelia." This suggests
that it might be possible to date, by the carbon-14 technique, those typhoons
in past centuries that were sufficiently intense and sufficiently "on target"
to yield gravel sheets upon atolls anywhere.

Vegetation. The principal broad-scale effects of the storm upon the vegetation is well summed up by Fosberg in the introductory portion of his report (now in manuscript). His remarks should be viewed in the light of the fact that prior to the storm Jaluit was densely vegetated [Plates 39 and 40], since it lies in an area where the rainfall averages close to 200 in. a year.

The effects of Typhoon "Ophelia," even on the same vegetation type, or on the same plant, were by no means identical in all localities and parts of the atoll. In general, the islets on the east side of the atoll suffered much more damage to their vegetation than those on north, south, and west. Also . . . narrow islets and parts of islets were far more affected than broad parts. This was well illustrated on Jaluit Islet, where the narrow parts south of Jabor were in places completely stripped of vegetation . . . [Plates 40 and 41].

Many trees were uprooted . . . Some were snapped off. Branches were broken or torn off of most of those that remained standing. Some exotic plants were killed or their above ground parts killed by salt. In places large scale burial of plants by gravel occurred. Elsewhere the soil with its vegetation was scoured away. Many tree trunks were seen in the lagoon on the shallower slopes along the east side [Plate 36]. Masses of plant debris were strewn at random on the shallower slopes along the east side.

From the observations of Fosberg, Wiens, and Blumenstock it is estimated that among those islets studied the greatest destruction was on Mejatto and northern Jaluit, both islets on the eastern reef, where 70 to 90 per cent of the trees were either completely uprooted or snapped off below the crown; while the least destruction was on western islets, where only 20 to 50 per cent were uprooted or snapped off. As for the comparative resistance of different tree species to the wind, Fosberg observes that *Pemphis, Cordia, Calophyllum, Casuarina,* and *Bruguiera* "perhaps stood up best," while *Pandanus,* breadfruit, and *Terminalia catappa* "perhaps fared worst."

Terrestrial fauna. Gressitt observed that there was no evidence that the storm had eliminated any terrestrial faunal species. There were, however, pronounced effects upon populations and breeding-rates, with local extinction where vegetation was eliminated. He states: "Groups which seem to have suffered most appear to be rats, soil insects, grasshoppers, and scale insects. The birds (sea and shore birds, dove, cuckoo), lizards (geckos, skinks), brackish water shrimps, amphipods, land crabs, and spiders seem to have suffered very little . . . *Culex* mosquitoes are breeding abundantly in cisterns which were inundated by sea water. House-flies and other filth flies are breeding abundantly, partly in privies as usual, and partly in some of the piles of accumulated decaying vegetation. Other insects found in the latter habitat, and under bark of dead trees, are breeding up large populations because of increase in their habitat as a result of the extensive killing and felling of trees and other plants. Still other insects, mainly moths and hemipterans, are breeding up large populations on new growth, apparently as a result of greater mortality among their parasites."

Submarine features and marine life. Banner examined the submarine conditions within the lagoon by diving to depths of 30 ft. and more in many different places. He also examined depositional materials on newly formed bars and upon the islets, with special reference to its probable derivation. It was not possible, however, to observe the submarine features along the reef front in the surge channel zone because of heavy surf conditions.

On the bottom of the lagoon below low low-tide there was no evidence of disturbed conditions. Even delicate corals were not broken. In contrast, it seems likely that the outer reef front suffered pronounced changes, at least in some sections, because more than 75 per cent of the coral rubble forming the new ocean-side bar off Jaluit Islet is comprised of materials newly wrested from the outer reef.

The storm seems to have had no great effect upon the fish life in the lagoon. The inhabitants report better fishing since the storm than there was before; but it is possible that they gain this impression through having to fish more intensively than before, since vegetable food is in short supply.

Demography and cultural effects. Fourteen Marshallese died in the storm. Two more died of exhaustion immediately thereafter. This toll was surprisingly light considering the fact that there were some 1,200 inhabitants living on the atoll when the storm struck.

The low fatality-rate was the result of three factors. Imroj, the most densely populated islet, was not completely under water. Further, about 150 natives of Mejatto happened to be visiting Imroj for a social event when the storm waves swept their islet. And the natives on Jaluit Islet were able to take refuge in sturdy Japanese, cement-block buildings that were the only structures to withstand the storm.

On islets not under water, nearly all habitations were destroyed. Buildings made of board and corrugated iron blew apart. Native buildings, of grass, fibre and pandanus, blew down; but according to informants these were readily pushed back up, reinforced, and thus re-established after the storm.

Many of the inhabitants on the eastern, inundated islets have been forced to move to Imroj. Already, however, a few are beginning to move back home. Great quantities of supplementary food are being supplied by the U. S. Trust Territory Government, and these supplies will have to continue for a long time. Though replanting is taking place and though new vegetation is sprouting from vegetative debris, it will doubtless be at least a decade before the atoll has really recovered. Meanwhile, it is planned to re-study the atoll at intervals to learn how an atoll recovers from a typhoon strike.

CHAPTER 7

PACIFIC EQUATORIAL CURRENTS, SWELLS, AND WAVES

On May 8, 1949, a bottle was tossed up on the shores of Likiep Atoll, Marshall Islands. It contained a note indicating that it had been thrown into the sea June 30, 1948, from a tuna-fishing boat 30 miles east of Guadalupe Island, Mexico. In 10 months and 8 days the bottle had drifted 4,500 miles (Feeney, 1952, p. 163). This incident merely illustrates the well-known phenomena of large-scale oceanic water circulation, in this case, the north Pacific equatorial current. It is also well known that associated with this current are the easterly tradewinds and that a corresponding current and wind are found south of the equator. The complete picture, however, is quite complicated, as is illustrated by the following incident.

In 1910 an adventuring traveler attempted to sail from Washington Atoll, about 5° north of the equator, to Makin Atoll in the Gilbert Islands slightly to the south and about 1,800 miles to the west. Following advice he first headed south across the equator to pick up an easterly wind. When he was within about 170 miles of his destination, he recrossed the equator northward. Here, however, the light wind failed him and was replaced by a westerly wind. He also encountered a 1½-mile-an-hour eastward-moving current which caused him to drift eastward at the rate of 30 miles in 24 hours on the average for a distance of about 700 miles, until he reached the vicinity of Baker Island. He then gave up the idea of going westward and sailed south again to get into the westward drift. Ultimately he arrived at Nonouti Atoll in the Gilberts. During this period, in the vicinity of Baker Island, he came upon a boat with some people from Nonouti. They had started for the adjacent atoll of Tabiteuea 20 to 30 miles southeast but their boat was caught during the night by the same eastward-moving current and carried far from their goal (Burnett, 1910, pp. 62–7). The significant effects of the equatorial oceanic circulation upon the atoll inhabitants are indicated by such an incident. What gives rise to this circulation, what patterns do the currents form, and what other effects do they have on man's habitat and environment on coral atolls? These questions are examined below.

Origin and nature of the Pacific equatorial circulation.

Ocean currents arise from wind friction upon the surface that produce wind drift and from differences in water densities that are brought about by differences in temperature or salinity or both. Dense water sinks to form convection currents that tend to mix the water until a homogeneous layer is achieved. At the surface the density decreases upon heating or upon the addition of large amounts of fresh water—rain or melting ice. Where intensive cooling occurs, as in the far north, vertical currents will penetrate to greater depths, until it has reached water of similar density. In the open ocean the temperature of the water on the surface is so high in low and middle latitudes that the density remains low, even where evaporation is high and salinity is high. In these latitudes, therefore, convection currents are limited to relatively thin layers near the surface. Sinking of water is characteristic of cold, high-latitude regions, thus filling the deep parts of the ocean with cold dense water, but sinking is not limited to the high latitudes. It occurs also where currents converge. Conversely, upwelling occurs both on the eastern oceanic regions, where trade winds carry the surface water westward, and at those zones in which there are diverging currents. Thus cold water along the equator in the western Pacific does not represent a continuation of the Peru Current but is due to a divergence along the equator within the south equatorial current (Sverdrup, 1942, p. 192).

In their essential features the surface currents of the ocean pursue the same courses as the winds that drive them but as a rule are more stable (McEwan, 1921, p. 495). Several authoritative books on oceanography cited in this report describe the current systems of the Pacific as a whole and discuss their origins. No attempt will be made to review the aspects outside the equatorial zone of relevance to the present discussion. In the trade-wind and equatorial-trough regions, the trade winds create a broad current flow westward with a velocity of about 1 mile an hour. This flow has a breadth of some 3,000 miles (Figs. 60 and 61). In the west the flow divides into two general streams, the north and south equatorial currents, which curve away from the equator in a northwesterly and a southwesterly current, respectively. In general, the westward-moving stream as a whole is displaced northward rather than being centered along the geographical equator. The south

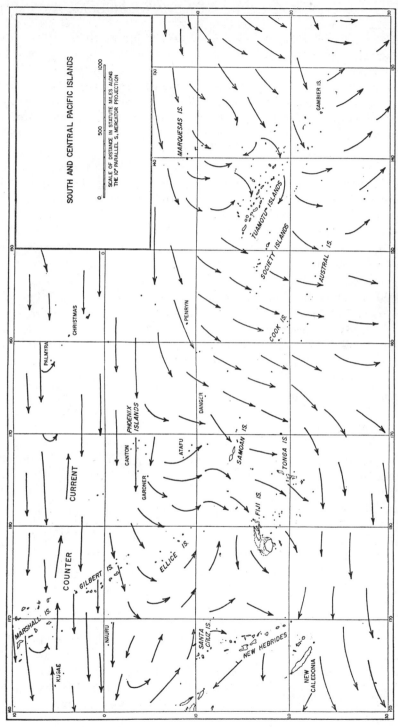

SOUTH AND CENTRAL PACIFIC ISLANDS

SCALE OF DISTANCE IN STATUTE MILES ALONG
THE 10° PARALLEL S. MERCATOR PROJECTION

0   500   1000

Fig. 61. Ocean-surface currents in south and central Pacific islands during February and March. [After Sverdrup (1942).]

Pacific equatorial drift extends southward as far as 20 to 25°S with the southernmost limits toward the eastern side of the ocean. In the north Pacific, the equatorial drift extends to about 25°N on the eastern side of the ocean and to about 20°N as the Asiatic islands are neared. The equatorial current is very strong in places; the southern current generally is the strongest. At times and at certain sections it may reach a velocity of 4 knots. The northern current may have velocities of 12 to 40 miles per day (U. S. Navy, 1952, p. 19). In the middle of the equatorial current a little north of the equator and corresponding to the zone of calms is the north Pacific equatorial countercurrent, which arises from the impinging of the main current on the land masses to the west (Fig. 61) and attains its maximum velocity in summer. In the eastern equatorial parts of the Pacific, the cold California Current and the cold Peru (Humbolt) Current converging near the equator from higher latitudes move westward with the general drift, adding water that is colder than the neighboring water by about 20°F (McEwen, 1921, p. 491). This inhibits reef coral growth in those parts of the eastern Pacific affected by cold water until, through intermixing and warming by the sun, a temperature above 64°F is reached, when reef corals can flourish.

The south equatorial current is present on both sides of the equator and extends to about 5°N. Among the island groups of the South Pacific the equatorial current is very irregular. East of the Tuamotu group the southern part of the current appears to turn off southward (U. S. Navy, 1952, p. 20). The north equatorial current, on the other hand, remains always in the Northern Hemisphere. There appears to be an "equatorial front" separating dense upwelled water near the equator from water of lesser density found generally in the surface layer of the south equatorial current. Horizontal convergence and sinking are apparently associated with this front, but the front does not coincide with the boundary of the equatorial countercurrent (Cromwell, 1953, p. 212).

According to a generalized diagram of ocean currents during February and March (Fig. 61), the north Pacific countercurrent flows eastward past Tobi and Sonsorol Atolls in the western Carolines, between Nukuoro and Ponape in the eastern Carolines, and between Ebon and Jaluit in the Southern Marshalls. A current-drift study during the period March to August 1946 indicated that at this time the north Pacific countercurrent was just south of Majuro and Arno in the southern Marshalls (Barnes, Bumpus, and Lyman, 1948, p. 875). "The boundaries of the equatorial countercurrent are located at about 2½°N. and 11°N. at the surface of the upper mixed layer and at approximately 1° and 11°N. at the bottom of the upper mixed layer." There appears to be a widening of the north Pacific countercurrent with depth, with portions of this countercurrent underlying the equatorial current (Yoshida, Mao, and Horrer, 1953, p. 116). One authority stated that more than one east-flowing current is indicated by his oceanic data, but that "The dynamic calculations indicate a major countercurrent with its northern boundary near 10½°N and 9°N" (Cromwell, 1953, p. 201).

The north Pacific countercurrent always lies north of the equator, but is farther north during the northern summer. Sometimes this countercurrent almost reaches the equator (U. S. Navy, 1952, p. 19). It has a general speed of about 1 knot but is higher in the northern summer and at this time may reach a speed of as much as 2 knots (Sverdrup, 1942, pp. 193–4). The velocity varies considerably within the system; the highest, about 2 knots, was found in March and August of 1946 to occur at the southern edge of the eddies associated with it, that is, at about latitudes 2 to 4°N. Earlier (1933 through 1941) Japanese surveys indicated the southern edge at between 4 and 6°N (Mao and Yoshida, 1955, p. 649). The north Pacific countercurrent is distinctive in that horizontal velocities are virtually constant with depth in the stirred layer (Yoshida, Mao, and Horrer, 1953).

Joseph L. Reid, Jr., of Scripps Institute of Oceanography (1960, 749–50), analyzed the South Pacific current systems and predicted that between 5 and 10 degrees south of the equator there would be found an eastward-flowing current that is the mirror image of the North Equatorial Countercurrent. During the last three months of 1960 the Institute's vessel Horizon carried an expedition to the oceanic areas off the coasts of Peru and Chile. This expedition confirmed the existence of a South Pacific Countercurrent with a flow about 300 miles wide. Its rate of movement was not as strong as that in the North Pacific, but it was powerful enough to drive the ship well to the east of her course (Pacific Science Association, 1961, 10).

Two other new Pacific equatorial currents of great significance and interest were discovered in the 1950's. One, an east-flowing current, is called the Cromwell Current after its discoverer, Townsend Cromwell, who found it in 1952 while making oceanographic studies on the Fish and Wild Life Service vessel Horizon. In 1958 the Dolphin expedition confirmed the discovery and traced it for 3,500 miles eastward from the Marquesas Islands. The core of the Cromwell Current at 140°W Longitude was found at a depth of 300 feet. The current layer is about 700 feet thick and 250 miles wide and flows opposite and underneath the west-flowing equatorial drift. Its speed averages 3 knots, as compared with the opposite surface stream which has a speed of 1 knot, and it transports about 30 million cubic meters of water per second, about equal to that of the Florida Current. Thus this subsurface "river" is as strong as a thousand Mississippi Rivers. Eastward the core of the current rises gradually until near the Galapagos Islands it is only about 140 feet beneath the surface. It disappears east of these islands. The Dolphin expedition located a second new current, a weak one flowing west beneath the Cromwell Current. Viewed in vertical profile, then, there are at least three current layers, two moving westward, with the Cromwell Current sandwiched between flowing eastward in the same direction as the surface north Pacific countercurrent (U. S. Navy, 1958).

That still other currents may exist beneath these is indicated by the discovery by the research staff of the Soviet oceanographic research ship *Vityaz* of a current with a velocity of about 43 feet per second or about 3 miles per hour at a depth of 33,280 feet in an undisclosed part of the Pacific. The Soviet discoveries included the location of a depth near the Marquesas of some 35,800 feet, so the current may possibly have been in this area (*The New York Times,* 1958a, p. 27). Hitherto, it had been thought that bottom currents were extremely slow, although ripple marks on sediments at depths as great as 750 fathoms were photographed on Sylvania guyot at Bikini (Menard, 1952, pp. 3–9).

The convergences and divergences of the ocean currents produce certain complexities in the generalized surface patterns. Theoretically, the countercurrent has been supposed to move with a transverse spiraling movement, with ascending water at its northern boundary and descending water on its southern side. Thus water is carried from the northern to the southern boundary on the surface and is carried back at depths between 160 and 640 feet. Similarly, in the equatorial drift westward, between the equator and the north Pacific countercurrent, the surface water appears to move from the equator toward the countercurrent, but at depths estimated to be between 320 and 480 feet. There is a region of divergence and upwelling in the equatorial zone (Sverdrup, 1942, pp. 193–5; Cromwell, 1953, p. 201) and, according to Sverdrup, also at about 10 to 12°N. However, the *Horizon* researchers reported that the surface flow of the equatorial countercurrent was almost entirely from west to east and that there was no appreciable north-south component to this movement (Yoshida, Mao, and Horrer, 1953). Cromwell (1953, p. 201) stated that there is no evidence to support Sverdrup's suggestion that there is upwelling at the boundary between the north equatorial current and the north Pacific countercurrent.

The north equatorial current branches off well before reaching the western boundary of the ocean, mainly to the north into the Japan Current, but also southward to feed the north Pacific countercurrent (Fig. 61). The strength of these flows varies with the season and depends upon whether the Asiatic monsoon winds are with or against them. The south equatorial drift (Fig. 60) is not so well developed as the one in the north Pacific and is also not as well known. Since more than half the equatorial drift is in the Northern Hemisphere, there is less warm surface water to move eastward in the Southern Hemisphere, and what does move eastward in southerly latitudes is merged with the Antarctic cold-water drift (Blair, 1942, p. 72). According to the Australian Pilot (U. S. Navy 1920), the southeast trade wind causes a north-going current which varies in strength from 1 to 2½ knots. During the summer months in the Southern Hemisphere this wind is spasmodic and may be replaced by a wind from a northerly direction, causing for a time a south-flowing current. However, the southeast winds have the prevailing influence, as indicated by the effects of currents in the formation of horseshoe-shaped reefs in the Great Barrier Reef in the path of the southeasterlies (Orr, 1933, p. 40).

Upon the pattern of the larger general flows are superimposed irregular currents due to changing winds and, furthermore, "eddies which are characteristic of the currents themselves and independent of wind action. A synoptic picture of actual currents can, therefore, be expected to be highly complicated" (Sverdrup, 1954, p. 503). Thus there appear to be large-scale horizontal eddies between 4 and 10°N, corresponding to the northern boundary of the countercurrent, each of which has an approximate radius of several hundred miles. "The size of these eddies seems to increase with depth and a large part of the territory of the countercurrent at upper levels is occupied by horizontal eddies at mid-depth" (Mao and Yoshida, 1955, p. 649). One of the most important of these is the cyclonic eddy (or several eddies) at the northern boundary of the countercurrent system between 6 and 10°N. Although the cause of these eddies still is uncertain, it is probable that eddies are generated by cutoff from the meandering current system and by disturbances caused by bottom topography, islands, or steady or unsteady meteorological conditions. Of these the predominance of the effects of the Marshall Islands is considered most probable (Mao and Yoshida, 1955, p. 654).

It has long been held that the limit of depths of currents resulting from wind drift has been about the so-called depth of "frictional influence," 650 feet. However, this limit may not be accurate, according to a theoretical study (Hidaka, 1955, pp. 208–9) which concluded that wind-driven currents can penetrate into a layer several hundred meters deep. "This implies that the motion of water in most parts of the oceanic troposphere could be produced by the stresses of the permanent wind system prevailing over the oceans." If this theory is accepted, previous computations on the volume of water movement in the westerly drift and in the north Pacific countercurrent may have to be revised. It was estimated from the Carnegie data that at about 160°W the volume transport of the north Pacific equatorial current above a depth of 1,000 meters is about 45 million cubic meters per second, approximately equal to the maximum transport of the corresponding current in the Atlantic (Sverdrup, 1954, pp. 718–9). The Carnegie section indicates transport to the east by the equatorial Pacific countercurrent of approximately 25 million cubic meters per second, comparable to that of the Florida Current. Surface observations seem to indicate that the volume transported is less in the western part of the ocean and that additional water is drawn into the current as it crosses the Pacific (Sverdrup, 1954, p. 711).

Local currents among the Pacific island groups

Near the islands the ocean currents sometimes are deflected and always are accelerated. Tidal currents in the western reef openings of atolls and barrier reefs usually are very strong and may not reverse with the tide. A heavy swell may throw so much water over the reef into the lagoon that there may be a constant set of the current out of the western openings and at times across the fairways. All these facts need to be considered when navigating among the islands (U. S. Navy, 1952, p. 21).

Currents among the six atolls of the Ninigo group appear to be influenced by the wind, with a little deflection near the islands. The average rate is reported to be about 1.25 knots (U. S. Navy, 1952, p. 212).

Aspects of the ocean currents in the Marshalls vicinity have been mentioned earlier. In general the currents vary from $\frac{1}{2}$ to $1\frac{1}{2}$ knots and set westward in the northern Marshalls and eastward in the southern Marshalls. When the northeast winds are strong, the westerly current is most strong between Likiep and Wotje Atolls. The easterly current is strongest between Mili and Ebon. North of Aur Atoll the north Pacific countercurrent is felt little (U. S. Navy, 1952, p. 214).

In the Caroline Islands the ocean currents are rather irregular because of the obstructing atolls, islands, and banks, as well as because of the monsoon drifts. This irregularity appears most marked and is considerable between 7 and 8°N (U. S. Navy, 1952, p. 256). This irregularity also is notable between the equator and 7°N, for the conflicting movements of the westward drift here meets the turn of the countercurrent, and these are complicated by the seasonal changes of the monsoon drifts (Fig. 60). This situation is illustrated by the experiences of several ships traveling between Ponape and the atoll of Kapingamarangi. In the course of the voyage of a German scientific expedition to Kapingamarangi in January 1910, the expedition ship *Peiho* was driven 15 nautical miles to the east of its course. Captain Blanc of the *S.S. Roque,* on which the writer traveled to Kapingamarangi in 1954, stated that while traveling south from Ponape to the atoll in August he had set his course for a point about 18 miles to the east of the atoll to compensate for the expected prevailing westward drift. However, a change of the current to the opposite direction, unknown to him, had brought him 32 miles off course to the east. On the other hand, the local atoll trading schooner, which had left Ponape at the same time as the *Roque* but which traveled much more slowly, had drifted far off course westward. As a result it lost its way and wandered westward and then northward, reaching Puluwat Atoll. It then managed to work its way back to Ponape 49 days after leaving the island (Wiens, 1956, p. 21).

In the western part of the Carolines and in the vicinity of the Palaus, the ocean currents also are variable, running with velocities of 1 to 1½ knots. South of the Palau group an easterly set prevails. East of the group the current is generally reported to be southerly, although an east or northeast current sometimes occurs. North of the group a westerly set prevails, while west of the group, reports have told of northwest and north currents (U. S. Navy, 1952, p. 303). Currents around the Palau Islands obviously are very confusing. As these reports are from different periods and not synoptic, a clear pattern cannot be discerned, although the chart shown in Fig. 60 is supposed to be accurate.

Among the large number of islands in the Tuamotu group the currents can be expected to be somewhat irregular. However, during settled weather and a steady southeast trade wind, the surface water moves westward at a rate of from 5 to 25 miles a day. From October to March, which is the rainy season, westerly winds and squalls are frequent, and the currents vary most at this season. Occasionally the currents may set eastward with a velocity of ½ to 2 knots (U. S. Navy, 1952, 3, p. 2).

The Gilbert group lies in a region in which the equatorial current begins to change its direction and to develop as the equatorial countercurrent. Thus the currents in the vicinity of the Gilberts are very irregular. At times easterly currents may be experienced with a velocity of 2 to 3 knots, although in general, the currents set westward, with a velocity of 3 to 4 knots (U. S. Navy, 1952, 3, p. 7). The former occurrence is most likely to take place with the southward shift of the countercurrent.

The Phoenix Islands lie squarely in the path of the westerly drift and the offshore currents here are generally westward, although their strength and direction varies with the wind. The usual velocity is about 1 knot, and the maximum not more than 2 (U. S. Navy, 1952, 3, p. 320).

Temperature and chemical character of sea water in relation to currents

In the trade-wind regions evaporation is very great and the salinity of the surface water is high. From these regions a vast quantity of water is thus removed and carried as vapor to be precipitated in the polar regions north and south of the equator and on continental and mid-latitude ocean areas as well. The highly saline surface water of the trade-wind zones drift westward and thence poleward in the two hemispheres until by reduction in temperature, the density becomes greater than that of the surrounding waters. According to Littlehales (1921, p. 499),

The systematically varying distribution of salinity and temperature giving rise to a systematic distribution of density or heaviness of the waters, is one of the basic factors in the sub-surface or inner circulation of the ocean, causing a systematic descent from the surface of the heavier waters which characterize the polar borders of the temperature zones, and a slow movement thence of the deeper waters, entirely distinct from the oscillations of the mass of the ocean set up by seiches and tides, both toward the equator and toward the pole in the south Pacific and toward the equator in the north Pacific, where ascending currents rise from the depths. The characteristics of this system of circulation may be interpreted by profiles showing the distribution of temperature in the depths and confirmed by profiles showing the distribution of oxygen in the depths. In the former the isothermal lines show a pronounced downward trend in the polar borders of the temperate zones and a pronounced upward trend in the equatorial regions; and in the latter it is evident that the waters in the depths of the ocean in the equatorial regions have been much longer out of contact with the atmosphere than the waters of temperate latitudes which, descending from recent contact with the atmosphere, contain by absorption about three times as much oxygen as the deep equatorial waters which have ascended from the depths as the close of the long circuit of the bottom waters towards the equator.

"Some oceanographers think that the bottom current takes a thousand years to travel from the poles to the equator, but that is not certainly so" (Graham, 1956, pp. 487–9).

The general aspect of the water character associated with circulation features produces regional peculiarities which in the Marshall Islands region occur in the area of the large eddies, between about 5 and 10°N. Here, with the exception of the surface temperature, the most outstanding feature of the distribution of temperature and salinity for the upper 250-to-300-meter layer is the appearance of a band of low temperature and low salinity.

The primary causes of this outstanding feature are thought to be
a. High precipitation.
b. Absence of saline Tropical Water tongues from either north or south.
c. Ascending of the North Intermediate Water mass with decreasing latitude, thus enabling the cool and fresh water associated with this water mass to come up to a level which in all other areas is occupied by warm and saline (northern and southern) Tropical Water masses.
d. Upwelling associated with mean current (Defant, 1936; Yoshida and others, 1953).
e. Upwelling associated with cyclonic eddies (Uda, 1940; 1949; 1952).

It is reasonable to assume that both types of upwelling originate at some intermediate depth, thus bringing cool and fresh water into the upper levels. The pushing and ascending of both the northern and southern Intermediate Water masses may further strengthen this upwelling (Mao and Yoshida, 1955, p. 669).

Data taken during the Great Barrier Reef Expedition (Orr, 1933, p. 61) showed that the surface water down to a depth of about 160 feet on the ocean outside the Barrier Reef was essentially the same as that inside the lagoon. The only important difference was that the outside water was somewhat more saline, especially during the rainy season, when fresh water mixed with the shallow lagoon water. However, an abrupt change took place in almost all the conditions between 160 and 320 feet; salinity rose, temperature fell, pH value and oxygen saturation fell, and the proportion of phosphate and nitrate rose. The discontinuity layer remained at the same depth both in the rainy and dry season, indicating little effect of surface mixing on the lower layer. The above changes all continued except for salinity to the greatest depth sampled, about 2,000 feet. Below 300 to 600 feet, however, salinity showed a decrease.

In general, salinity of the surface waters over the tropical Pacific does not vary more than 1.5 grams per thousand grams of sea water. The coral reef realm north of the equator averages about 1 gram per thousand lower in salinity than the reef realm of the south Pacific. The Tuamotu area waters have especially high salinity. During the northern summer, for instance, the waters around the Marshall and Caroline Islands have a salinity of about 34.5 per thousand as compared with that around the Tuamotus, which has over 36 per thousand. The lowest salinities appear to be associated with the countercurrent regions.

Surface-water temperatures during the northern summer average between 0.5 and 1.0°C. higher in the Marshalls and Carolines than in the Tuamotus (26°C., as compared with 25 or 25.5°C.), but are about the same as in the Ellice Islands south of the equator. During the southern summer, surface waters are about the same in the Marshalls and Carolines and in the Tuamotus (about 27°C.). The waters around the Gilbert and Ellice Islands at this time appear to be 0.5 to 1.0°C. warmer.

Effects of ocean currents in the equatorial regions

The effects of equatorial ocean currents are more dramatic and more destructive in the eastern sectors of the Pacific, where cold currents from upwellings and from higher latitudes shift seasonally and vary in extent from year to year, bringing climatic changes affecting the adjacent continental areas and islands and often resulting in the death of millions of fish and other marine organisms, which in turn reduces the marine bird population and their guano accumulations. In the western Pacific the biological effects of equatorial currents are felt more importantly in higher latitudes outside the equatorial region but also are very significant in the equatorial region. In the contact zone between cold and warm currents, where convergences and divergences occur, a temperature situation arises that is liable to prove fatal to large numbers of organisms in the different water masses.

The water becomes too cool for those accustomed to living in the warm current and too warm for those accustomed to living in the cold waters. Thus all along the contact zones there is a constant drifting of dead organisms to the bottom, where they provide food for the animals in the deeps (Moore, 1921, pp. 529–30).

Cromwell (1953, p. 209) stated that

Graham (1941), using Carnegie data, has shown plankton population near the equator which he attributes to upwelling. Our results are in good agreement with this idea . . . The plant and animal life that is dependent on the meridional circulation just described should exhibit certain additional features in its distribution.

Following the introduction of nutrients into the euphotic zone, e.g., by upwelling near the equator, phytoplankton and then zooplankton would be expected to increase. If the current near the equator has a northward component, as during southeast tradewinds, the plankton will be displaced northward. In general, the maximum zooplankton concentration would be expected somewhere between the region of nutrient enrichment and the zone of horizontal convergence, the magnitude of the displacement northward being dependent on the time rate of zooplankton increase relative to the rate of flow northward. If this flow is relatively rapid, the zooplankton may be carried to the zone of horizontal convergence north of the equator or, if a front exists, to the convergent zone south of the front. Due to its ability of directed vertical swimming, the motile zooplankton can maintain its level against the slight downward flow associated with horizontal convergence and will tend to concentrate in the convergent zone.

From the above paragraphs it would appear that the marine food is enriched both by the destructive effects of temperature change and by the concentrative effect on zooplankton of the currents in the convergence zone north of the equator.

Data from a study of zooplankton abundance in the central Pacific by J. E. King and J. Demond have been presented in histogram form (Fig. 62) by Cromwell (1953, p. 210) who pointed out that "Apparently the maximum zooplankton concentration is related to the equatorial upwelling. Although the peak abundance occurs at the equator, the bulk of the plankton is displaced a little toward the north, which is consistent with the proposed meridional circulation." This appears to be substantiated by the striking abundance of large fish, particularly of yellowfin tuna (*Neothunnus macropterus*) north of the upwelling (Fig. 63). Cromwell concluded that generally, in that part of the central Pacific over which southeast trade winds blow, the greatest catches occur north of the equator in the region of convergence.

Although an absence of data precludes the discussion of the effects of nutrients borne by deep currents on fish life in the depths, an indication of the possibilities that await investigation in the equatorial Pacific is given

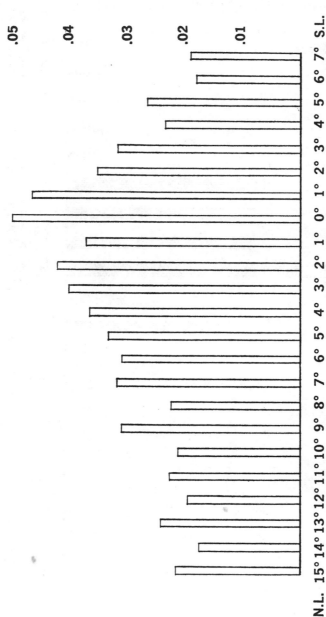

Fig. 62. Latitudinal abundance of zooplankton: millimeters of zooplankton per cubic meter of sea water netted from eleven crossings of the equatorial currents between 140°W and the 180th meridian. Data combined grossly, without regard for longitude or season. [From Cromwell (1953).]

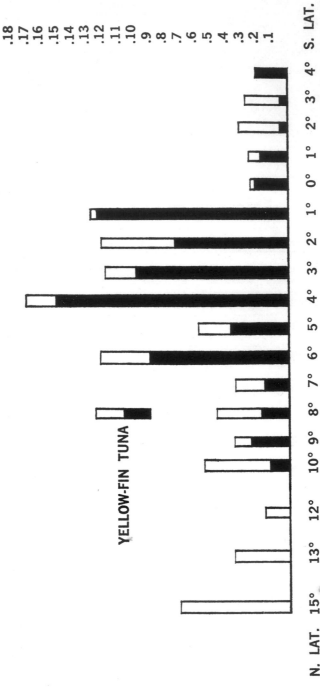

YELLOW-FIN TUNA

N. LAT. 15° 13° 12° 10° 9° 8° 7° 6° 5° 4° 3° 2° 1° 0° 1° 2° 3° 4° S. LAT.

.18
.17
.16
.15
.14
.13
.12
.11
.10
.9
.8
.7
.6
.5
.4
.3
.2
.1

Fig. 63. Abundance of fish per 100 hooks set along 150° longitude, as indicated by catching rate during Smith Cruise II across the Pacific equatorial currents. [From Cromwell (1953).] Black bars indicate the proportion of yellow-fin tuna.

by the comment of a Japanese oceanographer who with Lt. Comdr. George Houot of the French Navy in June 1958 descended to 6,000-foot depths in a bathyscaphe off the Japanese coast. The Japanese scientist reported seeing large numbers of horse mackerel and sardines between 1,500 and 6,000 feet depths and considered these lower regions a rich potential fishing ground not yet exploited. Normally fishing activities are restricted chiefly to depths not greater than 600 feet (*The New York Times,* 1958b, p. 45).

The upwellings associated with the countercurrent and the Cromwell Current appear to have had some unique effects in the marine history of the central equatorial regions of the Line Islands. Here atolls such as Howland, Baker, and McKean developed guano accumulations. Hutchinson (1952, pp. 21–9) stated that

The existence of bird colonies on such islands depends on the structure of the equatorial currents and the countercurrent between them . . . This pattern [of current movement on the north and south fringes of the countercurrent] implies divergences along the equator and along Latitude 11°N. Phosphate and silicate are brought to the surface in these latitudes, phytoplankton flourishes, and sea birds are more abundant in this region than anywhere else in the open Pacific. Arrhenius (1950) has obtained evidence that these divergences have remained in their present position and have contributed to a local increased biological productivity since the close of the Tertiary. During glacial periods, when the whole planetary circulation in the atmosphere was stronger, the divergences were probably more marked and the upwelling doubtless led to even greater productivity "on the line" than at present.

The distribution of postglacial phosphatization on slightly elevated atolls suggests very strongly that some climatic changes have taken place throughout the Pacific. Thus the existence of deposits under tropical forests on such places as the Purdy Islands implies a lower rainfall at the time of accumulation. "Arhenius' results are also of great interest in relation to the enormous depositions of millions of tons of phosphate rock on Nauru and Ocean Islands. These islands now lack bird colonies, but lying on the equator they are surrounded by ocean that would increase greatly in fertility if the equatorial upwelling became considerably more pronounced than today" (Hutchinson, 1952). Such increased upwellings would have occurred during periods of stronger trade winds associated with the greater vertical instability and temperature differentials of the atmosphere of the glacial periods. Fluctuations of ocean-water temperatures through several degrees is not unlikely to have occurred during the Pleistocene (Flint, 1957, p. 259), although what effects these changes might have had on the current systems is uncertain. A lowering of northern water temperatures would increase the differential between polar and tropical waters and might well increase the rate of upwelling. In any case, the glacial periods appear to have been times of maximum phosphatization.

The influence of ocean currents in the distribution of certain marine-life forms is of great importance, especially where the animals are free-swimming in their early or larval stages. Thus, in the case of the Mollusca, "Their future success in life after passing the free-swimming stage depends upon finding a suitable habitat for their subsequent existence—a habitat which would embrace all the necessary conditions of topography, temperature, salinity and food supply. It seems quite reasonable to suppose, and the insufficient data at hand indicate that the coasts washed by the great ocean currents have in the main a corresponding uniformity of temperature, salinity and food supply (plankton), the chief factors in the environment of marine animals. It, therefore, seems most reasonable to assume that it is due to the domination of these factors by the currents that we find the parallelism or coexistence of ocean currents and the faunal areas" (Bartsch, 1921, p. 508).

The widespread distribution of certain reef coral species in the Pacific without doubt is attributable to the ocean currents which carry their planulae (Yonge, 1940, pp. 384–5). In the case of the echinoderms, this also may occur in some, but on the whole their planktonic stage is too short to account for a dispersal over thousands of miles, and many of them are dispersed through drifting attached to seaweed or other floating material (Ekman, 1953, pp. 21–2). The similarity of many shallow-water-fish species in wide parts of the Pacific is partly attributable to the fact that large numbers of marine fishes deposit eggs that are lighter than the water and float. They are thus subject to the movements of the ocean currents (Moore, 1921, pp. 527–8). The current movement in the Hawaiian region of the Pacific is from the east or the northeast to the west or southwest. This is doubtless related to the observation that certain inshore fish species of Hawaii have traveled to Johnston Island, but it has not been proved that any Johnston Island species have ever got to Hawaii (Gosline, 1955, p. 479). The fact that Marshall Island shore-fish species have close affinities to the marine shore fishes of Indonesia but have a relatively distant relationship to Hawaiian shore fishes may be explained by the trade-wind drift and the countercurrent between the former areas. Between Hawaii and the Marshalls only a one-way traffic is likely (Strasburg, 1955, pp. 297–8). Similarly, the dispersal of plants by ocean currents (Safford, 1921b, pp. 535ff.) is so well known that it need not be emphasized at this point. This brief account is sufficient to indicate the very great influence of the ocean currents in the establishment of fauna and plant patterns in the Pacific. A more detailed consideration of these patterns is taken up in a later chapter.

The effect of ocean currents on atoll morphology has been discussed in an earlier chapter and is noted here only in passing as another aspect of the influence of currents. Yonge (1940, p. 378) pointed out that Wood-Jones (1912) considered that the form of Cocos-Keeling atoll was due entirely to the action of currents and that Krempf (1929) believed that atolls in the South China Sea were molded by the action of currents created by the alternating monsoons. Yonge himself had reservations on these answers. It is doubtful that the ocean currents have exercised important effects in molding the great Pacific atoll reefs, although in the case of islets or land areas on the reef, currents do influence their configuration (Fairbridge and Teichert, 1948; Orr, 1933), particularly in the case of sand cays and in the formation and changes in the shapes of sand and gravel spits.

Effects of ocean currents upon waves and swells

A contrary current decreases the lengths of waves and, because the amount of energy is not changed, makes them steeper. The periods of the waves are not altered, however, because the current decreases their velocities in the same proportion that it decreases their lengths. Following currents have the opposite effects: They increase the lengths of waves and decrease their heights. The effects of the current are proportional to its strength, whether it travels with or against the waves (Bigelow and Edmondson, 1947, pp. 53–6):

If a wave that has a period of 4.2 seconds, hence is 100 ft. long in deep water and is traveling at the rate of 13.4 knots, encounters a current flowing in the opposite direction at 2 knots [which is sometimes reached by the equatorial countercurrent], the height of the wave should theoretically be increased by a factor of 1.39 by the time a steady state was reached, but its length would be decreased to 67 ft. . . The steepness of the 100-ft. wave would very shortly be increased by about 2.07 if it ran into a contrary current of 2 knots and by 1.35 if it ran into a contrary current of only 1 knot [the ordinary speed of the countercurrent].

Steep, tumultuous waves characterize the countercurrent region, since the current runs counter to the prevailing waves built up by the trade winds. However, in the westward equatorial drift regions, the current moves with the direction of waves as a rule and the waves tend to smooth out. At times the ocean surface appears as smooth as that of a pond or has only the mildest of undulations, but when a westerly wind develops, the surface of the westward drift roughens up. During cyclonic storms and typhoons, the high seas developed by the storm winds may be decreased or increased in those sectors of the cyclone in which the winds are blowing with or against the surface current.

Aside from the overriding factor attributable to the fact that the right front quadrant of any moving typhoon piles up the highest waves, it could be expected that, in the event of a typhoon, atolls lying in the counter-current zone would meet the highest waves during the period in which they were struck by the northern component of the storm whirl. Atolls in the path of the westward drift zone would suffer the highest waves when they were struck by the southern component of the storm whirl. Complicating these factors in the case of large atolls, however, are the local obstruction and the currents created by the atoll itself, and the direction of approach of the storm, since the protection of the reef may dampen the effect of the prevailing current of the open ocean.

Ocean swells and "seas" in the equatorial Pacific

The state of the sea surface during a period affected by irregular, steep, and often high waves driven by wind, with many waves breaking their crests, is a phenomenon known as a "sea"; thus one speaks of a high sea, low sea, rough sea, or smooth sea. However, when the wind dies down or when wave trains advance out of the wind systems originating them, the individual waves of the train are termed "swells" (Bigelow and Edmondson, 1947, p. 63). "The direction in which swells advance are reminiscent not of winds at the time of observation but either of winds that blew previously or of wind systems at a distance." Swells may run at any angle with the wind. If the swell keeps coming from the same direction it may be assumed that the storm area is advancing directly toward the observer, retreating directly away, or standing still. If the swells come from a passing storm, their direction of advance will change with the direction of the storm.

Swells may run for hundreds or thousands of miles unless they are beaten down by contrary winds. Heavy swells from storms of the westerlies in high latitudes of the south Pacific may run to the shores of the Tuamotus and intermingle with the trade-wind swells. Swells from heavy storms may still run 10 to 25 feet high after traveling over 1,500 miles from their storm sources.

In general, the summer swell is most often high in those parts of the north Pacific in which the sea is most often high, and low where the sea is most often low. In summer "the swell is so seldom heavy enough to be of any practical account along the western sector of the equatorial belt of the north Pacific that such of the August reports as mention it at all there class it as 'low' more than 80% of the time, all along from the longitude of the Gilbert group westward to the Moluccas and to the southern Philippines." Of regions of considerable extent north of the equator, the region bounded by the contour that represents the presence of low swells 80 per cent of the time may be called the most pacific part of the Pacific ocean (Bigelow and Edmondson, 1947, p. 85).

Atoll effects on waves and swells

Waves are often refracted around a small island that is more-or-less round in shape, although the height of the breakers the waves produce will decrease around the shore. Although the reduction is greatest on the most protected side, the surf may be made very confused there because of the interference that often develops between the two trains of waves that meet, as they are refracted around from the two sides. According to Bigelow and Edmondson (1947, pp. 170–3),

There may be a shadow zone of quiet water in the lee of an islet, if its shores rise abruptly from water so deep that the waves then running are refracted but little as they approach it . . . The more irregular the coast of an island is, and the more abruptly it alters from place to place, the more likely it is that one can find a place . . . that will be sheltered from the surf . . . The larger an island is, the lower the surf is on its most sheltered side, as a rule, partly because the sidewise expansion of the inner ends of the wave crests is greater around it than in the case of a smaller island, but also because the interference by irregularities of the coast operating through a longer distance drains the inshore ends of the waves of their energy more effectively.

The above account of surf around islands or around promontories applies equally to coral atolls. Some small atolls, such as Nukuoro in the eastern Carolines or Ebon in the southern Marshalls, are so small and round that the swell heaves right around them during the winter when the northeast trades are strongest, and there is no effective shelter anywhere around them. On the other hand, the largeness and irregularity of Arno Atoll in the southern Marshalls, with its long northeast promontory, affords a safe and easy landing along the southerly face when the swell is coming from the northeast, although not when swells are from any other direction (Bigelow and Edmondson, 1947).

However, southwesterly gales originating hundreds of miles away in high southern latitudes may transmit heavy seas to roll against the western atoll reefs in opposition to the trade winds. When this occurs, it may be more dangerous to attempt landings on the lee than on the weather side of the Tuamotu Atolls.

Tidal waves and oscillations

Oscillations of the sea level apparently unconnected to ordinary tides or to storms have been known to occur in the Arctic. Such oscillations also were discovered to take place in the Pacific (*The New York Times*, 1957a). The tidal station at Canton Atoll reported an unaccountable change in sea level that occurs every 3.8 days. Its rise and fall is 6 or 7 inches.

More familiar are the so-called "tidal waves," which have nothing to do with tides but are swells usually associated with earthquakes in some part of the Pacific. They are better termed "tsunami," a Japanese term. Although the tectonic movement on the ocean bottom may be only slight, it generates a tremendous wave. Whereas an ordinary sea wave is rarely more than a few hundred feet long from crest to crest—no longer than 320 feet in the Atlantic or 1,000 feet in the Pacific—a tsunami often extends more than 100 miles and sometimes as much as 600 miles from crest to crest. Although a wind wave never travels more than about 60 miles per hour, in deep ocean waters a tsunami may travel over 500 miles per hour. The tsunamis are so shallow compared with their length (only 2 or 3 feet from trough to crest) that in the open ocean they are hardly noticeable. But when they approach shore, especially where the water is shallow, they build up to terrifying heights.

The giant waves usually range from 20 to 60 feet in height, but when they pour into a V-shaped inlet or harbor, they may rise to mountainous proportions (Bernstein, 1954, pp. 61–2). The shape of a section of coast exposed to them is of great significance in relation to the degree of destructiveness. This applies also to the shapes of atoll reefs facing the approach direction of tsunamis.

A tsunami is not a single wave but a train of waves separated, because of the great length of the waves, by intervals of from 15 minutes to more than 1 hour. "This has often lulled people into thinking, after the first great wave has crashed, that it is all over. The waves may keep coming for many hours. Usually the third to the eighth waves in the series are the biggest" (Bernstein, 1954, p. 62). The first wave of a tsunami generally is a sharp swell, not different enough from ordinary waves to cause alarm to the ordinary observer. "This is followed by a tremendous suck of water away from the shore as the first great trough arrives. Reefs are left high and dry."

The effects of a tsunami upon the low atolls may be very destructive. Burnett (1910, pp. 91–4) reported that "the island of Nukunau was swept some years ago by what was probably a spent tidal wave, which caused considerable loss of life." The Tuamotus occasionally also are reached by tsunamis with resultant great damage. "[The last tsunami] that flooded Raroia occurred on April 1, 1946" (Danielsson, 1955, p. 27). That storm was the same one that cost the Hawaiian Islands 159 lives and 25 million dollars in property damage (Bernstein, 1954).

The epicenter of the earthquake causing this tsunami was in the Aleutian trough near the 162° meridian W. (Shepard, MacDonald, and Cox, 1950).

This means that the tsunami originated in the Aleutians was felt destructively over 5,000 miles away in the Tuamotus.

Between 1917 and 1957, 37 seismic waves were recorded in the Pacific, 16 of them between 1950 and 1957 (*The New York Times,* 1957b). Only a few of them are very destructive, fortunately. The Hawaiian Islands are struck severely on the average of once every 25 years (Bernstein, 1954). By the same token, it is likely that the Marshall, Gilbert, Line, and many of the Caroline atolls and possibly some of the south Pacific atolls suffer varying degrees of destruction at the same times, although with diminished effect the farther away they are from the epicenters of the quakes.

The earthquakes causing the Pacific tsunamis most often appear to come from the northern or northwestern Pacific, such as the areas of Japan, Kamchatka, and the Aleutians. In 1957 (*The New York Times,* 1957b) the discovery was announced of a major crack 2 to 3 miles wide in the bottom of the Gulf of Alaska 500 to 700 feet below the 9,000-to-13,000-foot-deep ocean floor and running for 250 miles, possibly 400 miles, to intersect the Aleutian trench. It was believed that this fault may shed some light on the destructive tsunamis that sweep southward over the Pacific.

The disastrous May 1960 earthquakes on the Chilean coast produced tidal waves that caused havoc not only in Hawaii but also in Japan and New Zealand. On the western coast of Hawaii the highest waves actually reached the coast 18 hours after the initial series of waves. Shepard (*The New York Times,* 1960a) said that "It can only be supposed that the waves represented a reflection from a submarine cliff off Japan and another reflection from an escarpment in Oceania . . . The danger of possible late wave arrivals, especially on protected sides of islands, cannot be minimized." Information has not been available to the writer on the damage, if any, caused by these tsunamis on coral atolls.

Tidal phases and the development of amphidromes in the Pacific

A review of the recorded tides of the oceans shows the pattern of the phases and amplitudes of a semidiurnal and a diurnal tide. These have been shown to be intrinsically constant, and they can be plotted in the form of cotidal lines (Dietrich and Kalle, 1957, pp. 376–8). These are lines connecting all points having high or low tide at the same hour. These cotidal lines meet at a point where the tide vanishes, called an "amphidromic point" (Sverdrup, Johnson, and Fleming, 1954, p. 581).

The semidiurnal and diurnal tides brought into being by the tidal forces evolve with few exceptions into amphidromes under the influence of reflection, the Coriolis effect, and collisions or interference. These revolve in the northern hemisphere in general toward the left and in the southern hemisphere toward the right. In most cases, the form of the amphidromes are not completely symmetrical. Bands of high-tide lines appear which, in extreme cases, change to nodes. However, in the ocean there are no true or complete oscillation nodes. Instead, through the influence of collision or interference of tides with each other, certain small bands occur in which the phase of the tide comes to a sharp end within a short distance (Dietrich and Kalle, 1957).

The charts in Figs. 64 to 67 show cotidal lines and amphidromes in the Pacific. Phase transition in the form of a node occurs in the semidiurnal tides between Japan and New Guinea. In Micronesia the node is in the vicinity of Nomwin, Pulap, and Puluwat. The amphidrome near the Solomons, shown on Fig. 64, is a seminode (Dietrich and Kalle, 1957).

The distribution of the tidal rise is closely related to the cotidal lines. In the center of the amphidromes and at the nodes, the rise is almost zero. With increasing distance from these points and bands, the rise increases. This has been shown by direct observations in the Micronesian islands and was plotted by Dietrich as shown in Fig. 64. In the immediate vicinity of the nodes of the semidiurnal tides between Japan and New Guinea, between Truk and Satawan in the Carolines, the lowest known spring tide (only 16 centimeters) occurs, according to Dietrich. Westward from the node it increases steadily. At Guam it is 44 centimeters; at Ulithi it is 100; at the Palau islands it is 152. Eastward, correspondingly, it increases to 60 centimeters in the area of Satawan and Nomoluk in the Carolines, 116 at Ujelang, and 176 at Mili in the Marshalls.

The peculiarity of the distribution of rise in the center of an amphidrome is clearly shown when it lies by chance near an island. In the Solomons the spring tide rises only 12 centimeters. However, since the amphidromes for the most part occur in the regions of the open sea, the highest tides are to be expected along the continental coasts. Nevertheless, the nodes may be on the coast, as in northwestern Sumatra, where the spring tide is reduced to 18 centimeters (Dietrich and Kalle, 1957).

About 200 miles east of Malden Atoll in the southern Line Islands there is another amphidrome, and cotidal lines radiate in all directions from it. The cotidal charts are useful in describing the elevation of water bodies but, strictly speaking, only in describing a single harmonic constituent of the many that affect tides; and the only constituent for which such charts have been prepared has been the so-called "M2," or principal semidiurnal lunar constituent. The cotidal charts referred to here are of this type. They are inexact, however, especially at large distances from coasts and islands where tide observations have been made. Another difficulty is that tides not only are often estimated by crude methods, but that tide gauges are frequently located in sheltered bays or atoll lagoons, where the arrival of high water

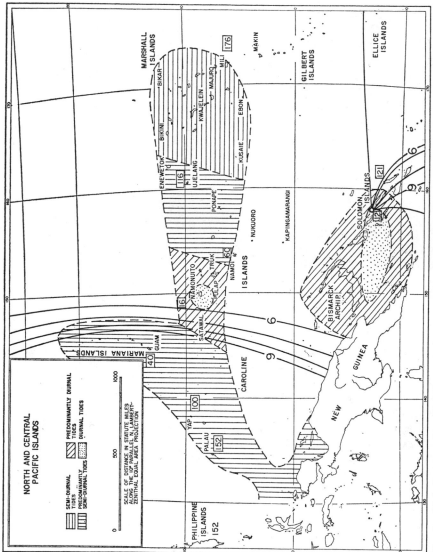

Fig. 64. Tide forms and cotidal lines of the semidurnal tides in north and central Pacific islands. Boxed numbers indicate centimeters of mean spring rise. Unboxed numbers indicate cotidal hours. [After Dietrich and Kalle (1957).]

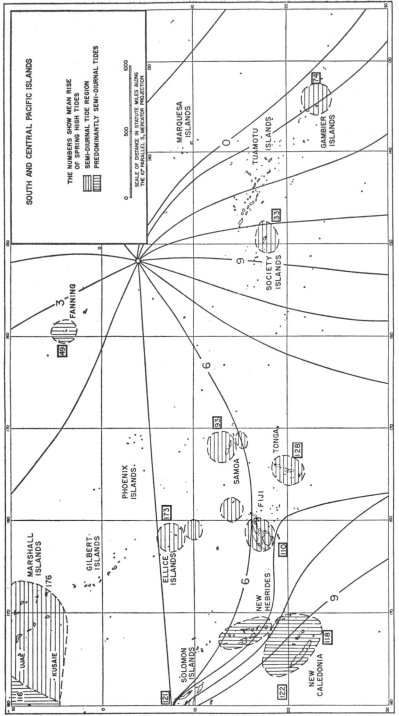

Fig. 65. Tide forms and cotidal lines of the semidurnal tides in south and central Pacific islands. Boxed numbers indicate centimeters of mean spring rise. Unboxed numbers indicate cotidal hours. [After Dietrich and Kalle (1957).]

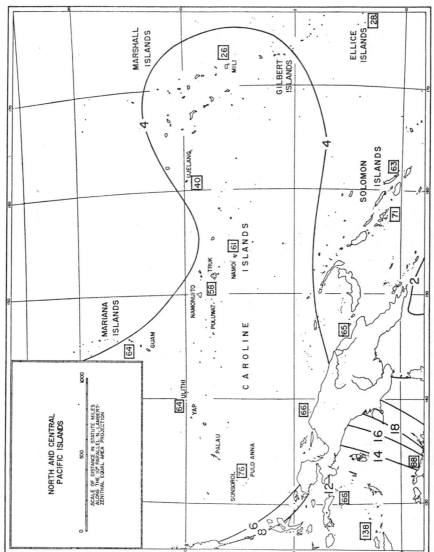

Fig. 66. Cotidal lines for diurnal flood tides for north and central Pacific islands (hours referred to Greenwich time). Boxed numbers indicate centimeters of mean spring rise. Unboxed numbers indicate cotidal hours. [After Dietrich and Kalle (1957).]

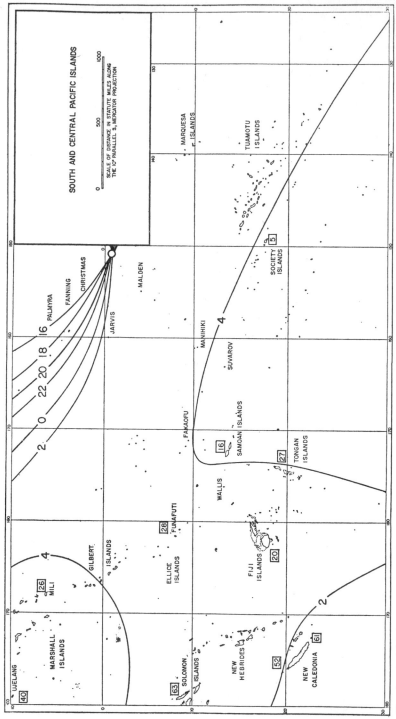

Fig. 67. Cotidal lines for diurnal flood tides for south and central Pacific islands (hours referred to Greenwich time). Boxed numbers indicate centimeters of mean spring rise. Unboxed numbers indicate cotidal hours. [After Dietrich and Kalle (1957).]

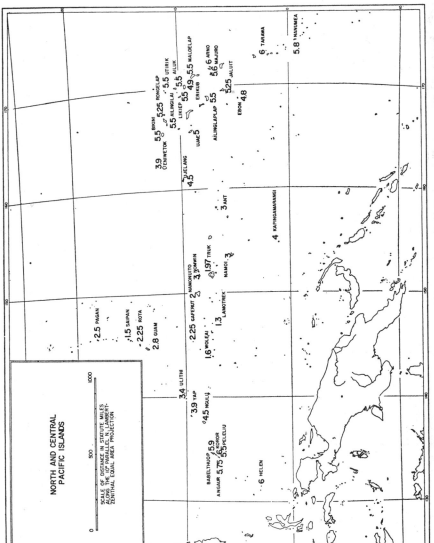

Fig. 68. Mean spring tide (in feet) in north and central Pacific islands. [From U.S. Navy (1952).]

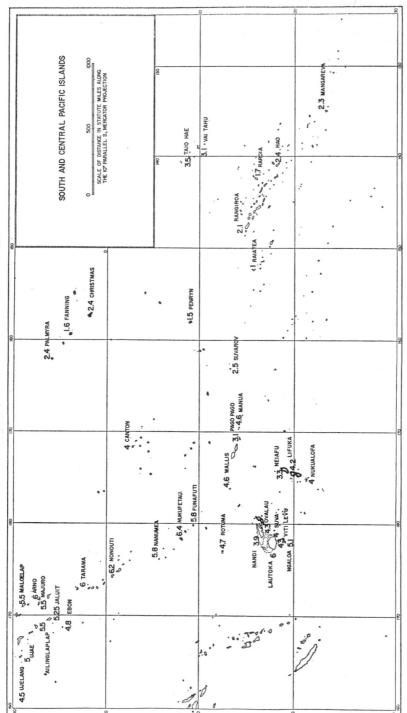

Fig. 69. Mean spring tide rise (in feet) in south and central Pacific islands. [From U. S. Navy (1952).]

may be delayed as much as several hours (Proudman and Groves, 1959, p. 201).

The charts in Figs. 68 and 69 show the height in feet of the spring tide rise, according to figures given by the U. S. Navy (1952) for various atolls and islands in the tropical Pacific. These figures do not correspond entirely with those shown by Dietrich. However, some of Dietrich's figures may have been interpolated. Moreover, there is some question of the comparability of the tide readings in all cases. Some of the figures in the sailing directions were for rises in atoll or other lagoon water levels. There are discrepancies in figures even where they refer to the same body of water. For example, for Arno Atoll the sailing directions give a spring tide rise of 6 feet and for three nearby atolls 5.5 feet. Cox (1951, p. 5) wrote concerning the tides at Arno that "An analysis of the tide records by the Coast and Geodetic Survey indicates that the mean tide range in the ocean is 3.8 feet and the spring range is about 4.1 feet. The mean water level in the lagoon is about the same as that in the ocean, but the mean tide range is 0.1 feet greater than that in the ocean. The explanation for this increase in tide range in the lagoon is not known."

According to Von Arx (1954, p. 270), while the ocean rises and falls as a simple harmonic oscillator, the lagoon surface, because of the restriction of the passes to water flow, probably oscillates through a slightly smaller amplitude than the ocean surface. McKee (1956, p. 28) found that the tide rises 6 to 13 inches higher within the lagoon at Kapingamarangi than it does on the seaward sides of the islands, probably because of the limiting constrictions of the passes through which the water moves. This may account for some of the differences in the spring tides recorded for certain places, as in the case of Erikub in the Marshalls. While the spring tide rise for Ailinglaplap in the southwest, Maloelap in the southeast, Wotje, Ailuk, and Likiep in the north and northwest all are given as 5.5 feet, or 138 centimeters, Erikub is reported to have a spring rise of 4.9 feet, or 125 centimeters. Truk also appears to have an anomalous spring tide figure when compared with Nomwin and Namonuito in the northwest and Namoi in the southeast. Of course, it is possible also that errors in recording may have occurred. As the sailing directions conclude, "The tides of the Pacific are complicated, partly due to the local conditions existing throughout the numerous islands" (U. S. Navy, 1952, p. 21).

CHAPTER 8

LAGOON CIRCULATION, TEMPERATURE, SALINITY, AND LIGHT

The physical marine influences in atoll lagoons and the immediate vicinity of reefs obviously differ from those of the open ocean. The shallower waters and enclosed circulations produce special conditions affecting marine life. These physical influences are examined in this chapter.

Lagoon water circulation

The most systematic published study that has been made of atoll-lagoon-water circulation to date is Von Arx's study of Bikini and Rongelap (1954). The following discussion, unless otherwise indicated, is paraphrased from his work. Obviously, lagoon circulations under given wind and ocean current situations would differ from lagoon to lagoon because of differences in reef configuration, lagoon depth, and the width, depth, number, and location of passes or gaps in the reef. Nevertheless, the Bikini and Rongelap examples provide significant clues to what might occur in other atoll lagoons with access to ocean water through the passes or over the reef. Figure 70 is a schematic diagram of the nature of the wind-driven overturning circulation in an atoll lagoon. Figures 71 and 72 show the generalized circulation of Bikini Lagoon in winter and that of Rongelap Lagoon during summer under east-southeast winds.

Winds, waves, tides, and the north equatorial current are the four sources of energy for driving the circulation in the lagoons. The wind is the most important in producing the water motion. During the winter, which here is the trade-wind season, the action of tides and waves accomplishes the exchange of water between ocean and lagoon. In summer, which is the doldrum season here, this is achieved by the tides and the north equatorial current. The seasonal migration of the northeast trades then leaves the northern Marshall Islands for the most part becalmed in the doldrums. This greatly modifies the lagoon circulation.

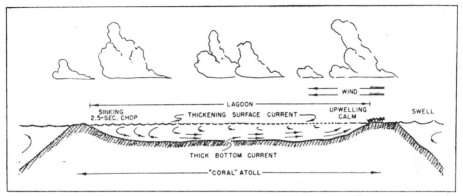

Fig. 70. Nature of wind-driven overturning circulation. Vertical exaggeration, 42 times. Length of section, 21 miles. Depth of section, 30 fathoms. [From Von Arx (1954).]

Both lagoons showed a primary and a secondary circulation pattern. The former is the overturning represented in Fig. 70. The secondary circulations are shown by the heavy arrows and the primary circulation by the light arrows in Figs. 71 and 72. The strength of both circulations was found to vary with the average wind strength recorded over the previous 24 hours. According to repeated measurements, the surface of the water on the windward seaward reef at high tide was approximately 0.5 meter, or 1.6 feet, higher than the level prevailing in the lagoon. This situation resulted in a steady head of water flowing over the reef between the islets into the lagoon at an average inward velocity of 50 centimeters per second. During the trade-wind season this is a continual flow and supplies about one-third the volume of the new ocean water added to the lagoon each day, the rest presumably being supplied through the passes or gaps in the reef. However, during the doldrum season, when the ocean swell is much reduced, this inflow becomes small or may even be reversed.

Over the leeward reefs, which are submerged, observations showed that the water transport across the reef alternates with the tides. Although the waves cross the leeward reefs, their approach after diffraction around the atoll is oblique and their energy is small. The surface wind-driven water moves predominantly westward and seaward from the lagoon, although dur-

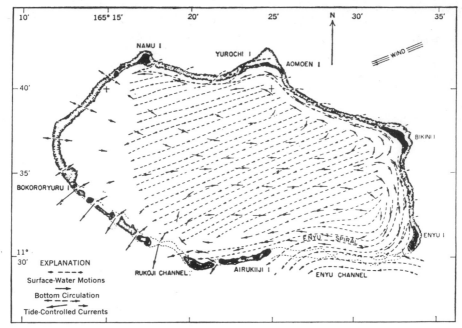

Fig. 71. Generalized circulation of Bikini Lagoon in the winter. [From Von Arx (1954).]

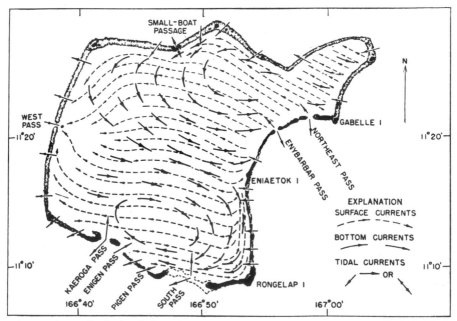

Fig. 72. Generalized circulation of Rongelap Lagoon under east-southeast winds. [From Von Arx (1954).]

ing the doldrum season this movement is slower and the tidal alternation of flow more symmetrical.

The thickness of the surface layer moving with the wind changes with the strength of the wind from 5 to 20 meters (16 to 65 feet). Its speed of movement is about 3 per cent of the average wind speed during the previous 12 hours. Characteristically, in winter a surface layer about 13 meters (43 feet) thick drifts with the wind at about 25 centimeters per second (about ½ mile per hour). During summer these values drop to an average thickness of 9 meters (29.5 feet) drifting at a speed of 15 centimeters per second (less than ⅓ mile per hour). The volume of water transported by the surface current is too large to be moved entirely over the leeward reefs, so some of it returns upwind along the bottom to form the closed circulation constituting the primary overturning circulation system illustrated in Fig. 70.

How much current movement actually takes place along the bottom of atoll lagoons depends in part upon the depth and size of the lagoons concerned. On the basis of sedimentary studies McKee (1959, p. 552) concluded that

No evidence of bottom currents in the deep parts of Kapingamarangi Atoll has been found. Relatively well defined boundaries between sedimentary belts at depths below about 90 feet indicate a general lack of mixing of their constituents. Analysis of mineral and biogenetic content of the facies belts confirm that little transportation of bottom sediments occurs; the uniform fineness of the calcium carbonate mud below 200 feet further suggests a lack of turbulence. . . . If such a circulation [as postulated by Von Arx for Bikini and Eniwetok] may be assumed to occur also in Kapingamarangi Lagoon, the lower, reverse movement does not appear to affect the bottom sediments materially, possibly because of greater depth (Kapingamarangi Lagoon is 240 feet deep and 8 miles long; Bikini is 180 feet deep and 21 miles long).

In the cases of both Bikini and Rongelap, the secondary circulation shown in Figs. 71 and 72 divides into two counter rotations, clockwise in the southern part and counterclockwise in the northern part. This sort of a pattern may very likely not apply to such elongated atolls as Namu or possibly Kwajelein, although secondary return circulations of a similar type no doubt are universal. In the case of Bikini and Rongelap, the turns at the western sectors into the body of the lagoon appear to be brought about by reef salients. With these turns, the current sinks and becomes part of the bottom current in the primary circulation system.

Although the leeward gaps at Bikini and Rongelap are direct openings to the sea and tidal currents move through them at speeds up to 150 centimeters per second (3.4 miles per hour), these tidal currents have little effect upon the lagoon circulation and the rate of its refreshment. The reason for this is that the tidal water entering through a pass does not get very far in before the tide changes and draws most of it out again. Von Arx (1954, p. 270) stated that

It is estimated that only 30 per cent of the water entering a pass on the flood tide remains in the lagoon at the completion of the ebb tide. This remainder is the quantity which was moved away from the influence of the pass by the primary lagoon circulation. On the flood tide, currents radiating from the southwestern passes were detected 5,000 meters (over 3 miles) inside the lagoon, but not all the water moving in response to the flow in the passes comes through them; hence, the radius of direct refreshment around the passes is probably somewhat less than 5,000 meters.

Intensive study from the air and from shipboard showed that the flow through Bikini's southwestern passes was 40 per cent stronger on the ebb tide than on the flood. This greater volume transport partly counteracts the continuous inflow of water over the windward reefs in winter and of the inflow from the southeastern Enyu Channel in summer. The tidal oscillation in the lagoon cannot keep step with that on the open ocean and probably oscillates through a smaller amplitude. It was found that "The turn of the current in the passes is 25 minutes later than high water in the ocean and 10 minutes later than low water in the ocean. The duration of slack water is less than 2 minutes" (Von Arx, 1954).

At Rongelap it was found that because the proportion of lagoon volume to the cross-sectional area of passes is 3.5 times greater than at Bikini, a much larger head of water occurs between the inside and outside of the lagoon during the mid-stage flood and ebb tides. This causes the water to penetrate farther into the lagoon and move in the form of a jet. The position of a pass along the leeward reef may give it unusual current flows. Thus West Pass in the middle of the west reef of Rongelap is always outflowing, probably because it is one of the chief exits for the surface water driven by the wind toward the west side of the lagoon. The current speed through this pass has been estimated at between 250 and 500 centimeters per second (5.6 to 11.2 miles per hour), and drift poles that were released as much as 5,000 meters (3 miles) on either side of this pass were drawn toward it and eventually floated out through the pass.

Volume computations indicated that during the trade-wind season about 3.8 per cent of the lagoon's volume is transported into and out of the lagoon per tidal cycle. Making due allowance for the fact that in the tidal cycle the passes exhaust about 70 per cent of the water they introduce, it is estimated that one lagoon volume is exchanged with the ocean in 39 days at Bikini. However, "This approximate value is valid only during the trade-wind season when a steady state can be assumed. Throughout the summer season no prolonged steady states exist, but it was found that the flow through the passes is reduced 50% and that over the reefs nearly 80%. The change in average wind direction from easterly to southerly occasionally forces water out of the lagoon over the northern reefs and makes Enyu Channel an important source of incoming water. It is estimated that the summer average exchange rate is approximately half of the winter rate" (Von Arx, 1954, p. 272). The situation at Rongelap was found to be remarkably similar to that at Bikini.

McKee (1959, p. 551) also found that the southern reef channel or pass affects sedimentation significantly and thus indicates the influence of the current movement into the lagoon from the ocean. This current is shown by a calcium carbonate silt-and-sand tongue extending lagoonward from the channel for about a mile. The type of sediment represented in the tongue has a different character from the bottom sediments in most other parts of the lagoon and thus may be assumed to result from movement and deposition by the current coming through the channel.

Utilizing salinity data gathered after the nuclear explosion on Bikini on July 25, 1946, Ford (1949, pp. 49–54) found that with the advance of summer, evidence indicated that the influx of ocean water through Enyu Channel became a dominating feature and that the influx was not a simple flow subject to tidal fluctuations. It was found that on at least three occasions during a 3-month period there were substantial intrusions over and above the normal flow, displacing lagoon water through the southwestern passes. Ford computed that during a period of 7 days on one of these occasions, 40 per cent of the lagoon water was displaced by lower-salinity ocean water. This appears to point to changed eddy conditions in the currents of the surrounding ocean.

McKee (1959, p. 551) found that the local tidal currents bordering the islands and lagoonal longshore currents paralleling the reef at Kapingamarangi appeared to affect greatly the distribution of sediment in shallow-water areas. These currents, formed by the tides, were found to fluctuate greatly both in speed and direction from place to place, influencing the distribution of beach and bar deposits.

Lagoon and reef water temperatures

The consideration of water temperatures is important in the study of the biology of the reef and of the lagoon. In the case of the zooplankton, temperature is a prime factor because of its action directly upon the physiological processes of the animals, especially upon the rate of metabolism and the reproductive cycle. The rate of metabolism may be increased two or three times for each 10° rise, within favorable limits. Indirectly, temperature operates through its influence on other environmental factors, such as gases in solution, viscosity of the water, and density distribution with all its important hydrographic implications (Sverdrup, Johnson, and Fleming, 1954, p. 843). In the diurnal migration, zooplankton may sometimes encounter a sharp gradient of temperature that may become a strong enough stimulus to prevent further ascent to the surface. Likewise, a sharp thermocline also limits the downward distribution of some surface forms.

Temperature influences are also important to the larger animals. Within the restricted temperature range found in the ocean there are temperature barriers segregating faunas into fairly well defined geographical regions of submarine climatic conditions that are controlled not only by latitude but also by depth of water and general circulation (Sverdrup, Johnson, and Fleming, 1954, p. 844). Temperature limits are much more narrow for reproductive processes and for survival of eggs and young than for the older stages. Temperature influences to a marked degree the rate at which calcium carbonate can be precipitated in the formation of shells, spicules, and skeletal matter. This is why in the tropical waters there are many marine animals that utilize calcium compounds in their supporting or protective structures. This also explains part of the reason for the exclusive occurrence in the tropical waters of coral reefs and of such giant clams as *Tridacna gigas*. The greater variety of species associated with tropical waters is another aspect of the influence of temperature conditions. "Not merely species but many general and even higher systematic groups are confined entirely, or nearly so, to the tropical region" (Sverdrup, Johnson, and Fleming, 1954, p. 867).

With these indications of the significance of temperature in marine ecology, we may proceed to examine some characteristic aspects of lagoon and reef temperature conditions. According to a study at Johnston Island by Emery (1956, p. 1514), surface-temperature measurements at 20 well-distributed stations in the lagoon showed no geographical variation. On the other hand, there was "a diurnal cycle in which the temperature of the lagoon and reef complex presented an average increase from 81.5°F at 0090 local time to 82.8°F at 1500. Temperatures of surface water in the deeper platform east and south of the islands showed a similar diurnal increase, but values were about 1°F lower. The daytime water temperatures lie in the range between daily mean and daily maximum air temperatures, 81 and 85°F, respectively."

It seems clear that while the Johnston example may fairly represent the more open lagoons or the deeper and larger lagoons, quite different water temperatures may characterize small, shallow, and completely enclosed atoll lagoons, just as temperatures in shallow reef tide pools show higher temperatures. For a shallow lagoon such as that of Onotoa (maximum depth about 8 fathoms), Cloud (1952, p. 35) found the temperature of the lagoon ranging from 23.5°C. (74°F.) just before daybreak to 34°C. (93°F.) at mid-day.

Characteristic water-temperature conditions on the Raroia reef and in the tide pools may be seen in the following excerpt from Doty and Morrison (1954, p. 3):

Water, in early July, coming in over the [windward eastern] reef edge in the morning was near, or a little below, 26°C [79°F]. Twenty meters inshore, in an incurrent area the water would be between one-half and one degree warmer and this warming of the water continued into the outer edge of the pool zone where the maximum temperatures were observed. In this case, they could be expected to be in the order of a degree and a half warmer than those obtained at the sea's edge.

Toward the inshore edge of the pool zone, the temperatures were measured in rills of water running out from the island conglomerate. In one case the temperature of a small pool near high tide line, but connected to the channel of the pool zone, was 29°C [84°F] in its central part; the inner edge, where the water was about 1 inch deep, was 27.8°C [82°F], and with the bulb just covered in a sandy incurrent rill of water running into the pool from under the island conglomerate the temperature was 27°C [80.5°F] . . .

As the channel along the inshore edge of the pool zone was followed toward the excurrent area, typically the temperature of the water was observed to increase in temperature about one degree. Then as the reef flat was crossed again, following the excurrent area out to the sea again, the temperature increased perhaps another degree, until at the most the temperature was about 30°C [86°F] . . . Beyond this point the repeated inwash of cooler water with each wave quickly lowered the temperature to that of the sea beyond and outside the reef.

From the above it is apparent that within short distances over the reef, temperatures change several degrees, this change being affected by the depths, currents, distance from incoming ocean water, and possibly by contact with cool fresh water draining out from the island fresh-water lens.

A study by A. G. Meyer at a reef in Torres Strait in 1918 showed that while daily temperature changes at the seaward margin have a narrow range (3.5°C., or 6.3°F.), the range increases toward shore to as much as 12.5°C., or 22.5°F. He concluded that the high temperatures experienced during part of the year must be sufficient to kill all corals within 450 feet of the shore (Wells, 1951, p. 12). A study by Wells at Arno Atoll's southwest leeward reef showed similar results. The richness of coral growth was found to be closely correlated to the temperature pattern, although Wells pointed out that water agitation and salinity conditions were also important among controlling factors. He found the fluctuation to be diurnal. Early in the morning, before the sun shines on the reef flat, temperatures across the reef are nearly uniform, but usually a degree less nearer shore than the normal 28°C. (82°F.) at the reef margin, but within a few hours temperatures near shore, even at high tide, are much higher than at the margin (Fig. 73). He also found that temperature measurements at intervals along a line more-or-less parallel to the reef margins and about 200 feet from shore showed great variation at low tide: from 28.2 to 30.9°C. (82.7 to 87.2°F.) at more-or-less regular intervals. These variations were found related to wedges of cooler water extending into the shoreward band of warm water (Fig. 74). The wedges were found to correspond with the re-entrants of the reef margin. Every wave of translation across the reef margin sent a wedge of cooler water inward.

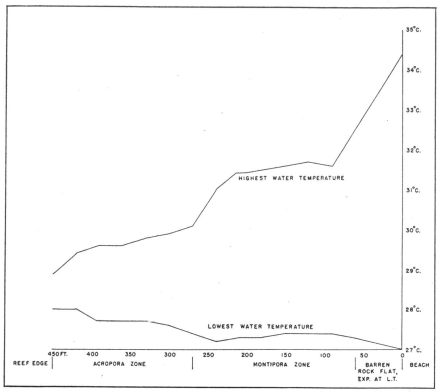

Fig. 73. Water temperatures across Ine anchorage reef, Arno Atoll, June 1950. [From Wells (1951).]

At Kapingamarangi, McKee (1959, pp. 552–4) found the summer surface water over deep areas of the lagoon to be between 29 and 30°C. (84.2 to 86.0°F.) and over patch reefs in the lagoon between 29.5 and 31°C. (85.1 to 87.8°F.). During an hour period of approaching storm followed by violent rain, the surface-water temperature dropped from 30.5 to 29°C. (86.9 to 84.2°F.). These figures compare with those for the temperature of the open sea around Kapingamarangi during summer months of 28.6 to 29.2°C. (83.3 to 84.2°F.). The lagoon surface water is 1 to 2°C. (1.8 to 3.6°F.) warmer than that of the open ocean. McKee concluded that lagoon waters here seldom drop as low as the normal of the sea, and locally may be 3 to 5°C. (5.4 to

9°F.) warmer, so that water entering the lagoon through the southern passes or over the reef probably affect both life and thermal currents.

As McKee has indicated above, the variation of water temperature from reef margin to shore also differs according to the weather. On overcast days

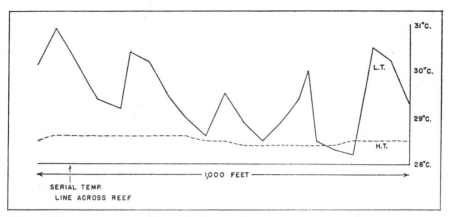

Fig. 74. Water temperatures along the inner edge of the Acropora zone, Ine anchorage reef, Arno Atoll. [From Wells (1951).]

the temperatures remain rather close to that of the ocean, but on clear days the tide-pool temperatures are far higher than at the margin. The runoff from the island fresh-water lens doubtless also tends to depress near-shore temperatures on the seaward reef. On the lagoon reef at Arno, fluctuations in temperature at low tide were found to be less pronounced because of the deeper water throughout (Hiatt, 1958).

Salinity of reef and lagoon waters

According to Sverdrup, Johnson, and Fleming (1954, p. 770), "The salinity of water is important in maintaining the proper osmotic relationship between the protoplasm of the organism and the water. The extent to which this osmotic relationship can vary depends upon the species. . . ." Corals living in the tropics have been reported to be tolerant of a 20 per cent reduction in the salinity of the water of their normal environment. Intertidal animals are subject to large fluctuations in salinity, owing to their frequent exposure to direct rains or runoff from land. At times, when low tide coincides with heavy rains, the lowered water salinity may be lethal to life on the exposed reef flats and tide pools (Sverdrup, Johnson, and Fleming, 1954, p. 840).

The salinity of lagoons obviously depends upon whether the lagoon concerned has open connections with the sea through passes or through reef tunnels or cavities, as well as to some extent upon its size and shallowness, and the amount of rainfall it normally gets. Where there are numerous openings for free exchange of water or where large increments of water come over the reef, one might expect little difference between salinity in the ocean and in the lagoon. This is substantially true, although salinity differences do occur. Research at Bikini Atoll revealed that marked salinity variations occurred within short periods of time, not only in the ocean surfaces near Bikini but also within the waters of the lagoon. A summer study at this atoll showed that during part of July the lagoon waters averaged 34.59 per cent salinity as compared with 34.30 per cent a few miles to the south of Bikini and up to 35 per cent northwest of the atoll. Within the lagoon, the highest salinity appeared to occur near the eastern reef, where upwelling of bottom water resulted from the wind-driven westward drift of surface water in the enclosed lagoon body (Ford, 1949, pp. 46–7).

In shallow lagoons especially, diurnal salinity variations take place. At Onotoa, where the lagoon is small and shallow, the range of salinity in the lagoon is 18,080 parts per million Cl^- in water coming over the reef just before daybreak and 20,680 parts per million Cl^- during the day. The pH was metered at 7.63 at midnight and 8.80 in mid-afternoon.

Some of the Line Islands lagoons are extremely saline. For instance, Arundel (1885, pp. 5–6) wrote that the ring of land on Sydney Atoll enclosed one large lagoon and several smaller ones, "the latter mostly dry; the former of very salt water, quite dead, with no communication with the sea . . . The water is very salt, nothing will live in it, and were it not for occasional heavy rains would in course of time evaporate; long arms of what was formerly the lagoon are now quite dry and a foot or more above the present level of the water."

Starbuck Atoll is described by the same author as having a lagoon that is drying up. "At the eastern end are some large salt lagoons (most weird-looking places), where thousands of tons of the purest kind of salt are found in various forms, coarse and fine. It has evidently been a large lagoon at one time, and either from partial upheaval or by the process of evaporation has become a series of small lakes and ponds, now nearly dry."

Niau Atoll in the Tuamotu was described by Friederici (1910, p. 104) as being very salty and apparently without any growing coral, although he stated that there were tasty fish in the lagoon. Although Canton Atoll has three breaks in the surrounding land through which sea water flows, Van Zwaluwenburg (1941) asserted that "The water within the lagoon has a higher salt content than the sea water."

In shallow lagoons and tide pools, water salinities vary diurnally. In an earlier chapter it was pointed out that Revelle and Emery (1957, pp. 703–6) had found diurnal changes in alkalinity/chlorinity ratios in tide pools. Banner (1952) and Randall (1952, p. 35) also found that at Onotoa, temperature, chlorinity, and pH all showed the same general pattern of diurnal variation, rising to a peak during the day and falling to a low at night. Samples tested for Ca^{++} and Mg^{++} showed that these varied directly with chlorinity.

Several decades ago Michael (1921, p. 555), quoting Mayor, wrote that: "Photosynthesis by marine plants in sunlight is a very important factor controlling the hydrogen-ion concentration of the water of shallow lagoons or tide-pools where the bottom is covered with seaweed; for the plants reduce the CO_2, thus setting free Oxygen and causing the water to become highly alkaline." He said that Mayor cited, as an example, the fact that "While the [pH of the] sea around the Tortugas is about 8.22, that of the lagoon rose at times to 8.35 by day and sank to 8.18 at night . . ." From these observations, it appears that, apart from other considerations, the activity of marine plants, including phytoplankton, brings about a fluctuating salinity situation in lagoons. This probably is slight in large, deep lagoons, but becomes significant on shallow reef flats and tide pools where such fluctuations may well be associated with limestone solution and precipitation processes (Cloud, 1952, p. 39).

In the shallow tide pools during the wet season, a sudden heavy fall of rain during a period of low water may cause a sudden change of salinity which will not be rectified for the marine life in it until the tide covers the flat. Extended heavy rains coinciding with an extended period of low water may have serious adverse effects upon those organisms in such tide pools which are intolerant of fresh water. The extreme change in chlorinity is seen in a fall of 15,000 parts per million in a tide pool at Onotoa during a day of rains, but the chlorinity jumped from 2,000 to 19,000 parts per million as the tide reached peak and flushed the pool again (Cloud, 1952, p. 38).

At Arno Atoll, Hiatt (1958) found that the tide pools and depressions containing water adjacent to the seaward beach of an islet were diluted to about 60 per cent of nominal oceanic sea water even during dry periods. This apparently was because of the great porosity of the seaward beach, which allowed considerable seepage from the fresh-water-lens head on the seaward side as compared with the higher head on the lagoon side. On the lagoon side of the islet, the salinity of the water over the lagoon reef was found to vary scarcely at all, regardless of the state of the tide. The relative impermeability of the fine sand and beach rock on the lagoon side almost completely dampened the runoff. During torrential rains the shallow water at the lagoon edge was slightly diluted at low water, but in no case did the dilution approach that on the seaward reef.

Influence of light on marine biota

The surface waters quickly absorb the red rays of the spectrum so that the subsurface animals live in a green, blue-green, or lightless world. In the

sea a red object appears black at a few meters' distance. Below the penetration of red rays, an object that is red at the surface would not be red at all.
Many animals adapt themselves by changing color appropriately to blend
with their background or to match the color of their background. Certain
species of surface plankton, such as the copepods Pontellopsis, Anomalocera,
and Corycaseus, and such fishes as the mackerel, bonito, and tuna have blue
or green colors. Other forms in plankton and in the jelly fishes are transparent or translucent and are almost indistinguishable to predators (Sverdrup, Johnson, and Fleming, 1954, pp. 825–31).

In the depths where daylight does not reach, many marine animals manu-
facture their own light. However, it is not always clear what the purpose
for the light is, since light producers are found in all marine communities
from the abyssal depths all the way up to the surface, and light is produced
by animals in all major groups from marine bacteria and the protozoans to
the vertebrates. The light is produced through the oxidation of some substance believed to be a simple protein, Luciferin. "The general phenomenon
wherein the water itself appears to glow is caused by innumerable microscopic organisms, mainly dinoflagellates of various types . . . Scattered
throughout the glowing waters are the larger brighter points of flashing
lights emitted by jellyfish, copepods, euphausiids, and annelids" (Sverdrup,
Johnson, and Fleming, 1954, pp. 833–5).

The influence of light on plant production is well known. The euphotic
zone, in which there is sufficient light for photosynthesis, extends down
to a depth of about 80 meters (about 260 feet). Beyond this depth, no effective plant production can take place, although in the clearest oceanic water,
light would still be perceptible at a depth of 700 meters and in average
oceanic water at 300 meters. Many of the pelagic planktonic organisms
migrate daily from deeper water to the surface at the approach of darkness
and begin their return to the depths at or near dawn. The greatest number
of individuals will be found concentrated at the level where conditions are
optimum with relation to light and other factors including temperature.
Moreover, it has been found that different species react differently, and
even different stages or different sexes of the same species have their characteristic behavior patterns in their diurnal response to light (Sverdrup,
Johnson, and Fleming, 1954, pp. 824, 826–38).

The presence or absence of light has been a most important factor in the
structural development and adaptations of most marine animals. It is found
that in the intertidal zone most animals are found in shaded situations in
holes, crevices, or the undersides of rocks or ledges. However, this type of
distribution may be due to a negative response to stimuli of heat and desiccation as well as to light (Sverdrup, Johnson, and Fleming, 1954).

CHAPTER 9

THE GEOGRAPHIC DISTRIBUTION OF ATOLL MARINE FAUNA

Wells has shown that there is great similarity among the corals of the Indo-Pacific region, especially in the Pacific reefs and atolls (1951; 1954). Taylor (1950, p. 8) pointed to the striking similarity of the marine flora in the Pacific, as exemplified by those studied at Funafuti in the Ellice Islands by the Royal Society of London and by those studied at Bikini in the northern Marshalls since 1946. Morrison (1954, p. 1) also found that in faunal species other than corals, such as mollusks, there appears to be a fundamental similarity in ecological conditions on the Pacific atolls. There is no doubt that species of fish also show great similarities in distribution. Since many of the larval stages of the different faunas are free-swimming for considerable periods, their widespread distribution by ocean currents throughout the Pacific is not surprising. Many other adult forms may be distributed by means of attachment to floating objects.

Geographic distribution of coral genera and species

The distribution of coral reefs and the conditions of their occurrence have been described in the first sections of this study. It is well known that the geographic pattern of occurrence of hermatypic corals is closely controlled by the pattern of minimum temperature isotherms (Fig. 75). Although emphasizing that deficiencies of data exist owing to incomplete collections from many parts of the Pacific and Indian Oceans, Wells concluded (1954, p. 389) that "The Indo-Pacific hermatypic coral fauna, so far as its composition on the generic level is concerned, is remarkably homogeneous. Its

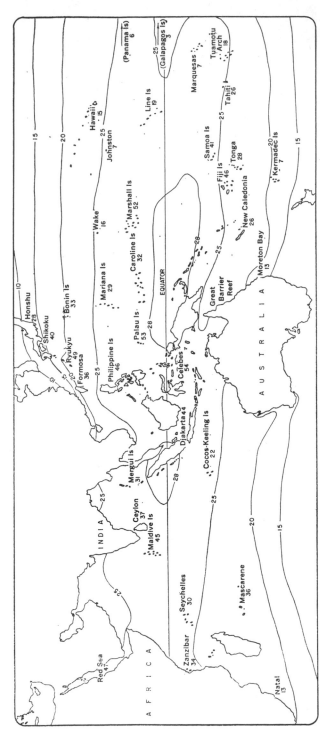

Fig. 75. Distribution of Indo-Pacific hermatypic coral genera based on the faunas of 32 areas. Isotherms are given in degrees centigrade. Numbers linked to areas indicate the number of genera known to occur there. [Adapted from Wells (1954).]

variations are principally radial gradients under temperature gradient controls, and there is no generic difference between a fauna from one extreme geographical situation and one from another within the same temperature range."

The known number of species in the Marshall Islands (surface species alone number some 150) compares well with those of other areas, such as the Palaus, the Philippines, Fijis, and Ryukyus, and may be about the number found on the Great Barrier Reef. Wells (1954, p. 396) found that within the Marshall Islands there are a few minor variations in the reef fauna from one atoll to another, although not enough data are available to exhibit any pattern of distribution. From the collections made, he concluded that no frondose or ramose species of Pavona occur at Bikini, but five such forms are found at Jaluit and other atolls, and they are common elsewhere in the Pacific. Another widespread species is *Fungia echinata,* which has been found at Jaluit but not at Bikini. He also found that the Actiniformis group of *Fungia* appears to be absent in the Marshalls, and that ramose species of Montipora are rare.

Fish distribution

In listing Tuamotuan fish collections prior to his own efforts, Harry (1953, pp. 42–4) noted that the number of species collected on 13 atolls ranged only from 1 to 4. On seven other atolls the lowest was 33 species and the highest 106 species. Yet he was able to collect about 400 species on Raroia, and on Kapingamarangi he found an even larger number. Randall (1955) recorded 396 species of inshore marine and pelagic fishes from the Gilbert Islands, but warned that "It should be emphasized that this is not even a near-definitive list of all the species which occur in the Gilberts, a fact which is readily apparent when the number of species in almost any family from the northern islands treated by Schultz and collaborators (1953) is compared with the same family in this report."

Randall goes on to state that

The fauna of the oceanic islands of the tropical Pacific is particularly uniform (the Hawaiian Islands excepted) for so vast an area. It is therefore not surprising that the fishes of the Gilbert Islands are very similar to those of the Marshall Islands, especially since only about 170 miles separate the northern Gilberts from the southern Marshalls. The similarity was evident from underwater observation by the writer in the southern Marshalls prior to and following the expedition to Onotoa. Subsequent study of the Gilberts collections and comparison with Marshall Islands material clearly demonstrated the high percentage of species of fishes common to both island groups. Disparity in the recorded faunas, such as the greater number of species known from the Marshalls, is undoubtedly a result of differences in the intensity of collecting.

Randall found that nearly all the Gilbert Islands fishes he recorded also occurred in the Indo-Malayan region. He viewed as fallacious conclusions that regard the faunistic connections between Polynesia-Micronesia and the "Indo-Australian centre of distribution" to be weak (cf. Ekman, 1953, p. 19). However, he stated that "Although there is no large number of species apparently endemic to Oceania in general, a sufficient number exists to indicate that some are truly confined to the oceanic islands of the tropical Pacific. A few of these, apparent examples being *Acanthus achilles*, *Pomacentrus vaiuli*, and *Apogon snyderi*, are abundant in the Pacific" (Randall, 1955).

Variations in local habitats may change the pattern of occurrence from one atoll to another. Harry (1953, p. 185) wrote that Raroia, which has a deep lagoon and major open passes to the ocean, provides ecological situations different from those in Takume, an atoll with a shallow enclosed lagoon only 15 miles away. Although the two may have the same species of fish,

Their relative abundance and ecological associations are clearly very different. Fishes that were seen only once or twice during the entire period at Raroia were noted to be common at Taukume and vice versa. These facts do not refer only to the lagoon since even certain physical aspects of the outer reefs were strikingly different and must have corresponding modifications of ecological conditions. In many ways, a comparative ecological study of atolls in one group would be more revealing than comparing islands from widely separated regions.

Sponge distribution

What may be generalized concerning fishes or corals may not necessarily be generalized concerning other fauna, however. This caution may be drawn from DeLaubenfels (1955, pp. 137–8) in the discussion of sponges. He said, for instance, that although there certainly is a significant resemblance between the sponge faunas of Ebon Atoll in the southernmost Marshalls and Onotoa Atoll in the Gilberts,

It has been my observation that each oceanic island that one visits has very few of the same species that occur on its neighbors, but still fewer from those islands that are yet farther away.

Mid-Pacific islands in general tend to have a certain type of sponge population; this consists of a few species that are peculiar to the island (perhaps having evolved there), a few species that are cosmopolitan, but these are a quite different assortment than the cosmopolitan species that are present on the nearest neighbors, and few species (such as *Stylotella agminata*) that are widespread in the Pacific. This situation is conspicuously different from that occurring in the corals.

Only one certainly new species occurs in the present collection, but it is also a new genus. Had the collecting been done by a sponge specialist, probably two or three others would have been found. It is to be expected that there would be about 40 species at such an island as Onotoa, whereas half that number are now available. Many sponges are so placed or characterized that they are likely to be overlooked. On the other hand, other marine objects often resemble sponges most deceptively.

Mollusk distribution

Randall (1955) pointed out that the enormous number of species of marine organisms of the Indo-Malayan region, along with the large number peculiar to the area, have led students of biogeography to designate this area as the center of distribution of the Indo-Pacific fauna. It is generally accepted that most of the fishes of Oceania have been distributed from the East Indies and the Philippines out into the Pacific. Moreover, Hedley (1896, pp. 400–1) wrote that east of Fiji the molluscan fauna indicates the abrupt termination of the Melanesian Plateau. The Samoas possess a distinctive oceanic molluscan fauna comparable to that of Tahiti, but the molluscan fauna of Fiji is distinctly continental. Although he felt that the route of the Polynesian fauna after its departure from the "continental" islands was too erratic to be exactly recoverable, he used an early tabulation of the range of three families of marine mollusks through 10 archipelagoes of the Pacific to show that there is a decrease in the number of species from west to east. Nearly one-fifth more species were recorded on the five western archipelagoes than on the eastern, with one exception (Hadley, 1896, p. 406). Apparently the wide and deep ocean between the easternmost islands and the west coasts of the Americas causes a sharp differentiation in a great many forms of animal life in these two regions of the east and west-central Pacific (Ekman, 1953, pp. 1–16). This emphasizes also the western origin of the Pacific island fauna.

Hedley (1896, p. 397), noting the poverty of the fauna of the atoll as compared with those of any "continental" area lying under corresponding latitudes (New Guinea, or the Melanesian Plateau), thought that, in addition, the mollusk shells found at Funafuti were smaller than the usual stature of their respective species on the "continental" islands. This accorded with findings of others concerning Gastropoda in the Tuamotus as compared with Tahiti, and of Gephyrean worms from Funafuti as compared with those of the volcanic island of Rotuma. There appears to be some ecological-environmental limitations for them in atoll habitats as compared with the more richly vegetated "high island" areas.

Distribution of other marine fauna

Caution is required when one is considering the poverty of species observed in many fauna, because so little work has been done in the Pacific. This is seen in the study of the annelids of the northern Marshalls (Hartman, 1954, p. 622): "Because of the considerable number of species (at least 100 indicated in the lists below), and since it must be concluded that these lists are at best only preliminary, one is inclined to question the generalization that the fauna of the Marshall Islands is small . . . Clark (1952, p. 265) recorded 80 species of echinoderms (excluding the holothurians); only 40% of the total number were found in two successive years, also indicating that the echinoderms have been incompletely collected."

When one compares the 100 species of annelids and the 80 species of echinoderms collected in the northern Marshalls with the 5 species of annelids and 28 species of echinoderms collected at Funafuti [up to Hedley's time the best surveyed atoll from a zoological standpoint (Hedley, 1896, p. 391)], it is easy to believe that the impoverishment of fauna thought to exist at Funafuti may be less of species than of records and collections. As Hedley himself remarked (p. 398), "Few realize how exceedingly rich the fauna of the tropical Pacific is, or how poor our knowledge thereof. . . ." These words appear applicable to the marine life of atoll reefs and their ecology.

Physiographic zones in atoll ecology

The physiography of an atoll reef forms the setting for the marine ecology. Certain conditions favor certain forms of sessile plant and animal life. As these forms are established and grow, they comprise additional elements of the environment favoring or discouraging the establishment and flourishing of still further forms of plant and animal life, or affect elements already present. Thus marine ecology is not static, even in a particular part of the reef, and it seems doubtful that one may recognize a climax situation, especially in the shallower parts of the reef, except by arbitrary definition. Nevertheless, ecological zones of semipermanence across a reef may be recognized, although these zones differ according to location with respect to windward or leeward situations, with submergence or elevation of the reef and with the occurrence of islands and of settlements on such islands on the reef. On the other hand, "Recognition of contiguous ecological field units within a given environment amounts to designating segments of a continuously variable sequence. Such units in large part express real central tendencies, but their boundaries are most indefinite, and to draw boundaries at all may be misleading" (Cloud, 1952, p. 58). However, if we keep in mind that there always are "suites of intergrading units," we find zonal differentiation a useful method in studying marine ecology.

The physiographic zones perhaps are most easily recognized and have been described in earlier chapters. Odum and Odum (1955, p. 293) gave cross sections showing a windward reef of Eniwetok without an island. Figure 76, a cross section of a Bikini reef, provides an illustration of the situation of a windward reef with an island. Figures 77 to 79 show three kinds of seaward reefs and three kinds of lagoon reefs. Newell (1956, pp. 332–3) showed nine profiles of different windward reef sectors and nine of leeward reef sectors. The physiographic zones these various reefs represent may be briefly summarized as follows.

Seaward-windward island reef. (1), the outer submarine slope, often accompanied by (2), a submarine terrace where sediment accumulates; (3), the windward buttress zone or zone of grooves and spurs, and (4), the coralline ridge or algal ridge, which together form the surf zone. The ridge may protrude in parts at low tide, and sometimes, as at Kapingamarangi, may rise shoreward slightly to (5), a narrow strip of algal mat kept wet by translation waves, sloping down into (6), the backridge trough or tide pool zone, sometimes connected by surge channels or tunnels with the sea, rising shoreward to (7), the offshore shelf, an intertidal zone drying at low tide and often veneered with gravel and boulders, which finally rises to (8), the wave-wet or spray-wet shore. Zones (5) to (7) comprise most of the "reef flat."

Seaward-leeward island reef. Similar to the above on the shoreward sections, but usually, although not always (Newell, 1956), lacks the raised ridge of coralline algae.

Windward inter-island reef. Where the central part of the reef is elevated and dries between high tides, the situation is similar to the two above. However, in the situation described by Odum and Odum for Eniwetok, there is no tide pool behind the algal ridge and the reef does not dry but deepens steadily toward the lagoon. The physiographic zones lagoonward of the buttress zone result from the organic growth. In addition to the submarine slope and possibly a terrace, they comprise (1) the buttress zone, (2) coral-algal ridge, (3) the zone of encrusting algae, (4) the zone of smaller heads, (5) the zone of larger heads, and (6) the zone of sand and shingle.

Lagoon-reef habitats may be exposed to the wind (windward lagoon reefs) or may be protected by an island (leeward lagoon reefs). Among the ecological differences between the two are the usually more active movement of sediment with resulting abrasion upon or burial of sessile organisms on the windward lagoon reef and the greater amount of fine-sediment deposition on the lagoon reef to the lee of windward reef islands, which results sometimes in mud flats. Alongshore currents may carry away sediments, so that in

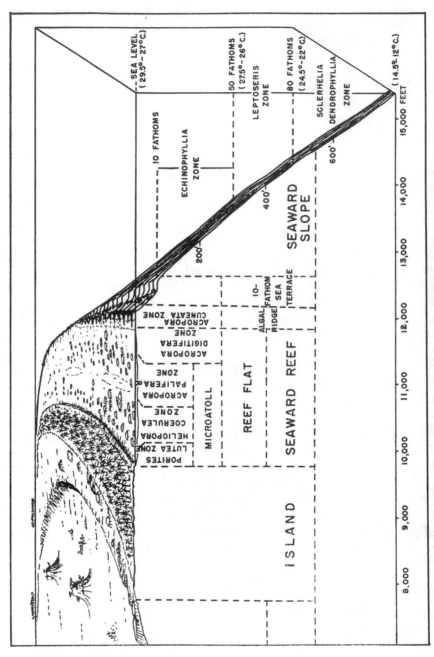

Fig. 76. Coral zones on the windward reef of Bikini Atoll. [From Wells (1954).]

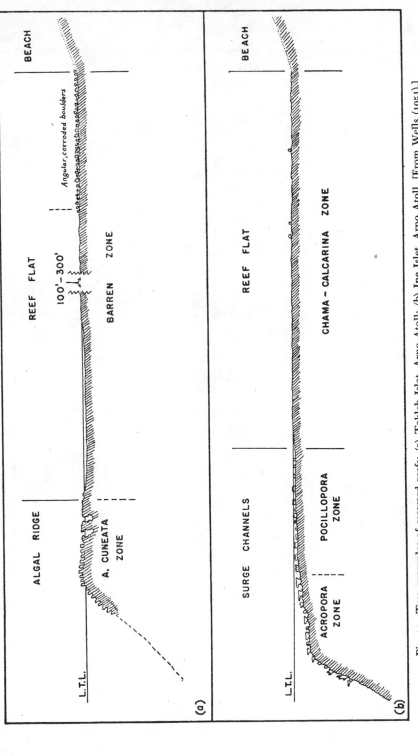

Fig. 77. Two examples of seaward reefs: (a) Takleb Islet, Arno Atoll; (b) Ine Islet, Arno Atoll. [From Wells (1951).]

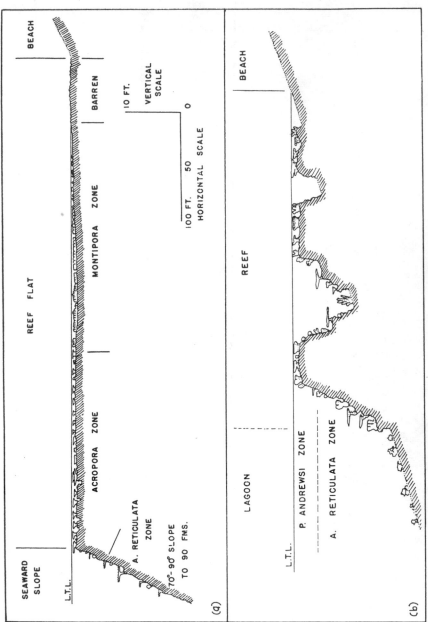

Fig. 78. Comparison of a seaward reef and a leeward reef: (a) seaward reef of Ine anchorage, Arno Atoll; (b) leeward reef of Takleb Islet, Arno Atoll. [From Wells (1951).]

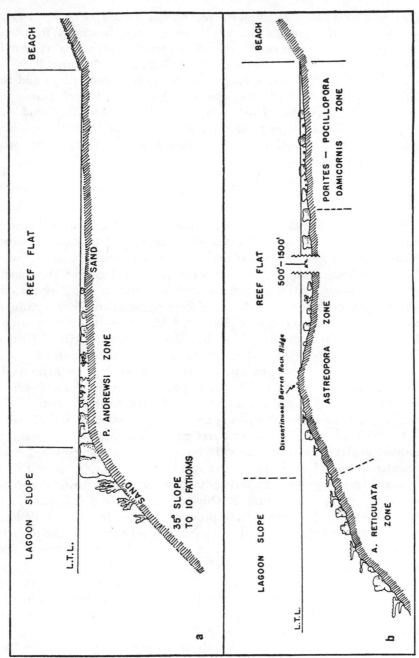

Fig. 79. Comparison of an enclosed lagoon reef and a windward reef: (a) enclosed lagoon reef of North Horn, Arno Atoll; (b) windward reef of Ine Islet, Arno Atoll. [From Wells (1951).]

many lagoon reefs bare rock forms the reef surface. Grading from the lagoon shore, the ecological zones may include either a sand or beachrock foreshore, sand or mud flats, decadent coral reef, and reef patches. Especially off heavily settled leeward lagoon beaches (as those off Tohou and Werua villages of Kapingamarangi), the debris, garbage, and waste from the village and the small nearshore current movement appear to have caused much suspended material and a heavy rain of sediment, which kills corals. The dead and decadent heads become overgrown with slimy soft algae. Shingle flats and Heliopora flats also may occur, either on the lagoon reef or on the inter-island channels and flats.

Reef coral zonation

The ecological conditions favoring particular coral genera and species within a particular reef depend upon water depth and turbulence, windward or leeward situation, occurrences of islets or inter-islet channels, and upon thermochemical zonal differences across the reef. Because a great many combinations of conditions can occur, no two reef cross sections are entirely alike. One part of the reef will contain different faunal and floral combinations from those in another part. For example, the descriptions of island reef zonation at Onotoa and Bikini show few similarities with the inter-island zonation at Eniwetok (Odum and Odum, 1955, p. 293). In emphasizing this diversity in a description of the reefs at Ine village on Arno Atoll, Hiatt (1958) pointed out that "They were not in any sense characteristic or typical except as influential conditions may be the same elsewhere. Such normally is not the case with roughly circular atolls within the trade wind belt. Dr. Wells has described several reef types which are more or less representative of Arno reefs; the Ine village reefs are but examples of formation under one set of conditioning factors."

However, certain general similarities in structure and zonation do occur. Cloud (1952, p. 24) found that at Onotoa, Tarawa, and Butaritari, the upper part of the reef frame was built primarily by the blue coral Heliopora, an alcyonarian, and not a typical stony coral or scleractinian. He thought that the observations by David and Sweet (1904) at Funafuti indicated that this might be true for the Gilbert and Ellice Island groups as a whole. In reviewing the studies at widely separated windward reefs (Aua in the Admiralties, Bikini and Arno in the Marshalls, Funafuti in the Ellices, and Rotuma north of Fiji), Wells (1954, p. 404) found similarity in the structure and zonation of reef corals, as shown in Table 11.

The horizontal distribution of corals and other forms of marine life across the reef is strongly influenced by great variations in living conditions. Changes in temperature and salinity from seaward margin to beach and across the lagoon reef were discussed in Chapter 8. In the inshore areas especially, the animals are exposed to the air for several hours at a time during the low-tide stage, and those that cannot migrate into the shallow pools or with the retreating tide must be able to withstand the desiccation. Those in the shallow pools must withstand marked and often abrupt changes in salinity and temperatures, although it is likely that the bottoms of the pools and the burrows in the rock tend to maintain their salinity because of the

TABLE 11

Structure and Zonation of Reef Corals

Shoreward		Seaward (windward)	
Inner reef	Intermediate reef flat	Outer reef	Algal ridge
Porites	Heliopora Seriatopora	Acropora	Pocillopora Acropora Goniastrea

absence of agitation and the difference in specific gravity of saline and fresh water. Moreover, reef animals in tide pools must be able to adjust to less than normal oxygen, because as the temperature rises the saturation value in grams of oxygen per liter of sea water decreases rapidly (Banner, 1952, p. 3). The shoreward areas also have inhibiting effects on coral growth because of the rasping, grinding abrasive action of the loose materials carried back and forth by turbulent waves and currents.

Qualitatively and quantitatively, the life of the outer reef edge flourishes to a greater degree and overshadows that of the reef flat (Hiatt, 1958). Although the population density in absolute value depends primarily upon the abundance of food available, the variety or species density depends mostly upon the selective action of the environment. Under optimum conditions, the species density is usually very great, but it decreases as the environment becomes less favorable. A study by Hiatt on the reef at Arno showed that a dramatic increase in species occurred seaward along a transect. The optimum conditions favoring speciation occurred on the outer slope of the reef. On the lagoon side optimum conditions were reached as soon as homogeneous physicochemical conditions were reached in the water away from the beach.

In the windward Eniwetok transect, Odum and Odum (1957) found only three species of coral along the breaker zone, which was largely covered by algae. In the encrusting zone they found seven species, with the encrusting Acropora and Millepora and small "doughnut-shaped" heads of Porites,

Favites, Plesiastrea, and Pocillopora being most conspicuous. In the next zone of deepening water lagoonward, they found twelve species. Here the massive types of Favids and Porites were characteristic, but branching Acroporas were conspicuous. Within the zone of large heads, in still deeper water, they found seventeen species, but also found a "noticeable sub-zonation with the Acropora, Porites, Pocillopora, and Stylophora in zone D while Heliopora and the two species of Millepora formed a distinct zone lagoonward which we designated as E."

Hiatt (1958) found vertical stratification of the corals areas even more striking than the horizontal zonation on the Arno reef and also found that considerable variation occurs between the lagoon and seaward reef-edge patterns.

Most significant, perhaps, is the far greater depth in which a variety of corals are abundant on the seaward slope as compared with the lagoonward slope. On both areas the uppermost strata, about 10 feet in depth in the lagoon and 35 feet in depth on the seaward slope, consists of a rather well mixed group of genera and species with Acropora and Astreopora dominating in the lagoon, but clear dominants are present in the seaward slope only in the topmost 20 feet (Pocillopora) with the next 15 feet so thoroughly mixed that no group dominates. The giant fans of *A. reticulata* form a veritable garden on the lagoon slope from 10 to 20 feet in depth, but on the seaward slope the same species, somewhat smaller in size, becomes dominant from 40–55 feet in depth. Beyond this depth in the lagoon the irregularly branched thickets of *A. formosa* take over, but on the seaward slope it is the rounded and encrusting Porites which cover most of the steep rocky slope, and these, interspersed with a few other genera, extend downward so far as is visible, some 250 feet. We may only surmise, without experimental evidence, what factors operate to so clearly differentiate coral growth on the opposite slopes of the reef platform. Certainly the seaward water contains less suspended material than does the lagoon water, and it is generally more turbulent since it receives the full impact of wave action. Moreover, sedimentary deposits are very different in size and composition on each side of the platform, and the substratum is exceedingly important in the location and growth of any sedentary form.

The above conclusions were from a study of a leeward island reef at Arno. Somewhat different conclusions were reached by Wells (1954, p. 407) from studies of a windward island reef at Bikini. He felt that

Three inferences are fairly certain: (1) the distribution of genera with depth is much the same in the lagoon as down the seaward slope to the equivalent lagoon depths, but the number of species diminishes more rapidly down the seaward slope than into the depths of the lagoon; (2) there is no specific depth at which there is a sudden diminution in number of genera or species, although the number of species does drop very rapidly from the surface to about 15 fathoms, increases slightly again to about 35 fathoms, then declines steadily and slowly to none at 85 fathoms; and

(3) the lower bathymetric limit for hermatypic corals is not imposed by the temperature gradient.

The first point made by Wells appears to be diametrically opposite to Hiatt's conclusion from Arno observations. On the other hand, one is a leeward reef, the other a windward reef. The seaward side of the leeward reef at Arno corresponds somewhat to the lagoon side of the windward reef at Bikini, both being sheltered, although the seaward side of Arno would have a somewhat different ecological situation, probably with less sedimentation.

The windward seaward side of the Bikini reef, however, would have a far greater water turbulence than the windward lagoon side of the Arno reef, so these would appear less comparable. However, since the windward, seaward reefs are too dangerous for detailed inspection by aqualung or masked swimmers, information still is inadequate for this region. More detailed knowledge would help establish whether Wells's first inference is certain or not.

The vertical distribution of hermatypic corals is controlled by the depth reached by light rays necessary for the growth of the symbiotic zooxanthellae and by the depth to which strong water movements reach. According to Wells (1954, p. 389) probably only the latter involves changes in fauna. Certain genera and species of other genera usually are found in quieter, deeper water than others. They include Leptoseris, Oxypora, Cycloseris, Anacropora, and special species of Acropora. In general, the more fragile types are in quiet, deeper waters.

The preceding general features of physiographic and three-dimensional zonation provide the setting for a more detailed examination.

Atoll foraminiferal fauna and their distribution

An important constituent of coral reefs are foraminifera and their tests, or shells, which form so much of the beach and lagoon sand. Some varieties are important also in the atoll marine ecology as planktonic forms. Few studies of atoll foraminifera distribution have been made. The most complete study, by Cushman, Todd, and Post (1954), on the recent foraminifera of the northern Marshall Islands is summarized and quoted from in part in the following paragraphs. Briefer discussions than theirs for the same area are found in Emery, Tracey, and Ladd (1954, pp. 79–80) and by Johnson (1954). Since these fauna are characteristic of the coral reef zone (84 per cent of the species are identified with known species from the tropical Pacific), the general distribution discussed probably is representative for Pacific atolls. The faunas of the four atolls studied do not differ significantly among themselves. However, some notable differences do occur between these atolls and certain other Pacific islands—"for example, the absence of Baculogypsina and various medium to large species of Rotalia, such as *R. calcar* (D'Orbigny), and the great variety of the miliolids . . . About 6% of the species and varieties found appeared new to science, and 10% which were undeterminable specifically also may be new" (Cushman, Todd, and Post, 1954).

Cushman, Todd, and Post felt that the samples provided a rather complete picture of the foraminiferal fauna present in the waters of and surrounding the atolls. Emery, Tracey, and Ladd (1954) stated that "The living foraminifer appears to be restricted to the reef, especially to barren flats carpeted by a thin veneer of a filamentous alga in which the tests are packed, usually one layer thick." However, Cushman, Todd, and Post described three faunal zones: (1) the reef flat and lagoon beach, (2) the lagoon and shallow outer slope, and (3) the deep water (where the fauna is chiefly planktonic with the addition of rare benthonic species). In each case, there is no sharp division, but faunas of each zone intergrade, or dominant species from the higher zones may work downslope into the lower ones.

Figure 80 shows the percentage composition for a typical beach sample and for a typical lagoon sample. In both beach and lagoon samples, *Amphistegina madagascariensis* comprises about half of the total. Amphisteginidae are present in large numbers on all the atolls, decreasing in numbers but increasing in variety of forms with depth on the outer slopes of the atolls. Next in abundance to *A. madagascariensis* D'Orbigny in lagoons is *Heterostegina suborbicularis* D'Orbigny, which in a few places is more abundant than the former. This local dominance probably is related to bottom conditions and to other unknown conditions according to Cushman, Todd, and Post (1954).

Leaving out of consideration the dominant one or several species, the remaining lagoon fauna may be rich in one or another of the Reussella-Bolivina, Textularia, milioid, peneroplid, or globigerinid groups. The reasons for these variations are also obscure but probably bottom conditions have a very important part in determining what foraminiferal species are to be found. Many factors other than depth affect these faunas, which are not entirely life associations.

Other species found in considerable abundance in the lagoons are *Calcarina hispida* H. B. Brady, *Marginopora vertebralis* Blainville, *Homotrema rubrum* (Lamarck), and *Miniacina miniacea* (Pallas). Certain samples, the shallower ones and those close to the reef, have rather large percentages of worn specimens of *Calcarina spengleri* (Gmelin) which appear to have been transported down into the lagoon from the reef flat. In general, the percentage of *C. spengleri* (Gmelin) decreases with depth and that of *C. hispida* H. B. Brady increases.

The percentage composition of the deep-water fauna is entirely different from that of the reef flat or the lagoons. Various species of the planktonic

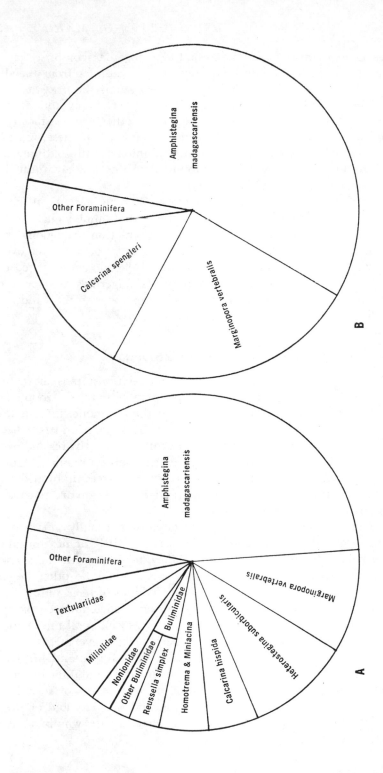

Fig. 80. Composition of typical lagoon-sediment sample (a) and typical beach-sediment sample (b). [From Cushman, Todd, and Post (1954)]

A

Amphistegina madagascariensis

Other Foraminifera

Textulariidae

Miliolidae

Nonionidae

Other Buliminidae

Reussella simplex

Buliminidae

Homotrema & Miniacina

Calcarina hispida

Heterostegina suborbicularis

Marginopora vertebralis

B

Amphistegina madagascariensis

Other Foraminifera

Calcarina spengleri

Marginopora vertebralis

families Globigerinidae and Globorotaliidae together comprise 50 to 98 per cent of the total foraminiferal fauna in the samples from the deeper locations. In the samples from the shallower locations the next most abundant species are *Amphistegina madagascariensis* D'Orbigny and *A. radiata* (Fichtel and Moll) and its varieties. Some 215 other species, mostly rare, form a relatively small part of the deep-water fauna. Of these, representatives of the families Lagenidae, Polymorphinidae, Ellipsoidinidae, Cassidulinidae, and Chilostomellidae are found almost exclusively in the deeper water (Cushman, Todd, and Post, 1954).

In spite of the percentage predominance of Globigerina tests in the outer deep water in the composition of samples, the actual numbers may be larger in the lagoons. Because of the semienclosed circulation of lagoonal waters and a continual replenishing of the lagoon water by ocean water over the reefs, there is an increase in pelagic fauna in the lagoon as compared to the ocean. Johnson (1954) estimated that living Globigerinas are about twice as numerous in the lagoon water as in the ocean water to the windward of the atolls.

Planktonic life forms and their lagoon distribution

In the over-all economy of the oceans, no relationship is more fundamental than that existing between the phytoplankton and the zooplankton. They form a vital part of the cycle between the inorganic, inanimate substances and the organic, animate forms and in the progression from chemical elements and compounds to plants, to plant eaters, to carnivores and detritus eaters, to bacteria, and back to chemical elements and compounds. Although in the open tropical oceans they may be as scarce as trees in an arid region, they are more numerous in atoll lagoons, and zooplankton are of considerable importance to the carnivorous corals.

The term "plankton" means "all the organisms, usually microscopic or semi-microscopic that float about in the sea with little or no resistance to water currents" (Johnson, 1949, p. 238). They, together with the sea water, form an enveloping environment among and around the other larger organisms and inorganic objects of the marine habitats of reefs and atolls.

Plankton consists of phytoplankton, the single-celled microscopic plants (diatoms) and various dinoflagellate protozoans, as well as all the small floating animals (zooplankton) that feed on them. On the average, the diatoms constitute about nine-tenths of the plankton (MacGinitie and MacGinitie, 1949, p. 10). Plankton consist not only of permanently planktonic forms (holoplanktonic) but also the transitory young or larval stages of such bottom-living forms as crabs, certain shrimp, clams, and the like, and of the eggs and young of fishes (Johnson, 1949). The diatoms are wholly unable to adjust themselves with respect to depth; the dinoflagellates are at best feeble, although they can move haphazardly about by waving their whiplike flagella. Both have adapted their structures to features which permit them to resist sinking. Their small size alone provides them a large proportional area of surface, which increases the drag through the water and slows down the rate of sinking. Special shapes and protrusions and the presence of oil in the late vegetative period of diatoms contribute to flotation ability. Without this ability they would quickly sink to the bottom.

In the presence of water and carbon dioxide the diatom can utilize the energy of the sun's rays to form organic carbon compounds, releasing oxygen from the water in the process. This oxygen is used in part in the respiration processes of the plant. Since there is always plenty of carbon dioxide dissolved in sea water, abundance of diatoms depends upon access to sunlight and upon certain dissolved salts, such as nitrogen and phosphorus, and perhaps to iron and other trace elements. Silicates used in forming the tiny shells of the diatoms never appear to be in short supply (Sverdrup, Johnson, and Fleming, 1954, pp. 762–73). In general the lack of diversity among the phytoplankton contrasts strikingly with the great diversity among the zooplankton.

Zooplankton include large numbers of protozoa, radiolarians, foraminifera, small crustaceans (copepods and others), jellyfish, many worms, a number of the mollusks, and the larval and egg stages of animals of all kinds, including fishes. In contrast to most members of the phytoplankton the planktonic animals usually have some power to swim, although this ability varies greatly with different animals. The manner of nutrition and ways of obtaining food differ widely among different groups of animals in contrast to the generally similar photosynthetic plant processes. The life cycles of the animals also are complex and differ widely.

Circulation patterns are important not only in the distribution of similar marine forms of life over wide areas, but also in the maintenance of an endemic population, particularly of planktonic forms, which are most affected by the circulation. Many partially landlocked bays or lagoons maintain certain characteristic populations through internal circulation patterns such as those associated with atoll lagoon currents.

The only studies of planktonic distribution in atoll lagoons known to the writer are those by Johnson (1949; 1954) based upon data from the northern Marshall Islands. In general, he found that most of the holoplankton species found in Bikini atoll lagoon also are found in the surrounding open sea, but that there are a number of endemic species not found outside the lagoon except where they have been washed out by currents. Moreover, many forms occurring normally in the outside ocean surface waters are concentrated in larger numbers within the lagoon. He found that these features correlated with the semiclosed circulation which the lagoon imposes upon the water coming in over the windward reefs. From a count of the 11 most common animal groups, Johnson found that the average concentration per cubic meter is four times higher in the lagoon than in the open sea northeast of the atoll. However, since the plankton concentration in the Marshall Islands area is relatively sparse, especially the phytoplankton, the lagoon plankton is not densely concentrated. Nevertheless, certain forms common both to the inside and outside of the lagoon may be as much as 27 times as numerous within the lagoon. "The restricted water flow within the lagoon is biologically important in conserving also the transitory planktonic larval stages of lagoon and reef fishes and bottom-living animals" (Johnson, 1954, p. 301).

The distribution of the plankton within the lagoon is closely correlated with the current patterns described by Von Arx (1954; Figs. 70 to 72), according to Johnson (1954):

A study of the vertical distribution and diurnal vertical migration of the endemic copepod *Undinula vulgaris,* and of the general plankton, reveals that much of the lagoon plankton lives mainly in the deeper, slowly (0.1 knot) eastward-moving counter current which as a water mass represents 70 to 90 per cent of the living space in the lagoon. Even during the night when much of the plankton migrates toward the surface into the faster (0.3 knot) westward-moving water, about two-thirds of the plankton still remains within the deeper counter current. . . . When we compare the number of specific organisms occurring per cubic meter of water at stations occupied inside the lagoon with the number found in the surrounding water just outside the reefs and passages, it is seen that the concentration is almost invariably smallest in the waters outside the eastern and northern reefs. It is nearly always largest by far at the stations within the lagoon, and intermediate at stations just outside the western and southern passages and reefs . . . In summarizing the average concentration by areas of the 11 most common animal groups, it appears that the ratios of concentration per cubic meter for (a) the outside eastern-northern area, (b) the inside lagoon area, and (c) the outside western southern area of principal outflow, are roughly a:b:c equals 1:4:2.

One aspect of reef character that the writer has not seen correlated with the question of whether corals are dependent upon an external supply of plankton is the greater width of the reef in the northeastern and northern sectors as contrasted to the poorer growth of reef in the southwest, leeward sectors. Since the southwestern areas of the reef are outflow regions where plankton appear to be more abundant, reefs here should grow more rapidly, and reefs should be wider and less fragmented if corals are highly dependent upon this plankton supply, even though the greater width of the northern reef in the northern trade-wind zone may in large part be attributable to current and sedimentation patterns, as suggested earlier. On the other hand, the abundance of patch reefs within the lagoon adjoining western and southern passes and the relative absence of such patch reefs adjoining eastern reef passes would appear to be correlated with the relative abundance of plankton in these sectors. This interpretation might not be valid if lagoon pass-mouth sedimentation were found to be the more basic factor in patch-reef formation at such locations.

Plankton-feeding fish naturally follow the movements and concentration of the plankton, and the carnivorous fish in turn are attracted by the presence of the plankton strainers, so it would appear reasonable to suppose that a knowledge of the lagoon current system might provide a guide to the best fishing grounds for predator fish as well as the plankton eaters. This correlation appears to explain the location of the schooling grounds for flying fish observed by the writer at Kapingamarangi in 1954. According to the local fishermen, the flying fish enter the channel from the open ocean after dusk to school in the lagoon area inside the passage and return to the sea by daybreak.

The prevailing surface flow in the pass area is outward, although at low tide there is a slack period or even a slight reversal of flow inward. The plankton rise from the deeper water into the surface flow at night, so the greater outflow of plankton at the southwestern passage would naturally attract the plankton-eating fish and their predators.

Another practical aspect of lagoon fishing sites for atoll dwellers is related to the current upwellings that occur in the eastern sectors of lagoons. Here a larger concentration of plankton should occur at all times. Most of the land areas and associated human settlements are situated along the eastern half of atoll reefs; the convenience to the fishermen is obvious.

Also affecting this aspect of the marine ecology is the fact that the lagoon waters near the settlements receive a higher amount of organic materials than the waters near uninhabited reef areas. This should result in more food for zooplankton as well as for detritus eaters among fish and other marine fauna. All these factors would seem to favor greater abundance of food for man in the lagoon areas most convenient to him. However, Harry (1953, p. 26) found the open lagoon at Raroia to have a relatively restricted fish population, so that the more important economic fishes for the human predators are associated with reef habitats rather than with open lagoon habitats.

Furthermore, it would appear that pelagic predators (bonito, tuna, sharks, and barracuda), which feed on flying fishes and plankton feeders, would be most prevalent outside the leeward reef and reef passages, since because of the outwash from the lagoon the plankton would be most numerous there. Harry (1953, p. 24) found this zone had the largest concentration of fishes of any restricted locality at Raroia and, in fact, that this is the favorite fishing ground of the natives. In the lagoon the coral heads near the deep pass and in the southwestern region "maintain the largest fish population, apparently receiving the greatest flow of nutrient materials." As these leeward areas near the atoll are most sheltered and there is less danger of rough surf than on the windward reef edge, the situation also favors the small craft of the atoll fishermen.

CHAPTER 10

ATOLL MARINE BIOTA, HABITATS, AND ECOLOGY

An apt introduction to this chapter is provided in the introductory paragraph of the discussion of the trophic structure of a coral reef by Odum and Odum (1955, p. 291):

The coral reef communities of the world are tremendously varied associations of plants and animals growing luxuriantly in tropical waters of impoverished plankton content. Under intense equatorial insolation the plants apparently grow rapidly and are eaten rapidly. Save for fluctuations the reef seems unchanged year after year, and reefs apparently persist, at least intermittently, for millions of years. With such long periods of time, adjustments in organismal components have produced a biota with a successful competitive adjustment in a relatively constant environment. The reef community is famous for its immense concentrations of life and its complexity.

The general features of physiographic and three-dimensional zonation described in Chapter 9 provide the setting for a more-detailed examination of ecological communities in the marine environment. Since there is a large variety of these, only some of the more-prominent observable ecological zones and communities that have been described by observers on different atolls will be presented. These may be regarded as characteristic examples of what may occur in various zones or situations on most open Pacific atolls. It is to be recognized, of course, that endemic species may occur on certain atolls or groups of atolls and that certain species may be prevalent on some atolls and not on others.

The seaward slope zone

Although data for reef biota on the seaward slope are limited, owing to the difficulties in their acquisition, three zones of growth for corals at Bikini were recognized by Wells (1954, pp. 398–9): (1) Echinophyllia zone, 10 to 50 fathoms; (2) Leptoseris zone, 50 to 80 fathoms; and (3) Sclerhelia-Dendrophyllia zone, below 80 fathoms. The first of these zones is the lowest into which surface reef species extend and grow with any degree of strength. In addition to the surface reef species, a number of species which occur also in the lagoon below the surface species are found here, notably species of Acropora. Certain species at Bikini occur only in this zone; the most abundant of these species are *Echinophyllia aspera* and *Oxypora lacera*.

There is a bench above this zone on the windward reef at both Bikini in the Marshalls and at Onotoa in the Gilberts. At Bikini (Emery, Tracey, and Ladd, 1954, p. 26) the terrace slopes gently from a depth of 15 to 25 feet at the reef edge to a depth of about 50 feet at the outer edge. Where well developed, the terrace here may be rather flat for several hundred yards from the reef edge. At Onotoa (Cloud, 1952, p. 64) the bench where examined sloped about 15° seaward from a depth of about 12 feet to the upper part of a 30-to-40° undersea slope at about 55 to 60 feet. This bench was found to be generally veneered with a mat of living and dead coral, the predominant types being stoutly branched *Pocillopora elegans* (Dana). Landward the bench extends to the buttress or grove and spur zone (Fig. 81).

At Raroia, Harry (1953, p. 22) found that "The greatest growth of coral was at this region and a large percentage of the total fish fauna lived on this shelf. Sharks constantly patrol this area . . . looking for food. Tuna, barracuda, and jacks also scout these waters, but normally keep nearer the surface. [These and] larger sea basses are in greater abundance in this zone than anywhere else [in the reef waters] and seem to hide in every hole in the coral." Naso and Balistes swim about immediately above the coral, and various species of the demoiselles that penetrate to deeper water, such as Dascyllus, form schools about the coral. The extent of fish fauna in this zone is seen to be about twice that found around coral heads in the lagoon.

This region at Raroia was observed to have a very characteristic fauna, typified by several sharks and carangids not noticed elsewhere around the atoll. Those at the surface included Sphyraena, thunnids, and schools of Hemirhamphus. Sharks wandered about just above the coral, moving from one surge channel to the next. Hovering above the coral were such species as Balistes, Naso, and often Acanthurus. Only very small fishes such as Dascyllus, Labroides, and Halichoeres were seen swimming about the coral. However, great numbers of small fishes less than 5 inches long (blennies,

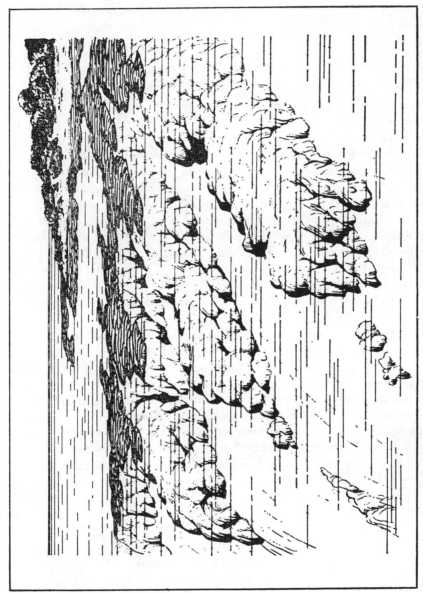

Fig. 81. Sea reef of Tufa Island, Rongelap Atoll, showing the relation of the marginal zone of reef and offshore algal ridges or spurs to the older surface. [From Emery, Tracey, and Ladd (1954). Originally adapted by P. B. King and Margaret Austin from a field sketch by Selwyn Taylor.]

gobies, a few cirrhitids, and a large number of wrasses) would come out of hiding when the water was blanketed with rotenone poison. Along with them would come some large sea basses up to 3 feet long. Parrot fishes were uncommon in this region, and chaetodontids and holocentrids were completely absent.

The groove-and-spur zone, or coral-algal ridge

Immediately inward from the seaward slope (Fig. 76) the characteristic coral growing on the ridge and in the dash of the surge at Bikini Atoll was *Acropora cuneata* (Wells, 1954). The only important branching scleractinian growing in the foaming surge of the ridge is Pocillopora. In the special ecological niche formed by the deeper parts of the surge channels and their cavernlike ramifications down to a depth of about 20 feet grow a number of species of corals found seldom elsewhere (Plates 14 and 42).

At the inward ends of surge channels that open into pools on the reef, bushy lithothamnion grows where there is some wave action; where there is no wave action, the crustose types are present. At Bikini, Taylor (1950, p. 29) observed that Halimedae and the Caulerpae were striking elements below the rim of the channels. Usually, he found a good deal of Udotea. Extending downward from the reef flat were Dictyospheria and Microdictyon also.

The ridges at Raroia were covered with Pocillopora and a species of Porolithon. Together they formed a rim which in places overhung the gorges of the grooves by 1 or 2 feet. Coating many of the higher parts of the spurs (Doty and Morrison, 1954, p. 5) was *Centroceras clavulatum,* but other than coralline algae were rarely present. Both at Bikini and Raroia the algal ridge was pink. Newell (1954, p. 7) found that at Raroia this was formed by blisterlike crusts of *Porolithon onkodes,* with small hemispheres of ramoze *Porolithon gardineri* here and there. The *Porolithon onkodes* clumps were as large as a man's hand and they partially enclosed open cavities, the refuges of numerous little crabs. He also observed many patches of an encrusting blue-green algae colored a light yellowish green. A narrow belt of discontinuous patches of encrusting Millepora followed the outer flanks of the ridge and extended around the heads of the grooves.

Characteristic of the area of the Porolithon, and often living under the surface level of the reef, on the sides or on the under sides of the small, rounded "heads" of lumps of the Porolithon growth were many species of snails (Morrison, 1954, p. 15). They include such species as the horse's hoof snail *Hipponix (Antisabia) foliacea, Hipponix (Cochlear) barbata,* and the small trochid snails Stomatia spp. and *Gena rosacea. Drupa clathrata,* the brown chestnut burr rock snail, is characteristic of the lowest normal low-tide level on the outer slope of the algal ridge, always in reach of the surf. A small red chiton was found only within the outer slope at Raroia by Morrison. He also recorded from the outer algal ridge or the reef margin just beyond such crabs as *Actaea cavipes, A. rufopunctata, Carpilodes ruga-tus,* the fuzzy, red-legged hermit crab *Aniculus aniculus,* and the smaller hermit crab with the brilliant blue-banded legs, *Calcinus elegans.*

Two species of shrimp, *Rhynchocinetes hiatti* and *Brachycarpus biungui-culatus,* apparently made their home in the surge channels outside the algal ridge at Raroia. They were not seen elsewhere on this atoll. Apparently, the spur or buttress zone outside the algal ridge, which has up to 30 feet of water over its outer slopes, is the normal habitat of many of the species of mollusks that are recorded as shells on Raroia but have never been seen alive. The most conspicuous of these, according to Morrison, are the small but very beautiful abalone shell *Padollus pulcherrimus,* the umbrella-limpet *Cheilea equestris,* the rare endemic *Drupa speciosa* Dunker, and the hand-some spotted cyclindrical cowry *Cypraea (Arabica) scurra.* Only rarely seen at Raroia, but undoubtedly cast up over the atoll rim by storms, were a few shells of the medium-sized scaly giant clam *Tridacna noae* (Morrison, 1954).

An illustration of the fish fauna in the surge channel zone is found in a description for Raroia Atoll by Harry (1953, p. 22) (Fig. 82). Since the open

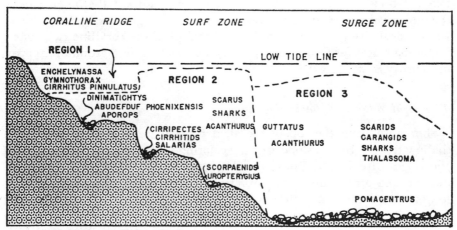

Fig. 82. Ecological zonation of fishes in surge channels at Raroia Atoll during the day-time. [After Harry (1953).]

mouths of the surge channels are dangerous places to swim about because of the presence of sharks, the description is mostly about the inner part of the zone. This zone contained the most distinctive fish fauna on the atoll. Many fishes found here were limited completely to this zone, and many fishes found almost everywhere else on the atoll did not occur in the surge channels.

The surge zone was completely dominated by cirrhitids and blennies (especially of the genus Cirripectes). They were not easily observable. In fact, during the day the surge channels looked practically barren except for sharks, scarids, and carangids schooling in the outer mouths. The presence of the other fishes became obvious when rotenone poison was thrown into the swirling water. The fishes in holes, in cracks, and under rocks of the buttress walls were quickly swept out of their hiding places. The high respiration rate of the fishes in the oxygen-impregnated surf waters made the fish here very susceptible to rotenone.

The narrow end of the channels also had a large population of echidnid eels, most of which appeared to be limited to this region and to the sea-urchin holes on the coralline ridge. Two pomacentrids were confined entirely to the channels, several scorpaenids were moderately abundant in the surge channels and in the sea-urchin holes of the ridge, and brotulids were prominent under the rocks and in the holes.

The broader, deeper section next to the outer mouths of the surge channels forms a distinctive subzone. Here a considerable population of larger fishes occur, none of which are confined to the surge channels. They comprise such types as surgeon fish, cirrhitids, carangids, scarids, and to a lesser extent labrids. At high tide these fishes move in toward the inner ends of the surge channels. Many species, such as *Acanthurus guttatus* and *A. achilles*, swim over the ridge onto the reef flat. The tops of the coralline ridge offers no hiding places for fish, but they are notable as a feeding ground for parrot fish (Harry, 1953, p. 23).

The algal ridge and backridge slope

Shoreward from the top of the algal ridge there is a slight slope to a shallow trough. In this slope area the coloring is not like the bright pink of the ridge. Often, as at Bikini (Taylor, 1950, p. 30), there is a coating of diatoms and other minute organisms on it. Pocockiella formed bright yellow-brown patches on which grew many crustose sponges and white soft corals. These surfaces back of the ridge also may support a growth of algae and other organisms which form a fine felt mat several millimeters thick. They include such minute organisms as Lautencia, Centroceras, and Jania. Over them commonly is found an immense population of the stellate Foraminifera whose abraded tests form the chief constituent of the beach sands. Few larger algae accompanied this turf at Bikini.

Doty and Morrison (1954, p. 6) reported that the smooth *Porolithon onkodes* cover of the algal ridge at Raroia extended horizontally inshore from the base of the algal ridge from a few inches to a few feet, ending in a rather definite border. This border could be located within a few centimeters, and they termed this the reef-ridge line. It was distinguished by a transition from the Porolithon surfaces dotted here and there by patches of blue-green algae to a surface dominated by an Amphiroa similar to *A. annulata*. In structure this Amphiroa zone was a turf about 3 centimeters deep over a room-and-pillar structure 10 to 15 centimeters thick. The cavities formed the habitats for a myriad of invertebrate species and small fish. In the solid structure of the reef here, the black boring urchin Echinometra appeared to be the most important inhabitant. The alga *Caulerpa urvilleana*, which appeared with some frequency opposite incurrent areas as green patches in the otherwise pink Amphiroa turf, and the Amphiroa itself seemed to be restricted to this zone. The other biota found here also are distributed farther inshore.

According to Doty and Morrison (1954), in this section of the reef *Turbo argyrostoma* was found to be rather sharply limited to within the reef line, the major distribution being in holes near the surface of the Amphiroa zone. Here also occurred a remarkable association between the shrimp *Crangon frontalis* and the alga *Lyngbya sordida*, which occurred both out in the groove of the surge channels and in the next adjacent inshore zone up to the backshore slope of the ridge. The algae took the form of perfectly developed simple or irregularly branched tubes which reached a width of 1 to 3 centimeters. These thin-walled tubes attach firmly but at isolated points to the structure beneath. Within the tubes live the commensal shrimps, usually solitary within each tube. This association, found also in the Marshalls by Taylor (1950, p. 111), was best developed on the underside of rocks. Tubes of this algae at Raroia reached a length of as much as 60 centimeters (Newhouse, 1954, p. 48).

Among the shell fish whose characteristic habitat is the top of the algal ridge is *Patella stellaeformis* (Morrison, 1954, p. 15). On the Raroia ridge it lived in little sockets on the surface and is discernible by the outline of its shell when the ridge is exposed at low tide. The surface of the shell as well as the rock on which it rests were covered with the pinkish algae. Also most characteristic of this zone at Raroia was the large, heavy-shelled white cat's-eye shell *Turbo setosus*. On every large Turbo shell were numbers of the hipponicid snail *Sabia conica*. These snails erode small sockets near the aperture of the Turbo shells and apparently feed as scavengers on the droppings of the Turbo. They have a shorter life span than the Turbo, for the oldest Turbo shells exhibited adult-size scars of Sabia animals that had completed their life cycle and dropped off. Small Sabia of the next generation were found attached in these scar cavities.

Three spiny species of rock snails of the Drupa species were found in this zone. One of these, the purple-mouthed *Drupa morum,* was restricted to the algal ridge, according to observations both at Raroia and in the Marshalls (Morrison, 1954). *Drupa elegans,* which in the adult form has a white mouth ringed by a red line, was restricted to the outer reef edge at Raroia. A third snail, *Drupa ricinus,* could be found in small numbers scattered from the shore completely across the reef.

The largest and most conspicuous animal of the algal ridge zone was the purple slate-pencil sea urchin, *Heterocentrotus trigonarius* (Plate 43). Also present was a more-reddish species, *Heterocentrotus mamillatus.* Commensal with the slate-pencil urchins was a small species of crangonid shrimp, also purplish in color, matching the general color of the urchins on which they live. Also, a parasitic snail, Stylifer sp., could be found attached to the oral side of the slate-pencil sea urchins (Morrison, 1954).

Because of the mobility of the crab fauna, they are harder to correlate into narrow zonations than are the slower-moving molluscan species. In the outer half of the reef on the lee side of atolls are the favorite hunting grounds of the native people for nighttime fish spearing and crab and lobster catching. The edible crabs hunted with the aid of torches, lanterns, or sometimes flashlights include the swimming crab *Charybdis erythrodactyla,* the xanthid crabs *Atergatopsis signatus, Carpilius convexus, Carpilius maculatus, Etisus splendidus, Juxtaxanthias tetraodon, Lachnopodus tahitensis, Zosimus aeneus,* and the plagusine crabs *Percnon abbreviatum* and *Plagusia speciosa.* Also important are the edible lobsters, such as the spiny *Panulirus penicillatus* and the shovel-nosed *Parribacus antarcticus.* On the mouth appendages of the Parribacus at Raroia a small species of commensal goose barnacle was found (Morrison, 1954).

The backridge trough, or tide-pool zone

Sloping shoreward from the algal ridge is a reef zone leading to a low-lying part of the reef termed a trough or tide-pool zone. From his study of the Bikini reef, Wells (1954) designated this the *Acropora digitefera* coral zone (Fig. 76; Plates 44 to 49). It includes the part of the reef flat supporting microatolls of varied composition and size growing in depths of 1 to 2 feet (awash at low tide). Although most of its surface is bare of coral colonies, this region has a great variety of corals. Anchored to the rock surface are encrusting nodular and stunted ramose colonies and microatolls from a few inches to many feet across. The larger colonies are formed by the growth of several adjoining colonies, often of differing species. On their dead parts still other species may grow, and their flat, rotten tops support other biotic forms, especially calcareous algae.

In a similar zone at Onotoa, Moul (1957, p. 31) found the part of the slope of this trough that extended back for about 100 to 150 feet from the algal ridge reddish colored from the mat of *Jania decussatodichotoma* that formed an almost continuous cover, which was especially heavy where the trough was always under water. Fleshy gelatinous red algae grew at the base of the Jania. Usually the only green algae present was Dictyosphaeria. A branched coralline alga, Goniolithon, was found to occur in solid stands where this zone was wide.

In the deepest part of the tide pool at Bikini, where at low tide the water was 2 to 3 feet deep, Heliopora formed compact colonies and microatolls of large size, 10 to 20 or more feet in diameter (Plate 51). Between this zone and the *Acropora digitifera* zone on the shallower outer slope of the tide-pool region there was a band 50 to 300 feet wide occupied almost exclusively by *Acropora palifera,* covered by about a foot of water at low tide. The *A. palifera* rarely formed microatolls greater than 10 feet in diameter, and scattered clumps of them mingled with the Heliopora in the shoreward slope of the tide pool. In the outer Acropora zone at Raroia, Newell (1954, pp. 9–10) found slate-pencil urchins occupying a zone 6 to 7 feet inward of the algal ridge, sitting in pits and depressions which they apparently had excavated. Presumably, they get their nourishment from food carried to them by the circulating water. In the next 80 or so feet landward the Porolithon-encrusted Pocillopora and Acropora were perforated by the numerous hollows of the boring urchin *Echinometra mathaei.* Both black and brown urchins occurred here.

The superficial deposits over the reef were found to form a superstructure of cellular material. This 10-to-20-centimeter-thick layer was built over a basement of solid rock in which the pores or crevices have been cemented over with foraminiferal sand. A variety of brittle stars, crabs, snails, fishes, and octopi found shelter in the open burrows and entrapped water at low tide, when much of the area is out of water (Newell, 1954).

Most of the other animals found in the hollows and borings were simply taking shelter until the next night's activities. Active and more abundant at night in this reef zone were the spotted cowry *Cypraea (Arabica) depressa,* *C. (Arabica) histrio,* and a few species of medium-sized shells of Mitra spp. Also found here, but rarely, is the common tiger cowry *Cypraea tigris,* which is widespread elsewhere, and colorful sea slugs (Nudibranch), including two species of the genus Glossodoris. One is opaque milk-white all over, but the other has red ring spots on a blue-black body about 2 inches long. A species of crab, *Daira perlata,* was seen only in or around the boring-sea-urchin zone. Their color and texture resembles coralline algal rock (Morrison, 1954, p. 15).

At Kwajelein on the windward reef east of Ebeje the author found long-spined black urchins occupying the deeper and shaded sides of hollows in the reef flat and seaward of perhaps thousands of short-spined brown urchins. The short-spined urchins were so dense that it was impossible to walk over this part of the reef without stepping on two or three at a time. The brown urchins resembled chestnut burrs, with sharp spines only about half an inch in length.

Some reef flats appear barren of organisms, yet upon closer examination are seen to have many forms of life. Long stretches of such reef areas at Arno were found by Hiatt (1958) to be covered by a thin carpet of brown-green alga, on the curly fronds of which clung myriads of pale salmon-pink Foraminifera, especially Calcarina, the dead tests of which are such an important part of beach sand. Scattered throughout this mat were small knobs the size of a man's fist. Closer examination showed them to be the solidly cemented shells of the rock clam Chama, which open only when covered by water. The author has seen similar Chama-studded reef flats on the leeward reef of Ebon in the Marshalls.

In the inner part of the tide-pool zone at Bikini, Wells (1954) (Fig. 76) recognized two other zones: a *Heliopora coerulea* zone and a *Porites lutea* zone. The former occupied a zone 100 to 500 feet wide in which water was 1 to 4 feet deep. Here innumerable colonies of Heliopora rose from the floor of the reef flat to form microatolls from a few feet to as much as 100 feet in diameter. In some areas, the coalescing of such laterally expanding micro-atolls formed surfaces an acre in extent, as at the western end of Namu Island at Bikini. This occurs also on lagoon reefs, and an example of this was photographed by the author on the windward shore of the lagoon of Ebon near the eastern end of Ebon Island (Plate 52). Wells found that pools or passages between colonies were covered on the bottom by a thin veneer of sand and coral fragments on which few if any corals grew. Where the microatolls have coalesced, the tops were compact, forming a firm platform at low tide.

In water less than a foot deep, nearer the beach at Bikini, the yellow and purplish-brown variants of *Porites lutea* were the only corals. They generally occur in small irregular nodules or microatolls up to several feet across.

In describing a tide pool at Onotoa in a protected region behind the windward reef, Banner (1952) found the dominant animal to be Heliopora, with one head to about every square yard. Porites also occurred but were only a tenth as plentiful. Other corals that were found, all infrequently, included Orbicella, Pocillopora, and Leptoria. In the exposed sand bottom the only animal was *Holothuria atra,* a sea cucumber. Other invertebrates were found under coral heads and in coral heads. Those that made their habitat under coral heads were stomatopods such as *Pseudosquilla ciliata.*

Tunicates, holothuroids, *Thais hippocastanum,* Tethys, and brachyuran crabs also were found under the coral heads.

In the coral heads Banner found crangonid shrimps ("pistol shrimps") and small xanthid crabs. Encrusting sponges of various types were common, as were black colonial tunicates. Annilid worms, such as Errantia and Sedentia, were moderately common. Between the inner branches of the coral were several species of clams, including Isognomon sp. and *Barbatia tenolla.* In the labyrinthian passages below the surface, where the Heliopora was becoming consolidated by coralline algae, lived numerous fish.

The inner part of the tide-pool zone is an erosional flat and the molluscan fauna is most easily collected in this area. The collection by Morrison (1954, pp. 12–15) at Raroia is probably representative for this zone elsewhere as well. Here he found several small species of Cerithium with *Pusia nodosa* (which probably feed on these small Ceriths), the small mitrid *Imbricaria punctata, Strombus maculatus,* and *Modulus tectum.* On the leeward side of Raroia, the most characteristic species of this zone of the seaward reef was *Vasum armatum;* the small, lettered mitre shell *Mitra litterata;* the black rock snail *Morula granulata;* a whitish rock snail with a purple mouth, *Morula uva;* and the little red-flammulate cone *Conus sponsalis.* The largest of the Vasum shells exhibited scars of formerly attached horse-hoof shells, *Sabia conica.*

According to Morrison, several frog shells, although uncommon, were found in this zone. Among these were the carnivorous *Bursa granularis,* the toad shell *Bursa bufonium,* and the small white toad shell *Bursa producta.* Although the first two are widespread in the Indo-Pacific, the third is only known in the region from the Gilberts to the Tuamotus.

Abundant locally here was the Hebrew cone, *Conus ebraeus;* the chaldean cone, *Conus chaldeus;* the flesh-colored *Conus miliaris;* and the darker *Conus coronalis.* All these were considered by Morrison to be separate species. He also found under the larger coral rocks in this zone the beautiful but dangerous *Conus retifer,* which has a poisonous sting; the tiny speckled *Maculotriton digitalis;* the small pink *Columbella pallida;* the black-spotted white ark shell, *Arca maculata;* and occasionally the large horse-hoof cowry, *Cypraea (Peribolus) mauritiana.* Under almost every rock of large size the black, poisonous sea urchins *Diadema setosum* take refuge during the daytime. These urchins move out to feed at sundown. Also found partly under these rocks was the long black sea cucumber, which stretches one end a considerable distance outward to feed. The largest and most conspicuous animal in the open in the daytime was found to be the common black sea cucumber, generally coated with a film of foraminiferal sand. At places there were as many as 15 to 20 of these per square meter.

Under the coral growths in the middle section of the tide-pool zone at Raroia Morrison found the money cowry, *Cypraea moneta,* quite common. Other mollusks commonly found in such habitats included the snake's head cowry, *Cypraea caputserpentis;* the whitish-tan sand cowry, *Cypraea schilderorum;* and the cones *Conus lividus* and *Conus miles.* Less common were the large *Turbo argyrostomus,* the tiny spotted cowry *Cypraea irrorata,* and the small blue-tipped, red-speckled starfish *Linckia multifora.* Examples of the latter were found in the stages of generating new arms from the body disks or the rest of the body from only one arm. Morrison found only in this zone, but rarely, the round sea urchin *Tripneustes gratilla,* a short-spined urchin that covers itself with pieces of algae or other debris, apparently for camouflage.

At the base of such coral rock could be found the white coral-boring snails *Magilopsis lamarckii.* These snails lived in a flasklike cavity in the coral with their heads directed toward the small opening to the exterior. In some of these cavities also were some clams living commensally with the snails. These clams, *Barclayia incerta,* have been found living commensally with these snails thousand of miles apart, from Reunion Island eastward to the Tuamotu Islands. The eggs of the Magilopsis snails are held in capsules in the chamber until they hatch, and the pelagic young swim away to find a new host coral in which to start their boring. In the same type of habitat as the Magilopsis was the coral snail *Quoyula monodonta* (Morrison, 1954).

On the leeward reef at Raroia, where the outer reef is lacking a definite algal ridge, some sections near the reef edge may have patches of colonial zoanthid anemones, so-called "soft corals." When they are exposed at low tide they are retracted and look like sandy, grit-filled patches of dirty grey-white paraffin about an inch thick. A symbiotic barnacle Baccalaureus spp. was found by Morrison to be living inside the colonial anemone. It was so much reduced from its normal appearance that he found it difficult to place it in a group. Its general shape was similar to that of the old Greek discus, with a symmetrical helicoid spiral ridge on each face.

The recording of crab life on the reef is easier than the attempt to localize species within certain habitats, since they range widely and move rapidly. Nevertheless, the following species were definitely recorded by Morrison (1954) from the inshore part of the leeward, seaward reef at Raroia. They included *Cryptodromia canaliculata, Dynomene spinosa, Micippoides angustifrons, Thalamita picta, Carupa laeviuscula, Actaea superciliaris, Chlorodopsis areolata, Cymo deplanatus, Eriphia sebana, Lophozozymus superbus, Lybia tesselata, Lydia annulipes, Xanthias lamarckii,* and *Pachygrapsus plicatus.*

Among the hermit crabs recorded in the same locality were the red, fuzzy-legged *Aniculus aniculus* and *Clibanarius corallinus,* the brilliant blue-legged *Calcinus elegans,* the ordinary-looking white-legged *Calcinus laevi-manus, Calcinus latens,* and *Calcinus seurati.* The feathery-appearing red-banded shrimp *Stenopus hispidus* also appeared in this zone. The red-eyed rock crabs, *Eriphia sebana,* were active on the exposed inshore reef flat at low tide. Morrison saw one in the act of crushing the shell of a small cone, *Conus sponsalis,* in its crushing claw and starting to eat it.

Like the crabs, many of the fish forms are hard to localize because of their free-ranging habits. In the middle reef sections (Fig. 83) at high tide

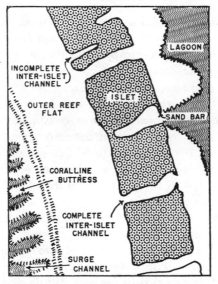

Fig. 83. Fish habitats of the reef zones at Raroia. [After Harry (1953).]

both night and day great numbers of the larger fishes swim over the reef to feed in the reef flat and tide-pool zones. According to Harry (1953, p. 23) these larger, free-ranging fishes included such species as the surgeon fishes (especially *Acanthurus triostegus, A. guttatus,* and *A. achilles*), wrasses (chiefly Thalassoma and Halichoeres), many species of parrot fishes and chaetodontids and also *Eulamia melanoptera,* all of which were prominent during the day. During the nighttime high tides the fish fauna over the flats were found to consist of Holocentrus spp., the mugilids, Belone, Hemi-rhamphus, Monotaxis, and a few cirrhitids. At low tide the middle flat region was characterized by great numbers of gobies of the general Parago-biodon and Gobiodon. Caracanthus were prominent to a lesser extent. Small labrids (usually Halichoeres) and Tetraodon hid among the coral in moderate numbers (Harry, 1953, p. 23).

In the inner flat and tide-pool zone certain blennies and gobies found nowhere else dominate the zone together with the echidnid eels *Lycodontis picta* and *L. flavimarginata*. Young *Cephalopholis argus* and the pomacentrid *Abudefduf glaucus* also are prominent here, according to Harry. Syngnathids rarely observed elsewhere are common here. Whereas during high tide these fishes may spread out over the reef flat to feed, the larger fishes from over the reef do not invade their realm.

The intertidal and spray-wet shore zone

The ecology of the intertidal and spray-wet shore zone is illustrated by the descriptions for Raroia by Doty and Morrison (1954, p. 13). Algal forms were found to be mostly microscopic blue-greens, generally *Entophysalis crustacea,* which give the rocks a black coloring. Between the low-tide pool level and about three-quarters the distance to the high-tide line, two common gastropods, *Thais hippocastaneum* and *Morula granulata,* had their habitat. A *Nerita plicata,* which was most conspicuous at night, migrated with the tides here so as to be exposed between waves that washed over it. In its upper shoreward fringe it overlapped the lower habitat of a Tectarius. Preying and feeding on the Nerita at its lower levels was a carnivorous gastropod, *Cronia cariosa.* The Tectarius, on the other hand, had its habitat in the spray-wet zone above the tides.

Doty and Morrison (1954) stated that the blue-green algae have a very significant role. They apparently soften the limestone, so that the snails rasp away the rock along with the algae. Both *Nerita plicata* and Tectarius appear to feed by ingestion of this algae. The darkening of the rock also appears to increase the temperature of the rock. While changing the pH locally, the algae also protect the rock somewhat from wave attack. Locally, the algae also affect the solution and deposition of calcium carbonate through their metabolic activities.

Inter-islet channel habitats

A great variety of habitats occur in the channels between islets because of great variances in channel depths and surface character. Some channels dry at low tide. At the other extreme are the deep ship passes through which a great depth of water flows at all times. Channels may have one-directional flow of water into the lagoon at all times, or there may be tidal reversals of water into and out of the lagoon. One-way tidal influx over the reef into the lagoon at Eniwetok Atoll has been described by Odum and Odum (1955, pp. 294–7). At this reef section there was a downslope of the reef from the low, ill-defined algal ridge, with deepening water toward the lagoon. The authors found five very clearly defined coral zones, as demonstrated by Table 12. The algal-coral ridge had only 3 coral species, marked zone A.

TABLE 12

Zonation of Corals at Japtan Reef, Eniwetok Atoll *

Species	Reef zone				
	A	*B*	*C*	*D*	*E*
Pocillopora danae (E. and S.)	X				
Acropora sp. (encrusting type)	X	X			
Millepora platyphylla H. and E.	X	X		X	X
Favites halicora (Ehrenb.)		X			
Pocillopora verrucosa (E. and S.)		X			
Plesiastrea versipora (Lam.)		X	X		
Favia pallida (Dana)		X	X		
Porites lobata Dana		X	X	X	
Favites abdita (E. and S.)			X		
Cyphastrea chalcidicum (Forsk.)			X		
Porites lutea M.-E. and H.			X		
Pocillopora elegans Dana			X		
Acropora tubicinaria (Dana)			X		
Acropora conferta (Quelch)			X	X	
Acropora humilis (Dana)			X	X	
Echinopora lamellosa (Esper)			X	X	
Favia stelligera (Dana)			X	X	
Acropora corymbosa (Lam.)				X	
Acropora recumbens (Brook) (?)				X	
Montipora verrilli Vaughan				X	
Montipora faveolata (Dana)				X	
Goniastrea retiformis (Lam.)				X	
Stylophora mordax Dana				X	
Lotophytum pauciflorum (Ehr.)				X	
Millepora murrayi Quelch					X
Heliopora coerulea (Pallas)					X
Turbinaria globularis Bernard					X

* Adapted from Odum and Odum, 1957, p. 2.

Zone B, an encrusting zone with only about 6 inches of water at low spring tide, had 7 coral species. As the water deepened in zone C, the number of species increased to 12, but most of them were in small heads. Among these heads small fish were numerous, and larger fish came into the area when the current was not too strong. Among the latter was the poisonous stone fish *Scorpaena gibbosa.*

In zone D, where the water was even deeper, there were 13 species of coral, 7 of which did not overlap those of zone C. The heads also became much larger, with channels of sand and cobble floor between them. Swimming becomes easy here for the larger fish, and the majority of parrot fish and surgeon fish were found to browse and school in this zone. This zone, which is about 400 feet wide, although it is a jungle of coral and fishes, is dominated by the plant world.

In zone E the number of species dropped off sharply, and the algae become less important. This zone, which was about 500 feet wide, apparently was a zone of sedimentation. Only 4 coral species were present and 3 of these were restricted to this zone. Foraminifera of large types were abundant but there were few fishes, except for schools of sardinelike fish that fed on fragments of pseudoplankton and a few of the larger carnivorous fishes such as sharks. Lagoonward beyond the 500 feet the slope took a sharp dip downward into the lagoon floor.

Differing from the reef at Eniwetok described by Odum and Odum are the common shallow inter-islet reefs, which are dry or nearly dry at low tide, but at high tide waves and currents are strong enough to sweep away the sand, leaving flattened and wave-worn coral cobbles and boulders. Concerning these channel areas at Onotoa, Banner (1952, p. 16) found that they were devoid of larger animals. In such areas, however, where there was some slight protection afforded by a bar formation, a feeble fauna developed. The animals represented included some xanthid crabs, a few sponges, and a few heads of Porites in the tidal basins or pools. Some life was found in the fine gravel zones near the zero tide levels. These comprised mostly sipunculids and annelid worms burrowing into the dead coral reef. In some of the pools might be found an occasional brittle star.

Between the extremes shown by the Eniwetok example and the Onotoa example are the channels that do not dry entirely, but in which there often are numbers of rather flat fragments of dead coral rock. In a situation of this kind at Raroia reported by Doty and Morrison (1954, p. 58), there almost always appeared to be a large population of grey spotted moray eels (*Gymnothorax picta*). Most of them tended to be small and clearly timid, as were the small black-tipped sharks (Eulamia), also found where the water is deeper. Also in the deeper portions of the completely cut-through channels were representations of coralline algae, such as *Porolithon aequinoctiale.* Such animal forms as Diadema, Vermetus, Drupa, and Chama also may be found. Near the central parts of channels there often occurred the algae *Caulerpa urvilleana,* and nearer shore *Microdictyon okamurai.* Under the edges of rocks and very near shore the most abundant macroscopic alga was *Dictyosphaeria cavernosa.*

The fish population in the inter-islet channels varies tremendously depending upon width and whether the connections between sea and lagoon are continuous or intermittent. The extent of sand-bar formation at the lagoon mouths of channels is important also. Conditions are so varied in channels that generalizations are difficult. Two greatly differing types, the shallow, narrow continuous channel, and the wide, deep channel as reported for Raroia by Harry (1953, pp. 24–5) are given as illustrations of differing ecological situations. In the former channels large numbers of gobies and blennies and even greater numbers of *Abudefduf imparipennis* are found. Parapercids were found only in this type of channel. Such channels form a nursery for the young of many species of echidnids and of Epinephelus and *Cephalopholis argus.*

Garue Pass at Raroia is 40 to 60 feet deep and about 400 yards wide. In such deep passes most of the time there is a strong flow of water, in this case out of the lagoon, but at extreme high tide the current reverses itself. Coral growth, especially on the two shore reefs, is very abundant in the pass. Harry found in this habitat the greatest concentration of fishes of any restricted locality on the atoll, and this formed the favorite fishing ground of the natives. All the large fish groups were abundant here, particularly the families Galeorhinidae, Isuridae, and Carangidae. Other families importantly represented include the Echeneididae, Balistidae, Labridae, Scaridae, Serranidae, Lethrinidae, and Lutianidae. The shore reefs had a distinctive fauna. Apparently only occurring in this zone at Raroia were *Dascyllus trimaculatus, Acanthurus lineatus, Amphiprion bicinctus,* and large sea anemones. Fish species such as *Chaetodon reticulatus, C. ornatissimus,* and *Acanthurus achilles* are more abundant in this deep pass than in any other locality on the atoll.

The shore line and adjoining land zones

Conditions on the lagoon sides of reefs have differing elements from those of the seaward sides, and the ecology of the marine flora and fauna presents as varied a picture as that on the seaward reefs. Beginning at the lagoon shore line and the adjoining land zone is the habitat of a few individuals of the common whitish shore-line snail *Melaraphe coccinea.* These were found at Onotoa (Banner, 1952, p. 16) together with a considerable population of the salt-marsh snails and a small number of the tiny golden snail *Syncera lucida.* They were most abundant where drift material accumulated from the lagoon.

The salt-marsh snails feed on the drift material and the algae on the rocks. They appear able to survive under the full heat of the sun by staying on the underside of rocks and in gravel layers 4 to 8 inches below the hot surface near the crest of the beach ridge. The commonest species of this snail were *Melampus luteus, M. violus,* and *Pira fasciata,* all found throughout the Indo-Pacific region. *Pira mucronata,* another species, appeared to live at all times under the gravel, even at night when all its relatives were moving about in the open to feed on the drift material. Two species, *Allochroa conica* and *Laemodonta mordax,* seemed to prefer the larger blocks of coral rock along the shore, according to Banner. The latter often were extremely abundant in pits on the underside of large coral rocks just below the normal high-tide line. Also abundant and living with it was another snail, *Planaxis zonatus.* Two small species of crabs, *Pseudograpsus albus* and *Cyclograpsus longipes,* were found to be living in the same habitat under the coral gravel and cobbles where Melampus and Pira flourished.

Along shores of this type at Raroia at or just below the low-tide line Morrison (1954, pp. 7–8) found the habitat of a number of crab species, including the rock crab *Eriphia scabricula,* the red-eyed rock crab *E. sebana,* the white rock crab *Xantho exaratus,* the speckled rock crab *X. gracilis,* the small rock crabs *Grapsus longitarsus* and *Pachygrapsus planifrons, Lydia annulipes,* young individuals of the common large red-clawed land hermit crab *Coenobita perlatus,* and the smaller hermit crabs *Calcinus laevimanus, C. latens,* and *C. seurati.* Where conglomerate rock occurred on the lagoon shores, Morrison (1954, p. 9) found the brown rock crab *Geograpsus crinipes,* together with smaller numbers of the red-spotted shore crab *Grapsus tenuicrustatus.*

Lagoon beach-rock and coral-gravel foreshore habitats

Collections of algae made from the surface of beach rock of the lagoon shore at Onotoa (Moul, 1957, p. 28) showed two species of Entophysalis as dominant, with *Calothrix pilosa* and *Nostoc muscorum* also present. Entophysalis also was shown by Newhouse (1954, p. 45) to be most prevalent on rock at Raroia from the high-tide line to below low tide on lagoon shores. At both atolls the dark coloration on the surface of the rocks was found to be due to the discoloration of sheath material of Entophysalis by exposure to sunlight.

Shoreward from the beach-rock ridge and sheltered by it, the lime-sand bottom was found by Moul to have become hardened to the consistency of hard putty. It had the same blue-green algae on the surface as was found in the beach rock. However, at about a quarter of an inch below the surface was a second layer of blue-green algae, which consisted of *Oscillatoria nigro-*

viridis, Lyngbya confervoides, and *Phormidium valderianum.* These blue-greens have been thought by some to bind the lime silt into beach rock.

Where erosion had produced small pools in the beach rock at different levels covered by salt water at high tide, a solid mat of an alga, believed to be *Enteromorpha compressa,* grew in the pools.

The lagoon beach-rock and coral-gravel foreshore habitats appear to have similar faunal associations. In these areas, when the tide is out during the day, the animals are subject to heat and desiccation, to rain, and to the out-flow of fresh water from the island fresh-water lens. On the other hand, when the tide is in, the organisms are subjected to the buffeting of waves, at times very violent storm waves.

Nerita plicata and *Grapsus grapsus* occurred in the higher beach rock just as they occurred on the seaward side, but the Nerita were not as numer-ous on the lagoon side. Together with another snail which shares the lower ranges of this zone, *Nerita plicata* scrapes off and ingests the blue-green algae. This second snail, *N. polita,* coexisted in the lower ranges with a carnivorous mollusk, *Cronia cariosa,* which feeds on *Nerita plicata* but which apparently is thwarted from eating *N. polita* by the thicker calcareous operculum, or "trap door," of *N. polita.* Normally, according to Morrison (1954, p. 9), *Nerita plicata* retreats with the incoming tide, both day and night, resting for the next night's activities at or just above the normal high-tide line.

Lagoon mud flats

At Onotoa Atoll, in a small area of soft mud slightly above zero tide level, where rich organic matter was decomposing, the mud was found to give off the odor of hydrogen sulfide. Banner (1952, p. 16) observed only one animal, the bright-hued fiddler crab, living in burrows in this habitat.

Lagoon sand flats

One of the most extensive habitats on the lagoon reefs of atolls is the sand flat. The flats extend outward from the beach as almost-level areas for from several hundred feet to as much as half a mile in places. On the outer edge they may merge into decadent coral reef rock or be covered with turtle grass or continue as sand bottom into the lagoon depths. The sand overlying the reef may be from a few inches to several feet thick and from about 2 feet above to several feet below zero tide level. According to Banner's ob-servations at Onotoa (1952, pp. 19–21) the fauna of this zone varies with the depth of water, the fineness of sand particles, the amount of wave action, and the depth of sand. The differences in fauna are not well demarcated and more often are quantitative rather than qualitative. That is, the same species are present in most cases but vary in relative abundance. However, with differences in depth of water, fauna changed markedly.

According to Banner, the fauna of the sand bottoms at Onotoa included four Porifera, or sponges—a purple, an orange, and two black species. Among the Annelida were tubeworms, two species of Errantia, and both small and giant sipunculids. The Crustacea included *Lysiosquilla maculata,* Calappa sp., and some Callianassids. The Echinoderm *Holothuria atra* were so numerous as to count 5 to 15 per square yard. Ptychodera sp. represented the Chordata. Only a few living mollusks were observed, mostly, according to Banner, because the Onotoan natives liked to eat the sand-flat mollusks. Shells observed included clams, *Gafrarium pectinata, Tellina crassiplicata,* Nautica, various species of Mitra, Terebra, Cymathium, and Trochus.

In similarly sandy lagoon reef areas at Raroia, Morrison (1954, pp. 7–8) reported that the conspicuous members of the fauna were *Strombus mutabilis, S. gibberulus, Cerithium columna,* and *Conus eburneus.* The latter were seen only at night, probably being buried under the surface of the sand during the day. Under rocks deeply imbedded in the sand, Morrison found annelid worms possessing needle setae that can stick painfully into groping fingertips. This pink species of annelid have golden setae and must be handled only with forceps in order to avoid painful stings.

In these sandy lagoon reef flats, where the bottom at low tide has at least a foot of water, various corals grow up from the bottom. These were found by Banner to include Porites (dominant), *Pocillopora damicornis, Acropora servicornis,* Orbicella, Pennaria, and other corals.

On dead parts of the coral heads were found tube worms in limy tubes, sipunculids, various species of Crangonid and brachyuran crabs, colonial tunicates and such mollusks as *Cypraea erosa, C. moneta,* and *Barbatia amygdalumtostum.*

The lagoon reef flat and tide-pool zone

This zone of the lagoon reef flat has a considerable variety of habitats. It is a region with a somewhat eroded bottom, often rocky and containing boulders, pooled in places with a foot of water at low tide. In places there is a thin layer of sand or sand and pebbles, and, between rocks, sand may fill the interstices. In such a situation at Raroia Morrison (1954, pp. 7–8) reported finding on and under the rocks abundant money cowries, *Cypraea moneta;* black rock snails, *Morula granulata;* purple-mouthed snails, *Peristernia nassatula;* and *Pollia undosa.* On the underside of the larger coral blocks he found the byssiferous clam *Isognomon perna* and two characteristic species of ark shells, the small black-spotted white *Arca maculata* and the small brown *Barbatia parva*. In nests deeply dug into the under surfaces of some of the coral blocks were many specimens of all sizes of the large turkey-feather ark shell, *Arca ventricosa*. The eastern gold-ring cowry, *Cypraea (Ornamentaria) obvelata,* was found together with the money cowry, also under such rocks. Two species of sea slugs, the pulmonate Onchidium and the green half-shelled tectibranchiate *Smaragdinella calyculata,* shared this same habitat.

Morrison also observed that two large species of hermit crabs, one a white-eyed *Dardanus deformis* and the other the giant red *D. megistos,* ranged widely over the inner reef flats. Both were fast-moving and scurried away when disturbed rather than withdrawing into the large snail shells they used, such as those of Turbo, *Charonia tritonis,* and *Lambis truncata.*

In the shallow tide pools in parts of the intertidal flats at low tide, certain swimming crabs were to be found. These included *Portunus granulatus* and *P. longispinus.* A handsome fiddler crab at Raroia, *Uca tetragonon,* is whitish in color but has a brilliant crimson-orange "fiddler" claw. It was active when the tide went out, running over the surface of thin conglomerate rock and hiding in holes in this conglomerate. Great numbers of tiny water striders, Halobates sp., may be seen at times in this intertidal zone (Morrison, 1954).

Lagoon turtle-grass areas

Turtle grass may form dominant growths over lagoon reef sand bottoms from zero tide level to depths between 6 and 10 feet. The deep green grass (Thallasia sp.) seldom grows over a foot or more high, but makes dense stands over surfaces of sand in which its creeping rhizomes form an interwoven mat. According to Banner (1952, pp. 21–2) the turtle grass proper at Onotoa was relatively devoid of invertebrate life. The most abundant visible animals were a papillose green-black holothurian, although on the grass fronds were occasional black colonial tunicates, and on the fronds and bases of the grass several varieties of sponges. The few burrowing animals in the sand substrate appeared to be limited to a small squillid (Lysiosquilla) and some burrowing worms.

Rising out of deeper portions of the turtle-grass beds were some solitary coral masses rich in life, both fish and invertebrate. The corals were mostly Porites, but these were partly covered by other corals such as Acropora, Pocillopora, Orbicella, and the like. The invertebrate fauna were generally similar to those in the coral heads of the sandy reef flats.

Over the sandy lagoon reef and gravelly areas near the shore line the largest percentage of fish fauna appeared to be schools of mullet and young Lutianus. Buried in the sand of the reef at Onotoa, Harry (1953, p. 25) found two species of moringuids abundant. Over both the sandy and dead coral rock areas of the lagoon reefs the fishes wandered at high tide to feed, but Harry found them limited in species here. Aside from the moringuids the fish were chiefly *Acanthurus triostegus,* and *Pomacentrus nigricans.* The former wandered about in large schools over the reef when it was submerged. The latter chiefly was found to be restricted to definite coral heads or sections of coral heads.

Lagoon shelf margins and lagoon slopes

The broad picture of lagoon coral zonation at Bikini Atoll has been found by Wells (1954) to be similar to that found on other Marshall Islands atolls. The zones (Fig. 84) include a *Porites andrewsi* zone extending from the beach outward for 300 to 500 feet or more on a gentle slope in depths of 2 to 18 feet, where patches of coral rise close to the surface. Calcarous algae were found to be uncommon and insignificant along this slope. From about 4 to 5 fathoms to the lagoon floor at 27 to 30 fathoms, *Acropora formosa* was plentiful, often forming dense thickets. This slope may be further divided into two subzones. The shallower one, from 3 to 15 fathoms, was marked by abundant handsome, delicate vasiform *Acropora reticulata.* The deeper zone, with a quiet water environment, was characterized by *Acropora rayneri* and the related *A. rambleri,* both also found in deep quiet water outside the reef on the seaward slope. The surface species were either not found in this zone or occurred in small colonies in the upper part of this deeper zone.

On the steep vertical face of the lagoon reef adjacent to the leeward side of Raroia Atoll and living in pockets of live massive corals, large flat ark shells, *Barbatia complanata,* and the byssiferous clam, *Pedum spondyloideum,* were found conspicuously present by Morrison (1954, p. 6). *Tridacna maxima,* the brightly mantled but smallest of the giant clam species, grew on or near the edge of the lagoon reef. Because it is often subjected to great wave force from the waves traveling across the lagoon, it needs the strong byssal attachment it has developed. A few species of boring clams resident in the extremely hard coral rock include the mytilid *Lithophagus teres* and *L. mucronatus,* and the smaller *Gregariella bakeri,* the latter reported so far only from the Hawaiian Islands and from Raroia in the Tuamotus.

The boring sea urchin *Echinometra mathai* and the black, poison sea urchin *Echinothrix diadema* occurred near the lagoon reef margins, but were not common, according to Morrison. On each of the latter urchins one can expect to find two species of the commensal crustaceans *Stegopontonia commensalis,* a shrimp which generally lives between the spines of the sea urchin, and *Eumedonus convictor,* a small spider crab which lives on the anal plate

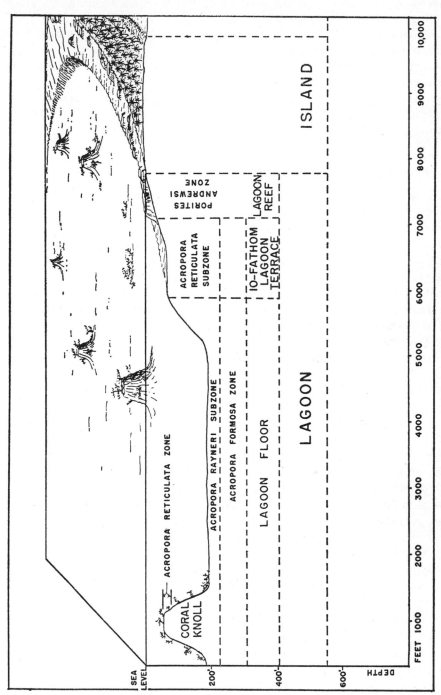

Fig. 84. Coral zones in the lagoon of Bikini Atoll. [From Wells (1954).]

region of this sea urchin. Morrison found both species of crustaceans of almost the same color as the very dark greenish-black sea urchins.

Among the invertebrate fauna occurring in this habitat, Morrison reported the poison cone *Conus textile,* a small sand clam (Tellina sp.), and a species of balanoglossid worm living in pockets of sand between the corals. With these, of necessity also present, were the many small annelid and other worms that make up the food of the carnivorous *Conus textile.*

Lagoon patch reefs and knolls

The lagoon patch reefs are similar to the well-developed lagoon reefs, but appear to have a more luxuriant flora and fauna. Patch reefs may be described as coral and coralline assemblages that grow to the surface to cover areas that are sometimes extensive. Before these assemblages reach the surface they may more properly be called "coral knolls." Where they have reached the surface extensively, they tend to develop the same kind of flats as on peripheral reefs, and much of the surface may be dead and covered with sand. A lagoon may contain hundreds or thousands of knolls and patch reefs, as was discovered by soundings in the northern Marshalls atolls. The 180,000 soundings made in the 24-mile-diameter lagoon of Eniwetok revealed more than 2,000 coral knolls, descriptions of some of which are given by Ladd, Tracey, Wells, and Emery (1950). The top of one of these, rising from a depth of 150 to 200 feet in the lagoon to within about 30 feet of the surface, was rough and irregular, with a maximum relief of about 15 feet. Corals were dominant and covered 75 per cent of the area, but Lithothamnion bound their bases in places. Spreading out from the bases of the coral column, the surface was covered with green, living Halimeda and calcareous sand and debris.

On the knoll a great variety of corals was present, including such massive forms as Porites several feet in diameter, great fragile brackets of *Acropora reticulata* 6 or 7 feet high and 5 to 15 feet across, and large thickets of *Acropora palifera.* Over large areas Lithothamnion formed a hard crust, and white segments of dead Halimeda were scattered over the knoll. Among the commonest mollusks were Tridacna, some measuring 1 to 2 feet across (one large specimen was 3 feet across). Some of these were loose, but others were fixed and hemmed in by coral growth. Soft corals (alcyonarians), usually absent on seaward reefs and not common on lagoon reefs, were common on coral knolls in the lagoons.

Below 10 fathoms the surface species decrease in number and the *Acropora reticulata* subzone is succeeded by the *A. rayneri* subzone. Wherever coral knolls occur in environments that are very well sheltered, according to

Hiatt (1958), species of the solitary loose-lying mushroom coral, Fungia, are to be found, both on coral knolls and in other reef environments.

The other forms of biota on the patch reefs in general appear similar to those of the well-developed lagoon reefs, according to Morrison's observations (1954, pp. 5–6). He found that on the patch reefs at Raroia that were exposed at low tide, the green cat's-eye shell *Turbo ptholatus,* the large spiny oyster *Spondylus varius,* and the blackish plicate oyster *Ostrea sinensis* were among the most conspicuous species of shells. An occasional individual of the large "leather urchin" starfish, *Culcita novaeguinae,* was to be seen. The commercial pearl oysters, *Pinctada margaritifera,* lived in the lagoon here from a depth of a few feet to more than 100 feet. (Where there is no danger from sharks, and where overfishing has not extinguished the abundance of the pearl oyster, the atoll native engages in commercial pearl diving.) Commensal shrimps live in the mantle cavities of both the pearly oyster and the *Spondylus varius.* In the former a pair (male and female) of the shrimp species *Conchodytes meleagrinae* is found in each large specimen of oyster. In the latter a similar pair of the shrimp species *Pontonia hurii* lives commensally.

Fish life on and about a coral knoll appeared to vary much more than that of other fauna, depending upon the position of the knoll in the lagoon, according to Harry (1953, p. 26). He found that at Raroia coral knolls situated on the eastern and northeastern sides or upwind sections of the lagoon had a considerably reduced fish fauna as compared with that elsewhere. The knolls situated in the southwestern and downwind sectors of the lagoon had the greatest variety of fish species. The characteristic faunal variety at Raroia is shown in Figs. 85 and 86.

Harry reported that the open lagoon appears to have a relatively restricted fish population. Bottom dredging down to 40 feet brought up small gobies but no other fishes. The dominant open-water groups in the lagoon probably were sharks, carangids, and Spratelloides sp. It appeared to him that near the coral knolls and lagoon shore reefs schools of large parrot fish slowly followed rather definite routes. He noticed also that the eastern sand flats at Raroia were particularly inhabited by mantas, eagle rays, and sting rays.

Rock-cavity habitats

Long ago Gardiner (1903, p. 336) concluded that perhaps the most important boring animals of the coral rock were the Polychaeta, which include most of the marine annelid worms, even though their actual forms are inconspicuous and of small diameter. Almost every rock below and between tide lines on a coral reef can be expected to have some specimens. The surface at the edge of the reef is perforated with their borings. Although all rocks and corals are attacked, the Polychaeta animals chiefly affect the finer-textured corals. Their total effect must be enormous, and Gardiner considered them as the prime and most effective agents in the breaking down of coral rock.

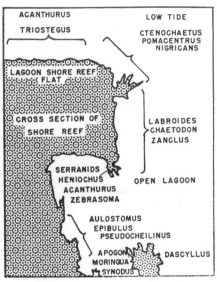

Fig. 85. Ecological zonation of fishes at the windward lagoon reef face, Raroia Atoll. [After Harry (1953).]

The annelid fauna of the Marshalls are larger in number of species than were supposed by some observers. Over 100 species of marine annelids have been collected from the northern Marshall Islands. Eniwetok was the most intensively investigated (up to 1954), and 72 species were recorded from this atoll alone, 41 from Bikini, 20 from Rongelap, and 5 from Rongerik, the latter having been only cursorily examined (Hartman, 1954, p. 619).

Undoubtedly, inadequate examination also accounted for the poor collection of annelids (5 species) from the Ellice Islands atoll of Funafuti during the Royal Society study at the turn of the century (Hedley, 1896, p. 391). According to Hartman, who studied the collections in the northern Marshalls, there were no obvious differences in the annelid faunas of windward and leeward islands, nor on seaward and lagoonward sides of the islands, so far as the limited numbers taken permitted generalization. This would appear to be entirely probable in view of the fact that annelids are largely crevice dwellers or limited to the substratum. Factors of current, wind drift, and similar general environmental factors would have less physiological influence than such ecological conditions as the kind of substratum or the associations of other organisms. Hartman (1954, p. 621) said that Martin Johnson thought them most abundant in the coral zone on the platform just

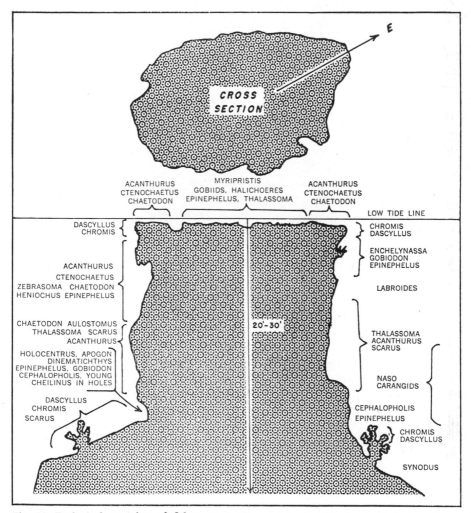

Fig. 86. Ecological zonation of fishes on small coral heads, Raroia Atoll. [After Harry (1953).]

shoreward of the Lithothamnion ridge and in the pot-holes of the reef flat. The surge channels, however, have been little sampled.

The annelids of the northern Marshalls show a clear affinity with fauna from other parts of the Indo-Pacific and notably included some new forms belonging to genera not limited to tropical seas. Some of the small individuals bore a close resemblance to the species of temperate or boreal seas, and Hartman believed that the coral-reef region might represent the extreme limits of their ecological ranges.

The species of annelids destructive to calcareous structures, and thus affecting the ecology of numerous other biota of the coral reef, include the following: *Pseudonereis gallapagensis, Lysidice collaris, Eunice afra, Palola siciliensis, Aglaurides fulgida,* Polydora spp., *Dodecaceria laddi,* and *Hypsicomus phaetaenia.* (In some parts of the central Pacific the Palola worm swarm to the surface in vast numbers during certain seasons and phases of the moon, and they are relished as food by the natives, who gather them in large amounts.) The blue coral (*Heliopora*) and the white pillared corallines are especially riddled by Palola, Lysidice, and Dodecaceria. Pseudonereis were found especially abundant in Heliopora on Eniwetok Atoll. Possibly the most destructive of these is the Palola, which has a conspicuously large and strong ventral mandibular plate that in the Eunicidae family may function as a rasp. The Aglaurides comparatively have the smallest plate and may be proportionately less destructive, according to Hartman.

The other annelids that do not do any excavating are "nestlers," or crevice dwellers. They occupy natural shelters among the calcareous structures and by very reason of their presence the annelids cause destruction of their environs, Hartman reported. Many derive their nutrients from the corallines or coral clumps, or from micro-organisms within the clumps. Such worms are the Amphinomids, of which one of the commonest present is *Eurythoe complanata,* a fire worm. Others secrete mucous, as in the case of the phyllodocids. Still others deriving nutriment from their environments are most of the Eunicea, the capitellids, and terebellids.

Only a few contribute to reef growth by building calcareous tubes. Examples are the serpulids, such as Salmacina and Eupomatus. On the other hand, Hartman noticed that certain reef-building forms, such as the sabellarians and maldanids and most Sedentaira, were not represented or conspicuously scarce in the collections from the northern Marshalls.

CHAPTER 11

MARINE BIOLOGICAL RELATIONSHIPS AND NUTRITION

In the biological sphere there are many different environmental conditions affecting marine life which serve to separate characteristic communities fostered by particular sets of conditions. The communities are more-or-less unstable, however, since the forces operating to mold their character do not remain unchanged. The portion of the marine environment in which a characteristic community of organisms is fostered by more-or-less-uniform conditions is called a "biotope" (Sverdrup, Johnson, and Fleming, 1954, pp. 879–80).

An important aspect of certain biotopes is that of commensalism. This word indicates that two organisms live together, the first benefiting from the second, the second being neither benefited nor harmed by the first. One of the remarkable associations of this type seen at both Bikini (Schultz, 1948, pp. 304–5) and at Ifaluk (Bates and Abbott, 1958, p. 192) is that between a fish and an invertebrate host—a globular, nearly armless starfish, *Culcita novaeguinae,* which reaches the size of a man's head. Inside the body cavity of about half of those examined on Bikini was a nearly transparent fish, Carapus, 5 to 10 inches long. The latter has adapted itself to a sea-water environment with a low amount of dissolved oxygen. The starfish lives in the lagoon in depths from a few feet to 20 feet or more.

Sea cucumbers (Plate 47) such as Thelenota (Bates and Abbott, 1958) use their hind intestine for a sort of "breathing." Muscles pump water into the anus and hindgut and thence to a pair of respiratory tubes, from which it is expelled after being held for a certain time. This cycle of water breathing keeps the hindgut flushed and clean, and a slender fish, Jordanicus, hides out in this pulsing cavern in between feeding periods outside the sea cucumber.

An association between a fish and a coral at Bikini is described by Schultz (1948):

Living in the branching polyps of the coral Acropora, was the little yellowish goby *Gobiodon citrinus,* which had during July and August prepared a nest and laid eggs in it. Gobiodon cleared off a small area, three-fourths of an inch by 2 inches long, at the base of a coral branch arising near the center of the colony. On this carefully prepared spot, a thin growth of green, purplish, or brownish-colored algae occurred.

The Acropora responded to the presence of Gobiodon and formed a slightly raised rim around the nesting area. This goby, only about an inch long, then deposited a small cluster of eggs in the shallow depression, and both parents remained to protect their home.

There may be even closer association between two or more organisms, however, in which the association is obligatory and mutually beneficial. Both types are very common among marine forms of life. Examples of the latter type are found in the association between the zooxanthelae, or green algal plants, and such animals as radiolaria, sponges, corals, sea anemones, and even bivalves and echinoderms, where the algae may grow directly in the subcutaneous or other cells of the animal, giving the flesh characteristic coloring. The significance of the relationships is not always known. It is believed that the alga derives benefit by utilizing wastes such as carbon dioxide and possibly nitrogenous wastes created by the animal. The animals may gain by the removal of wastes and by utilization of the products of photosynthesis, such as oxygen. In the case of *Tridacna gigas,* the clam apparently absorbs the plants to utilize their carbohydrate contents (Sverdrup, Johnson, and Fleming, 1954, pp. 879–82).

Nature has provided specialized apparatus to ensure success among the higher animals in the food chains. Thus fish such as herring, sardines, and anchovy and even the large mantas feeding upon zooplankton, are equipped with straining gills to strain out the plankton while water passes through. The fast-swimming predators on the smaller fish of this type include the tuna, jacks, sharks, and barracuda found in tropical waters. These predators are equipped with well-developed eyes and efficient teeth to seize their prey and are also fast swimmers. Among the bottom-inhabiting animals, the sea stars are voracious feeders on clams, which they exhaust and force open by applying continual pulling pressure on the two halves. Predacious snails, distinguished by their long siphons, are able to drill holes into bivalves and other mollusks, insert their siphons, and eat the soft contents.

Bacterial activity in lagoon sediments

There is substantial evidence that some forms of bacteria are truly marine and not merely derived from the runoff from land. Although the concentration of dissolved organic matter in the sea is much smaller than that occurring in soil surfaces, the total amount of dissolved organic matter is several times greater than the total bulk of living organisms present at one time. Bacteria appears to be the only form of life that makes substantial use of this dissolved organic matter, and bacteria are important in maintaining a continuous return of organic material to the mineral state (Sverdrup, Johnson, and Fleming, 1954, pp. 911–12). Bacteria function in several ways. Under certain natural conditions bacterial precipitation of calcium occurs in the sea and especially in tropical lagoons, where organic material is more abundant. Bacteria also can utilize ammonia nitrogen to form nitrates and nitrites. Moreover, although the process of nitrogen assimilation is primarily a function of plants, bacteria can do this also (Sverdrup, Johnson, and Fleming, pp. 914–18).

In the lower parts of the food chains of coral reefs and atolls there still is much uncertainty with regard to interrelationships, especially the relation between two of the most important elements of the reef, the corals and the algae.

Reef and lagoon food production and consumption

It is generally recognized that tropical ocean waters are relatively barren and desertlike with respect to planktonic food sources. An atoll, on the other hand, is like an oasis in the aquatic desert (Schultz, 1948, p. 314). Corals, as far as is known, are carnivores rather than herbivores. The food chains build up in pyramid fashion, so that the quantities of lower animals must logically be much larger than the higher ones, and each step up represents a smaller number of individuals. Since corals feed upon lower animals in planktonic form, the bulk of the plankton present must be larger than the bulk of the coral animals themselves. However, measurements of the zooplankton movements over the reefs and the amount of animal food available in comparison with the bulk of coral animals on a reef show that, contrary to the expected pattern, coral animals appear to be more numerous than their food sources —if animals are assumed to be the only source of food for corals. This does not appear to be logical. The solution to this puzzling situation has not been definitely settled, and there are conflicting opinions concerning the nutrition of corals.

Much of the controversy is centered upon the question of the role of the zooxanthellae, which are symbiotic algal cells living in the coral tissue. They are so numerous in reef corals that under suitable illumination a coral will behave like a plant, producing an excess of oxygen and taking up carbon dioxide from sea water (Marshall, 1930, p. 35). The zooxanthellae are highly specialized for life within the endoderm cells of corals and other coelenterates; they never occur free in the sea. These algae obtain from the coral animal carbon dioxide (only during periods of light) and available phosphate and nitrogenous compounds (at all times). The zooxanthellae thus find protection and inorganic food within the animal cell, and the association is essential to the zooxanthellae (Yonge, 1940, p. 366).

Yonge asserted, however, that the association is certainly not essential to the life of the individual coral colonies, since examples of coral living in darkness without zooxanthellae are known. However, he suggested that the association may nevertheless be of fundamental importance to reef corals. First, corals may obtain nutriment from the algae, either normally or under exceptional circumstances, or, second, the oxygen liberated by the algae during photosynthesis may contribute to the respiratory needs of the animals, or, third, the rapid removal of waste products of metabolism may be of great importance to the reef corals.

There appears to be universal agreement that corals capture and devour living zooplankton. Moreover, Yonge and Nicholls (1931, pp. 78–9) found that the feeding mechanisms of the different genera of reef builders are specialized for dealing with zooplankton of all sizes.

Corals . . . are specialized for a carnivorous mode of life in the properties of their digestive enzymes as in the nature of their feeding mechanisms. Protein is digested with great rapidity, fat can be digested slightly, while the only carbohydrate which can be assimilated is that which occurs in animal tissues, namely glycogen. No carbohydrates of vegetable origin can be digested . . . The energy requirements of corals are exceptionally low [and the chief function of carbohydrates is to afford energy] . . . Protein, on the other hand, is required in great amounts for growth, which is rapid in corals, for the replacement of worn tissues and for the formation of the reproductive products . . . Carbohydrates have a very minor role to play in the digestive processes of the Madreporaria.

Yonge and Nicholls (1931, p. 175) felt that the coral animals probably obtained "a large proportion of the carbohydrates needed for metabolism by the breaking down of protein which they digest with great rapidity," in this process liberating nitrogen, phosphorus, and sulphur in a form immediately available to the zooxanthellae.

In any case, the symbiosis of coral animals and the algal zooxanthellae differs from that of the Tridacna clams, which also have zooxanthellae in their endoderm cells but which "farm" the algae in their extended mantle edges and absorb them directly as food matter (Yonge and Nicholls, 1931).

The reef-forming corals such as the Madreporaria, however, obtain no nourishment from their contained zooxanthellae, nor are these necessary for the initial budding and early growth of newly settled colonies, according to Yonge and Nicholls (1931, p. 210). They found no evidence of any digestion of zooxanthellae by the corals, or any transference of material from the plants to the tissues of the animal. In experiments, the Madreporaria when starved quickly showed a reduction in the bulk of their tissues, and this was shown equally whether or not they possessed zooxanthellae. Moreover, zooxanthellae, including living ones, were expelled in large numbers immediately after starvation began, owing to the lowered metabolism of the coral and the consequent lack of inorganic food material for the plants. The role of the zooxanthellae was conceived by Yonge and Nicholls to be primarily to use waste products of the coral metabolism and thus increase the efficiency of the reef-building community of corals.

In contrast to these conclusions, other students of marine biology (Sargent and Austin, 1954; Odum and Odum, 1955) believed that atoll reefs are essentially self-sufficient communities, producing as much organic matter as they consume, or more. Sargent and Austin (1949, p. 246) showed evidence indicating that

The rate of consumption of organic matter by the reef community as measured by the oxygen consumption is much larger than the rate of supply of organic matter by the current driven across the reef. Neither the amount of material caught by a plankton net nor the amount available for oxidation by bacteria in the biochemical oxygen-demand measurement is sufficient to satisfy the requirements of the reef community. We have further found that between the surf zone and the lagoon the reef community as a whole produces in a 24-hour day probably somewhat more organic matter than it consumes. The picture of the reef as a self-supporting community, depending on the current only for dissolved nutrients (in a broad sense), and not for particulate or dissolved organic matter, is reasonably clean cut.

The importance of marine plants is indicated in the oxygen production of the reef surface as measured in the oxygen content of the water before and after it crosses the reef. Sargent and Austin (1954, p. 295) calculated that this reaches 23×10^{-6} milliliters per second per square centimeter of reef surface. This seems rather large when so much of the reef appears to the eye almost barren of plants. They found that the rate of oxygen production appeared to be of the same order of magnitude even on somewhat dissimilar reef areas, however. Closer examination revealed that matted filamentous Myxophycea and other minute algae are commonly embedded in the foraminiferal sand and in other locations partly protected from direct sunlight, while the zooxanthellae are abundant in corals, tridacnids, and other animals. Blue-green filamentous algae abound in the surface rock layers as well as under the coral polyps.

Sargent and Austin believed from their study that the zooxanthellae of the corals produce organic matter at a rate quite comparable with its rate of consumption by the coral colony and, under favorable circumstances, even exceeding it. They felt that their evidence points to the retention of the products of photosynthesis by the zooxanthellae within the coral colony, and that some of Yonge's own experiments indicated a "closed cycle of events within the colony." In short, although Yonge concluded that corals do not derive organic matter directly from their zooxanthellae, they believed that the weight of evidence is on the opposite side (Sargent and Austin, 1954, p. 299).

This view was supported by Odum and Odum (1955) whose study of Eniwetok reefs convinced them that the coral is "almost a whole ecological unit in itself with producer, herbivore (utilizing food from symbiotic algae), and carnivore (plankton feeding at night) aspects" (p. 318).

They recognized, however, that direct evidence had not been obtained to prove that coral animals benefited from diffusion of organic substances from the algae, although the quantities of algae present relative to coral protoplasm would make one suppose this to be the case. Moreover, these authors point out that in addition to the zooxanthellae within the coral cells, there also are filamentous green algae growing in bands in the pores of the inert skeletons of the living polyp zone of all the species of hard aragonite corals examined by them, only Dendrophyllia being without them. As stated by Odum and Odum (1955),

Comparison of live and dead corals provides indirect evidence of symbiotic relationship between coral animals and filamentous algae in the skeleton. Algae occur in characteristic bands under living polyps, and the bands show patterns which are characteristic for a given species. These subsurface bands disappear if the coral animals above them died to be replaced by other algae which grow on and near the surface of the dead skeleton. Thus, the bands are not present on the sides of the head where there are no live polyps . . . Since the green filaments are tightly enclosed within the coral colony, any organic matter produced by them as growth or surplus diffusable products cannot escape without going through the enclosing polyp zone. There is no room for such growth except as the whole colony grows and there is no visible accumulation of organic products. The situation leads to the supposition that either the plants are growing close to the compensation point or are supplying coral animal polyps with organic materials.

From quantitative measurements Odum and Odum (1955, p. 298) found that the total plant protoplasm exceeds the animal biomass (about 3 to 1), and that the filamentous green algae have a greater biomass than the zoo-

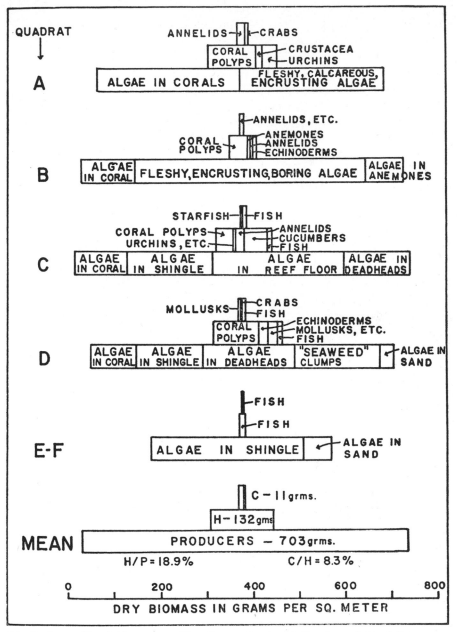

Fig. 87. Pyramids of biomass resulting from estimates of the dry weight of living material (including dead skeletal material associated with protoplasm). For each quadrant, A through F, the weight of "producers" (bottom layer), "herbivores" (H) (middle layer), and "carnivores" (C) (top layer) is shown plus the average dry biomass for the reef. [From Odum and Odum (1955).]

xanthellae (about 16 to 1). "If the filamentous skeletal algae are considered an integral part of the coral colony along with the zooxanthellae, a reasonable biomass pyramid is obtained which is in line with the high photosynthetic activity shown by most coral colonies."

Even if it were conclusively proved that the corals derive food from their symbiotic algae, they "still need to obtain some food and critical nutrients such as nitrogen by ingesting plankton, since there is not enough plant material to completely support the coral and since the coral requires a higher nitrogen content" (Odum and Odum, 1955, p. 299). However, at Eniwetok's windward reef, where the water movement over the reef is one-directional, the Odums found that the amount of plankton leaving the back of the reef was about the same as or slightly greater than that in the incoming water at the reef front. This supports the view that the reef is self-sustaining and deriving no net gain of larger planktonic material from the inflowing ocean water (p. 313).

On the basis of their calculated figures for dry biomass of different plants and animals in five quadrats across the reef, the Odums constructed an interesting chart showing the various nutrition pyramids invariably formed (Fig. 87). Although quite different taxonomic components were present in the different zones across the reef, similar biomass figures were obtained. "The mean standing crop for the reef as a whole in gm/m² was: producers, 703; herbivores, 132; and carnivores, 11. The ratio between standing crop trophic levels was H/P, 18.9% and C/H, 8.3%."

CHAPTER 12

MARINE FAUNA DANGEROUS TO MAN

For the discussion of atoll marine fauna that are dangerous to man, it is convenient to classify as follows: (1) dangerous predatory fishes, such as shark and barracuda, which attack man; (2) venomous marine fauna, which injure, when stepped on or touched, by means of poison spines and stings; (3) poisonous invertebrates that cause injury when eaten; and (4) poisonous vertebrate fishes that cause injury when eaten.

Almost all tropical reefs are characterized by a few or many species of animals in each of these classifications. Most students of tropical reefs, however, probably feel safer with the dangers of an atoll environment than in driving about in an automobile in more sophisticated regions of the world. Nevertheless, caution must be exercised concerning several types of reef animals. As will be seen below, there is still much disagreement and many unconfirmed suspicions about the amount of danger present, and different atolls or even different sectors of an atoll may have dissimilar hazards.

Dangerous predatory fishes

Although sharks commonly are present around most tropical reefs, the majority appear to be relatively harmless species, such as the white-tipped-finned *Triaenodeon obesus* (Harry, 1953, p. 48) or the little sand shark with the black-tipped fins, *Charcharhinus melanopterus* (Plate 53) (Bates and Abbott, 1958, p. 205; Randall, 1955, p. 3). These species generally are small, and the natives often swim or wade among them without fear. Randall (1952, p. 56) wrote that on Onotoa Atoll, only five cases of attack by sharks

on men were recalled, even by the older Gilbertese. These involved large
sharks, not the common smaller reef forms, but the dangerous species were
not identified. At Ifalik apparently only one of the inhabitants living at
the time of the inquiry had been attacked by a shark (Bates and Abbott, 1958,
p. 60).

On the other hand, Harry (1953, p. 178) reported that the natives at
Raroia were afraid of the sharks and always left the water whenever sharks
came into the region in which they were swimming. He found that the
sharks were especially abundant and aggressive in Garue Pass and around
the outside of the atoll over the coralliferous outer bench and in the surge
channels. He was charged twice by sharks while in surge channels. One
woman in the village had had an arm bitten off by a shark when she was a
girl. Morrison (1954, p. 18) also reported on the "extreme reluctance of the
Raroian natives to dive here [in the surge channels] in the known presence
of all the dangerous sharks of the region. . . ." Friederici (1910, p. 131)
wrote that sharks were very numerous among the Tuamotu atolls and that
some lagoons were overrun with them.

Dangerous sharks are more likely to be present in large lagoons with deep
passes than in the smaller lagoons. In some atolls, such as Rangiroa (44 by 17
miles), the lagoon is reported to be infested with sharks (U. S. Navy, 1952).
At Kapingamarangi Atoll the natives in 1954 were unafraid to swim for
long distances in the middle of the lagoon or even in the deep pass and
outside the leeward reef. The sharks seen were mostly small sand sharks.
One shark 2 to 3 feet long was caught.

Fosberg (1954) wrote that from all observations, sharks must be regarded
as a very minor danger in the northern Marshalls. The writer saw only one
shark of significant size in 13 islands and atolls in the Marshalls. This was
one about 3 feet long caught by a line off the leeward reef at Likiep. However, it is not advisable to enter the water if one has an open or bleeding
wound. According to Bates and Abbott (1958, p. 159), sharks cruise around
slowly and hunt mainly by scent. They become excited when there is blood
or when raw flesh is exposed. When excited or close to food, sharks begin
to depend to a greater extent on sight and are likely to strike at any moving
object.

Harry (1953, p. 182) urged that shark repellent be used in tropical regions
and that, despite contrary reports, it has repeatedly been proved that copper
acetate repellent is very effective against sharks. The dye used as a shark
chaser clouds the water and blocks the vision of the shark fairly effectively,
because the shark's eyesight is not too good (Bates and Abbott, 1958).

Schultz (*The New York Times*, 1960b) stated that sharks have a mechanism by which they can detect slow motions in the water, such as those made
by bathers. He asserted that there can be no question that sharks are ter-

ribly dangerous in most warm and temperate ocean waters. Probably the most dangerous, he said, is the great white shark, *Carcharodon carcharias,* followed by the tiger shark.

Barracuda occur in the northern Marshalls and no doubt at most Pacific atolls. According to Fosberg (1954), they are dangerous and will attack swimmers without provocation. Other dangerous marine vertebrates include moray and conger eels. The latter are rare in the northern Marshalls, according to Fosberg, but can bite severely. The wicked-looking moray eels often inhabit holes in the coral rock, and a hand thrust toward such a hole may be bitten.

A recurrent story in the tropical Pacific tells of a giant grouper that is mostly mouth, which lurks in the outer openings of coral caverns. Legend has it that its habit is to suck in any live object that comes near it, including people, but this has not been confirmed. It has been known to swallow small sea turtles.

Fish large enough to give rise to such tales include the giant sea bass, *Epinephelus lancelatus,* which has a bulldog-like head. Parrot fish may be over 6 feet long and weigh several hundred pounds, but they are harmless (Bates and Abbott, 1958, p. 193). Surgeon fish are harmless but have lancetlike erectile projections on the sides near the narrow part of the tail. By whipping the tail, the fish can inflict painful cuts when caught and carelessly handled.

Venomous marine fauna

When the Reverend William Gill was traveling in the South Seas (1876, p. 275), he was told of the funeral of a man in the Hervey Islands who died as a result of picking up a large cone (*Conus textilis*). He had been stung by "the numerous barbs" on its mantle. These barbs injected a virulent poison into the man's skin. He felt a painful sensation running up his right arm to the shoulder, and the pain increased after he went home until he writhed in agony. His body swelled a great deal and by daylight he was dead.

Cone shells and Terebra cones are quite dangerous to handle while the animals are still alive. These shells are abundant on most atoll reefs, and the animals are capable of poisonous stings with their darts. Because they ordinarily do not do this, the danger often is not known. Fosberg (1954) pointed this out and urged caution in handling them, since a number of deaths are on record from cone-shell stings. Even the native people sometimes are unaware of the stings. Banner (1952, p. 32) said that *Conus striatus,* one of the poison cones, is gathered and eaten by the Gilbertese at Onotoa and that these people had no knowledge of its sting.

Sea urchins, except for the purple-red slate-pencil urchins, are to be avoided. The long-spined black Echinometra species have very brittle sharp spines which easily penetrate the skin and break off in the flesh, remaining painfully evident until they fester out. Apparently, the long-spined varieties have poison in their spines, since to merely brush against them with the bare leg brings wasplike stings, although of short duration (Fosberg, 1954). Sea urchins are very common in tide pools. The black ones wave their spines in an undulating fashion. The writer observed a small tan or brown variety with short, stubby half-inch spines on the windward reef at Ebeje, Kwajelein Atoll. There was literally a carpet of these urchins, and one could not walk there without stepping on them. However, their spines did not penetrate the rubber soles of canvas shoes.

Fishes with venomous spines reported at Onotoa (Randall, 1952, p. 56) and undoubtedly present in most reef areas include the sting ray, the siganids, and certain scorpaenids such as Pterois. The stone or rock fish, *Synancea verrucosa*, is reported from Tarawa and Raroia and probably occurs on most atolls. Harry (1953) reported that they appear to be completely unafraid and refuse to move even when poked. When disturbed, they remain perfectly stiff and can be pushed or hit and not made to move. However, if hit with the hand or stepped on with bare feet, they can cause painful wounds with their spines. This fish was especially feared by the natives at Raroia, who gave it the name "pugapuga." Other venomous fish named by the Raroians were the Pterois ("tataiaihau"), *Scorpaenopsis gibbosus* ("pugapuga veve"), Siganus ("marava"), some Acanthurus, all Ctenochaetus, Aetobatus ("taperota"), and the large moray eels.

Catala (1959, p. 111) wrote that at Tarawa the leaves of *Triumfetta procumbens* were boiled until soft and then applied as a dressing to limbs swollen from the sting of the stone fish, *Synancea verrucosa*. The leaves and dressings were renewed as necessary, and treatment for a week was said to be sufficient to stop the pain. Without treatment pain was said to continue for three weeks. Hedley (1896, p. 39) reported that at Funafuti Atoll wounds from the spines of the Monocanthus sp. were treated with a poultice of the *Psitolum triquetrum* plant. Another mode of treatment for this was to burn the plant and hold the wounded limb in the smoke.

Sting rays are chiefly dangerous to humans when stepped on or when a person's foot accidentally touches the spine. The spines can inflict a very painful wound. According to MacGinitie and MacGinitie (1949, p. 417), it is best to treat such a wound by applying a disinfectant and then letting it alone. To squeeze the wound to "get the poison out" is said to make it worse.

A common source of infectious wounds in atoll reef areas are the corals themselves, since many have very sharp and jagged skeletons. A person stepping on and breaking through fragile corals, or brushing against them with bare skin may get badly scratched, and the wounds often heal slowly. Such infections may bring on a high fever. Coral cuts should be washed with alcohol as soon as possible.

Invertebrates that cause food poisoning

A great many mollusks and other invertebrates such as the Palolo worm are eaten by the inhabitants of Pacific atolls. A few have been reported to be poisonous in some localities, but little information is available on this subject. At Onotoa Atoll in the Gilberts the large conch, *Charonia tritonis,* is considered poisonous and is not eaten by the natives (Banner, 1952, p. 31). At Majuro the natives do not eat the black sea cucumbers, but they pound or mash them to a pulp to use as fish poison. This method of fish poisoning is used on Guam also (Smith, 1946, p. 7). Gill (1876, p. 273) stated that "The most poisonous marine animal in the Hervey Islands is 'the white-shelled' sea crab (Angatea). The native dictum is 'All land crabs are good, sea crabs doubtful.' Occasionally, a native in a fit of passion or jealousy commits suicide by eating 'the white-shelled' crab, and yet, strangely enough, some have been known to eat these dangerous crustaceans with impunity."

Fish that cause food poisoning

The most significant danger to man from atoll marine fauna is the poisoning that results from eating toxic fishes. Because of the great dependence of man upon fish for food in the Pacific atolls and the frequent uncertainty as to the toxicity of the fishes caught, poisoning by fish is one of the most widespread hazards to health on these islands. The problem is not limited to the atoll dwellers, of course, but is serious to all who dwell or travel in the tropical reef realm and eat the fish of these regions.

Dr. Guy Loison, Research Officer for Health to the South Pacific Commission, has written an informative article on this subject (1955). He pointed out that during World War II about 400 Japanese died in Micronesia from eating poisonous fish. In the Marianas, an American ship was held up because half of its crew were sick from eating barracuda. In 1949, 57 Filipinos became ill and two died from eating moray eels. The flesh of a black moray eel caused the death of five people in the Marshall Islands in 1953. In 1950, 35 cases of fish poisoning were reported from Kwajelein, six from Majuro, and three from Ponape. At the United States air base on Johnston Island in 1950 there were 20 cases of fish poisoning. On Sydney Island in the Phoenix group, fish poisoning was held responsible for the high infant-mortality rate. At Palmyra (U. S. Coast Pilot, 1950) many cases of violent fish poisoning have occurred, some with fatal consequences. At Raroia (Harry, 1953, p. 177) the natives reported that an average of about six cases of fish poisoning occurred each year, but they mentioned no deaths.

Aside from the health hazards, poisonous fish also result in economic losses and uncertainties. In 1944, according to Loison (1955), poisonous fish from Midway and Christmas Islands caused a panic on the Hawaiian market, which led to loss of unsalable fish valued in thousands of dollars. Obviously, the economic potential of the tropical Pacific cannot be fully developed until the problem of poisonous fish is solved.

Unfortunately, the problem is more complex than the difficult task of recognition of poisonous species alone. Only certain well-recognized fishes are known to be always poisonous. Smith (1946, p. 91) wrote that of the approximately 2,000 species of fish and other marine animals in central Pacific waters, at least 125 are said to be poisonous when eaten. Loison (1955, p. 30) reported approximately 300 species reputed to be poisonous. Among the species that he found most often mentioned were the swellfish (Plate 54), or puffer (Tetraodon) (an ounce of its flesh can kill a man within 20 minutes), boxfish, horned boxfish, moonfish, porcupine fish, trigger fish, and barracuda.

Unfortunately, fishes eaten without ill effects on some atolls cause violent illness on others. At Raroia, the Tuamotuan natives informed Harry (1953, p. 177) that the number of poisonous species varied from atoll to atoll and from season to season. They stated very definitely that certain fishes were poisonous when found in one locality of an atoll but completely edible in another region of the same island. They claimed that the poisonous properties were due to what the fishes eat, but they were not sure what food caused the damage. The natives attributed the scarcity or absence of population on some of the southern atolls of the Tuamotu group to the fact that the people were able to eat only a few species. Emory (1939, p. 56) said that South Marutea is noted for its numerous species of poisonous fish, but that all Tridacna, oysters, and lobsters may be eaten. Certain species of fish from some areas of the lagoon were good but the same species from other areas were toxic. Earlier, Friederici (1910) had gathered generally similar information in the Tuamotus. His men suffered some fish poisoning although they ate only fish said to be safe by two native crewmen. He stated that it was thought the poison was caused by certain algae on which the fish fed but did not know whether this had been scientifically established. Tuamotu lagoons reported to have poisonous fish included Manihi, Apataki, the two Maruteas, Toau, Aratika, and Mururoa. Mangareva also had some objectionable species.

At Arno Atoll in the southern Marshalls, about 15 species were said by the natives to be poisonous. These included many commonly known to be poisonous in tropical waters (Hiatt, 1951, p. 7): *Ctenochaetus strigosus,* several species of Tetraodon, Athigaster, and Diodon, some scorpaeonids, *Synancea verrucosa,* Pterois, certain muraenid eels, and certain balistids. No seasonal differences in toxic character were reported but certain species that were poisonous on one side of the atoll were not poisonous on the other side.

In his survey of the central Pacific, Smith (1946) found the toxic-fish problem baffling:

Only the puffers (family Tetrodontidae) and their spiny relatives, the porcupine fish (family Diodontidae), seem to be universally regarded as dangerous. Other species are poisonous in one locality but harmless elsewhere. Even the virulence of the poison varies from place to place, and with the season of the year. As far as could be determined, there are no poisonous species in the Palaus. Elsewhere, it is good judgement to follow the recommendations of the native people, who from long experience have come to know the harmful local varieties. The only other generalization is that surface-feeding fish, taken by trolling offshore, are not known to be harmful. The poison evidently originates in the food of reef and lagoon fish.

Catala (1957, p. 118) reported that there were few species of poisonous fishes in the Gilberts and that in eating fish, the Gilbertese "will not scorn even such species as Diodons and Tetraodons, in which there is really very little to eat once the toxic parts have been removed. It is an interesting fact that cases of poisoning by shell-fish or fish are extremely rare." This report appears to be confirmed by Randall's findings (1952, p. 55) at Onotoa Atoll in the Gilberts, where the only fishes considered poisonous by the Onotoans were the puffers, and then only the internal organs, especially the gonads. He observed the natives catching, preparing, and eating many species known to be poisonous elsewhere. In interviews, he found out that a certain section of the reef near the northern part of the atoll harbored poisonous fishes for several years, but that during the preceding two years the fish taken from there were not toxic.

South of the Gilberts are the Ellice Atolls. Here fish poisoning was reported in 1922 to be very prevalent (O'Connor, 1922, p. 43) and the poison was not limited to specific fish, although only rock fish was constantly poisonous and shark's liver occasionally so. It was found that cooking fish does not affect the poison and that the head and liver were particularly dangerous; cats often died from eating these discarded parts.

Among the Marshallese (Steinbach, 1894, p. 157) there exists a belief that many fish caught outside the lagoon are poisonous, although this does not apply to those caught on the open ocean away from the reefs. Loison (1955, p. 28) also reported that fishermen in the tropical Pacific believed that big fish or deep-sea fish are more poisonous than smaller ones or lagoon fish. In parts of the Marshalls the fishermen say that the only poisonous fish are those found in the passes.

According to Loison, the tail end of the fish is considered less toxic than the head or middle parts. The poisonous substances circulate in the blood. Also, once the fish is dead, the toxins contained in the viscera spread rapidly through the adjacent flesh. Although warm-blooded animals are liable to be affected by eating this flesh, fish, crabs, and sea snakes are not harmed by eating it. Cats and dogs poisoned by fish suffer loss of hair, and this also has been observed with humans.

The preceding discussion appears to suggest that there may be a connection between fish and their local ecology, but this hypothesis has been rejected. Ecology and toxicity do not seem to be interrelated, according to Loison (1955, p. 30). He pointed out, for instance, that up to 1946 the 224 people inhabiting Fanning Atoll had eaten all species of fish caught, but that between February 1946 and April 1947 an epidemic of 95 cases of fish poisoning occurred. Obviously a new element had entered the picture. As nerve and sensory disturbances are more predominant in cases of fish poisoning than digestive disorders, bacteria must also be ruled out as the cause of poisoning. On the other hand, Halstead's research indicated that fish poisoning definitely originates in the diet of the fish. It is considered possible that fish poisoning is caused by *Gonyaulax catenella,* "the only plankton element that has been proved fatal for man. It has already been recognized as the cause of toxicity in mussels. It is particularly abundant along the coasts of the Pacific Islands, forming long rusty-coloured trails on the sea. Fish, crabs and shell-fish are permeated with its poison, a more dangerous one than that of botulism." According to Loison, Dr. Yoshio Hiyama, who studied the fish-poison problem in Micronesia, suggested a possible connection between the poison and the nematocysts or the filamentous stinging organs of the coral polyps. Whatever the source of the poison, the chemical nature is still unknown, although it is neither protein, protamine, nor alkaloid. The maximum concentration of toxins is in the liver and intestines of the fish.

In view of the seriousness of this dietary problem throughout the atoll realm, it seems useful to give an example of the symptoms of a nonfatal case of fish poisoning suffered by Loison (1955):

I diagnosed the cause of my own particular case on the very first day, when I got up and washed my hands. It was certainly the cold tap I had turned on, and yet I started at the excruciating burning pain experienced. This sensation was to last for several weeks. Similarly drinking a cold beverage caused an unbearable impression of agonized burning.

Gastro-intestinal troubles were of minor importance, and ended after

48 hours, leaving me to cope with a far more unpleasant symptom: a general itching that continued constantly for a fortnight, forcing me to contort my body into the most grotesque positions and scratch without stopping. Moreover, I would wake up every night, not because of the spasmodic twitching of my legs, but because I had the impression my teeth had become loose and were about to fall out of their sockets.

The final and most difficult effect to bear was the ensuing state of exhaustion which lasted some three or four months. My thighs in particular were weak and painful as though they had been given a thorough beating. Those familiar with fish poisoning tell me I was lucky to get away with few and such slight symptoms: I might have suffered from vomiting, abdominal pains, fever, excessive perspiration, pains in the joints, numbness of the lips and tongue, motility incoordination, various paralysis of the motor and vegetative systems, temporary blindness, and other similar troubles.

As for antidotes or remedies, no effective ones have been discovered. O'Connor (1922) suggested an early purging with Epsom salt. Loison tried

the most popular remedy in all the Pacific islands: *Messerschmidia argentea*, Linne. I cannot say it hastened recovery appreciably . . . A handful of the velvety leaves is allowed to stand in boiling water, which is then boiled down to one-third of its original volume until a brownish, bitter liquid is obtained. Drunk ice-cold and sweetened with sugar, it is not unpleasant.

Some Micronesians prefer to chew the bark of the tree. In the Marianas, the dried leaves and bark are roasted before macerating. In the Marshalls, patients eat a mixture of raw leaves and crushed coral . . . Analysis of *Messerschmidia argentea* would probably make it possible to extract a useful palliative . . . It is interesting to note that after being poisoned by fish, several patients have recovered from rheumatic pains or oxyuriasis.

The Gilbertese natives on Sydney Atoll in the Phoenix group used *Morinda citrifolia* to treat fish poisoning (Groves, 1951).

It is obvious that intensive research needs to be done to obtain a remedy for one of the most serious afflictions of the coral atoll inhabitant. Since his very food supply is involved, the atoll dweller cannot avoid taking chances with fish poisoning, and he must anticipate that he may suffer from it occasionally and that it could cause his death.

CHAPTER 13

ATOLL SEA AND SHORE BIRDS

Birds, especially sea birds, have an important role in atoll ecology, both in the marine environment and on the land. Sea birds and shore birds prey upon the fish and other reef fauna and eat large numbers of them. When the birds die they fall on the water or on the land. Those that fall on the water are consumed in turn by the marine fauna. The sea and shore birds compete with predator fishes for the smaller fish that are their prey. The excreta of the birds in part drop back into the lagoon or ocean and are consumed by lower forms of life. They also enrich the water for the phytoplankton and the bottom sediments for bacteria. On land, the sea and shore birds as well as the land birds roost and some may nest. Here, although little concerned with obtaining their food from the land, the sea birds generally are still far more important in affecting the land ecology, if because of nothing other than their enormous number compared with land birds. The sea and shore birds take out of the sea and add to the land significant amounts of organic material. Soil and vegetation are changed by the excrement added to the land.

Especially in the drier atolls, guano accumulation and phosphatization of the soil and rock in some instances have led to their large-scale exploitation as commercial fertilizer. Hutchinson (1950, p. 192) believed that the fertility of many wet atolls "doubtless depends on such phosphatization, followed by bacterial nitrogen fixation" and that the possible role of excess phosphate in regulating competition between *Pisonia grandis* and other trees deserves study. To a small extent certain sea birds and their eggs are a source of food for human beings. The feathers of some birds also have been utilized in the past for millinery and for other decorative purposes.

Sea and shore birds have become adapted to their environment in a re-markable fashion. The most wonderful aspect of this adaptation is their ability to survive on islands having no fresh water. According to Schmidt-Nielsen, Jorgensen, and Osaki (1957), sea birds normally find their drinking-water needs in the flesh of the fish they devour. However, the birds acci-dentally take in large quantities of sea water while feeding. This would prove toxic to them were they not equipped by nature with a complicated filtering device. Although the birds are able to excrete a reasonable amount of sea water naturally, the oversupply of salt-laden fluid flows constantly from the nostrils to the tip of the beak. Frequent shakes of the head toss the drops away. This biological ability in part explains the nesting of sea birds on desert or semiarid islands and atolls in the Pacific, where, if other conditions are right, they may flock in hundreds of thousands, so that they completely dominate the land.

Interrelation of climate, current, marine fauna, and birds

In an earlier chapter it was shown that north of the equatorial counter-current and near the equator there are divergences in the ocean current which are regions of high biological productivity (Sverdrup, Johnson, and Fleming, 1954, p. 712). Because of the upwelling, these are regions of rela-tively high silica and phosphate content. Hutchinson (1950, pp. 160–3) showed the direct correspondence of these features with the high plankton and sperm-whale catches and with the low rainfall of these regions.

Figures 62 and 63 show graphically the latitudinal abundance of zooplank-ton and fish caught in the area bounded by longitudes 140 and 180°W, and latitudes 7°S and 15°N. Planktonic hauls were richest between 1°S and 4°N when averaged without regard to meridian. Along the 150°W meridian (about 500 miles east of the Line Islands), the zone of abundance was sharply demarcated between 1 and 6°N. Since fish abundance depends upon plankton abundance, the average haul without regard to meridian does not as accurately reflect the boundaries of rich plankton life as the fish-catch abundance along one meridian. The latter also would show more accurately the bounds of upwelling currents, and the relationship of island situation to the zones of upwelling, if any islands are nearby. To study the relation-ship of the irregularly distributed islands, however, the averages must be used. In general, the Line and Phoenix groups fall within the zone of very productive marine fauna at all seasons (Hutchinson, 1950). These atolls are rich in guano and low in rainfall. The islands south of the Phoenix group have higher rainfall and with few exceptions are generally lacking in guano accumulations. They also fall in zones of relatively low silicate and phosphate content in the ocean water and in much reduced plankton hauls and whale catches.

The cause-and-effect relationships here are obvious. The upwellings associated with the equatorial countercurrent and other currents and, possibly, locally the obstruction presented by the submarine slopes of the islands cause nutrient-rich water to be brought to the photosynthesis, or euphotic, zone of phytoplankton. The rapid growth of the plants causes rapid zooplankton production, which provides the basis for the large fish population on which the vast numbers of sea birds depend. The birds, in turn, deposit guano on the islands where they roost and nest. A wet climate leaches and washes guano away from the land and also has adverse effects upon the rearing of some types of young birds, and dense vegetation growing on wet islands may interfere with the ground-nesting habits of certain sea birds. Pandanus, Pisonia, and coconut palms may directly and successfully compete with ground-nesting boobies and sooty terns for the limited space available. Where large numbers of an arboreal species occupy an island, phosphatic soils probably always develop, but on such wet islands neither workable guano nor significant phosphatization of coral rock is apt to develop (Hutchinson, 1950, p. 166). Thus islands with dry climates appear to favor large bird populations, and also the preservation of accumulated guano.

The final link in the relationship is that between the climate and the ocean currents. Upwelling of the colder deep ocean water over large areas directly affects the atmospheric conditions over the water. Contact with cool water cools the air and makes it more stable. Since atolls provide no orographical uplift, and there is seldom frontal development in the tropical atoll realm, rainfall depends largely upon convection and the resulting turbulence. The increased stability of air over cool water would naturally lead to reduced rainfall and drier conditions on low atolls situated in such waters.

Although much more information is needed to elucidate the equatorial pattern of bird distribution, Hutchinson (1950, p. 167) felt that the records available "clearly indicate the paucity of birds in the southern part of the tropical Pacific." This paucity appears to be related to the fact that upwellings associated with the northern and southern divergences are mainly in the northern hemisphere. Of the two divergences, the equatorial divergence probably is biologically more important, since both the plankton and surface phosphate contents are slightly lower in the divergence north of the equatorial countercurrent.

The rate of accumulation of guano, if ascertained and if no loss takes place, presumably could be used to date the colonization of any island by marine birds in large numbers. Information on this subject appears scanty.

Hutchinson (1950, p. 193) tells of one instance in which a ship's captain had, after 20 years, revisited an uninhabited island colonized by huge swarms of birds. He found that the floor boards of an unroofed structure abandoned 20 years previously had accumulated guano to a depth of about 20 inches. This made an average depth of about an inch a year. From comparisons with the rate of phosphatization of guano on dry islands off the Peruvian coast, Hutchinson concluded that "It is certainly reasonable to suppose that phosphatization on Baker and Howland Islands has proceeded for but a few millennia."

This estimate would seem to accord with Fairbridge's conclusion given earlier in this study that about 3,600 years before the present time, the sea level was about 10 feet higher. The highest parts of Howland are only about 10 to 12 feet above present high-tide marks (Hutchinson, 1950, p. 167). The same is true of Jarvis, which has a filled lagoon floor about 7 to 8 feet above sea level. Jarvis is interesting also in that it has at least two and possibly three phosphatized guano layers separated by coral gravels. These indicate the recent eustatic fluctuations of sea level above and below the level of the present Jarvis "lagoon" floor as claimed by Fairbridge and suggested by Hutchinson (1950, p. 173). Baker Island, whose central lagoon was also filled in, has a flat surface covered with guano and phosphatized rock at about the same level above the sea.

Although the drier atolls and large bird colonies are definitely related (Plate 55), particularly for contemporary bird colonies, phosphate occurs also on wet atolls, although these deposits mostly appear to have ancient origins (Hutchinson, 1950, pp. 161, 184). Fanning Atoll was exploited commercially for phosphate. Washington Atoll also has deposits, although apparently not of commercial interest. Hutchinson cited a phosphate expert, Elschner, who appears to have visited Washington Atoll in 1915, as the authority for the belief that a colloidal calcium phosphate was being formed by the contemporary washing of guano into the water of Washington Atoll. This forms a plastic mud from the precipitate which acts as a seal over the bottom and apparently prevents marine-water infiltration, thus keeping the lagoon water fresh. If this is correct, said Hutchinson, Washington Island is the wettest island for which there is clear evidence of contemporary phosphatization, which he attributes to the existence of a completely closed lagoon.

Hutchinson found it strange that while a wet island such as Fanning had phosphate of commercial quality and quantity, drier Christmas Atoll to its south appears not to have produced phosphate. Even at Palmyra, a section of one of the islets had been phosphatized into a hardpan 10 to 20 centimeters deep under 2 inches of black humus (Hutchinson, 1950, p. 186; Rock, 1916, p. 22). Hutchinson felt that it was only reasonable to believe that whatever phosphatization took place on Palmyra must have been subsequent to the latest emergence of the land and before a dense forest came into existence (1950, p. 194):

The profile of Rose Atoll strongly suggests that, though a phosphatic soil might result from a bird colony nesting on a richly vegetated island, the phosphatic hard-pan observed on Palmyra would not develop. Moreover, it seems unlikely that an island without a closed lagoon would become phosphatized under the present meteorological conditions of Palmyra, even if a forest cover had not been immediately established. The most reasonable explanation of the Palmyra phosphatization would seem to be that the climate was drier at some time after the emergence. The same reasoning might perhaps be applied to the Fanning Island phosphate deposit, if more was known of it. It seems unlikely that phosphatization would have occurred on Fanning and not on Christmas Island under present meteorological conditions.

Hutchinson hypothesized that the paradoxical absence of phosphatization on Christmas and its existence on the wetter Fanning and Palmyra north of it as well as the islands south of it, such as Jarvis, Howland, and Baker, could be explained if it could be shown that earlier the equatorial rain belt was farther south and that its center was over Christmas rather than Washington (Hutchinson, 1950, p. 195): "Fanning and Palmyra being somewhat drier than they are today would more easily acquire phosphatic guano; Christmas Island being wetter would acquire none. The three dry islands on the equator may have been wetter, but if the shift of the rain belt to its present position occurred a few thousand years ago there would be ample time for accumulation of the deposits found in the nineteenth century." He recognized, however, that this was merely a working hypothesis that might meet insuperable climatological difficulties, but that "the alternative hypothesis of a post-Pleistocene dry period throughout the Pacific fits the special case of the Line Islands less neatly."

The most important guano bird species

Hutchinson (1950, p. 165) concluded from an examination of the literature that the two species of terns *Sterna fuscata* (sooty tern) and *Sterna lunata* (bridled tern) are the most abundant on the barren atolls. On Phoenix Atoll they were found to occupy separate areas, although they were about equally common. Their absence on Howland and Baker (in 1862) apparently was due to their destruction by rats, whereas on Malden the colony was decimated in 1877 by domestic cats run wild.

The next most abundant bird on undisturbed dry atolls appears to be *Anous stolidus* (common noddy), but noddies are generally far less numerous than terns. On the wetter atolls, such as the northern Line Islands, the terns were confined largely to littoral bare areas of sand and broken coral. Since these areas tended to slope into the sea or lagoon, rain water washes much of the guano into the sea or lagoon, so that they are unfavorable sites for the accumulation of guano. On the wetter atolls with richer vegetation, noddies often nest in trees, whereas certain terns, such as the *Gygis alba* (fairy tern), prefer Tornefortia branches to the ground (Plate 56), although they breed on the bare coral rock on such atolls as Christmas and Phoenix. On Gaferut Island the writer found Gygis nesting apparently exclusively in the Tournefortia trees. The noddy *Anous minutus* was found entirely arboreal in its nesting habits on Fanning and Christmas, as was *Procelsterna cerulea* (blue-gray fairy ternlet). It is seen from this that, although terns are common on all the islands, there is some progressive substitution as well as change of habits in passing from the dry and barren to the wet and richly forested islands. Only on the dry atolls, however, are the great colonies that could form relatively pure guano deposits likely to be present (Hutchinson, 1950, p. 165).

Boobies are also extremely common. Those that breed on the ground, *Sula leucogaster* (the brown booby) and *S. dactylatra* (blue-faced booby), are commoner on the dry islands, but they also nest on the wet islands. *S. leucogaster* possibly was the most common guano bird on Howland in its virgin state, but on Fanning, *S. sula* (red-footed booby), which nests almost invariably in trees or bushes, was the most abundant bird (Hutchinson, 1950, p. 166).

Another bird that has been regarded as a significant contributor to guano deposits in the Line Islands is the *Fregata minor* (frigate bird or Pacific man-of-war) (Plate 57). Others occurring in significant numbers include *Nesofregata albigularis* (white-throated storm petrel), *Pterodroma alba* (Phoenix petrel), *Puffinus pacificus* (wedge-tailed shearwater), *Puffinus nativitatis* (Christmas shearwater), *Puffinus lherminieri* (dusky shearwater), and *Phaethon rubricauda* (red-tailed tropic bird). The sole albatross found in the region is the gooney *Diomedea nigripes* (black-footed albatross). This is found only at Johnston Island (Hutchinson, 1950). According to Schultz (1948) the fish supply around the Pacific Islands has been about the same since Pleistocene times. Baker (1951, p. 31) concluded from this that the population of guano-depositing birds was about the same in ancient times as it is today. However, it is more probable that the absence of man and the destructive rats, cats, dogs, and hogs which he brought with him allowed much larger populations in the Pacific atolls in ancient times than are present today, particularly on the now-inhabited atolls.

Probably most of the birds of the Pacific atoll realm have been recorded and described in Ernst Mayr's field guide (1945) and in Baker's monograph (1951). However, Mayr (1945, p. 3) asserted that "Our knowledge of the seabirds of the Pacific (their relationships, distribution, and life histories) is still very incomplete." Until his volume was printed there was no single book in English available on the birds of the area of Micronesia, western Polynesia, and the islands of Melanesia east of New Guinea and the Bismarck Archipelago. Hutchinson's study (1950) also contains a great amount of information on the birds found on the phosphatized atolls and raised coral-liferous islands of the tropical Pacific. Baker (1951, p. 21) believed that most existing bird species in Micronesia have been recorded and that "The heyday of the taxonomist in ornithology in Micronesia is over." However, he said, "The field of avian ecology in Micronesia has barely been scratched." He has, therefore, made an effort in his monograph to fill part of this deficit. On the basis of available data, he has analyzed the distribution, origins, migrations, speciation, and the conservation problem of Micronesian birds. The following discussion is largely derived from Baker's study (1951).

Distribution and range of sea birds

Of the 206 types of birds found in Micronesia, 30 are sea birds, 29 are migratory shore birds, and 147 kinds are land or fresh-water birds. Of the 30 sea birds, 18 kinds are resident and 12 are regarded as visitors to Micronesia. Further field study, however, may show that some of the supposed visitors are actually resident birds. The presently believed division into genera is shown in Table 13.

TABLE 13

Genera of Birds in Micronesia *

Genera	Resident types	Nonresident types
Diomedea (albatross)	0	1
Puffinus (shearwater)	4	1
Pterodroma (petrel)	1	1
Phaethon (tropic bird)	2	1
Sula (booby or gannet)	3	0
Fregata (frigate or man-of-war)	1	1
Larus (tern)	0	1
Chlidonias	0	1
Sterna (tern)	2	4
Thalasseus (crested tern)	1	0
Procelsterna (blue-gray fairy ternlet)	0	1
Anous (noddy)	2	0
Gygis (fairy tern)	2	0

* From Baker (1951, p. 29).

The sea birds may be divided into three groups: inshore, offshore, and pelagic. The inshore group generally remains within 4 or 5 miles from shore and within sight of land. The offshore birds have a range that takes them beyond the sight of land but not as far as the extensive flights of the pelagic birds, although in practice it is hard to draw the line between the latter two.

In Micronesia the majority of the Laridae are of the inshore zone and include such residents as *Sterna sumatrana* (black-naped tern), *S. anaetheta* (brown-winged tern), *Thalasseus bergii* (crested tern), *Anous stolidus* (common noddy), *A. tenuirostris* (white-capped noddy) (Plate 58), and *Gygis alba* (fairy tern). The latter spends considerable time ashore and eats insects as well as crustaceans and fish. The brown-winged tern, the crested tern, and the noddies may venture into the offshore zone beyond sight of land. Sea-bird visitors to Micronesia include some that normally range inside the outer reef areas of atolls as well as offshore. These include *Chlidonias leucopterus* and *Sterna hirundo* (black-billed common tern) (Baker, 1951, pp. 29–30).

The birds that frequent the offshore zone but may not range extensively at sea include Fregata, Sula, *Sterna fuscata* (sooty tern), *S. hirundo, S. anaetheta,* and others. Birds that spend much of their time at sea and may seldom approach land except when breeding include *Diomedea nigripes* (black-footed albatross), the petrels and shearwaters, and possibly the tropic birds. Although 12 of the 18 resident sea birds appear to prefer the offshore zone and only 6 apparently are restricted chiefly to the inshore areas, there are more numerous individuals of the latter (Baker, 1951, p. 30). This would correspond with the more abundant food supply in the inshore areas of the atolls and other islands.

There are no sea birds endemic to Micronesia. Those found here have ancestral homes in the Palearctic region, in the north and central Pacific, in Polynesia, in Melanesia, in Malaysia, or they have uncertain homelands because of their circumtropical occurrence. Sea birds having a Northern Hemisphere range and reaching the northern and western edges of Micronesia as winter visitors include *Larus argentatus, Chlidonias leucopterus,* and *Sterna hirundo* (Baker, 1951, p. 31).

Sea birds restricted in their distribution to Polynesia and adjacent islands but which range to Micronesia, either as residents or as visitors, include *Puffinus tenuirostris* (short-tailed shearwater), *P. nativitatis, Pterodroma rostrata* (Tahiti petrel), *P. hypoleuca* (stout-billed gadfly petrel), *Sterna lunata* (bridled tern), and *Procelsterna cerulea.* In the vast area of Polynesia, especially in the high islands of its margins, there appears to have been considerable speciation among sea birds. Only a small part of these bird species have reached Micronesia (Baker, 1951).

Two birds with ranges restricted to the western Pacific and the Indian Oceans have reached Micronesia from somewhere in the Melanesian or Malaysian area. These are *Sterna sumatrana* and *Thalasseus bergii*. Other birds have circumtropical ranges. They include *Puffinus pacificus, P. lherminieri*, Phaethon, Sula, Fregata, *Sterna anaethetus, S. fuscata, Anous stolidus, A. tenuirostris,* and *Gygis alba* (Baker, 1951).

Migratory shore birds

In atoll marine ecology, the shore birds play quite a different role from that of the sea birds. Although there is an overlap in their food sources, the sea birds are more exclusively fish and crustacean eaters, while the shore birds feed on a greater variety of reef fauna as well as shore fauna such as insects and lizards not ordinarily sought by sea birds. This lack of competition from local island birds has made the reef-bound islands and atolls attractive to migratory shore birds. Shore birds also differ in being resident only part of the year in the tropical atolls and islands. The tropical islands of the Pacific are the favorite wintering grounds of many species of shore birds, although for some they are merely stepping stones on the annual migration from breeding grounds in northern Asia or Alaska to the winter homes in Australia and New Zealand (Mayr, 1945, p. 28). In the southwest Pacific, all the migratory species, with the exception of the Australian stilt, are visitors from northern Asia or Alaska. They begin to arrive in the southwest Pacific in late August and depart again in April and May. Some individuals of all species, however, stay on throughout the summer. These are nonbreeding birds, either because they are too young or because of poor health. Since their plumage differs from that of the breeding adults, they may be hard to identify.

Mayr listed 31 species and subspecies of shore birds and adds six other species that may occur in the southwest Pacific. Of the possible 37 species, 29 are found in Micronesia. Of these, 28 species are from two families, Charadriidae and Scolopacidae. The other species, apparently present in Micronesia, is of the family Phalaropodidae. Of the 28 recorded shore birds, 17 are classed as regular visitors and 11 as uncommon visitors. Of the 28 species recorded, 18 come from northern Asiatic breeding grounds. Seven have circumpolar breeding ranges, and three come from American (Alaskan) breeding grounds. Moreover, 21 of the 28 waders have their winter ranges on the Asiatic side of the Pacific, with eastward extensions into Micronesia and other parts of Oceania. Of the other seven three have circumpolar winter ranges, one is restricted to a winter range in Oceania, and the other three winter range in America (Baker, 1951, pp. 32–3).

Baker (1951, pp. 34–42) suggested three migratory "flight lanes" for the Micronesian shore birds: (1) the Asiatic-Palauan Flyway, (2) the Japanese-Marianan Flyway, and (3) the Nearctic-Hawaiian Flyway. Since banding records for Pacific migratory birds are scanty, these have been deduced from sight records. The information available indicates that migrant shore birds which use the first flyway move east into the Carolines from the Palaus (examples: *Tringa nebularia* (greenshank), *Charadrius leschenaultii* (large sand dotterel), but this eastward movement may not be very pronounced. Eight species of shore birds that reach the Palaus and the westernmost Caroline islands are not recorded from other parts of Micronesia. Shore birds migrating via the second route through the Mariana Islands probably fan out to the southeast, south, and southwest, some even reaching the Palau (i.e., *Heteroscelus incanus,* or wandering tattler). The last flyway is probably the one which supplies the largest wintering populations of shore birds to central and eastern Oceania. They may fly from the Hawaiian Islands directly south through the scattered islands to southern Polynesia or southwesterly to the Marshall Islands, feeding en route, moving thence through the Gilbert, Ellice, and other more southerly groups rather than westward into the Carolines. Thus, *Numenius tahitiensis* (bristle-thighed curlew), which characteristically migrates from the Hawaiian Islands through the Marshalls, seldom is found west of the Marshalls (Baker, 1951).

Tables 14, 15, and 16 list the species of shore birds which Baker suggests may use the three flyways (Baker, 1951, p. 37).

TABLE 14

Shore Birds That May Use the Asiatic-Palauan Flyway

Regular visitors	*Uncommon(?) visitors*
Pluvialis dominica fulva	*Charadrius dubius curonicus*
Charadrius mongolus stegmanni	*Charadrius alexandrinus*
Charadrius leschenaultii	*Chlidris tenuirostris*
Numenius phaeopus variegatus	*Erolia ferruginea*
Numenius madagascariensis	*Erolia subminuta*
Limosa lapponica baueri	*Limicola falcinellus sibirica*
Tringa nebularia	
Tringa glareolia	
Actitis hypoleucos	
Heteroscelus brevipes	
Arenaria i. interpres	
Gallinago megala	
Erolia minuta ruficollis	
Erolia acuminata	

Since the shore birds are generally rather shy of people, they are less easily seen and identified, and numerical counts are harder to obtain. There is little question of their numerical insignificance compared to the vast colonies of sea birds that characterize some uninhabited atolls and the rela-

TABLE 15

Shore Birds That May Use the Japanese-Marianan Flyway

Regular visitors	*Uncommon(?) visitors*
Pluvialis dominica fulva	*Squatarola squatarola*
Charadrius mongolus stegmanni	*Numenius tahitiensis*
Numenius phaeopus variegatus	*Numenius madagascariensis*
Limosa lapponica baueri	*Tringa glareola*
Actitis hypoleucos	*Gallinago gallinago gallinago*
Heteroscelus brevipes	*Erolia minuta ruficollis*
Heteroscelus incanus	
Arenaria i. interpres	
Gallinago megala	
Crocethia alba	
Erolia acuminata	

TABLE 16

Shore Birds That May Use the Neartic-Hawaiian Flyway

Regular visitors	*Uncommon(?) visitors*
Pluvialis dominica fulva	*Squatarola squatarola*
Numenius tahitiensis	*Charadrius hiaticula semipalmatus*
Heteroscelus incanus	*Charadrius v. vociferus*
Arenaria i. interpres	*Limosa lapponica baueri*
Crocethia alba	*Tringa melanoleuca*
Phalaropus fulicarius	*Gallinago delicata*
Phalaropus lobatus	*Erolia melanotos*
	Erolia acuminata

tively large numbers of sea birds that nest even on inhabited atolls. The importance of the shore birds in atoll marine ecology thus is far less than that of the sea birds, although at their particular reef and shore habitats the shore birds may exercise a more significant local role.

Aspects of marine and shore bird ecology

The relationship between the frigate bird and the booby is a peculiar one and deserves mention. The frigate bird is easily identified (Plate 57). Its flight is an effortless glide through the air, sometimes for hours without a wing beat, the deeply forked tail opening and closing like a pair of scissors. Although Mayr stated that they "never settle on water but pick their food with the bill from the surface" (1945, p. 19), Degener and Gillaspy (1955, p. 50) give different information: "It is commonly reported that frigate birds, lacking webbed feet, never land on the surface of the water because they cannot take off again. This is not true. I have seen a small flock of them playfully land, float and rise again from the placid surface of the lagoon." It has a well-developed homing instinct and Tuamotu natives rear them in captivity and use them after the manner of homing pigeons to carry messages among the islands (Townsend, 1919, p. 156).

All reports agree that the frigate bird is a robber of other birds' catch, diving on the boobies, attacking them, and beating them with beak and wings until the boobies drop the fish they have caught or disgorge what they have swallowed. The frigate then dives and retrieves the food in mid-air or from the water surface and gorges itself (Arundel, 1885). In the rookery the frigate not only may rob the nest of boobies, but may seize the young of other frigates and fly away with them to eat on the wing (Degener and Gillaspy, 1955). The booby's reaction in being attacked must be a deeply ingrained instinct. Arundel wrote: "It is very curious that when you come on a booby sitting on its egg or nest, and it cannot rise and fly away, it utters very harsh cries, pecks vigorously at you with its long, sharp-pointed beak, and then, if you do not go away, it at last disgorges the fish it has recently caught at your feet, as much as to say, "There; you are no better than the man-of-war hawk, my natural enemy. . . ." Bryan (1903) wrote that the old birds seldom go far out to sea. "If this species is to be seen in numbers, one may be certain of being within 50 miles of land, usually, though not always, a low coral island." The Pacific man-of-war may prey on other animals also. Rabbits introduced onto Laysan are caught by these birds. Dill and Bryan (1912, p. 10) wrote: "Several times we saw them pick up full-grown rabbits, and we found young ones dead on the nest of the red-footed booby." The man-of-war birds "are all cannibals, and will quickly devour any egg or young bird left unprotected; hence constant vigilance is necessary on the part of the parents who take turns in guarding the nest" (Dill, 1916, p. 153).

Albatrosses appear to become completely attached to a nest site that has been used previously. DuMont and Neff (1955) wrote that they found 172 black-footed and 77 Laysan albatrosses banded in previous years returning to the same spot on Midway to nest. Many had been banded 10 to 16 years ago. None of the banded birds were noted on other islands on Midway, so that they concluded that there was no exchange of birds between the islands of the Midway Atoll. The forming of distinctive colonies of sea birds in

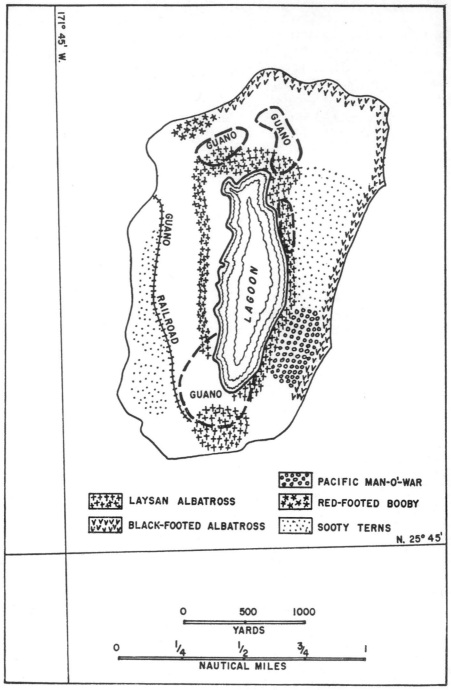

171° 45' W.

GUANO

GUANO

GUANO

GUANO

RAILROAD

LAGOON

GUANO

PACIFIC MAN-O'-WAR

LAYSAN ALBATROSS

RED-FOOTED BOOBY

BLACK-FOOTED ALBATROSS

SOOTY TERNS

N. 25° 45'

0	500	1000

YARDS

0	1/4	1/2	3/4	1

NAUTICAL MILES

Fig. 88. Location of bird colonies at Laysan Atoll. [After Dill and Bryan (1912).]

breeding sites without intermixing, except for some overlap where different species adjoin each other, is shown by Fig. 88. This map shows the data plotted by Dill in 1912, redrawn by Hutchinson, and further redrawn by the writer on a U. S. Coast and Geodetic Survey base map of 1942. The outer circumference of Hutchinson's map very roughly corresponds with the Coast and Geodetic Survey's map, but there is little resemblance between the shapes of the lagoons. The guano patches were taken by Hutchinson from Elschner (1915). Hutchinson (1950, p. 206) said that Dill's map was based on a population of the Laysan albatross that was much reduced after 1909. It is clear from the restriction of the sooty terns to one side of the guano rail-road that these also had been disturbed by the guano operations. In any case, as Hutchinson suggested, the distribution of the Laysan albatross sug-gests that most of the guano was derived from this bird and from the sooty tern. An interesting aspect of the colonization sites is the apparent prefer-ence of the albatrosses for sites near the shore of the sea or lagoon. As shown in Fig. 90, the black-footed albatrosses on Laysan all are found on a narrow strip along the north and east or windward shores, except at the extreme southern tip of the lagoon where they appear to have been displaced south-ward by the guano digging and here occupy the seashore area. The southern and western or leeward sea shores appear not to be favored nesting sites. These observations appear to be in accord with the need of the birds for take-off space, and, apparently, these sites facing the prevailing winds are most favored.

In listing habitat conditions that contribute to high populations, Frings and Frings (1959, p. 16) included the following characteristics observed on Midway, which has the highest density of Laysan albatrosses: "1. the sand is covered with grass or other low ground cover which holds the sand and affords materials for protecting the nests; 2. there are not too many low, dense shrubs such as Scaevola, to form hazards to walking and landing or taking off in flight; 3. ironwood trees are present in reasonable numbers, providing overhead cover which Laysans seem to prefer to completely open terrain and providing 'needles' for the nests; 4. there is available nearby some relatively clear area, such as a grass-covered meadow, a road or a runway, for take-offs and landings." These authors sample-measured space require-ments for albatross nesting territory and found that the diameter of the average nesting territory under conditions of high population density was 64 inches, encompassing an area of about 25 square feet, although the nest itself was only about 40 inches in diameter, and the distances between the nests varied from 0 to 60 inches.

Captured banded birds provided information indicating that the majority of young albatrosses return to nesting islands for the first time sometime between the ages of 4 and 6 years. Adult albatrosses, once they have selected a nest site, appear to return to the same site year after year, over 90 per cent sampled returning to sites within 10 to 12 feet of former locations. A large proportion of Laysan albatrosses nesting in any one season, whether success- ful or not in rearing a chick, return to nest the following year. Since breed- ing birds appear always to return to the same island to nest, it would appear that population spread to other islands must be by young birds which have never nested before rather than by adults which have nested previously. "Divorced" albatrosses are few, numbering only about 5 per cent. Some 95 per cent of breeding pairs return intact to nesting sites. It therefore appears that the pair bond normally remains intact until broken by the death or disappearance of one of the partners (Rice, 1959, pp. 7–11).

Some idea of the number of sea birds on undisturbed barren atolls can be imagined from the reduced number on Laysan in 1911, estimated to be approximately 946,000. About 334,000 of these were sooty terns; there were 180,000 Laysan albatrosses, the next largest group. Two species of shearwaters totaled 175,000 birds. The stout-billed gadfly petrel numbered 160,000 and the bridled tern 50,000. None of these are represented on the map given by Hutchinson. The 12,500 Pacific man-of-wars and 125 red-footed boobies are represented on the map. Some 300 red-tailed tropic birds were not included. The criteria for inclusion or omission in the showing of colonization groups on the map is not given.

The terns are the most conspicuous sea birds in tropical waters. Although terns are competent swimmers and divers, they like to rest on floating ob- jects. They are often seen on pieces of driftwood or floating coconuts and will be seen flying and diving wherever a school of small fish churns the water. Their slender, graceful shapes, long tapering wings and long, usually forked tails, and their jerky nonsoaring flight make them easily recognizable (Mayr, 1945, p. 21). Their loud voice belies their small size, however, and their constant cry and movement, day and night, is never absent from a colony. Arundel (1885) said of the sooty tern that he believed its common name, "wide-awake," was taken from the cry of the tern, which resembles these two words, as well as from "its habits and state of mind, which these words correctly describe."

Moul (1954, p. 6) found the common noddy tern the most common bird on Onotoa. Many of these birds perched in the palms and pandanus during the middle of the day, resting and preening, but some restless individuals were moving to sea and back again during all daylight hours. The greatest movement occurred in the early morning and late afternoon, when the largest numbers shuttled back and forth between roosting area and the sea, reef, or lagoon. Moul said that they fluttered about at all hours of the night, whether the moon was bright or not. At Midway during November and December, DuMont and Neff (1955) found the air relatively free of sooty terns and other birds from 1 A.M. to at least an hour after sunrise. Most stout-billed gadfly petrels were in the air from near sunset to about 10 P.M., although they continued to fly about until past midnight. However, scarcely any albatrosses fly about after dark.

When the sea is rough beyond the reef, according to Moul (1954), the noddies often were seen feeding over the reef at ebbing tide. They dived to pick up their food from the surface but did not submerge like the common Atlantic tern. Other individuals would stand near tide pools and wait for a small fish to move into open water. On one occasion Moul found them quite active even during a rain storm. As they flew about in the rain, occasionally they would drop, shaking the water from their wing and tail feathers and then, recovering, gain altitude.

Moul wrote that three times during his stay on Onotoa he saw the long-tailed New Zealand cuckoo flying about followed by a group of black-naped terns which kept diving at it. The former apparently ignored their attackers. The black-naped terns here seemed to prefer habitually to rest on the coarse coral gravel ramparts on the seaward side of the two islands and habitually to fish in the shallow water at one end of the lagoon. Marshall (1951, p. 16) noted that these terns rest on sand spits or gravel exposures near large expanses of shallow water where they feed. When on the wing over fishing areas, they dive from about 25 feet. Sometimes they swoop low to catch small flying fish.

The crested terns feed mostly on mullet and sometimes chase flying fish. According to Marshall (1951, p. 17),

> They hunt by diving from a height of 25 to 75 feet as follows: a bird over a favorite water fishing site swings into the wind, poises and rises, suddenly faces down and rolls about a half turn as it plummets down to sink half way under the water, rises into the wind, swallows, shakes out its feathers (clearing them of water), flies straight on, then circles back to the starting point . . . Prodigious distances are covered in foraging, and single birds can be seen in the middle of the lagoon, bound from one end of the atoll to another. They are widely distributed in the lagoon, but do not go far out over the ocean. They do not join the noddy fishing flocks, but feed on their own or in company with black-naped terns. They are active from dawn to dusk, but spend much time sitting together on rocks.

Noddies feed in large milling flocks on "bait fish" scared up by schools of tuna. They follow tuna movements until new schools of bait fish are chased to the surface, and they are always ready to scoop the fish from the surface. Noddies also will make individual forages in the patrolling of shallow tide pools, so that they cover vast areas in their feeding. The smaller noddy, *Anous Tenuirostris,* differs from the large noddy, *Anous stolidus,* in that the larger birds make continual whining cries while circling the fishing area.

Both species nest in trees (Marshall, 1951, pp. 17–18). Where trees or bushes are not available they nest on the ground (Moseley, 1892, p. 299).

Marine-bird destruction by rats and by man

The sea and shore birds are not so susceptible as the land birds to extinction, because they are not confined to an island or a group of islands near each other and because their habitats are not destructible or as destructible as are those of the land birds. The ground-nesting birds, however, are especially vulnerable to man and to other enemies introduced by man accidentally or intentionally, especially rats and cats. Rats are particularly destructive because of their ability to survive without fresh water; the blood of birds can satisfy the need for moisture. A visitor to Howland Island in 1854 was almost overwhelmed both by the birds and by the rats (Howland, 1955, pp. 95–103):

Next to the birds and living in close and constant proximity to them, the only fauna we observed were armies of rats. They appeared to be the gray Scandinavian variety and to be subsisting and thriving on the eggs and fledglings it was only too easy for them to obtain . . . Occasionally the birds would make a raid on a band of rats engaged in these depredations and succeed in seizing some of the younger robbers. They would, we observed, kill the rats by tearing them to pieces with their beaks and talons, or more often where the rat was of a small size, fly off to a point at a considerable height above the reefs and drop their prey into the pounding surf . . . The vast armies of rats were as unafraid of us as the birds and squealed and bit at us as we trod on their squirming tails . . . The rats were in one great common army, squirming and squealing wherever the birds nested and making common warfare on the birds. Their complete fearlessness of us would indicate their antiquity . . . During the day when not engaged in shading the eggs or feeding the young the bird in charge of the nest spends his or her time beating off the attacks of the rats. In cases where a band of well grown rats is on the warpath and makes an attack on a nest or group of nests, the sea fowl in that vicinity will band themselves together and make a concerted attack on the rats using wings, beak, and talons and keeping their enemies quite busy until they have moved off. The young rats of small size have a hard time of it, as the birds often kill these under-sized enemies outright . . . I am of the opinion that the young of each is the prey of the other and that except where eggs are cracked by the birds themselves the rats do not affect an appreciable amount of damage by their destruction of eggs. I only observed a few cases where the rats were successful in rolling a whole uncracked egg to a point where it was pushed over a ledge with sufficient drop to break it when it landed below.

The very fact that rats had increased to such enormous numbers (a companion of this man killed some 500 rats in protecting his camp during 4 hours of the afternoon) indicates that rats were increasing at the expense of the birds. Whether there is a saturation point where the birds and rats balance each other is not clear, since birds and rats appear to coexist on some islands for long periods of time. However, Hutchinson (1950, p. 165) indicated that on Baker and Howland the rats exterminated the terns.

The effects of periodic decimations of sea birds from natural causes or by man is not always easily evaluated, because of the difficulties of estimating bird populations and of mortality rates. The subject of albatross population dynamics, for example, "is one in which we are almost totally ignorant," according to Rice (1959, p. 13).

Fairly good estimates may be made of breeding birds by sample counts of nests or nesting pairs, but Rice (1959, p. 5) pointed out that "It is difficult to determine what this figure means in terms of total population—breeding and non-breeding. Present data suggest that the total [albatrosses], including all categories of unemployed birds, is at least three times the number of birds nesting in any one season . . . On this basis the total world population of Laysan albatrosses is tentatively estimated at 1,500,000 and that of black-footed albatrosses at 300,000." This was over 100 per cent more than the world populations of each of these species estimated in 1958, when it was not evident that such a large proportion of the birds during a season roamed at sea and were not nesting. In a personal communication to the writer, Johnson A. Neff of the U. S. Fish and Wildlife Service at Denver, Colorado, wrote that "annual population variation in density of population occurs on each of the Leewards," in his firm opinion, and that it was his theory "that the non-nesting but sexually mature population at sea varies greatly: probably due to physiological variations that may be caused by feeding conditions at sea—a phase never studied."

A study at Midway by Frings and Frings (1959) indicated that population estimates also may err when they are made at the wrong time of the nesting season. The buildup of the nesting bird population for albatrosses, for instance, takes place over a longer period than was generally thought earlier, more than a month as compared with the 2 weeks believed earlier. Later counts, thus, should be larger.

In view of the aspects mentioned, the value of some of the earlier estimates of different kinds of bird populations is greater for their qualitative assessments than for their quantitative reliability. Thus, Dill's estimate (1916, p. 173) of a decline of earlier albatross population on Laysan from over a million to about 180,000 after 1911 as a result of guano-mining operations may be several hundred per cent off, but it still showed a major decline in population. Estimates of Laysan albatross population (as distinguished from the black-footed albatross) on Laysan Island in 1951 amounted to 103,000. In 1955 it was the impression of air observers that the density of Laysan albatrosses on Laysan was less than that at either Sand or Eastern

Island on Midway, each of which had only an estimated 22,000 to 25,000 individuals (DuMont and Neff, 1955).

However, in 1957–1958 the breeding birds alone on Laysan Island were estimated at 260,000 Laysan albatrosses and 67,000 black-footed albatrosses (Rice, 1959, p. 6). Neff sent to the writer on Nov. 2, 1959, tabulated recent estimates for Sand Island of Midway as given in Table 17.

TABLE 17

Estimate of Birds on Sand Island

Observer	Year	Laysans	Blackfoots	Total	Comments
Fisher	Dec. 1946	145,000	69,000	214,000	All birds
Sheehan	1952	30,000	25,000	55,000	All birds
DuMont-Neff	1954	22,600	7,700	30,300	All birds
Kenyon, Rice et al.	1956–57 *	236,000	18,000	254,000	All birds
Rice et al.	1957–58 *	200,000	17,000	327,000 (sic)	Breeding birds
Frings	1958–59	33,700	6,500	40,200	?

* Includes both Sand Island and little (350 acres) Eastern Island.

The mortality of juvenile birds from egg to fledging is high, averaging about 51 per cent among the black-footed albatrosses and 37 per cent among the Laysan albatrosses, whose mortality rates are lower. These rates do not take into consideration the apparently high mortality of young birds immediately after they leave the island, for many young birds are found floating dead in the lagoon or washed up on the reef and beaches. Sharks, which were said to throng into the lagoon when the young gooneys were learning to fly, were reported to have killed large numbers of young birds. "On the basis of general impressions, it would seem that the majority, probably at least two-thirds, of the albatrosses which reach the flying stage are successful in leaving Midway Atoll" (Rice, 1959, pp. 14–18).

Natural catastrophe such as typhoons and tsunamis at times may cause heavy mortality. Typhoon Ophelia, which generated high storm tides at Midway and throughout the Leeward Islands on January 11–13, 1958, sent waves over the beaches and part of the nesting area, accounting for a mortality of 42 per cent, of which 35 per cent of the young dead were from the inundations (Rice, 1959, p. 19).

Man's activities have greatly added to the death rates of sea birds. Half a century ago on Marcus Island, Bryan (1903) wrote that except for an occasional solitary individual bird, a Japanese fertilizer company had virtually exterminated both types of albatross on Marcus by killing them wholesale and boiling them in large kettles. "The resultant, consisting of flesh, bones,

and viscera, was barrelled and shipped to Japan where it was used for fertilizer. Within six years the entire colony of these splendid birds has been
exterminated."

At the same time the Japanese on Marcus also engaged in killing the
sooty terns and fairy terns and preparing their skins and wings for export to
New York, Paris, and Berlin for millinery purposes. In an earlier day the
red-tailed tropic bird suffered a similar fate at Motu-iti near Tahiti from
where the royal chiefs of Tahiti derived the tail feathers of this beautiful
bird for their adornment (Bennett, 1840, p. 365). The red tail feathers of
these birds once fetched good prices in Europe as plumes for riflemen's hel-
mets in the old Imperial German Army (Luke, 1945, p. 224). As late as 1928
the tail feathers of this bird were in commercial demand (New Zealand
Journal of Science and Technology, 1928, p. 371).

The hazards presented by the sea birds to aircraft operating from Midway during World War I caused 80,000 albatrosses on Eastern Island to be
killed in an attempt to remove or control nesting birds. The operation
proved to be a failure, because birds from outside the area and from the sea
promptly moved in. A variety of methods to remove them have been tried
since then, apparently with little success. However, estimates in December
1958 indicated that the effects of the harassment and killing campaigns
started three or four years previously were then beginning to show up.
Frings and Frings (1959, p. 16) concluded that "It looks very much as if
the black-foots, at least, on Sand Island will leave under pressure of harassment by man. This could probably be speeded up . . . The Laysans seem
likewise to be leaving, and this process, too, could be speeded up. The
driving of these birds from Sand Island, at least, seems desirable for the
benefit of the birds themselves, in view of the unintentional or occasional
malicious harassment to which they are being subjected."

Laysan Island is the most important breeding station for North Pacific
albatrosses. It is utilized by 46 per cent of the total breeding population of
Laysan albatrosses, and by 61 per cent of the breeding population of black-
footed albatrosses. Midway Atoll ranks second, with 36 and 15 per cent,
respectively, of the total breeding populations of the two species. Only four
atolls—Laysan, Midway, Lisianski, and Pearl—and Hermes Reef are the
breeding ground of 96 and 94 per cent, respectively, of the total world populations of Laysan and black-footed albatrosses (Rice, 1959, p. 7).

In view of this situation and the fact that the necessities of aircraft operations at Midway might compel the complete extermination of all the 420,000
albatrosses in the colony (The New York Times, 1959), Rice suggested improving the albatross habitat on Laysan, Lisianski, or Kure Island, so as to
avoid reduction of the world breeding populations of these birds. Whether
the destruction on Midway would solve the problem of aircraft strikes of
flying birds is uncertain. "Indications were found that other sea birds, par-

ticularly noddy terns, which nest on the ground and thus compete with the albatrosses for territories, may be increasing. If the albatrosses go, these may increase" (Rice, 1959, p. 17).

Marine birds as sources of food

Marine birds are among the various species of birds captured by atoll dwellers for food. The eggs of various birds also may be gathered for food.

Sooty tern eggs, which are about an inch long, are described by Arundel (1885) as "uncommonly good eating, especially when boiled hard and curried. It has not the slightest taste of fish about it." In April 1958 while the writer was visiting Jaluit, he sailed with some of the inhabitants to a small uninhabited islet on the northwestern reef of the atoll, where the islanders gathered eggs and captured about 20 sooty terns to take home for eating.

Gardner Island natives are said to domesticate the boobies and avoid the fishy flavor of the flesh and eggs by tethering the birds (U. S. Navy, 1952, p. 331). Danielsson (1955, pp. 179–80) said that on Raroia the boobies have been almost exterminated by the natives, who catch them or take their. eggs for food, and that the reason frigate birds are still numerous is probably that their meat is regarded as poor food. Noddies, however, nested in huge numbers on certain uninhabited islets of Onotoa Atoll, and during the breeding period, October to December, small groups of young people sailed once or twice a week to these islets. "Each person brings back at least four or five dozen eggs and half a dozen young birds from such a trip. The eggs are all eaten irrespective of the stage of development of the embryo. Some of the birds may be kept in captivity and fed for some time before being killed, but most of them are eaten immediately" (Danielsson, 1955).

Burrows and Spiro (1953, p. 34) mention the noddy as being used for food on Ifalik in the western Caroline Islands. Burnett (1910, pp. 52–3) wrote that Polynesian natives traveling on his ship between Rakahanga and Manihiki caught noddies flying low by throwing a line at the end of which a stick had been tied, so as to wrap the line around the neck of the bird and bring it down. These noddies, "though of an intensely disagreeable flavour to European taste," upon being dressed and soaked for a few days in salt water, were evidently very palatable to the natives, "indeed, are considered quite a delicacy by them."

Birds, on the whole, did not furnish an important or steady food source to the atoll dweller. Krämer (1905, pp. 140–6) claimed that in the Marshalls eggs were disliked as food everywhere. In most inhabited Pacific atolls, certain varieties of birds and their eggs were eaten as a supplementary food. In some instances, however, a constant drain on birds and eggs resulted in much-depleted bird stock.

CHAPTER 14

ATOLL LAND: THE FRESH-WATER PROBLEM

Some aspects of land ecology have already been discussed, especially with regard to the life of marine and shore birds. The following chapters concern chiefly the land aspects of atoll ecology. The marine and land ecologies of atolls cannot be discussed as entirely separated phenomena, however, since they are intricately interlocked in a great variety of ways, and, of course, there are intermediate zones of transition in which both marine and land elements together form various habitats. This is evident in the shore and intertidal zone and also in the avian aerial interchange between sea and land. As it affects the land, the transference of organic matter from the sea to the land in the guano of sea birds is especially significant. In an entirely different and inorganic manner, the buoyancy that is given fresh water in the porous coral rock of reef islets by the pressure of denser infiltrating sea water makes it possible for important economic plants to exist on oceanic coral rock and debris and to help answer the fresh-water problem.

Ground-water conditions on atolls

Atoll islet material is generally so porous that drainage by percolation down through the ground is "perfect and almost instantaneous" (Fosberg, 1954). There is no running surface water, except that driven by storm winds and waves across the land. Normally there is no standing surface water except where pits have been dug down below the surface of the water table. Exceptions are known: one example is that of islets subject to intensive military motor traffic, such as Kwajelein. The surface road materials may become "so compacted and, apparently, cemented as to become more or less impervious. Here water puddles may stand as long as 24 hours after heavy rains" (Fosberg, 1954).

Catala (1957, p. 35) mentions instances on Gilbertese atolls where "The water supply formed above the shallow bed-rock may remain stagnant at root level and injure the palms which are as sensitive to water-logged conditions as they are to drought." He noted that old taro pits might acquire an impermeable floor and kill once-productive coconut palms through "asphyxia." Another unusual situation is illustrated by the central depression on Kili Island, which is a single reef island. Here, tidal fluctuations of the ground-water level normally noted in pits and depressions appear to be quite minor. Where the normal fluctuations would be several inches, a series of readings during spring tides and at the end of a dry period showed maximum fluctuations attributable to tidal effect between one-half and three-quarters of an inch. This hints at an unusually dense rock formation beneath the surface. "Ten or twelve days previously, during a period of daily rains it was noted that the ground water stood several inches higher. In fact shallow pools formed over extensive areas . . . The water rose 6 and ½ inches over the average level . . . Apparently rain water drains very rapidly to the center of the island, and accumulates there . . ." (Bach, 1950).

Normally, when rainfall on atolls drains down through the ground, some of the water is held in capillary openings in the soil and remains available to shallow-rooted plants which withdraw this moisture and transpire it to the atmosphere. It is estimated that less than half and perhaps only about a quarter of the rainfall is available after evapotranspiration losses are deducted (Arnow, 1954, p. 4). The surplus seeps quickly to a body of more-or-less fresh water saturating the rock and sand. This "basal ground water" makes contact at its lower face with marine water that has infiltrated through the porous rock from the sea and lagoon. Fresh water poured upon an open body of salt water will quickly spread over the surface of the salt and through currents and waves become thoroughly mixed with the salt water. Porous rock, however, interposes an obstacle to this rapid spread and restricts the mixing of the light fresh water with the denser salt water. The fresh water is only about 40/41 as heavy as salt sea water and floats on the salt water, displacing 40 parts of sea water for each part of fresh water floating above the normal salt-water level. That is, fresh water seeping to basal ground-water level on coral atolls and other porous islands has a depth that is about 40 times the head or elevation of its water table above sea level. This head or hydraulic gradient of water tends to seek sea level by lateral flow through the restricting rock. This principle of fresh-water displacement of salt water in islands and coastal areas is known as the Ghyben-Herzberg law, after its first discoverers (Cox, 1951, p. 11). As the head of water moves outward, the depth of the fresh water becomes less until at the edge of the shore, where the fresh water seeps into the sea, it is just about at sea level, disregarding the fluctuations of the tide. In a roughly round island of uniform permeability, the body of fresh water floating upon the salt water assumes the shape of a lens, the edges of which coincide with the edges of the island, with the upper face of the lens only slightly convex compared with the deeply convex lower surface at the salt-water interface.

Actually the shape of the fresh-water body varies, depending upon local geologic conditions, the shape of the island, and variations in rainfall. Also the 40-to-1 depth ratio is modified by a transition zone of variable thickness in which there is a mixture of fresh and salt water resulting from the vertical movement of the tides (Arnow, 1955, p. 8). On an island of uniform permeability the maximum head and thickness of fresh water will be greater if the rainfall is greater, smaller if the rainfall is less. It also varies with seasonal changes in the rainfall. "In two islands of the same size, the one with the lower permeability will have the higher head and the thicker fresh-water lens. In two islands of dissimilar size but having the same permeability and receiving the same rainfall, the larger island will have the higher head and the thicker fresh-water lens. Because of the change in shapes of the fresh water lens with change in size, the relationships of rainfall rate, island size, shape, and permeability to the thickness of the fresh-water lens are complicated and not those of direct proportionality" (Cox, 1951, p. 13).

Since the fresh water floats on the sea water that seeps through the underlying reef rock, the level of the fresh-water lens is controlled by a base that varies with the tidal movements. The fresh-water surface thus rises and falls according to the tide but with a lag and a smaller degree of fluctuation. This lag and the degree of dampening of the tide depend upon distance from the coast and the porosity of the ground or rock. Greater distance and smaller permeability produce greater lag and tidal damping (Cox, 1951, p. 14). Arnow (1954, p. 4) wrote that a comparison of tidal fluctuations in the ocean and in the ground-water body in four islands of the northern Marshalls indicates that the ocean tides are damped by about $\frac{9}{10}$ as they move through the land. On small islands this damping is greatly reduced. On Ailuk the mean tidal range of water in a well 115 feet from the lagoon shore was only 0.32 feet, as compared with the mean tidal range of 4 feet in the ocean. The comparable ranges for water from a well on Lae 1,035 feet from the lagoon shore was 0.16 foot and 2.1 feet, respectively.

Tidal movements of the lens and the alternate swelling and shrinking of the lens by rainfall or drought result in the raising and lowering of the salt-water and fresh-water contact, or interface. This movement of the interface up and down alternately brings the invasion of salt and the dilution of salt water with fresh water. Thus the contact zone is not sharply defined in terms of salinity or freshness, but shows a transition in salinity. At the center of an island of uniform permeability, the tidal fluctuation is at a minimum, and the depth of fresh water is at a maximum. The rate of salt transfer is at a minimum, and there may be not only a low salt content but comparatively little change in salt content as compared with near-coast situations, where the tidal range is greater. At the shore, of course, the tidal range is at a maximum and there also is a reverse hydraulic gradient at high tide carrying salt water into the island. "Consequently all of the water emerging at the shore is brackish, and the change in salt content with depth and time is complex" (Cox, 1951, pp. 14–15).

In summary, to quote Cox (1951, p. 16),

The average salinity at any point in a Ghyben-Herzberg lens in a small island is, therefore, complexedly controlled by the size of the island, the horizontal location of the point on it with reference to the coast lines and the vertical location of the point in the lens, by the average recharge (that is, the average excess of rainfall over transpiration losses) and by the variability of the recharge, by the permeability and porosity of the rocks, and by the tidal range in the surrounding water,The salinity at the point may be at a particular time greatly different from the average salinity at the point. Near the surface of the lens, except at the shore, the salinity will depend principally on the time elaspsed since the last rainfalls and the magnitudes of those rainfalls in relation to the porosity and permeability. Soon after a rain the salinity will drop fairly quickly and then return gradually to a normal value which will be determined, like the salinity deeper in the lens, principally by seasonal changes of recharge, again with relation to the permeability. As has been already indicated, the salinity at the shore will be greatly influenced by the tides. [See also McKee, 1958, p. 263.]

Cox stated also (1951) that the relatively impermeable beach rock serves as a barrier to the outflow of fresh water, especially where the underlying reef platform is impermeable also. In such a situation, encircling beach rock acts like the sides of a tank, effectively sealing off fresh water from the ocean. This causes a high head, very little tidal effect, and low salinity. He suggests that beach rock in such situations related to old shore lines now buried in interior parts of the islands might make similar barriers within the islands, resulting in the separation of two or more independent fresh-water bodies. This would seem to present a very plausible explanation for the situation earlier described for Kili Island, since "Such layers of beach rock might also result in the perching of thin bodies of fresh water above sea level."

Since atoll islets range from tiny sand cays to areas half a mile wide and many miles long, an important question is what size an islet must be to have a fresh-water lens and how fresh the water can be. A standard for freshness of water needs first to be set for comparative purposes. The U. S. Public

Health Service recommends 250 ppm. of sulfate (SO_4) and chloride as upper limits for water used in normal domestic consumption, although water considerably higher in these components may be used without harm by people who have become adjusted to it (McKee, 1958, p. 268). Cloud (1952, p. 32) found that on Onotoa in the Gilberts "A well toward the center of parts of the larger islands that are wider than about 1000 feet has a good chance of producing a fairly continuous supply of potable ground water under the normal draft of the native population. Wells in narrower land or near the beach are apt to be brackish." Onotoa is a rather dry atoll. The average of 8 years of rainfall records showed only 44 inches per year. On Ifalik in the western Carolines, Arnow (1955, pp. 2,. 7–12) found fresh water in two wells dug 175 feet from the ocean and lagoon, respectively, on an islet only 700 feet wide. On the same islet, where the land was only 350 feet wide, the fresh-water lens was practically undeveloped, and it did not exist on a small islet 75 by 150 feet in its largest dimensions. Ifalik has an average annual rainfall estimated from partial data to be between 100 to 120 inches. The wider islets here are between 1,200 and 2,000 feet wide. Arnow wrote, "Even allowing for errors due to surveying and shortness of record, the lens on Ifalik undoubtedly attains a head of at least 1 foot and possibly 1 and $\frac{1}{4}$ feet above mean sea level. The depth to salt water below mean sea level, therefore, probably is 40 feet or more . . . The 40-foot figure is a wet-season figure, and the depth undoubtedly decreases during normal dry seasons and during extended periods of drought. Native informants state that they have no recollection of a drought on Ifalik."

At the eastern tip of Airik on Ailinglaplap Atoll (Wiens, 1957, p. 3), the writer tasted fresh water with hardly any brackishness in a well only 30 feet from the lagoon shore. The islet width was about 300 feet here and near the end of a mile-long islet section several times wider.

The water table at Arno in the southern Marshall Islands was studied by Cox (1951, pp. 18–23) from wells dug along two profiles across Ine Island, a long but relatively narrow islet. One profile crossed the islet where it was nearly 1,400 feet wide. Another crossed it where it was only a little over 300 feet wide. In the first profile a well about 550 feet from the lagoon shore contained 8 ppm chlorides, the same concentration of salts as in the original rainwater,

and an amount astonishingly low to anyone accustomed to the range of salinities to be found at far greater distances from the sea in the Ghyben-Herzberg lenses of volcanic islands like Hawaii. Water of 250 ppm chlorides or less could be found within 70 feet of the lagoon shore but no closer than 750 feet from the ocean shore, and water of 1000 ppm chlorides within 60 feet of the lagoon shore but not closer than 400 feet of the ocean shore. The salinity at the center of the narrow part of the island [second profile] at the same time was 5500 ppm . . . indicating the very great importance of the width of the island on the minimum salinity in the Ghyben-Herzberg lens.

Cox found that the water-table gradients on the two sides of Ine Island indicate an effective permeability 10 times or more greater in the zone occupied by the Ghyben-Herzberg lens on the ocean side than on the lagoon side. Moreover, he found that the permeability coefficients computed for this zone are much greater than those expected in the kinds of sediments found near the water table, indicating that in the reef platform here must be a permeability discontinuity below which the permeability is greater than that above. The tidal effects indicated that the high permeability continued to a depth greater than that of the Ghyben-Herzberg lens. Cox (1951) concludes:

These observations, with a number of scattered observations of tidal fluctuation, salinity, and hardness of water . . . indicate that on the wide parts of the islands of Arno Atoll, and probably on wide atoll islands with similar climate generally, there is a well-developed Ghyben-Herzberg lens with a maximum head of about a foot above mean sea level containing fresh water in its upper part . . . The highest head and freshest water is to be found toward the side of the island under which the average permeability is lowest, which on Ine and Arno at least, and probably very commonly, is the lagoon side.

Arno Atoll's rainfall is incompletely recorded even for a single year, but from partial records and from the full records of Majuro, 10 miles west, it is estimated at about 160 inches per year or more. It is, thus, a fairly wet atoll climatically. In the drier northern Marshalls (50 to 80 inches of rainfall per year) the average height of fresh water above mean sea level is less than a foot, according to Arnow (1954, p. 3). McKee (1958, pp. 260–8) described his observations of ground-water conditions at Kápingamarangi. Climatically, this atoll is intermediate between Ifalik and Onotoa. Complete rainfall records are not available for a full year nor for a number of consecutive years. Partial records and the nature of the vegetation provide a rough basis for an estimate of between 80 and 100 inches of rainfall annually. McKee confirmed the observations and conclusions of Cox, Arnow, and Cloud on the other atolls. Three wells were analyzed by McKee on each of two large islets: Werua (900 feet wide) (Fig. 30), and Taringa (540 feet wide) (Fig. 31). A single well was dug in each of two small islets, Parakahi (400 by 300 feet) and Hukuniu (250 by 150 feet).

The spacing (in feet) of the wells in relation to the coasts on these islets was as given in Table 18. The analyses of water samples from the test wells provided information on the quality of atoll water in different sites and under varying rock and soil conditions.

The data presented in Table 19 are from analyses by the U.S.G.S.

(McKee, 1958, op. cit.) and are given to indicate the characteristic composi-
tions of atoll ground water.

McKee found that here, as on other atolls, there is an asymmetry in
the permeability of atoll islets. In most islands the lagoon shores are
composed of beach sands, whereas the seaward shores are composed of

TABLE 18

Position of Wells

	Lagoon to well 1	Well 1 to well 2	Well 2 to well 3	Well 3 to sea
Taringa	68	250	160	125
Werua	65	500	300	125

	From lagoon (W) side	From sea (E) side	From north side	From south side
Parakahi	136	288	145	156
Hukuniu	100	164	91	54

stratified rocks, boulder ramparts, or both. Moreover, water from wells
on the seaward side is definitely brackish, as shown by wells 3 on both
Taringa and Werua, and mostly not potable. This suggests that seawater
"enters through sizeable cavities or cracks with free circulation rather than
by the slow percolation that constitutes intergranular movement in the
sands. In contrast, ground water on the lagoon sides of these islands is fresh
and drinkable almost to the beaches."

TABLE 19

Analyses of Water Samples from Test Wells and Comparative Data for Normal Sea Water

	Taringa			Werua			Parakahi	Hukuniu	Normal sea water
	(1)	(2)	(3)	(1)	(2)	(3)			
Chemical components, ppm:									
Calcium (Ca)	89	174	255	132	194	268	258	517	400
Magnesium (Mg)	24	63	249	12	13	204	54	1,160	1,270
Sodium (Na)	38	560	2,010	22	23	1,580	400	9,390	10,560
Potassium (K)	2.4	18	75	3	2.4	55	12	359	380
Sulfate (SO$_4$)	16	4.1	459	1.2	4.1	288	30	2,290	2,650
Chloride (Cl)	55	1,100	3,810	20	18	2,980	875	17,500	18,980
Physical characteristics:									
Hardness, ppm	320	693	1,660	379	538	1,760	866	6,060	6,215
Sodium, %	20	63	71	11	8	65	50	76	79

The data from the smaller two islands suggested to McKee (1948) that on these islands

Permeability of the rock or sediment, rather than size of the island, controls the amount of water-level rise and fall . . . The real significance of island size in regard to the fresh-water problem is whether or not a lens can develop and be maintained.

Because continued operation of a lens depends largely on the amount of recharge, a sizable surface area for catching precipitation and a sufficient amount of precipitation are necessary. Parakahi, a small island in a region of only moderate rainfall, is noteworthy for having a lens of fresh, potable water. Hukuniu, which is still smaller, has highly saline water, but this may be due as much to contamination from free circulation through large channels in limestone as to small size of the island. Thus, only a rough qualitative measure of the minimum size requirement, furnished by the example of Parakahi, is available for Kapingamarangi Atoll.

Arnow (1954, pp. 4–5) thought that in the islands south of Eniwetok in the Marshalls, infiltration from rainfall is adequate to maintain a permanent lens if the island is at least 0.1 square mile in area. In places on the main islands in Likiep, Lae, Ailuk, Wotho, Eniwetok, and Ujae Atolls, ground water was found to contain less than 250 ppm of chloride, and on Utirik, Ujelang, and Kwajelein to contain less than 500 ppm of chloride. Such waters are definitely potable and contain less dissolved mineral matter than is present in public water supplies in parts of Guam.

Table 19 shows that well waters on the two larger islands are progressively higher in chemical components, total hardness, and salinity . . . "The hardness of water from wells on the lagoon sides and in the island centers ranges between 300 and 700 ppm. By comparison most water classified as soft in the United States is below 50 or 60 ppm. The island waters would require 'water softeners' for domestic use in the United States. They are similar to waters from the northern Marshall Islands recorded by Arnow (1954, p. 7)" (McKee, 1948, p. 267). Arnow reported that in 53 ground-water samples tested in the northern Marshalls, all had a total hardness of more than 200 ppm and 50 exceeded 300 ppm.

Both McKee and Cox agree that excessive hardness of atoll ground water reflects contributions of calcium and magnesium from limestone and lime sand. McKee (1948) found that calcium is much higher than magnesium in the near-lagoon water samples, "reflecting solution of calcium carbonate and relatively little mixing with sea-water, whereas calcium exceeds magnesium only moderately in the near-sea samples, reflecting mixing with sea water, which has proportionately more magnesium."

Hardness of water from nine wells on Raroia in the Tuamotus at the close of the dry season ranged between about 240 and 360 (plus or minus 13) (Newell, 1954, p. 17). Rainfall for the year averaged 43 inches, which is comparable to that on Onotoa in the Gilberts and less than that in most of the northern Marshalls.

In a personal letter to the writer, Cox (Sept. 2, 1955) wrote:

The hardness of the ground water on an atoll can be derived only by admixture of calcium and magnesium ions from sea water or sea salt, or by solution of these ions from the carbonate sediments. That derived from sea water or sea salt may be computed from the chloride and calcium ions in sea water and the practically constant balance between the chloride and calcium ions in sea water. The calcium derived from solution may thus be computed as a difference.

I found in the ground water of Ine Island, Arno Atoll, hardness values of 200 to 2,400 mg./liter as $CaCO_3$, with excess of 200 to 900 mg./liter above what was expectable from the chloride content if the hardness were all derived from the sea water. I assume that these excesses represent solution of calcium and magnesium carbonates. Assume a rainfall of 120 inches/year (of the right order of magnitude at any rate), this is equivalent to 10 cu. ft./yr./sq. ft. of area. Allow 50% for evapotranspiration, there remains 5 cu. ft./yr. of ground water discharge per sq. ft. of surface area. If this water dissolves sufficient $CaCO_3$ to raise its concentration on discharge to 300 mg./liter or 8 and ½ gr./cu. ft., there is a loss of 40 gr./yr./sq. ft. Assuming the sand has 30% porosity, and the grains 2.7 gr./cc. density, this loss represents a deduction of the surface by 2.5×10^{-4} ft. per year, or, in other words, ¼ ft. per millennium. This rate is easily sufficient to explain the prevalent central depressions of atoll islands and in fact must indicate a continuing supply of sediments from the bordering beaches to maintain a central area above water level.

There is no doubt in this writer's mind concerning the fairly rapid rate of rain-water solution of island rock. On a visit to Jaluit in 1956 the writer found a Japanese concrete gun emplacement over which were piled blocks of reef rock to a depth of many feet. Hanging from the entrance of one such emplacement were limestone "icicles" or stalactites about a foot long and ¾ inch thick near the center, formed presumably since the 1940's when the Japanese fortified Jaluit. As to the explanation of the central depressions of some atoll islets through the solution process, several other factors may be involved also, as indicated by the discussion of the dynamics of atoll morphology in Chapter 3.

Arnow (1954, p. 6) pointed out that, as would be expected in islands composed almost exclusively of limestone or its derivatives, the ground water is slightly alkaline. The average pH of 50 samples tested was 7.4. Of these 45 had a pH between 7.0 and 8.0, and 39 between 7.2 and 7.6. Two of the samples had a pH of 6.7, which is slightly on the acid side, but both of these came from taro pits with a mucky peat having much decaying vegetal matter. Two samples having a pH of 8.3 were mixed with sea water. Well water from Kapingamarangi (McKee, 1958, p. 267) had pH readings ranging from 7.0 to 7.5, and those from the relatively brackish wells on the seaward side were consistently high, reflecting the intermixture with sea water. On Raroia Newell (1954) found that the water from nine wells ranged from about 14 to 17 parts per thousand salinity, with pH of 7.6 to 7.8. The average pH of water from eight wells at Onotoa was 7.6. The range was between 7.4 and 7.98 (Cloud, 1952, p. 33).

The temperature of ground water in the northern Marshalls averaged 81°F. This is 1 degree less than the mean annual air temperature (Arnow, 1954, p. 6). At Onotoa (Cloud, 1952) the ground water averaged 79°F. At Raroia it averaged 78.3°F. At Ifalik (Arnow, 1955, p. 14) the temperature of the ground water ranged from 76 to 81°F., averaging 79°F. At Kapingamarangi temperatures for all well waters was 81.5 to 83°F. in the early morning but commonly rose 1.8 to 3.6°F. during the day (McKee, 1958, p. 267). No particular pattern may be derived from these figures, since ground-water temperatures in exposed wells may be influenced by sun or shade conditions, or such events as the recency of rains.

Use of fresh water on atolls

It is the exceptional instance that ground-water or fresh-water bodies can be found exposed on the atoll surface naturally. It is not unknown, however. Wilkes (1845, p. 335) reported that fresh water on Aratika Atoll in the Tuamotus was procured from a large pool, about 50 feet in diameter and of considerable depth. Seurat (1903, pp. 1, 3, 10) described a fresh-water lake on South Marutea Atoll about 100 meters long situated on the northwest reef and called Vaipu by the natives. Taro, banana, and sugar cane were planted in the mucky soil of its fringes. Burnett (1910, p. 58) said that Washington Atoll, which is covered with a dense tropical vegetation exhibiting the most luxuriant growth, had "in place of the usual salt lagoon with an outlet to the sea, a beautiful fresh water lake . . . It is quite unique; there being no other coral atoll in the South Pacific similar in this respect."

Fresh ground water was known to the inhabitants of all atolls where "swamp taro" cultivation was carried on in pits. The digging of wells to tap the ground water very likely arose from the practice of digging pits for taro. Actually, in some areas, as on Kapingamarangi and Nukuoro, a corner of the taro pit may be deepened to provide a well for laundry or bath water. Arnow (1954, p. 6) wrote that none of the wells in the northern Marshalls was reported to antedate the German period of control. The writer feels doubtful that this could be so, unless it could be shown that the taro pits dug down to below the ground-water surface on such islands as Meijit, Ailuk, Utirik, Maloelap, and Likiep (Wiens, 1957) were post-

German developments. On Kwajelein a century ago Hammet (1854, pp. 59–61) found a small pool or well of water next to a pathway whose water tasted like rain water. It is true, however, that he said the only water offered him at Wotho was from a coconut shell and that he found that the natives on Rongerik hollowed out basins in the lower trunk of large trees to collect rain water running down the trunks. Hedley (1900, p. 28) illustrates a method used by the Funafuti people of obtaining rain water by tying a coconut frond stem downward to a leaning coconut tree and thus leading the dripping water collected by the frond down the stem and into a large hollowed wooden bowl set on a platform.

This method probably was a widespread one before tanks and other large containers were introduced by Europeans. Hague (1868, p. 41) wrote that the natives on Atafu Atoll in the central south Pacific collected rain water by cutting out an excavation in the trunk of an old coconut tree just above the ground. He saw a number of trees so prepared. Each such excavation, he said, might have held 4 or 5 gallons. However, he pointed out that, having coconut juice to drink, they did not depend upon rain water for subsistence.

In the Gilberts half a century ago, according to Hercouet (1896, p. 435), the natives obtained drinking water by digging wells about 2 meters deep in the ground, but the water was always brackish. At Niutao in the Ellice Islands south of the Gilberts, Moresby in 1876 is quoted by Hedley (1896, p. 7) to have said that although the people had "an unlimited supply of coconut milk" and did not need ground water, they "cut the coral rock to a depth of 20 feet, and make an opening wide at the top and narrowing into three small holes below which fill with brackish water as the tide rises. They do not have any other supply."

On Sydney Island in the Phoenix group, Arundel (1885, p. 6) found that "near the fish pond on the west side of the lagoon is an old water hole where excellent fresh water is still obtained." Although Sydney then was uninhabited, about a quarter of a mile beyond the water hole was a large collection of "graves" (moraes?) showing that earlier they had been used occasionally at least.

Wilkes (1845, pp. 323, 325) also found wells in use in the Tuamotus. On Taiao Atoll his party found two "springs" (wells) of fresh water near the lagoon and a good supply of coconuts. At Napuka Atoll he said that water (presumably from wells) was to be had in small quantities on the eastern section of the island. On Faaite Atoll, Cuzent (1884, p. 71) found that he could get "rather good drinking water and more of it than on most other islands where is it usually difficult to obtain water."

In more recent times, both the old and new methods of obtaining fresh water are used. The newer methods are to collect rain water in discarded steel oil drums or in concrete tanks 6 or 8 feet square and 4 to 6 feet high set on or near the surface of the ground. The catch water dripped from the eaves of houses or from corrugated sheets slanted directly into the tanks. Many of these were built by or under German or Japanese supervision during their periods of rule and, when old tanks have deteriorated, new tanks have been built by the island dwellers themselves. These tanks are a conspicuous feature of Marshallese settlements especially.

According to Cox (1951, p. 23) and Arnow (1954, p. 6; 1955, p. 14), the Marshallese prefer rain water to well water for all purposes and draw directly only a small quantity of ground water. However, they will wash and cook with ground water during the dry season and drink it when the cisterns are completely empty. According to Cox (1951, p. 23) there were no wells in the densely populated parts of Ine Village on Arno Atoll; here the entire water supply comes from rain catchment. In the more rural areas of Ine and Arno Islets, however, a number of dug wells are used almost entirely to supply laundry water. Two wells seen were lined with beach rock. Most were sunk in low places and lined with oil drums with the ends cut out. None extended more than a few feet into the water.

Fosberg reported (1946, pp. 85–9) that on Eniwetok shallow wells had been dug near the centers of most islets. On Aomon Islet, which he visited in May, the well water was slightly brackish. Since the rainfall is generally low here, cistern water is of necessity a poor and uncertain source of water. Tobin (1955, p. 5) said that on Ujelang Islet at Ujelang Atoll southwest of Eniwetok, water was obtained from two manmade wells. Both furnished potable water, although the smaller one was slightly brackish. These wells supplied the villagers adequately even during the prolonged dry season. A small well on nearby Raij Islet also furnished potable water. He found that there also were nine cement cisterns, one inoperative and the others in fair to poor condition. However, even in very wet Ebon Atoll, the writer found a well near the center and lowest part of Ebon Islet which was used by at least some inhabitants for bathing. The well was neatly lined with coral blocks.

The end of World War II found cisterns in bad repair or demolished on many atolls in Micronesia. Some of these have been repaired, others have been abandoned. Many found abandoned in the Marshall and Caroline Islands (on Jaluit, Maloelap, and Kapingamarangi) were those used by the Japanese near their now-demolished installations. Today they breed large swarms of mosquitoes.

Wells are widely used in the Gilberts (Catala, 1957, p. 8) and in the eastern Carolines—on Mokil, as reported by Murphy (1950), and on Kaping-amarangi and Nukuoro, as observed by the writer. Buck (1950, pp. 49–50) was told that on Touhou, the chief residential islet on Kapingamarangi (where there was only one well in 1954), there once were a number of wells. As concrete tanks are now widely used, most of the wells have been abandoned and covered.

On some atolls in the central south Pacific, such as Danger, Manihiki, and Rakahanga, concrete cisterns furnish water collected from church and meeting-house roofs (*New Zealand Journal of Science and Technology,* 1928). However, Collombet (1924, p. 702) reported that each of the islands of Danger Atoll had wells of brackish water which the natives could drink. He also reported that on Fakahina in the Tuamotus there was a masonry cistern which held 200 tons of water.

"One or two wells in the center of [Baker Island] supply water but with too much lime and salt in it for Europeans to drink, or to be useful for vegetation; our natives drank it without any apparent ill effects" (Ellis, 1936, p. 19). In Canton Atoll the inhabitants have to depend upon stored rain water for fresh water (Van Zwaluwenberg, 1941). Farther north, Christmas had no fresh water and was uninhabited 120 years ago (Benson, 1838, p. 66), and even Palmyra, a rather wet atoll, apparently had no well and was uninhabited 30 years ago (Rock, 1929, p. 364).

Although atoll water supplies at times present problems to the inhabitants, under the old conditions water was not so important as one might imagine. The atoll dweller cleaned his fish and shellfish in sea water and did not need to wash coconuts and pandanus fruit. "He replaced his simple garments with new ones when they became soiled, and washed his body daily in the sea . . . the people spent so much of their time in salt water that their skins became inured to what was unpleasant to others. When rains occurred, they availed themselves of a natural shower bath and, at times, a scooped-out excavation in a fresh-water seepage on the beach with a coconut-shell dipper provided all the necessities of bodily ablution. The earth oven, with its heated coral or shells, did not require water for cooking purposes. The beverage required by man was supplied by the coconut" (Buck, 1938, pp. 139–40).

Water was a necessity only on atolls that did not have a luxuriant growth of coconuts. Even though the water obtained by digging shallow wells might be somewhat brackish, it was not unpalatable to those accustomed to it, according to Buck. Laborers on Malden Island preferred well water to rain water caught in tanks, because they attributed medicinal properties to it. This belief in the medicinal quality of atoll ground water also was found at Rakahanga in the Tuamotus, where a beach well was thought to benefit people suffering from rheumatism, asthma, and certain skin diseases (New Zealand Journal of Science and Technology, 1928, p. 371).

Arnow (1955, p. 14) was surprised to find that on the wet atoll of Ifalik practically no rain water is caught or used directly. Ground water is used for drinking, cooking, and washing, and bathing is done in the lagoon or in a well. Gressitt (1952, p. 3) found a similar situation in the wet atoll of Kayangle west of Ifalik, where the chief water supply for the community consisted of a pool of slightly brackish water about 3 yards square, walled by large square blocks of coral rock. Possibly because the ground water was too brackish on this narrow island, an oil drum was used next to a small shelter to catch rain water.

Changes in the practices of fresh-water use undoubtedly are among the more important aspects of atoll acculturation processes during the past century. Since native atoll materials are not adaptable for the construction of large water containers to catch rain-water runoff, steel drums are desired by atoll dwellers who do not have the use of concrete catchment tanks. Tanks are expensive to construct and so generally are located in village settlements. In more isolated areas, especially on outlying islets away from the main settlements, smaller containers, if available, are used. House-roof catchment also has led to increased use of corrugated tin roofs. Among the most prominent users of concrete tanks are the Marshallese. The writer noted the conspicuous presence of these tanks on all 13 islands of the Marshalls group he visited in 1956 and can confirm the Marshallese preference for rain water. Moreover, if he can afford it, the Marshallese householder will have a separate bathhouse near his residence. The nearest approach to Western luxury in Marshallese bathhouses seen by the writer was at Likiep. The leading man in the community had a large cemented-over concrete cistern from which a hand pump brought water by pipe to a shower tank above his bathhouse.

The importance of the use of rain water from catchment tanks lies in the avoidance of contaminated ground water, which results from unsanitary surface conditions and practices. Also, soap lathers easily with rain water as compared with the hard ground water, so less soap is used, and the atoll dweller appreciates the softness of the water for laundry purposes and hair washing. However, open tanks also are great mosquito breeders and collectors of dead lizards and insects.

Importance of ground water to atoll plant life

As Cox (1951, p. 24) has pointed out, the small draft of ground water by the people in the Marshalls and other atolls is no indication of the over-all importance of the water that seeps into the ground. Although the moisture in the unsaturated part of the soil is probably primarily responsible for the support of vegetation on wetter atolls, some atoll plants are wholly or partly dependent on ground water from the saturated zone. The most obvious plants of this type are the wet-land forms of taro, which are widespread economic plants on Pacific atolls. Taro culture is found throughout Polynesia, Micronesia, and Melanesia, although it has declined in many areas in favor of imported rice and flour, particularly in the Marshall Islands. There are several taro-like plants that grow on atolls, but only two are generally considered edible. Of these, *Colocasia esculenta* is the smallest in size and is the only one that deserves the name of taro, according to Krämer (1928, pp. 165–72). The other is a giant form, *Cyrtosperma chamissonis*, which often is of greater importance as a source of atoll food (Drews, 1944, p. 571; Murphy, 1950, pp. 64–5; Niering, 1956, p. 12) and which is less exacting than Colocasia in that it better tolerates slightly brackish ground water (although both do best in the freshest water).

Ground water also apparently plays an important part in sustaining breadfruit trees (Cox, 1951, p. 25). Although breadfruit is not generally thought to require ground water from below the water table on wet atolls and high islands, on the drier atolls or on atolls with an extended dry season, the distribution of productive breadfruit trees appears to correspond closely with the pattern of salinity of ground water. Cox believed that generally the tree did not extend from the island interior beyond a zone where the ground water has a content higher than 200 to 400 ppm of chloride. This compares with the fresher limits of a few tens of parts per million of chloride for Collocasia and Cyrtosperma cultivation. Banana and papaya show control by ground water similar to that of taro. No other economically important plants seem to be limited by the availability of fresh ground water (Cox, 1951, p. 26). Such important food trees as the coconut palm and the pandanus obviously can grow on islets without fresh ground water, although they do best on atolls with wet climates.

CHAPTER 15

ATOLL LAND: SOIL CHARACTER AND TYPES

Relatively little attention has been paid to atoll soils in past scientific study. Casual descriptive notes incidental to vegetation studies and occasional analyses, mostly concerning guano soils, comprised all available information until 1950 (Fosberg, 1954, p. 99). Since then the most comprehensive study of atoll soils has been the Arno study by Stone (1951). Other notable contributions include those of Fosberg (1954), McKee (1958), and Catala (1957).

Characteristic topographic features of atoll islets have been described in Chapter 3. These are briefly reviewed here. As pointed out by Fosberg (1957, p. 420), most islets appear to be erosional remnants of higher reef platforms left by a fall of sea level following the post-glacial climatic optimum. Loose sediments have been heaped on top of these by storm waves and tsunamis. Some sediments have been consolidated into conglomerate rock. On a given atoll most of the erosional remnants are about the same height above sea level, except where local differential erosion has occurred.

Other islets are of a more ephemeral type—the rock platforms are more-or-less sea-level reefs onto which storms have piled rubble ramparts and sand. Still less permanent and at lower elevations are islets which are mere sand and pebble cays arising from accumulation of gravel drift carried by currents and waves to initially form a bar on a wide reef flat.

Once established, an islet of any of these types may accumulate additional drift or storm-tossed sediments, which results in increased elevation or areal expansion or both; or, to the contrary, current and wave scour may eat away and reduce an islet or cut channels across a large islet and fragment it into two or more separate islets. Islets may be wiped off the reef entirely by typhoon waves. On the other hand, sand cays and islets without emerged rock platforms may become stabilized for greater permanence by vegetation growth producing roots that bind the sediments together. Chemical processes cementing beach rock often provides a protecting peripheral. Finally, excess erosion on the seaward side and accretion of sand through current drift on the lagoon side of an islet, especially on the windward reef, but also on the leeward reef, may cause a gradual migration of the islet lagoonward, or along a reef.

Because the seaward sides of islets (especially on the windward reef, where most islets are situated), are washed by stronger currents and larger waves as a rule, coarser debris accumulates on the seaward and exposed parts of islets. The finer materials from this side are washed farther lagoonward and, in the case of larger islets, into the interior of the islets. On the lagoon and leeward sides the reduced strength of currents and waves results usually in sand and pebble accumulations. Thus in most cases one may say that the lagoon half of an islet tends to have the finer, more-impermeable soil constituents, while the seaward half tends to have bouldery, cobbly, and coarser pebble soil constituents (Plates 22 and 59). Also, because during storms the stronger waves come from the open sea, the sediments are heaped higher and form higher ramparts than those on the lagoonside. The land surface thus slopes gradually from the seaward side toward the lagoon. Often, however, ramparts built by storms on the entire periphery of islets may result in a depression in the islet interiors that rises to the surrounding ramparts. On windward lagoon sides this may be accentuated by wind-formed dunes. Over the course of a long period of time, storms may produce a succession of more-or-less concentric ramparts and dunes. Atoll islets may therefore not have a very even surface.

The processes of rampart, sand shelf, beach ridge, and lagoon dune formation often create structural inland basins. In general, a profile from seaward to lagoon shore might be expected to show high land on both shores and a lower center. This orderly process actually is far from common, owing to storm catastrophes; current, wave, and wind activities; and natural and manmade burials and excavations. The resulting pattern of atoll soils may be very complex, although the soil types may be relatively few and simple.

Stone pointed out (1951, p. 7) that soils developed on uplifted reefs and limestone areas over long periods provide an indication of the similar processes that would transform atoll soil should they remain above the sea for a long enough time.

In the oldest such areas the calcium and magnesium carbonates, which make up such a large part of the present atolls, have been entirely dissolved from the surface layers and often from a considerable depth; the soil then consists of combinations of aluminum, silica, iron and other constituents originally present as only small percentages. The time required for such formation is great, and the solution of several feet of limestone may yield only an inch or two of soil. In contrast the present atoll soils are extremely youthful and are classified as lithosols and regosols. The surface layers have been darkened by addition of organic matter and there has been some solution of carbonates but in the main the materials of the soils have been little altered.

Thus the concept of a weathered soil such as one finds on continental areas, with a surface zone of leaching (A horizon) and a depositional zone (B horizon) overlying the partly broken up parent material (C horizon), needs some alteration. Normally the B horizon is absent in atoll soils (Stone, 1951, p. 19; Catala, 1957, p. 5; Fosberg, 1954, p. 100). The A horizon generally passes directly into the C horizon.

Parent materials: physical and chemical nature

Aside from the humus or organic material, the soils on most atolls are derived almost entirely from rock or sediment composed of calcium (and some magnesium) carbonate. On Kapingamarangi, McKee (1958, p. 255) found that

Much of it is limestone derived from the bed rock; the rest of it occurs as unconsolidated sediment including gravel, lime sand, and lime mud. Large clastic fragments include blocks broken from the reef, coral heads, and masses of coralline algae. The small gravel is almost entirely coral rubble. Lime sand consists of shell fragments and tests of Foraminifera, with local contributions of the alga Halimeda and other organisms. The lime mud apparently results from the decomposition of stratified rock or of limestone blocks. All of these clastic materials mixed with humus are relatively undecomposed, even though they are in an area of prevailing warm, humid climate. This indicates a very youthful soil.

Soils formed from "coral mud" or lime mud were not found on Arno but occur in areas other than Kapingamarangi (Stone, 1951, p. 8).

Aside from the textural differences represented by different source materials—stony corals, Lithothamnion rock, ground up or unaltered shells and coral, Foraminifera tests, and Halimeda fragments—the different elements become especially significant when the results of chemical analyses of various organisms are compared. Thus, for instance, the inorganic parts of the reef-building corals consist almost entirely of calcium carbonate, whereas some of the Lithothamnion group have up to 25 per cent magnesium carbonate. However, Halimeda, another alga, contains only about

1 per cent magnesium carbonate. Calcite and aragonite, two minerals characteristic of different reef organisms, differ somewhat in solubility. Certain reef organisms which may contribute relatively little mass to the reef nevertheless are sources of phosphorus or other chemicals needed for plant growth (Stone, 1951, pp. 8–9). Thus an atoll dominated by Lithothamnion rather than corals, such as Rose Atoll, may have soils of quite different chemical components from an atoll dominated by corals. The chemical analyses of some typical soils from Arno are given in Table 20.

In summarizing the chemical nature of parent material of atoll soils, Stone (1953, p. 2) wrote

Analyses of the reef organisms, . . . indicate that calcium carbonate, while predominant, is by no means the only compound of importance in their composition. Some of the Lithothamnion group may contain up to 25% magnesium carbonate and some of the Foraminifera up to 11%. Although phosphorus is generally low, some of the Crustacea may contain up to 27% calcium phosphate in their skeletons and there are appreciable amounts in some of the Alcyonarian corals. Nine samples of non-phosphatic subsoils from Arno contain from 0.01 to 0.02% phosphorus. Soluble potassium is found in moderate amounts whenever appreciable exchange capacity is present. Traces of most elements are of course to be expected by reason of their presence in sea water.
As a source of plant nutrients these materials have certain apparent advantages and disadvantages. The calcareous medium tends to be favorable for some nitrogen-fixing legumes and Azotobacter. However, it limits availability of certain nutrients such as iron, of which there is a conspicuous deficiency whenever organic matter content in the soil is low.

Iron is of vital importance to cultivated atoll plants, according to Catala (1957, p. 8). Also, he claimed, the excess of calcium carbonate in these soils is often "the cause of trophic disturbance, more often called 'chlorosis.'" More likely, however, lack of iron or nitrogen is the cause.

In all atoll soils the water-holding capacity is important, because soil porosity is so great that "drainage is almost perfect." Cassidy, Department of Agriculture, Suva, Fiji Islands, who analyzed 29 soil samples from Tarawa Atoll (Catala, 1957, p. 7), wrote that "It is a little unexpected to find that even the coarse samples have a water capacity equal to, or better than, that of pure sand (0.5 to 1.0 mm.) or even than many sandy soils, which hold only about 35% of their weight before run-off occurs."

The different water-holding capacities (in percentages) were as follows: 2 samples, 35 to 39; 8, 40 to 49; 7, 50 to 59; 3, 60 to 69; 1, 70 to 79; 3, 80 to 89; 3, 90 to 99; and 2, 100 to 136.

From these figures, 65 per cent of the samples had a water-holding capacity of at least 50 per cent of their weight, and 27 per cent of the samples had capacities of over 80 per cent of their weights. The explanation for these unexpectedly high figures "is clearly to be found in the many inter-

TABLE 20

Chemical Analyses of Some Soils from Arno Atoll *

Profile no.	Soil type or designation	Depth of sample	pH	Organic matter, %	Total matter, N, %	Organic matter/ nitrogen	Pounds per acre								Soluble salts, $K \times 10^5$
							P	NON³	NHN³	Mg	K	Mn	Fe	Al	
16	Mangrove peat, L'angar Island	0–6	5.90		1.51		1,600	35	130	12,000	976	5	1	5	2,700
		16–22	5.75		1.24		1,200	15	100	16,000	1,200	5	1	5	3,000
26	Coconut-Pandanus peat, Ulen Island	0–8	6.25		2.60		280	30	190	2,000	436	5	.1	5	225
24	Taro-pit coconut-pandanus peat, Arno Island	0–8	5.40		2.95		320	15	220	1,400	310	5	1	5	345
25	Arno loamy sand, Arno Island	0–6	7.45	16.68	0.88	19.0	80	100	40	750	110	8	1	5	80
		6–11	7.55	11.32	0.59	19.2	25	30	40	425	63	8	1	5	60
		14–19	8.40	0.28	0.04		25	8	18	5,000	18	5	1	5	19
		24–30	8.65	0.14	0.04		40	8	20	3,750	15	5	1	5	17
6	Arno gravelly loamy sand, Ine Island	0–6	7.40	32.92	1.16	28.4	110	100	50	1,800	203	25	1	5	104
		6–12	7.50	20.44	0.70	29.2	25	40	45	750	80	20	1	5	74
		20–26	8.35	0.28	0.04		30	5	20	5,000	18	5	1	5	15

* From Stone (1951, pp. 5–6).

stices of the coral fragments and shells. . . ." Nevertheless, Stone considered the moisture-holding capacity of the mineral soil low, increasing the effect of rainfall distribution and ground water. But he also emphasizes (1953, p. 1) that where fresh water is available at shallow depths, textural considerations "obviously do not have the significance for deep-rooted plants that they often have elsewhere."

Extraneously derived materials in places may add an unknown significance to soil quality. The most conspicuous and abundant foreign rock is pumice. Its occurrence is widespread. Since it contains a great number of air bubbles, it floats to atoll shores from far-distant volcanic eruptions. Sachet (1955) has cited numerous instances in the literature of its occurrence and included descriptions of its chemical composition. Silica (SiO_2) comprises about two-thirds of its composition, followed by aluminum oxide (Al_2O_3), which amounts to 15 to 17 per cent. No other constituent appears to constitute more than 6% of it. McKee (1958, p. 255) wrote that the influence of pumice on atoll soils is unknown. Stone (1951, p. 10) stated that although on Arno the amount of pumice in the soil was not significant, locally its mass may be great enough to affect the soil or plant growth. That some Micronesians attribute to it a beneficial influence on soil is shown by Wilkes (1845), who wrote that the Gilbertese gathered pumice stones, pounded them into small particles and mixed them with the soil around coconut roots to fertilize the palms. Sachet (1955) suggested that this indigenous practice points up very strongly the ecological significance of this material and that the effects of pumice on atoll plants should be investigated.

Other rock materials in atoll soils derived from outside sources probably are insignificant except very locally. Occasional rocks and gravel have been transported in the roots of floating tree trunks to atoll strands. In some instances, soil and earth have been brought as ballast in ships traveling to atolls—by Germans to Jaluit and by Americans to Johnston and Kwajelein. But in the ecological picture of atoll soils, these imports have little importance.

Cementation produces brown phosphate rock on many atoll islands, formed by phosphate leaching from guano deposits into limy materials below. There it forms insoluble calcium phosphates, often in the form of a hardpan. The calcium carbonate is replaced wholly or in part by the phosphate, so that acid soils, if found at all (excepting peat accumulations), occur on phosphate areas (Stone, 1951, p. 10). In texture and structure the phosphate rock, or phosphorite, resembles the limestone from which it developed but is lighter in weight, owing to its high porosity (McKee, 1958, p. 258).

Other types of cementation by precipitation of dissolved carbonates in the upper layer soil, except for beach-rock formation, were considered by Stone (1951, p. 12) to be inconsequential on Arno, although at depths of 40 or more inches strongly cemented sandstone was encountered in some places. However, he stated that "In a sense cementation is merely an incidental consequence of secondary lime deposition and can be expected wherever water saturated with calcium bicarbonate evaporates or loses carbon dioxide, as by warming or escape of excess acquired under the higher carbon dioxide pressure in the upper soil."

Solution is the dominant physical process acting upon the land. The carbonic acid released by roots and organic-matter decomposition converts calcium carbonate to soluble bicarbonate. Rainwater then moves this into the ground water. Some of this is precipitated along the shores, cementing sand and rubble to beach rock, but it is lost from the island interiors according to Stone (1951, p. 12). This solution progresses rapidly in the upper layers, so the innermost margins of the belt of stony land, because of their greater age and longer period of weathering, are much less coarse than the outer beach. The pebbles found within the upper organic horizon of older soils often are soft and easily crushed, and readily penetrated by roots, whereas the sand particles are most disintegrated in this zone. From his discovery that on Arno Atoll the most highly weathered soils often contain much more gravel in the surface horizon than immediately below, Stone concluded that there was a concentration of gravel because of the solution of finer particles.

Older soils buried by recent sand or storm debris are not unusual on atolls and are often discovered when digging a well or trench or because of scouring by typhoon waters. Burial was observed by the writer on Jaluit as a result of Typhoon Ophelia, January 7, 1958. McKee and Fosberg, on the same expedition, found that storm scour had exposed "an undisturbed soil profile overlain by coral rubble to provide a disconformity that is precisely analogous to that produced by Ophelia" (Blumenstock, 1958, p. 3). Buried profiles also were found on at least three islands of Kapingamarangi by McKee (1958, p. 257).

Soil formation and soil properties cannot be considered apart from climatic influences, particularly those of rainfall. The constancy of rainfall is as important as the amount, "with the effect of variation being more drastic the lesser the amount" (Stone, 1953, p. 2). This, of course, is not limited to island areas. However, on atolls the effects of variation are of special importance on narrow islands, where the nature of the groundwater lens is more easily affected by short droughts. It is obvious that rainfall affects the leaching of salts formed in the soil and those added by spray. Salinity, according to Cassidy (Catala, 1957, p. 7), will naturally be a function of the amount of leaching by rainfall prior to sampling.

The values he obtained from Gilbertese samples (presumably after rain following a dry period) "and the general physiography of the islands, coupled with the available description of the vegetation, suggest that salinity is likely to be one main factor in plant production."

The Gilbert atolls are relatively dry compared to Arno, of course. At Arno, Stone (1951) found that "To date conductivity measurements seldom show sufficient concentration of salts in the surface of soil to be injurious to the plants, although these do not represent the temporary conditions that may result from flooding or heavy spray during severe storms."

Organic matter and biological factors

The importance of living vegetation and decaying organic matter in the solution of calcium carbonate through the formation of carbonic acid has been noted. The abundance of algae in moist areas also leads to the solution of the rocks they mantle. Organic matter obviously has the greatest cation-exchange capacity and thus is of great significance in soil formation (Stone, 1951, p. 16). The consideration of organic matter is almost inseparable from that of nitrogen, since there is a fixed carbon to nitrogen ratio of approximately 10 or 12 to 1 and organic matter to nitrogen ratio of 20 or 30 to 1 (Stone, 1953, p. 3). Figure 89 shows the relationships among organic matter, biological organisms, and nitrogen in different atoll soil types. Figure 90 shows the sequence of soil development and its relationship to soil properties. The latter indicates the considerable accumulations of humus and nitrogen. The dark soils of Arno contain at least 2,000,000 pounds of organic matter per acre. Stone (1951) concluded that the percentage composition as well as depth of the organic layer tends to increase with age and suggested that a few centuries may have been required for such accumulation. Moreover, he found no evidence of any rapid decline in the long-occupied areas of Arno Island.

Apart from rainfall, Stone described four sources of nitrogen on atolls. These are the following:

1. Flotsam and dead marine organisms. Chiefly of significance to the early stages of strand vegetation.

2. Legumes. *Sophora, Canavalia,* and *Vigna* are often common in the earlier stages of soil development, but only *Intsia,* a leguminous tree, persists in the dense forest. In open areas and near-shore areas the former three may form dense stands.

3. Certain terrestrial algae are abundant, although the contribution of nitrogen-fixing blue-green algae is unknown.

4. Sea birds may add appreciable amounts of nitrogen to the land surface generally, apart from the marked guano or phosphate areas.

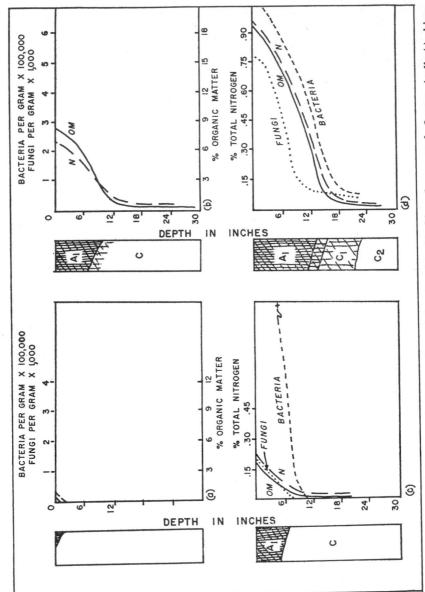

Fig. 89. Characteristics of some atoll soil profiles: (a) beach sand; (b) shioya loamy sand, Onotoa Atoll; (c) shioya sand, Arno Atoll; (d) Arno loamy sand, Arno Atoll. [From Stone (1951).]

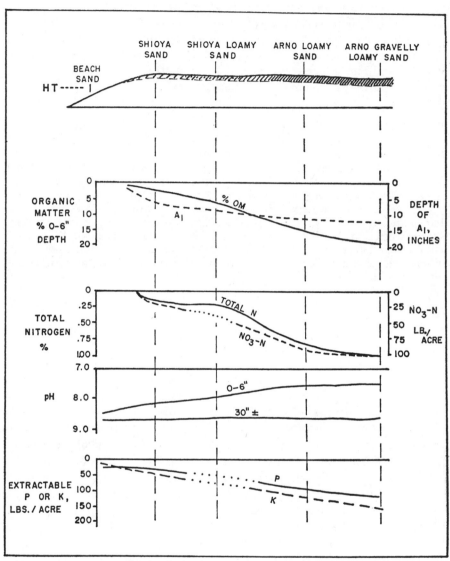

Fig. 90. Synthetic sequence of soil development and soil properties. [From Stone (1951).]

Stevenson (1953) examined 25 soil samples from 15 Arno Atoll profiles and concluded that the "total numbers of bacteria and actinomycetes were relatively low. Ammonifying bacteria were present in all but one profile, and usually in both surface and subsurface layers. This was true also for denitrifying organisms. Nitrifying bacteria were found in only four of the 15 soils examined, and they occurred only in the surface layers. Cellulose-decomposing organisms were detected in 12 of the soils. Azotobacter types [nitrogen-fixing] were found in nine of the soils."

With regard to soil samples from Onotoa, Moul (1957, p. 25) stated:

Of particular interest is the fact that the numbers of bacteria were in all cases lower than those of actinomycetes and that with 3 of the 4 soils more than 80% of the colonies that developed on the agar plates were those of actinomycetes. A similar observation was made with soil obtained some years ago from Bikini. This is contrary to what one expects to find in soils of temperate regions, particularly those of humid climates . . .

The predominance of actinomycetes is interesting in view of the fact that many of these organisms produce antibiotics. It is possible that the actinomycetes affect the transformations of material in the soils by their antagonistic effects. It is also possible that some actinomycetes may be obtained from these soils that will serve some useful purpose as products of new chemotherapeutic substances.

Although the fungi may be more properly discussed in relation to the plant life of atolls, their closeness to soil processes justifies their inclusion in the present discussion. Fosberg (1946, p. 12) has pointed out that fungi are of enormous importance in an agricultural economy. "They may cut production to such a point that financial failure results. On the other hand the control of certain weeds and insects may be affected or aided by certain disease-producing fungi. Soil fungi and those which produce mycrorhizae (a kind of filamentous mycelium symbiotically associated with roots of seed plants) may determine whether or not certain crops can be grown in an area." Prior to 1946 very little was known of the fungi of coral atolls. Two papers analyzing collections from the Marshall Islands have increased this knowledge, but much remains to be done in collections and analyses.

Rogers (1947) indicated previous knowledge of 16 species of fungi hitherto reported from the Marshall Islands. His own paper listed 34 species identified at the time of writing and indicated that possibly there were more. Of these, *Glaziella aurantiaca* was a Phycomycete belonging to the Endogonales, 17 of the others being Myzomycetes, 19 Basidiomycetes, and 2 *Fungi imperfecti*. The *G. aurantiaca*, an algal-like Phycomycete, was found in humid Ebon on the surface or under loose fragments of well-decayed vegetation, chiefly leaves of coconut palms. Rogers thought that "It is less than certain that the Ebon collection is conspecific with those reported from the American tropics." Sparrow (1948) subsequently examined 44 soil specimens from four atolls of the northern Marshalls for the presence of soil Phycomycetes. He found no filamentous Phycomycetes in any sample. Of the Phycomycetes found in 22 of the soil samples, 20 were species of the chytrid genus Rhizophlyctis and the other two were chytridiaceous parasites of these species. One of the latter was considered by Sparrow to be the "first undoubted species of Olpidium parasitic on another Phycomycete and, with *O. uredinis,* one of the only two species known to attack fungi."

Rogers did not find any of the 17 slime-mold Myxomycetes collected sufficiently uncommon or unusual to be worthy of comment.

Among the Basidiomycete fungi, one appears to be worthy of notice as a food for human consumption. This is *Auricularia ampla,* found usually on coconut palm wood. Rogers described it as a "thin, leathery, often ear-like basidiocarp, pilose and ashy to nearly glabrous and brownish black above, and rosy to purplish black below . . . Strangely enough, it is not eaten in the Marshalls, whereas in Hawaii the same species . . . is regarded not mistakenly as good food."

It is natural for the fungi to be most abundant in the wetter atolls. On the drier atolls of the northern Marshalls, such as Ailuk and Wotje, lichen incrustation was found to be sparse or lacking.

The breaking down of organic remains is carried on in large part by micro-organisms, according to Stone, but earthworms are often abundant, and small snails are numerous in some areas. Both earthworms and land crabs burrow and thus mix soil materials. Termites are common and break down the dead woody tissues (see Niering, 1956; Usinger and La Rivers, 1953; Marshall, 1951). The hermit crabs forage everywhere on the smaller islands but are not common in the interior of the larger densely vegetated islands on atolls.

Man has been a most important biological agent in atoll soil change. Soils once supporting natural forest now support dense groves of coconut or breadfruit palms, bringing obvious soil changes, particularly with the development of the export trade in copra, for important chemical elements are exported with the copra from the atoll land. Each ton of copra exported carries away the equivalent of 25 or more pounds of superphosphate. Taro-pit excavation and taro cultivation bring profound soil alterations. The occupation of land for houses and the use of fire in cooking and the burning of debris and weeds importantly affect the soil. The practice of many atoll peoples of defecating on the beaches below high-tide line, however sanitary, reverses the good work of the sea birds in fertilizing the land by permitting the sea to wash away plant nutrients (Stone, 1951, p. 18). Man, however, also adds in many ways to the fertility of atoll soils. While he may defecate on the beaches, he urinates generally in the bushes. Urea is

the chief nitrogenous end product of the metabolism of proteins. Moreover, the burial of the dead on land also adds organic plant nutrients
utilized by trees and deep-rooted plants.

Catala (1957, p. 36) adds the following:

A special case may be discussed at this point, that of Betio Islet, scene
of the battle of Tarawa. This was completely devastated during the battle,
and has been replanted to coconuts since the end of the fighting. In many
places the young palms are developing with remarkable luxuriance. Some
only 6 years old were already producing nuts and toddy. This may be attributed to the 3,000 bodies buried on this islet and also to the sanitary
habits of the Japanese garrison during the occupation, which may have
added as much as 40 kg. of excretia per month per man for 20 months.
There may have been also some benefit gained from the indirect action
of nitro-explosives abandoned scrap iron, etc. Whatever the reason, the
fertility of some areas of Betio is probably the best in the archipelago. On
the contrary the coconut palms planted on the site of an airstrip in the
center of the islet are not very flourishing.

The domestic animals of man, such as the pig, the dog, and the cat, add
manure to the soil, although on many atolls they are insignificant in
number. These various additions to the soil affect significantly only a few
of the islands on any atoll, since village settlements localize such effects.
In sum, the Arno observations and studies on other atolls, such as Kapingamarangi, indicate that atoll soils are not as "impoverished" as often believed, although some mineral deficiencies are known or suspected.

Soil types

Fosberg (1954, p. 100) defines four principal areal units of atoll soils: (a)
essentially unaltered sands and gravels, (b) stony and very stony complex,
(c) Shioya series, and (d) Arno series. In addition to these Fosberg adds the
Jemo series and minor units such as taro-pit mucks, mangrove peats, and
exposed reef rock or beach rock. The exposed rock surfaces are not considered soil properly speaking, although they often serve as a substratum
for one species of tree, *Pemphis acidula*.

The stony complexes are commonly on the seaward side of islands. The
interstices among the rocks may be empty, may be filled with sand and
pebbles, or may have soil that is highly organic and black near the surface.
The cobbles and boulders are white on their undersurfaces but gray to
black on exposed surfaces, owing to the presence of blue-green algae in
surface layers.

The Shiowa series was first identified on Okinawa and was applied to
similar Arno soils, with the difference that on atolls these soils lack the
quartz sand found in some of the Okinawa soils of the series. Fosberg stated

that the soils of this series are by far the commonest and most widespread soil found on atolls. They consist of grayish-brown sands or gravels, rarely loamy sands (or even silts), which are only slightly weathered and have a very low organic content. They naturally support most of the mixed forest and the Lepturus grassland vegetation characteristic of atolls. In the sequence of development this series runs inland from the beach sand to Shioya sand and Shioya loamy sand, plus varying amounts of small-size gravels. Stone relates them to the Arno series as younger stages of development nearer the beach in contrast to the older Arno loamy sand and Arno gravelly loamy sand of the central parts of larger islets (Fig. 89). The following descriptions are largely from Stone (1951):

1. Shioya sand: This includes dune sands and medium and coarse beach sands with the following typical profile:

0–3–6 in.:   Single-grained pinkish-gray (75YR-6/2–7/2) sand or loamy sand, recognizably a mixture of decomposing organic matter, brown roots, and white sand. pH 8.2. Changing abruptly to
3–6–30 in.:   White or pinkish (75YR-9/1–9/2) white lime sand

On Arno, areas of Shioya sand adjacent to loamy sand have been planted to coconuts; elsewhere the vegetation typically consists of scrub-forest sedges and grasses. Development of this soil into a loamy stage is most rapid when the soil adjoins older land and shares its outflowing ground water, leaf litter, and seed supply.

2. Shioya loamy sand: This is a well-drained alkaline soil formed on lagoon-laid sand and is an older stage of Shioya sand. The profile shows a surface horizon 5 to 8 inches deep darkened by organic matter to a light gray, gray or brownish gray, resting on light-colored limesands. It is typical of younger narrow lands and windward lagoon coasts but usually is absent from seaward coasts and wider island interiors. The following is a typical profile:

0–7 in.:   Friable loamy sand, dark gray (10YR-4/1) in color when moist, single-grained or weakly aggregated. pH 7.8
7–8 in.:   Transitional
8–40 in.:   Single-grained pinkish white (75YR-9/2) loamy sand composed of Foraminifera and ground-up shells, coral, and Halimeda fragments. pH 8.4

The present vegetation of this unit is usually open coconut grove, but in poorly maintained stands a dense undergrowth of scrub forest and grasses often forms.

3. Arno loamy sand: This is a well-drained, dark-colored calcareous soil formed on old beach and dune sands under the vegetation of wider island

interiors. There is extreme contrast between the well-defined surface horizon and the light-colored sands beneath. A typical profile follows:

Surface: Scattered twigs and breadfruit leaves
0–11 in.:   Highly organic, granular loamy sand or sandy loam, somewhat plastic when worked. Black when moist, very dark gray (10YR-3/1) when dry, heavily flecked with lighter-colored sand particles. Earthworms plentiful. pH 7.5
11–13 in.:   Abrupt transition from above to
13–21 in.:   Single-grained, light-gray loamy sand stained with organic matter, becoming white (10YR-8/2) at a depth of a few inches. pH 8.4
21–54 in.:   Friable, pinkish-white (75YR-9/2) limesand becoming coarser at 40 inches.

Where gravel is present, it often is much more abundant in the surface layer, where it is weathered and easily crumbled. The presence of relatively unweathered surface gravel can usually be related to former house sites, since it is a common practice to spread fresh, clean gravels over a yard. In almost all cases there is fresh ground water, and taro pits are located in these areas. The debris dug from the pits generally forms a slight bordering ridge around the fields. The breadfruit zone also is found in this soil area. Pandanus, intermixed with coconut palms, are common, and even in well-cleared groves, small secondary-forest trees are abundant. Untended groves may be crowded with many species of trees, ferns, and weeds. Mosses may be abundant also. This is the most fertile of the atoll soil series, with the exception of small areas of phosphatic soils.

The development and weathering exhibited by the Arno soils are evidence of their considerable age, according to Stone. They were formed under a native mixed broadleaf forest replaced in part by the indigenous culture and then almost completely by "copra culture." These soils are essentially the same as those of adjacent Majuro in the same relative positions on islets. Similar soils, but much older (possibly 3,000 years) and with organic layers 18 to 30 inches thick, were found on Kapingamarangi by Niering (1956, pp. 2, 28). The organic matter of this type of soil is high for tropical soils (16 to 32 per cent at Arno).

4. The Jemo series, as defined by Fosberg (1954), was partially described by Hutchinson earlier (1950) and occurs on numerous Pacific atolls in small patches, almost invariably under forests composed predominantly or entirely of *Pisonia grandis*. The surface is marked by a dark-brown to black layer of pure organic matter that is spongy or peaty in texture; the original material, leaves and twigs, is altered virtually beyond recognition and is often filled with living rootlets. When not mixed with significant

amounts of calcareous sand, the pH is 4 to 6. Most often the upper layer of sand and gravel are cemented by a dark-green cement into a hardpan or sandstone which is strongly phosphatic. According to Fosberg (1954, p. 102), "The correlation between the occurrence of such a hardpan and strong guano staining on the surface layer of litter is striking. In most well-developed examples of this hardpan, lumps, boulders, and slabs lying at random or in small concentrations on the surface are also common. Occurring thus, they are commonly somewhat weathered. These have apparently been pushed up by growing Pisonia root systems or heaved up by roots of Pisonia trees that have been tipped over by wind."

From his field observation, Fosberg concluded that *Pisonia grandis* is one of the few trees capable of producing a raw humus or "mor" layer in the lowland tropics. This is normally acid. The presence of or absence of the raw humus seems to be independent of the accumulation of phosphate, since layers of it were observed without guano staining and with uncemented sands and gravels beneath. However, sea birds roosting on Pisonia trees drop finely divided calcium phosphate onto the litter. This is carried down into the litter by rain water, which in contact with the humus becomes diluted carbonic acid. The calcium phosphate becomes soluble in this acidic rain water. As the solution filters down and comes in contact with the calcium carbonate materials below the litter, the solution becomes alkaline and precipitates the phosphate as a cement that binds the sand and gravel into a hardpan. On the other hand, Fosberg stated, "Where no humus has accumulated, the guano falling on the lime-sand or gravel would not become soluble, as neither its own reaction of pH 6 nor that of rain water is sufficiently acid to dissolve it, and the environment is alkaline." The almost colloidal calcium phosphate, Fosberg suggested, is washed down through the loose coral sand and gravel to the ground-water lens, from which it is gradually flushed out by outflow of ground water and tidal action. Where these processes are impeded, large accumulations of fine-grained phosphate may be formed directly, with no relation to the vegetation, as on some of the elevated "phosphate islands." On the other hand, the presence of a phosphatic hardpan, if found in an atoll soil, would probably indicate the former existence of a Pisonia forest, as well as of large nesting colonies of sea birds.

Soils of this series have been found on Jemo, Taka, Kwajelein, Ujae, Wotho, Ujelang, Bikar, Pokak, Ebon, and Arno in the Marshalls, as well as on Wake to the north. Literature references to such types indicate their occurrence on Palmyra, Fanning, Rose, Butaritari, Onotoa, Washington, and Ngatik. Niering (1956) wrote: "On Pumatahati [at Kapingamarangi] a dark-brown humus layer 6–8 inches in depth, free of the usual sand and rubble, overlies a highly phosphatic cemented layer. The organic material

is also phosphatic (100% apatite, McKee, 1956) and acidic (pH 4.5). . . ."
Pisonia covered the island until 1920 and sea birds still roost here in huge
numbers as they did before 1920.

A typical profile from Jemo Island (Fosberg, 1954) follows:

Surface: 3.5–3 in.: Loose twigs and leaves of *Pisonia grandis* conspicuously
stained by spatterings of guano, chiefly from red-footed
boobies roosting and nesting in Pisonia trees

3–0 in.: Dark-reddish-brown (5YR-2/2–3/2 to dark-brown (10YR-
2/2) spongy, elastic (when dry) raw humus, or "mor."
pH 4.5 to 6.5. Transition to B horizon abrupt

0–5 in.: Cemented coarse sand, cement dark brown (10YR-2/2),
grains white (10YR-8/2); weakly to strongly consolidated, continuous or shattered by growing roots; pH 8.
Transition to C horizon abrupt

5–36 in.: Very-dark-brown to very-dark-grayish-brown (YR-2/2–
3/2), sandy loam or loamy sand, with some white grains,
some gravel included, amount increasing downward; pH
8. Depth not determined, holes not dug more than 3 feet

Obviously, many variations of this soil must occur, depending upon age,
Pisonia tree density, and bird population as well as upon subsoil conditions
and the vagaries of storm wash and wind-blown sand.

5. Mangrove peat (Stone, 1951): This is a somewhat fibrous woody peat,
moderately well decomposed and saline, formed under *Bruguiera conjugata*.
When moist, it is dark red in color, drying to dark reddish brown (5YR-2/2–
3/2). The odor of hydrogen sulphide is present in the deeper layers. The
fresh peat commonly has a pH of 7.2 to 7.4, but this changes upon drying
to pH 5.6 to 5.9. This type is usually less than 2 feet in depth but occasionally
can be as deep as 40 inches or more. The shallower areas are often somewhat
more decomposed and may contain lime fragments. The ground water fluctuates with tidal changes but is usually 1 to 2 feet below the surface. Except
for a few epiphytic Asplenum ferns, the interior vegetation is wholly Bruguiera. This soil type is useful only as forest for mangrove trees.

Mangrove mucks also may develop on atolls, but there is seldom enough
fine material to create significant areas of muck. The writer saw only two
fairly extensive areas of such muck, at an islet adjacent to the pass at Nukuoro Atoll in the eastern Carolines and on one end of Elizabeth Island
of Jaluit Atoll.

6. Coconut-Pandanus or fresh-water peat (Stone, 1951): This unit may
be found in interior swamps, such as in abandoned taro pits. The peat is
shallow, usually 1 to 2 feet deep, and fibrous. The more-decomposed por-

tions are bound together by a mass of living and dead roots. A typical profile from Arno follows:

0–24 in.: Well-decomposed peat with many root fragments; pH 6.5 at time of sampling, 5.4 after drying. Color after drying and grinding is brown to dark brown (7.5YR-4/5). Water level at 2 inches at time of sampling following heavy rains, which was much higher than on a previous visit

24 in.: Mucky limesand

The potential fertility of the peat is high, and cultivation and exposure to sunlight would probably change the peat to well-decomposed muck in which taro normally grows well. The Arno peat swamps grew taro before their abandonment early in the century. Peat accumulation appears to have been a rapid process here.

Peat swamps originating naturally are represented by the situation found on Washington Atoll. Wentworth (1925, p. 137) described this as follows:

In the interior of Washington Island, an emerged atoll of the North Pacific, is a fresh-water lake several hundred acres in extent and three feet above sea level. The remainder of the area of the former salt lagoon is occupied by a peat bog of nearly equal extent. The arrangement of the vegetational zones around its margin and the presence in the middle of the bog of an "island" of coconut palm forest growing on a basement of normal peat indicate that the area is being stabilized and converted into dry land. The peat is three or four feet in thickness, rests on a rolling surface of clean coral sand, and is composed mainly of bullrush stems with very little silt or other rock debris.

7. Taro-pit mucks (Stone, 1951): These artificial mucks, created by long-continued additions of organic material for taro culture, vary considerably in the admixture of mineral matter and relative wetness. The ground water is fresh, and its level fluctuates with the tide, the maximum often being within a foot or less of the muck surface. Where pits have been abandoned, peats may develop over a period of time with dense vegetation, such as *Pandanus* and coconut palms. Such mucks can easily be returned to taro cultivation. In their present condition, the drier mucks and the margins are well suited for bananas, but on Arno they are not being utilized extensively for this purpose. A typical taro-muck profile follows:

Surface: Scattered breadfruit leaves and seedlings of *Colocasia* and a grass

0–10 in.: Mucky limesand with some coral gravel less than 1 inch in diameter. Matrix very dark gray flecked with light lime particles. pH of moist sample 7.6

10–32 in.: Light-gray sand changing to white sand; the organic matter content diminishes gradually with depth; pH 7.4 at 30 inches. Strong smell of hydrogen sulphide at 30 inches. Ground-water level 28 inches when sampled, but the following day, with the rising tide not yet full, 15 inches

Soil conditions and effects on plants

Shallow-rooted plants and those growing some distance above the ground water must depend exclusively on water held in the soil. It is quite possible for some atoll plants to grow in salt-free soil of considerable depth overlying brackish ground water. On dry atolls or those having a prolonged drought, plant survival depends to a great degree upon the moisture-holding capacity of the soil and the moisture content of surface organic layers. In many areas, however, the ground water is close to the surface, and here the problem is not water but salinity. Ground-water salinity often increases during the dry season, if there is such a season. In such situations, salinity, like soil moisture, should be considered a fluctuating soil property for the critical levels that determine plant survival, and these levels may persist only for brief periods (Stone, 1951, pp. 41–2).

Where outward-flowing sheets of ground water reach near shore, as is frequently true of sandy lagoon shores of wetter islands, some sensitive plants may grow almost to the shores. Breadfruit, which is not regarded to be salt-tolerant, has been observed within 15 to 25 feet of the lagoon shore on Kapingamarangi (Niering, 1956, p. 10). Stone (1951) warns that salinity, important as it is in controlling plant distribution, should not be over-stressed. Thus certain plant species or plant communities growing in an area of limesand or Shioya sand may be exposed to atmospheric and ground-water salinity, but these soils also have little nitrogen, a low exchange capacity, little potassium, and display other characteristics of low fertility. A plant may not grow in a certain soil for reasons other than salinity. In a similar sense, the occurrence of certain plants in island interiors may be a response to the higher fertility there as well as to salt-free ground water. Deficiency of iron may influence plant competition on areas of exposed limesands, since Thuarea, Vigna, Tacca, and Centella are at least moderately affected by this deficiency. Iron deficiencies produce chlorotic plant conditions especially in village areas and clearings, where organic-matter additions are lacking. The practice of keeping residential yards covered with clean gravel and the removal of all fallen leaves and debris may produce iron deficiencies. Yellow leaves on palms have often been attributed to excess salinity, whereas nitrogen deficiency may be the trouble. Long use of the land for copra cultivation may result in a phosphorus deficiency, and in a number of instances that have been reported, palms have suffered unexplained maladies in the central parts of larger islands where they once were productive.

The most marked cases of malnutrition in the coconut palm appear to have little relation to total rainfall, according to MacMillan (1946, p. 32), and they seem to be accompanied by symptoms of malnutrition in the associated plants in the area, with the exception of Pandanus.

Many vegetables and plants introduced from continental areas fail on most atoll soils because of some chemical deficiency, whether of phosphorus, iron, or certain minor elements. In the absence of specific information on limiting elements, Stone (1951, p. 45) suggested the use of "complete" fertilizers, or, in their stead, heavy applications of organic matter incorporated with the soil or as mulches.

MacMillan (1946) wrote that among the vegetables and smaller plants there are a number of striking examples of nutritional deficiencies. "Anemia due to lack of iron, and indicated by pale green and yellow to white leaves, is frequently observed in sweet potatoes. The papaya is of a distinctly anemic appearance. Throughout the Pacific area a squash has become established and is widely planted by the natives. This squash is consistently very low in production, and though it flowers profusely, the blossoms fall with no fruit formed. With the squash it has been demonstrated that fertility is directly related to fruit setting and production, and that a minimum of balanced fertilizer will bring worthwhile results."

Potash is of special importance in the production of starch in taro, yams, arrowroot (tacca), sweet potatoes, and breadfruit. Coconut trees require mineral fertilizers; nitrogen is needed for the leaf structure, phosphorus for the nuts, and potassium for general well-being and the production and storage of carbohydrates and fats.

In summary, the atoll islands are at the very margin of nonfertility. None of the nutritive elements is abundant and fertility is unbalanced. With abundant rainfall the vegetative growth is greater, the resultant plant residues are greater, and there is an exaggerated appearance of fertility and vegetative well-being (MacMillan, 1946, p. 31).

CHAPTER 16

PLANT ORIGINS ON ATOLL ISLANDS

Merrill (1945, p. 89) wrote the following of the Pacific Ocean area:

Botanically the low islands are very uninteresting and monotonous. The flora of one is usually quite the same as that of another, although these islands and islets may be separated by many hundred and in some cases several thousand miles. The native vegetation may be scanty or reasonably well developed, depending on the size of the island, the quality of its soil, and whether or not it is permanently inhabited. Just how poor the total flora of an isolated group of small islands may be, in spite of the vegetation being actually luxuriant, is illustrated by Palmyra Island. This group is located about 1,000 miles south of Hawaii and consists of 52 islets, the largest being 46 acres in extent. The highest land is only five feet above sea level. Its flora consists of only fifteen different species, but most of the species occur in great abundance. . . .

While admitting that atolls are characterized by small floras with very few endemic species and a preponderance of widely dispersed strand plants, Fosberg (1949, p. 89) repudiated the idea that the plant cover is a strand vegetation that is uniform and uninteresting. "Actually, however," he wrote, "this uniformity exists only in the minds of those who have visited very few atolls or who have observed them only superficially." He pointed out the striking contrasts between the vegetation of the driest atolls, such as Malden, Jarvis, Howland and Baker, with their sparse desertlike vegetation of a few grasses, herbs, and dwarf shrubs, and the luxuriant jungles on atolls in the central and eastern Carolines and southern Marshalls.

Despite Merrill's remarks, Palmyra is not typical of all the atolls, nor is the total number of plants on Palmyra only 15 species, as Merrill stated. Rock (1916, p. 30) stated that aside from 12 marine algae, he collected on Palmyra 3 fungi, 7 lichens, 1 moss, 2 ferns, and 13 flowering plants. If Rock had stayed longer than 16 days and continued to search the several dozen islands, it is possible he might have found a few additional species. As examples of the differences among atolls, Fosberg found only 8 or 9 types of seed plants of the xerophytic type at Taongi in the northern Marshalls, which has about 40 inches of rainfall and a semidesert climatic regime. At Bikini which has about double this amount of rainfall but is not as wet as Palmyra, Taylor (1950) found some 57 species of flowering land plants, but no gymnosperm, no fern, and only one moss. At Arno, with a rainfall of about 160 inches, Anderson (1951) found 125 different plant species, exclusive of lichens and fungi.

Although there is, then, considerable diversity in flora from atoll to atoll, there is no doubt that atoll floras are very limited compared with those of high islands, but all the islands of Micronesia and Polynesia, high and low, have a very restricted flora compared with the larger island groups in Malaysia. The flora of all the small islands of Micronesia number less than 1,300 species, as compared with some 8,500 species of the Philippine flora (Merrill, 1945, pp. 210–1). Nevertheless, the question still arises as to how the various plants on atolls have become scattered over the vast expanses of the Pacific Ocean.

There are six obvious ways in which plants or their seeds may reach an isolated oceanic atoll: (1) by floating with ocean currents and being thrown up onto the strand, (2) by being blown there by winds, (3) by being carried there by sea birds or migratory birds, either as undigested seed through the alimentary tract or through attachment of seed to bird feet or feathers, (4) by transport on other floating objects, such as trees, (5) by accidental transport by man, and (6) by intentional transport and introduction by man.

Wind can be safely postulated to be an agent of plant distribution, but there are definite limitations here, and few seeds are actually adapted to very wide distribution through the medium of the wind. In some groups of flora, such as the ferns, one can safely postulate effective wind distribution for a distinctly high percentage of both low- and high-altitude species found in the Pacific islands. Many fern species are common to the flora of these islands and to the larger islands of Malaysia, whereas some of them are found in the tropics of both hemispheres. It seems probable that their microscopic spores may be carried by the wind for vast distances (Merrill, 1945, p. 214). Although it is true that the direction of the prevailing winds at low altitudes may not be favorable to an eastern distribution from the western Pacific, high-altitude winds of the stratosphere may carry such spores in the reverse direction of the trade winds. The strong swirling winds of typhoons also may be effective in the dissemination of large seeds as well as microscopic spores.

An interesting example of one large tree that has been spread by birds is the *Pisonia grandis*. On many atoll islands, stands of Pisonia form the favorite roosting place for boobies and terns. The slender fruits of this tree are covered with a very sticky substance which causes them to adhere to the feathers of the birds and thus be transported to other islands. A noddy seen at Wotho was literally plastered with them (Fosberg, 1953, p. 4). Hatheway (1953, p. 34), however, thought from his observations on Arno that this mechanism of dispersal is not very effective in the short run. Koidzumi (1917) thought that seeds of *Cassytha filiformis* must have been dispersed by birds. At Canton Atoll Lister found attached to the feather of a booby the seed of the trailing plant *Boerhavia tetrandra,* which has many glandular hairs (Hedley, 1896, p. 410).

Schnee (1904) pointed out that waves throw many fruits and seeds on shore and that the tropical strand flora has the capacity to remain in sea water for a long time—weeks and months. Some seeds seemingly never sink. He cited a typical atoll plant seed *Morinda citrifolia,* which floated in laboratory salt water for 123 days, at which point the experiment was stopped. Schnee collected seeds of 30 species of plants tossed up on the strand at Jaluit, including some that never grew in the Marshall Islands, but grew at Ponape, 1,000 miles away. At Canton Atoll Van Zwaluwenburg (1942) wrote that "Between December 1940 and February 1941 there were some weeks of strong westerly winds which attained a velocity of 55 knots. The effect of these prolonged gales on the normal ocean currents, though temporary, must have been considerable. Drift-borne seeds were absent or at least inconspicuous on the Canton beaches the year before, but by August 1941 they were a striking feature of the shoreline everywhere. It is assumed that their presence is a result of the gales of the previous winter."

If oceanic currents are postulated as the chief distribution agency for the tropical strand-plant seeds and fruits from the western Pacific to the central and southern Pacific islands, one must give the equatorial countercurrent primary responsibility for their distribution to such areas as the Marshalls and Gilberts. The Fijis and southern Ellice Islands perhaps could more easily have acquired their drift seeds from the southeast current running past northern New Guinea and other Melanesian islands, such as the Solomons and Santa Cruz groups.

Since the countercurrent path fluctuates north and south seasonally between the southern Marshalls and northern Gilberts, it is easy to see how it could bring a uniform strand flora to these groups. The countercurrent continues eastward between Christmas and Palmyra, and these atolls and Fanning and Washington may receive the flotsam of this current, including seeds and fruits. The closeness of the east-west chain of the Carolines to the northern fringes of the countercurrent brings all these atolls and islands into range of its flotsam.

However, the character of the countercurrent itself and the divergence to its north and convergence to its south, respectively, are important aspects to consider with regard to plant dispersion. Because of its clockwise spiraling motion, the surface of the countercurrent is constantly moving southeastward toward the convergence zone, where the current sinks and moves at depth in a northeasterly direction. The floating seeds and fruits and other flotsam, however, do not sink and hence cannot follow the current at depth back northeastward to the northern boundary of the countercurrent, where a divergence takes place. It is clear that the general southern region of convergence will be marked by a broad zone of floating debris brought there from both the southern equatorial current and the countercurrent. The farther eastward the countercurrent flows, the fewer seeds and fruits are left to drift eastward, until, somewhere past the Marquesas and before the Galápagos Islands are reached, no more seeds will be found in the countercurrent drift. All the floating objects of western origin by this time will have reached the convergence zone and be moving southwestward or along a local vortex. This zone develops large surface vortices or whirls, which help to distribute floating seeds and fruits to any island in the path of the whirls. The seasonal fluctuation of this zone widens the zone south of the countercurrent affected by these vortices.

To the north of the countercurrent, the divergence zone, by contrast, would carry little flotsam and fewer and fewer floating seeds and fruits of western origin would remain the farther eastward the current moves. That is, in a longitudinal cross section of the surface current, the northern part theoretically should contain fewer floating objects, and the divergent current flowing away northward would have little to carry away from the countercurrent compared with the southern vortices developing from the convergence. Nevertheless, vortices also develop in the surface current in the Marshall Islands, and what floating seeds and fruits do occur may therefore be more widely distributed.

In the countercurrent region, the predominant winds are easterly or northeasterly and thus add a vector increasing the southerly drift of objects floating on the surface. In the western Pacific, also, during January, February, and March, westerly or northwesterly winds may be important as far east as Samoa (Guppy, 1906, p. 65). These combined influences tend to make the southeasterly spread of plants from the west Pacific easier than the northeasterly spread. Hedley (1896, p. 403) traces the direction of faunal dispersion from the Ellices to the Tuamotus. This may help explain the reason for the greater paucity of western Pacific tropical plant species in Hawaii as compared with Tahiti, which is actually farther east.

Also important in this dispersal pattern are the differences in the apparent prevalent paths of tropical hurricanes north and south of the equator. The general direction north of the equator is toward the west-northwest, and hurricanes seldom originate east of Hawaii. Most of them apparently originate or attain significant wind speeds in or west of the region of the Marshall Islands (Fig. 57). Thus, although within the surface vortices associated with hurricanes dispersions of a few hundred miles from island to island may easily be accomplished, the long-range drift eastward with the countercurrent would be aided by the southern quadrants of the northwestward-moving hurricanes. The northern quadrants of the same hurricanes, however, would aid the northwestward spread of floating seeds and fruits. That is, seeds that have been carried from the Philippines or Halmahera as far east as Ponape, say, may then be carried westward by hurricane-blown drift to the northern islands of the Carolines and to the Marianas. The Hawaiian Islands would not be likely to get much aid in such plant dispersals.

In the south Pacific, however, if we may accept the paths of hurricanes drawn from meager data (Fig. 58), the directions of such paths are toward the south and southeast. Although normal prevailing ocean currents in such areas as the Tuamotus and the south-central Pacific atolls from Malden to the Cooks and Palmerston (Fig. 61) appear to be from the northwest, the occasional hurricanes would bring currents crossing this drift almost at right angles. Together with the normal vortices south of the countercurrent, the hurricanes would aid the southeastward dispersal of floating seeds and fruits from the western equatorial zone.

Although many of the strand plants of the atolls are carried by ocean currents to distant islands, Merrill (1945) cautioned that not all the Malaysian strand plants whose seeds or fruits are adapted to dissemination by ocean currents reached the remote small islands in the Pacific, for there apparently are limits to the amount of time that certain seeds or fruits will float and retain viability. Safford (1921b, p. 535) also pointed out that the existence of many strand plants of southern Polynesia in the flora of Hawaii has been attributed not to ocean currents but to human agencies. Guppy (1906, p. 62) thought that the total number of plants in the Pacific area with seeds or fruits that could be transported unharmed over wide tracts of sea would not much exceed 100, and that the shore plants with buoyant seeds or fruits of the tropical Pacific islands numbered only about 70.

Guppy (1906, pp. 562–3, note 35) listed the following littoral plants with buoyant seeds or fruits which are found distributed in the Fijian, Tongan, Samoan, Tahitian, and Hawaiian groups. This list, he said, probably contains nearly all the species of the Polynesian region, but it is not implied that these plants have been recorded from all the groups.

1. Species found only in the Old World: *Calophyllum inophyllum, Hibiscus diversifolius, Thespesia populnea, Heritiera littoralis, Kleinhovia*

hospita, Carapa moluccensis, C. obovata, Smythea pacifica, Colubrina asiatica, Mucuna gigantea, Erythrina indica, Strongylodon lucidum, Dalbergia monosperma, Pongamia glabra, Inocarpus edulis, Derris uliginosa, Afzelia bijuga, Barringtonia racemosa, B. speciosa, Rhizophora mucronata, Bruguiera rheedii, Terminalia katappa, T. littoralis, Lumnitzera coccinea, Pemphis acidula, Morinda citrifolia, Guettarda speciosa, Wedelia biflora, Scaevola koenigii, Cerbera odollam, Ochrosia parviflora, Cordia subcordata, Tournefortia argentea, Ipomoea glaberrima, I. grandflora, I. peltata, Aniseia uniflora, Clerodendron inerme, Vitex trifolia, Hernandia peltata, Excaecaria agallocha, Tacca pinnatifida, Cycas circinalis, Pandanus odoratissimus, Scirpodendron costatum.

2. Species occurring in both the Old and New Worlds: *Hibiscus tiliaceus, Suriana maritima, Ximenia americana, Dodonaea viscosa, Canavalia obtusifolia, C. ensiformis, Vigna lutea, Sophora tomentosa, Caesalpinia bonduc, C. bonducella, Entada scandens, Gyrocarpus jacquini, Luffa insularum, Ipomoea pes caprae, Cassytha filiformis, Cocos nucifera.*

3. Species occurring in America to the exclusion of the Old World: *Dioclea violacea, Mucuna urens, Rhizophora mangle.*

4. Species that are found only in Polynesia: *Canavalia sericea, Mucuna platyphulla*(?), *Cynometra grandiflora, Serianthes myriadenia, Parinarium laurinum*(?), *Premna tahitensis.*

Merrill (1954, p. 251) added Casuarina and Tephrosia to the list of sea-transported plants in the Pacific.

Koidzumi (1917) listed the following Marshallese strand plants as being disseminated by ocean currents: *Barringtonia asiatica, Calophyllum inophyllum, Hibiscus tiliaceus, Triumfetta procumbens, Canavalia ensiformis, Erythrina indica, Pemphis acidula, Guettarda speciosa, Morinda citrifolia, Scaevola frutescens, Cerbera lactaria, Cordia subcordata, Tournefortia argentea, Ipomoea grandiflora, Euphorbia sparmanni, Hernnandia peltata, Cocos nucifera, Pritzchardia pacifica, Pandanus tectorius, Mariscues albescens, Lepturus repens, Stenotaphrum americanus, Bruguiera gymnorhiza.*

Merrill (1954, p. 254) believed, moreover, that Hibiscus, Thespesia, Suriana, Ipomoea, Cassytha, *Ximenia americana,* and *Bacopa monnieria* were panhemispheric long before man appeared.

The Pandanus appears to have reached most atolls by way of ocean currents, although man also has aided its spread. The Pandanus seed grows in segments of fruits which have a spongy material. This acts as a most efficient float (Hawkes and Degener, 1950, p. 103). According to Catala (1957, p. 49) "It is logical to think that the presence of the Pandanus in the Gilbert Islands, as in other regions, dates from long before that of the coconut palm. Many authors believe that the germinative properties of the Pandanus seeds are preserved even after long periods in sea water, whereas those of the coconut are more rapidly lost in the same conditions. From this it may be deduced that the Pandanus did not, like the coconut palm, need human intervention and that the majority of them which colonized these islands grew from seeds which drifted on to their shores."

Professor St. John informed Buck (1951, p. 305) that there are scores of Pandanus species on the different Pacific Islands, most of them occurring on only one or a few islands but few being widely distributed. This speciation indicates the ancient introduction of the Pandanus long preceding man in Polynesia. However, the preferred edible varieties favored in various localities cannot be reproduced from seed, but must be planted from slips and cuttings. Hence, these must be disseminated through conscious human transport.

The coconut is too large and heavy to have reached the isolated atolls except by floating or by man's introduction. However, botanists are still at variance on the question of whether coconuts drifting at random with the currents can retain their germination powers long enough to create spontaneous groves on the shores where they finally come to rest (Massal and Barrau, 1956, p. 10). Bates (1956, p. 792) contended that the coconut is "more dependent upon man than it might, at first glance, seem. Its tropicopolitan distribution is now generally acknowledged to be a consequence of deliberate dispersal by man. Where coconuts occur on uninhabited Pacific islands, there is frequently evidence that they were planted by transient visitors; and, where there is no evidence one way or another, it is difficult to rule out the possibility of planting." Buck (1938, p. 138) also asserted that "Botanists now hold that coconuts are not endemic to atoll islands and must have been transported and planted by early Polynesian mariners." He pointed out that although Captain Fanning saw coconut trees on then uninhabited Fanning and Christmas Atolls in 1798 and Captain Cook saw them on Christmas Atoll in 1777, both remained ashore so briefly that they did not see the archeological remains on these islands, which indicated previous visits or habitation by Polynesians.

Hedley (1896, p. 22) went so far as to say: "I doubt whether, despite popular opinion to the contrary, a wild coconut palm is to be found throughout the breadth of the Pacific. Certainly it is most rare, again contrary to popular theory, for a drifted coconut thrown upon the beach by winds and waves to produce a tree." This seems a somewhat extreme statement, since the writer has observed numerous instances of coconuts sprouting on the strand on islets in southeastern Kwajelein that had no mature palms. These nuts undoubtedly floated to their sites from adjoining islets several miles to the north.

Bates concluded that "The coconut now certainly seems perfectly capable of persisting as a part of strand vegetation with no interference from man. But man does so frequently interfere that it is difficult to be sure what would happen to the coconut if this interference ceased."

According to Buck (1938, pp. 304–16), the plants that were present in Polynesia when man arrived offered little in the way of food. On atolls the only edible plants were purslane (Portulaca sp.), the roots of the Boerhavia, seaweed, and possibly Pandanus. The first Europeans to come into contact with the Polynesians and Micronesians on the low islands found that they had the coconut, breadfruit, banana, taro, arrowroot, and sweet potato. All these have been introduced by man to the atolls. The breadfruit that came into Polynesia was seedless and could be propagated only from young shoots that sprang up from the spreading roots of the parent trunk. The banana had to be propagated in the same manner. The taro and the sweet potato are grown from tubers which could only reach the atolls through man's transport.

As to the source of these and most other atoll plants of the Pacific, Merrill (1954, p. 205) said that familiarity with the floras of Malaysia, Papuasia, Micronesia, and Polynesia, impresses one very strongly with "the evident fact that the vegetation of the Pacific islands is made up, on the whole, of western elements . . . For all practical purposes the floras of the different islands in the tropical Pacific basin are greatly attenuated Malaysian ones."

The analysis of the distribution of Pacific strand plants by ocean currents provides several clues to the origins and dispersal of atoll plants in the Pacific, although for the distribution of plants in general the agency of ocean currents may not have been important (Guppy, 1906, pp. 62–71). Guppy said that of the 70 strand plants among the Pacific islands, Fiji has only 65, Tahiti 40, and Hawaii only about 16. This indicates the eastward attenuation of plant species from the Indo-Malayan source in the west. Five of the species found widespread among Pacific atolls and islands, *Barringtonia speciosa*, *Cerbera Odollam*, *Guettarda speciosa*, *Hernandia peltata*, and *Tournefortia argentea*, are found as far eastward as Pitcairn, Elizabeth, and Ducie Islands, but do not occur in the Galápagos.

Moreover, of the 70 strand plants listed above, 45 are exclusively Old World species, 16 occur in both the Old and the New Worlds, 3 are exclusively American, and 6 are Polynesian.

Guppy propounded the principle that the New World does not receive strand or shore plants dispersed by Pacific currents, although it has contributed some to the Pacific islands. With the Indo-Malayan strand plants are *Ipomoea pes caprae*, *Canavalia obtusifolia*, and *Sophora tomentosa*, which occur in America also.

Since, however, their seeds are not better adapted for floating from the Old World to America than the equally buoyant fruits of the Old World strand plants that have failed, the presumption arises that their home is in America and that they have made the easier passage across the Pacific westward from America to the Old World.

The only exception to the rule that America does not receive shore plants dispersed by currents from the Old World are presented by the three Australian genera, Dodonaea, Scaevola, and Cassytha . . . They offer, however, but little difficulty, since . . . *Dodonaea vicosa* has probably been in part dispersed by man, whilst the other two species are as well fitted for dispersal by birds as by currents. The occurrence, therefore, of these species in America does not necessarily raise the question of the currents.

The western origin of the strand flora and the indigenously introduced flora of the pre-European period appears well established. This is not necessarily true of more recent introductions. Thus, Kapingamarangi, with 98 species (Niering, 1956, p. 30), and the Hall Islands atolls, with 94 species (Stone, 1959), in the eastern and western Carolines, respectively, do not have the variety found in the Marshalls, which are still farther away from the western source areas. Arno, for instance, has 125 species of vascular plants, of which 57 species were introduced from many source regions east and west during the past 100 years (Hatheway, 1953, p. 3). Arno, with its better commercial connections, received these plants through man-manipulated transportation, whereas Kapingamarangi and the Hall Islands, more isolated, were not exposed to so many recent introductions.

On the other hand, atolls farther west may have species not found in the east. Thus, *Eugenia javanina,* a large tree unknown in the Marshalls or in the atolls of the Carolines east and south of Ponape, grows in the Hall Islands as a codominant with giant Pisonia trees (Stone, 1959).

Buck stated that the only exception to the western origin of atoll food plants is the sweet potato, which came from South America. The sweet potato had reached Hawaii by 1250 A.D. and reached New Zealand from central Polynesia by 1350. The sweet potato is known in the Kechua dialect of north Peru as "kumar." Since the general Polynesian name for the sweet potato is "kumara," the tuber must have come from the north Peruvian coast. Buck believed that Polynesian voyagers must have reached this coast some time before 1250 A.D. and brought the sweet potato back to Polynesia on a return trip (Buck, 1951; see also Merrill, 1954, p. 194).

Plant introductions by man have continued with the coming of Europeans, Japanese, and Americans to the Pacific atolls. This process began with the Spanish and was continued by such people as Captain Cook and the naturalists of French Admiral d'Entrecasteaux's expedition, as well as by later explorers and missionaries (Barrau, 1958, p. 16). Of some 57 ornamental plants (Plate 60) found on Jaluit Atoll, Okabe (1941) stated that 26.9 per cent were introduced by Germans. The ornamental hedges on Arno Atoll are said to have been introduced by Japanese (Mason, 1957). In speaking of continuing introductions in the Gilberts, Catala (1957, p. 82) said: "When the Gilbertese return from working abroad, they generally bring back new plants. A remarkable fact is that they almost always choose plants with either ornamental leaves or fragrant flowers which may be fashioned into the leis and garlands required for the dances and songs that form so important a part of the daily life in these islands. . . ."

According to Fosberg (1956, p. 190), the total number of presumably indigenous species of flowering plants and ferns known from the northern Marshalls is 42, with 7 more of presumably aboriginal introduction. However, there are 57 naturalized species, with about 15 more occasionally persisting after cultivation. In addition, there are about 41 cultivated species.

Of the 98 species on Kapingamarangi in the eastern Carolines, Niering estimated that only 38 were indigenous. Of the remaining 60, at least 58 were introduced.

Of the 94 species from the Hall islands 52 were considered probably indigenous, 22 consciously introduced for food or ornamental use, and the remaining 20 accidental weed introductions (Stone, 1959).

Nearly half of Arno's 125 species were considered introduced during the past 100 years, about 38 coming as cultivated plants and 19 coming accidentally as weeds. Thus, in 1850, Arno's flora must have consisted of only about 68 species of higher plants (Hatheway, 1953).

Obviously, not all introductions are desirable. Numerous weeds have been brought into atolls to add to the vegetation already struggling for room and water. Weed species that probably are indigenous very likely include *Lepturus repens, Fimbristylis atollensis, Triumfetta procumbens, Vigna marina, Wedelia biflora,* and *Cassytha filiformis.* They have been found growing on sand freshly deposited along the lagoon shores and probably are brought by ocean currents. *Euphorbia chamissonis* and *Thuarea involuta* also may be in this category. Weeds of possible aboriginal introduction perhaps coming in as "stowaways" with breadfruit or banana slips transported to new atolls might include *Centella asiatica, Hedyotis biflora, Ipomoea littoralis,* Oplismenus sp., *Portulaca samoensis,* and *Cyperus polystachyos* (Hatheway, 1953, pp. 20–2).

Arno Atoll in 1952 had about 26 species of unwanted alien weeds. Most of these had been introduced after 1873, when an Hawaiian mission was established at Ine Island (Hatheway, 1953).

An example of a noxious weed that has come into the Marshall Islands in recent times is the sand burr. Another is *Paspalum vaginatum,* an aggressive weedy grass introduced into Likiep Atoll. It was partially attributed with causing the failure of attempts to revive taro culture there (Fosberg, 1956, p. 191).

MacMillan (1946, p. 36) has pointed out that plants which develop from introductions can become preferred hosts for diseases and insect pests struggling for existence on native crops; or they can be the means of introduction of parasitic plant diseases which will flourish on established native plants and the initial source of insect pests which become fatal to the plants they accompany as well as new hosts among the useful plants in the island economy.

Since new plant introductions will inevitably take place in the future, great care must be taken that they will be a genuine benefit and not a curse to the atoll inhabitants.

CHAPTER 17

ATOLL LAND PLANT DISTRIBUTION AND ASSOCIATION

In spite of a considerable amount of work by numerous botanists, ethnographers and others in the islands of the Pacific (see Sachet and Fosberg, 1955), it still seems premature to attempt a comprehensive analysis of the distribution of plants among the low coral islands of the Pacific. The reason for this is, first, that collections have been made on relatively few atolls and reef islands, and, second, that time or equipment limitations, inadequate training, or other more primary interests have conspired to make most of the collections superficial and the identifications highly incomplete. When a comparatively wet atoll (Palmyra) is reported to have only 15 species of plants while a much drier atoll (Bikini) has three or four times as many species reported, it is obvious that only a partial picture of the distribution of atoll plants can be given. On the other hand, enough has been done to provide a fairly good idea of what plants are likely to be fairly universal on Pacific atolls under given rainfall regimes. The requirements or the tolerances of certain other plants are such that while they may occur on a dry or a wet island, they may be sparse or absent under opposite moisture conditions.

Rainfall and vegetation zonation

The relation between rainfall and the number of plant species on an atoll has already been pointed out, and it is further illustrated in Table 21. The collections represented in the table were made carefully, so only inconspicuous species are likely to have escaped attention. Even though the figures may be not entirely complete, they are complete enough for correlative purposes, and the important correlation between rainfall and the number of species of land plants on coral atolls is sufficiently obvious. We would expect from this correlation that the northern Marshalls generally have only about half the number of species of land plants present in the southern Marshalls, and that the northern Gilberts have about twice the number of species of the southern Gilberts, since in the Gilberts the rain fall decreases toward the south. We might also expect that there would be a roughly comparable number of species of land plants in atolls having about the same amount of rainfall. That is, the northern Marshalls and southern Gilberts should have species variations similar to those of the Tuamotus.

TABLE 21

Relation of Rainfall and Plant Species

Island	Rainfall, inches	No. of species	Source
Canton	19	14	(Hatheway, 1955)
Wake	39	16	(Christophersen, 1931)
Bikini	80	58	(Taylor, 1950)
Kapingama-rangi	80–100	98	(Niering, 1956)
Tarawa	115	97, plus 10 European garden vegetables	(Catala, 1957)
Arno	160	125, exclusive of lichens and fungi	(Anderson, 1951)

These expectations, however, may not necessarily follow. In the first place, since atolls nearest the western Pacific sources of introduction have the advantage of closeness to the sources, such atolls theoretically should have the largest number of species, while those in the eastern parts of Micronesia and Polynesia should have relatively fewer species (Fosberg, 1949, p. 91). Some that are near large high islands might obtain drift seeds retaining their germination power, whereas some seeds may not be able to retain this power if the water gap over which they must drift to an island is great. Second, correlations between rainfall and species number may be subject to considerable error, owing to differences in opportunities and practices in conscious introductions. These, in turn, depend upon opportunities to travel to the right places and transport facilities from such plant sources to the atoll. Where transportation is convenient and frequent, introductions may occur more often.

An example of this difficulty of correlation is that of Wake, which in

1923 had a reported flora of only 16 species of vascular plants (19 flowering plants) (Bryan, 1959, p. 5). By 1956 introductions had resulted in the establishment in the wild state of 26 new species, while 47 other species were being cultivated in pots or under some sort of human protection (Fosberg, 1959, p. 3). Thus the total number of plant species at Wake in 1956 was 89. Since the original vegetation of most of the atolls consisted largely of a few species of strand vegetation, the number of plant species on many inhabited atolls today must be attributed largely to man. Correlation of rain fall with plant variations thus presents uncertainties and pitfalls.

However, there are distinctions in adaptations and associations between wet and dry islands. Thus, Taylor (1950) in analyzing studies of Marshallese plant distribution by Koidzumi (1917) stated that the southern atolls are notably different from the northern atolls in several respects; on the southern atolls Barringtonia is an important element, Allophyllus is a major woodland type, and Suriana, Fimbristylis, Taca, Pisonia, Boerhaavia, Dodonea, Clerodendron, Occhrosia, and other genera are apparently absent. On the other hand, he said, the Koidzumi records of Solanaceae and Euphorbiaceae in the southern Marshalls have no counterparts to the north.

Fosberg (1956, pp. 186–8) wrote that Wake Island and the northern Marshall Islands, which stretch roughly in a north-south line, may be divided rather naturally into four east-west trending belts of rather uniform vegetation. The northernmost consists of Taongi and Wake, where the aridity is such that the coconut appears not to thrive. The general aspect is a sparse vegetation of a few species. Scrub makes up most of the cover, with grass being prominent on the sand and scattered herbs, such as the morning glory (Ipomoea tuba), on stony openings.

The second belt consists only of Bikar Atoll, where coconut trees will grow but will not produce normal nuts during dry periods. The dominant vegetation is pure Pisonia forest, the crowns of the trees forming a complete canopy. (An example of vegetation on a semidry atoll in the Phoenix group is seen in Plate 61.) Other plants of zone 1 also are found.

In the third belt a line of atolls stretches from Eniwetok in the west to Utirik in the east. A more diverse and larger flora occurs (Plate 62). Forest types, aside from coconut plantations, are Pisonia forest, Cordia forest, mixed forest, and Pemphis forest. Scrub succeeds the mixed forest in exposed situations, and along the tops of the beaches Scaevola may form pure stands. Coconuts generally are small and the palms stand rather far apart, so that the crowns do not form a closed canopy (Plate 63). During the dry season the grass turns brown, as do the tips of coconut-palm leaves, and the Pisonia and Cordia lose most of their leaves. Arrowroot (Tacca) forms a ground cover and, together with Pandanus, contributes importantly to the food supply.

In the fourth and southernmost belt of the northern Marshalls are such atolls as Likiep, Kwajelein, and Maloelap (Plates 64 and 65), all of which have a moderately moist climate (120 inches of rain fall per year). This group has all the species of plants appearing farther north plus several others and is luxuriant in appearance. Ochrosia may be found in pure stands. Introduced plants are more numerous, and coconut plantations, where not destroyed during World War II, occupy most of the larger islets and many of the smaller ones as well. Breadfruit becomes an important tree, although not growing to very large size. Around village houses it may dominate the vegetation (Plate 77).

In the southern Marshalls the writer believes one may recognize two additional zones. The northern one includes Namu, Ailinglaplap, Majuro, and Arno, all of which have a moderately high rainfall (160 inches per year). One is impressed with the marked increase in vegetation luxuriance from Kwajelein and Maloelap to Namu. Coconut trees become tall and have rich green crowns. Breadfruit trees grow to over 90 feet and have trunks 5 or more feet in diameter at waist height from the ground. The rich dark soil in central parts of the larger islets supports a great variety of large trees, and the undercover is rank. There are large pure stands of breadfruit in the central parts of larger islets.

The wettest atolls in the Marshalls, and the most luxuriant vegetationally, are the four southernmost, Jaluit, Mili, Namorik, and Ebon (Plates 39, 66 to 68). These, together with the single-reef islet of Kili (Plate 69), have a rainfall that probably averages over 180 inches per year. This wetness, together with the fact that Jaluit was the center for the Marshalls administration under the Germans and the Japanese, has led to numerous plant introductions and to probably the largest number of species in the Marshalls. Many of these introductions were wiped out by Typhoon Ophelia in January 1958. The storm seriously damaged Jabwor Islet, on which most of the introductions were made.

As indicated above, at least six fairly well distinguished vegetational zones occur in the north-south stretch of atolls from Wake to Ebon. As temperature differences are slight, the critical factor causing the difference is the amount and perhaps the seasonal distribution of rainfall. The latter is less significant in the wetter south than in the dry north.

The Caroline Islands stretch in a relatively narrow zone in an east-west direction, so vegetational zonation is less marked than in the Marshalls. In general, the Carolines lie in a belt corresponding to the southernmost two zones of the Marshalls. However, in the eastern Carolines, Nukuoro, Mokil, and Pingelap tend to exhibit a more luxuriant vegetation than Kapingamarangi (Plates 10, 70, and 71) in the drier equatorial region. In the north-south chains, such as the Gilbert and Ellice Islands, one may expect well-marked zonations in accordance with progressive rainfall changes. Catala

(1957, p. 30) divided the Gilberts into three rainfall zones. These would presumably be reflected in the vegetation, although he said that "It would seem that as regards the behavior of the coconut palm, these distinctions are less sharp, and might even be reduced to one group for the northern and central islands and another for the southern islands." Insufficient data are on hand to allow comment by the writer on vegetation zonation in other atoll groups of the south Pacific. However, the rainfall-distribution chart (Fig. 51) may be used to get an idea of likely similarities and differences.

No attempt is made in this report to describe or map the geographic distribution of particular plants among the Pacific atolls. The discussion will be concerned with the geographic "zonation" of plants, with characteristic plant associations, and with plant ecology on atoll islands.

Salt tolerance of atoll plants

Salt water not only influences atoll plants through the ground water but also through spray. While the dominant strand vegetation of atolls is tolerant of saline influences, there are degrees of tolerance among the different species. For example, Niering (1956, p. 23) pointed out that

The foliage of Guettarda is more easily damaged than that of Scaevola. Oceanward the leaves of the former show a general browning of the margins while lagoonward this is not at all evident. In contrast, Scaevola is unaffected except for occasional shrubs with dwarfed rosettes of leaves. Along the marginal areas as well as in the interior of some of the smaller islets the lower coconut fronds are often brownish and dying. However, the success of these species along the marginal areas would suggest that these effects are relatively superficial. In contrast, other marginal species of lesser importance such as Cordia and *Terminalia samoensis* are more adversely affected, which may account for their minor role. . . .

Whenever typical interior species such as Premna and Morinda occur in the marginal zone, probably as a result of erosion inland, dead or dying branches are evident, and leaves show marked salt spray damage. A similar condition is present where the marginal vegetation is absent and the full force of the salt-laden winds directly strikes the unprotected undergrowth in the interior. Where the breadfruit canopy projects above the surrounding coconut, dead or defoliated branches are evident. According to the natives, the upper branches frequently lose their leaves following a severe storm. However, new ones usually appear later . . . Another species very sensitive to salt spray is Calophyllum which is planted exclusively along the lagoon shore [at Kapingamarangi]. The lone specimen observed oceanward showed both salt-spray damage and serious insect infestation.

Niering also made the following list giving the relative salt tolerance of the more-common species, beginning with the most-salt-tolerant group: (1) *Cocos nucifera, Pandanus tectorius, Messerschmidia argentea, Scaevola seri-*

cea, and *Guettarda speciosa.* (2) *Cordia subcordata* and *Clerodendrum inerme.* (3) *Terminalia samoensis.* (4) *Premna obtusifolia* and *Morinda citrifolia.* (5) *Calophyllum inophyllum.* (6) *Artocarpus altilis.*

In pointing out the effect of the year and a half of drought (1949–50), Moul (1957, p. 2) stated that on a stretch of South Island at Onotoa only 50 feet wide, nearly all the coconut palms were dead, but the Scaevola, Pandanus, and Guettarda did not show any serious effects.

Spray planing of vegetation canopies produces striking profiles and patterns. On Nukuoro Atoll the writer observed that breadfruit trees in island centers, whose crowns towered above the coconut canopy by 10 or 20 feet, appeared as though their foliage had been sheared at an upward slant rising from the seaward side of the groves toward the lagoon side. On numerous aerial photographs of the Marshalls examined by the writer, pure stands of strand shrubs, apparently Scaevola, Pemphis, or *Suriana* plants on the smaller islets having no palms, formed windrow patterns, whether from salt-spray planing or wind-influenced alignments. These effects were observed on photos of Ailingalae, Arno, Rongelap, Ujelang, and Wotje.

The process is confirmed by Hatheway's observations on Arno Atoll (1953, p. 29):

On the windward islands these forests reflected in their growth the prevailing direction of the wind. The canopy of the forest and of the Scaevola scrub to windward was in effect a plane of leaves dipping toward the ocean beach at angles of 9 to 13 degrees. On Langar, *Barringtonia* and *Hernandia* were prominent in a small portion of the native forest. These trees appeared to have been restricted in their upward growth by the salt-laden winds, for although they were massive, with trunks over two feet in diameter, many were scarcely 25 feet tall. Their trunks were inclined at dangerous angles or actually prostrate on the ground, and branches projecting above the canopy of the forest were mostly leafless.

Relation of species number to island size

Fosberg (1949, p. 90) has pointed out that important differences occur in vegetation association between small or narrow islets and large land areas. "The smaller the area of an islet the more extreme is the strand character of its vegetation, and the larger the area the more divergence is shown from this type. This divergence may be of different sorts, as in the extensive Lepturus-Messerschmidia savannah on dry Christmas Island, the dense moist forest of Nomwin, the tangled swamp on Ailinglaplap, or the solid forest of a single species on isolated Vostok Island."

The only quantitative study seen by the writer relating island size to plant occurrence and association was that made on Kapingamarangi by Niering (1956) with whom the writer cooperated in the mapping of this atoll's vegetation. Tables 22 and 23 and Figs. 91 and 92, taken from Niering's article, lead to some highly interesting conclusions. Table 22 lists species of trees and shrubs arranged along the ordinate of the rectangle according to frequency of occurrence on atolls. Table 23 lists herbs along the ordinate in the same manner. Along the abscissa the 33 islets are listed in order of size from 0.03 to 79.5 acres, respectively (see also Fig. 14, p. 36).

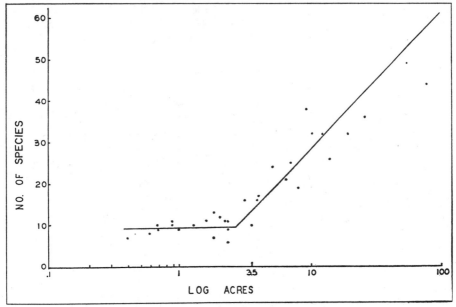

Fig. 91. Number of species of plants on Kapingamarangi Atoll plotted against islet size. Note the two linear relationships: There is little variation in species per islet on islets 3½ acres or less in size, whereas on islets 3½ acres or more in size, the number of species is proportional to the size of the islet. [From Niering (1956).]

Figure 91 shows a bar graph giving the number of species according to size of islets, while Fig. 92 plots the same thing in a line graph. The latter two indicate that islets of 3.5 acres or less in size show very little variation in the number of species per islet. Islets larger than 3.5 acres in size show a progressive increase in the number of species with increase in size of islets. Thus the 19 islets of about 3.5 acres or less in area each have between 5 and 16 species of plants. These islets varied from 25 to 350 feet in width and 100 to 500 feet in length, mostly elongated in the ocean to lagoon direction across the reef. The largest eight islets, betweeen 9.2 and 79.5 acres, have between 27 and 61 species. The line graph clearly points to a critical size of about 3.5 acres as the turning point in increased species number and may indicate something like a minimum size for a significant fresh-water lens in

TABLE 22

Species of Trees and Shrubs on Kapingamarangi Atoll * †

ISLETS

Trees	Origin	% frequency	Hare	Werua	Ring.	Toro.	Nuna.	Taringa	Matiro	Touhou	Tetau	Tang.	Puma.	Hukuh.	Taka.	Here.	Ramotu	Para.	Sake.	Hepepa	Niku.	Tariha	Turu.	Tirakau	Toko.	Tipae	Tirakume	Matuket.	Hukun.	Riku.	Pepeio	Mata.	Tiahu	Pungu.	Matuker.
Cocos nucifera	AI	100	A	A	A	A	A	A	A	F	A	A	A	A	A	A	A	A	A	A	A	A	A	A	A	A	A	A	A	A	O	A	O	R	R
Guettarda speciosa	I	97	A	A	F	A	A	A	F	R	A	A	A	A	A	A	A	A	A	A	A	A	A	A	A	A	A	A	F	O		F	O	O	R
Morinda citrifolia	AI	97	F	F	A	A	A	A	O	O	A	A	A	A	F	A	A	O	O	F	O	O	O	O	O	O	O	O	O	O	O	O	O	F	O
Premna obtusifolia	I	97	A	A	A	A	A	A	A	O	A	A	A	A	A	O	O	O	O	O	O	O	O	O	O	O	O	O	O	O	O	O	O	O	O
Pandanus tectorius	I-AI	97	A	A	F	A	A	F	A	A	O	O	O	O	A	A	A	F	O	O	O	O	O	O	O	O	F	O	O	O	R	O	O	O	R
Barringtonia asiatica	I	63	R	R	R	R	R	R	R		R	R		R	R	R	R	R			R		R		R	R	R	R		R	R		R	R	R
Calophyllum inophyllum	AI	51	R	O	O	O	O	O	O		R	R	R	R	R	R	R	R	R		R		R			R	R	R	R		R				
Hibiscus tiliaceus	AI	48	O	O	O	O	F	O	F		O	R	O	O	O	R	R	R	R											R					
Cordia subcordata	I	45	O	O	O	O	O	O	O	R	R	R	R	O	O	R	R	R			R	R								R					
Artocarpus altilis	AI	42	R	R	A	F	A	F	A	F		F	F	O		R	R																		
Messerschmidia argentea	I	39	O	O	O	O	O	O	O		R		O	O		R	R				O	O	O	O	O		R	R				O	O		
Terminalia samoensis	I	27				R	R	R	R		R		O			R										R									
Hernandia sonora	I	24	R	R	R	R	R	R	R				R	R	R		R																		
Cerbera manghas	RI	15			R	R	R	R		O																									
Pisonia grandis	I	15	O	O	O	O	O	O	O	O		O	O	O																					
Terminalia catappa	AI	15	R	R	R	R	R	R	R	R	R																	R		R					
Carica papaya	RI	12	O	O	O	O	O	O	O	O																									
Thespesia populnea	I	12	R	R	R	R	R	R	R		R	R	R									R													
Intsia bijuga	D	12			R	R	R	R	R								R																		
Erythrina variegata	RI	9		R	R	R	R	R																											

Species	No. of islets	Origin
Pandanus dubius	6	AI
Plumeria rubra	6	RI
Ochrosia oppositifolia	6	I
Adenanthera pavonina	3	RI
Barringtonia racemosa	3	D
Kleinhovia hospita	3	D
Pemphis acidula	3	RI
Pongamia pinnata	3	I
Soulamea amara	3	I
Shrubs		
Scaevola frutescens	97	I
Allophylus timorensis	36	I
Clerodendrum inerme	33	I
Pipturus argenteus	27	RI
Hibiscus sp.	15	RI
Polyscias fruticosa	12	RI
Caesalpinia bonduc	9	I
Polyscias scutellaria	6	RI
Sophora tomentosa	6	I
Capsicum frutescens	6	RI
Codiaeum variegatum	6	RI
Vitex negundo	6	RI
Cassia alata	6	RI
Tabernaemontana divaricata	3	RI

* From Niering (1956).

† Species arranged according to frequency of occurrence. Islets arranged according to size, from smallest to largest. Relative importance of each species indicated by letter: A, abundant; F, frequent; O, occasional; R, rare. Probable origin of each species also indicated by letter: I, indigenous; AI, aboriginal introduction; RI, recent introduction; D, drift seedlings not yet established as mature specimens.

TABLE 23

Species of Herbs on Kapingamarangi Atoll * †

ISLETS

Herbs	Origin	% frequency	Hare	Werua	Ring.	Toro.	Nuna.	Taringa	Matiro	Touhou	Tetau	Tang.	Puma.	Hukuh.	Taka.	Here.	Ramotu	Para.	Sake.	Hepepa	Niku.	Tariha	Turu.	Tirakau	Toko.	Tipae	Tirakume	Matuket.	Hukun.	Riku.	Pepeio	Mata.	Tiahu	Pungu.	Matuker.
Asplenium nidus	I	54	O	A	A	F	F	F	F	R	F	F	F	F	F	F	R				R						R			R					R
Tacca leontopetaloides	AI	39	O	F	O	A	O	R	R	O	F	F	F			R	R					R					R					R			R
Lepturus repens	I	36	O	O	O	F	F	O	O	O	O	O	O	O	O	O					R	R		O	R					O	R				R
Stenotaphrum micranthum	I	36	F	F	F	F	F	F	F	R	F	F	O	F	O						R			A						R					
Thuarea involuta	I	33	F	F	F	F	F	F	F	O	F	F	F	O	O	F								A											
Cyrtosperma chamissonis	AI	33	A	A	A	A	R	F	F	F	F	F	R	R	R	O		R									R								
Crinum sp.	AI-RI	30	A	R	R	O	O	R	R	R	F		O	O													R								
Fimbristylis spathacea	I	21	O	O	O	O	F	O	O	O	O	R	R	R				R																	
Musa nana	RI	21	O	O	O	O	R	O	O	R	F	F	O	O																					
Vigna marina	I	21	A	A	A	F	O	O	O	O							O																		
Cassytha filiformis	I	18	O	O	O	R		R	R									O					A	A						R		R			
Triumfetta procumbens	I	18	O	O	O	R											R																		
Fleurya ruderalis	I	12	O	O	O				R																										
Hemigraphis reptans	RI	12				R	R		O	O	R	R		R		R																			
Ipomoea pes-caprae	I	12	R	R	R	A	O	R	R	R	F	O		O		R																			
Ipomoea littoralis	I	12	R	R	A	O	O	R	R		R	R																							
Hedychium coronarium	RI	9	O	O	R	R	R	R	R																										
Canavalia microcarpa	I	9	R	R	R	R	R	R	R																										
Eleusine indica	RI	9	O	O	O	A	A	A	A																										
Nephrolepis hirsutula	I	9	A	R	A	R	R																												
Polypodium scolopendria	I	9	R	R	R	R	R	R	R																										
Wedelia biflora	I	9	O	A	A	O	O																												
Zephyranthes rosea	RI	9	O	O	O	R	R	O	O																							O			
Digitaria microbachne	AI	6	O	O	O	R	R	R	R																										
Eragrostis amabilis	RI	6	R	R	R	R	R	R	R																										

Species								No.	Importance/Origin
Euphorbia chamissonis	R				R			6	I
Fimbristylis miliacea						O	O	6	RI
Ipomoea tuba			R				O	6	I
Jussiaea sulfruticosa						A	A	6	AI
Mucuna gigantea						R	R	6	D
Musa sapientum	O				F			6	RI
Pteris tripartita						R	R	6	I
Vernonia cinerea				O		O	O	6	RI
Achryanthes aspera					R		R	3	RI
Adenostemma lavenia						R		3	RI
Alocasia macrorrhiza	R							3	AI
Alternanthera sessilis						O		3	RI
Angelonia angustifolia						O		3	RI
Asclepias curvassavica	R							3	RI
Blechum brownei						O		3	RI
Colocasia esculenta					R			3	AI
Cucurbita sp.							R	3	RI
Cymbopogon nardus						R		3	RI
Cyperus brevifolius						R		3	RI
Eclipta alba	R							3	RI
Gomphrena globosa	R							3	RI
Lindernia antipoda					O			3	RI
Ocimum sanctum	O							3	AI
Panicum ambiguum				O				3	RI
Paspalum vaginatum					R			3	RI
Phyllanthus niruri	R							3	RI
Portulaca oleracea	R					R		3	RI
Psilotum nudum							R	3	I
Saccharum officinarum	R							3	RI
Dioscorea sp.		R						3	RI

* From Niering (1956).

† Species arranged according to frequency of occurrence. Islets arranged according to size, from smallest to largest. Relative importance of each species indicated by letter: A, abundant; F, frequent; O, occasional; R, rare. Probable origin of each species also indicated by letter: I, indigenous; AI, aboriginal introduction; RI, recent introduction; D, drift seedlings not yet established as mature specimens.

the rainfall regime of Kapingamarangi. It is not Hare, the islet with the greatest acreage, however, that has the most species, because this islet has its large acreage by virtue of great length. It is Werua, the second largest islet, but the one with its center farthest from all shore lines, that has the greatest number of species. Its huge Cyrtosperma and taro pit also indicate that it probably has the best-developed ground-water lens.

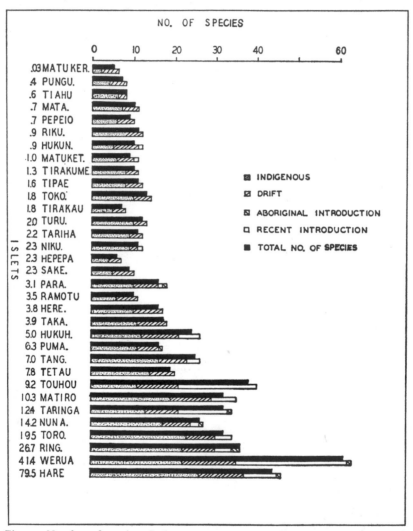

Fig. 92. Number of species of plants on each islet of Kapingamarangi Atoll and their presumed origin. The number preceding the name of an islet is the islet size (in acres). Note the continuous increase in the number of species on islets over 3½ acres in size. Recent introduction of species is most common on Touhou and Werua, the most densely populated islets. [From Niering (1956).]

In analyzing these figures, Niering divided them into those with 3.5 acres or less of area, those of intermediate size (between 3.5 and 9.5 acres), and the larger ones (over 9.5 acres in area). The 19 small islets were completely dominated by coconut trees averaging 55 to 65 feet in height. On some of these islets, notably Pepeio, all of which had immature sandy and recent soils built up through sand accretion only during the preceding 35 years, chlorotic palms were very conspicuous. Breadfruit, except in one instance, was absent, another indication of a poorly developed ground-water lens.

The understory on these islets varied considerably in development. In general, Guettarda (Plate 72) was most characteristic, with scattered Morinda and Premna. Periodic clearing of the undergrowth left only occasional taller Guettarda and Pandanus (Plate 73) scattered throughout the understory. In two instances of very narrow islets the understory is practically wanting except for an occasional Pandanus, although old stumps indicate previous vegetation that has been cleared or that may have been killed by salt water inundation. "In general, the herbaceous cover is absent or comprises scattered specimens of Tacca, Asplenium [Plate 74], Crinum, and *Lepturus repens*. *Cassytha filiformis* [Plate 72] occurs as a parasite. Only on one islet, Turuaimu, which is extremely sandy and open, is herbaceous cover abundant. Here *Triumfetta procumbens* occurs as an important ground cover" (Niering, 1956, p. 7).

The islets intermediate in size tend to be under 500 feet in length and under 800 feet in width. A slightly larger number of plant species correlates with a slightly more favorable environment. Although coconut plantations were dominant, on a few islets a breadfruit-coconut association occupied parts of the interior. Coconut trees are somewhat taller, 75 to 85 feet high. According to Niering (1956),

The most striking change occurs in the understory. Although Guettarda still occurs as scattered trees, Premna and Morinda, 5 to 7 inches in diameter or larger and 25 to 30 feet in height, predominate. In addition, *Pisonia grandis* is locally abundant, especially on Pumatahati, which was formerly covered by a Pisonia forest. Pandanus is scattered or localized. Sucker and sprout growth of Morinda and Premna often form a shrub layer 3 to 4 feet in height. Again, land management practices account for the variation from a relatively open shrub layer with scattered larger Morinda and Premna to a relatively dense undergrowth.

Herb cover increases compared to that of the smaller islets. In addition to those species found on the smaller islets the two grasses Stenotaphrum and Thuarea are most frequent, especially in the openings. Other species which appear for the first time include *Fimbristylis spathacea, Ipomoea littoralis,* and *Ipomoea pes caprae*.

On the larger islets of the third category, coconut plantations at Kapingamarangi reach their maximum development, but the breadfruit-coconut association may occupy a larger total area than the coconut-dominant zone.

Werua islet is the best example of such a situation (Fig. 93). As on the previous islets, Premna, Morinda, and Pandanus are the typical understory species, although variants occur. Occasional associates include Pisonia and *Hibiscus tiliaceus*. Scattered trees of *Hernandia sonora, Cerbera manghas,*

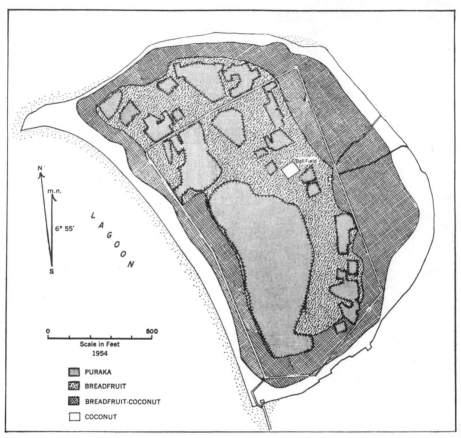

Fig. 93. Dominant vegetation zones on Werua Islet, Kapinmarangi Atoll. [From Wiens (1956).]

Thespesia polpulnea, and *Ochrosia oppositifolia* usually occur as isolated trees.

On these larger islets the herbaceous cover increased markedly compared to the smaller islets. Considerable variation also occurs between the wide and narrow islets. On the narrow islets the two grasses Stenotaphrum and Thuarea, Wedelia, *Vigna marina,* and occasional ferns are most typical. On the wider islets ferns attain a lush development in the more-shaded plantations with scattered grasses in the openings. The ferns Nephrolepis and Asplenium (Plates 74 and 75) form a continuous ground cover 2 to 3 feet high. Further variation occurs from the ocean side to the lagoon side. Herbaceous cover is usually less continuous on the recently deposited sandy areas, in contrast to the highly organic rubble areas oceanward. In openings around abandoned house sites, now within the plantations, Vigna often forms dense tangles which completely engulf the other vegetation. This plant together with Wedelia forms the most troublesome weeds (Niering, 1956, pp. 7–8).

Werua is the only islet having four rather clearly discernible vegetation zones (Wiens, 1956, p. 45):

These are arranged in a generally concentric zonation with the exception of the outermost zone of Guettarda and Scaevola, which have been permitted to grow here only along the north channel and seaward fringe. Aside from this fringe zone a coconut-trees-dominant zone completely encircles the islet, occupying the outermost 50 to 100 feet. Inward of this, breadfruit trees form an intermixed stand with coconut trees in a zone whose innermost bounds may roughly be delimited by a line running around the entire area of puraka (Cyrtosperma) [Plate 76] fields and pits and coming close to their outer edges. The area inside this line is dominated almost completely by breadfruit trees [Plates 67 and 77], among which coconut trees are much less prominent, but under which Pandanus trees occasionally form dense understory vegetation.

On the larger islands diverse vegetational associations result from differing soil conditions. Aspects of some of these associations have been indicated in Chapter 15. Some special situations are described below.

Land use and vegetation types

In speaking of Mokil Atoll in the eastern Carolines, Murphy (1950, pp. 65–7) stated that 95 per cent of the land above high tide falls in the category of coconut land. "Coconut land is, in short, all of the land of the atoll outside of the wet gardens. All of it is potentially coconut producing even though locally bananas or breadfruit may predominate and pandanus is everywhere abundant." While these generalizations may be applied to most atolls in the wetter climates, it is more descriptive of the remarkable adaptability of the coconut to varying conditions than of the actual vegetational cover and land use on most atolls. Two examples of vegetation distribution in terms of areal coverage are given in Tables 24 and 25. Although not comparable in categorization, they point out the diversity existing in land use and in plant cover and also indicate the differences resulting from the pressure of high and low population on the food resources.

Several aspects in the tables contrast with each other. First, Kapingamarangi is a small atoll with a small land area and a dense population—

about 0.65 acre per capita. Arno is a large atoll with a relatively large land area and relatively low density of population—3.8 acres per capita. Arno may have up to twice the annual rainfall of Kapingamarangi and thus has better coconut-palm growing conditions. At Kapingamarangi, except for

TABLE 24

Kapingamarangi Land Use *

		Percentage
1954 population	426	
Total land area:	276.4 acres	
Coconut-dominant land	157.03 acres	56.8
Breadfruit-coconut land	76.01 acres	27.5
Breadfruit-dominant land	18.29 acres	6.6
Taro, Cyrtosperma swamp	25.11 acres	9.0
Rainfall per year	80–100 in.	

* From Wiens (1956).

TABLE 25

Arno Atoll Land Use *

		Percentage
1952 population	850–1,000 (approx.)	
Total land area:	3205.3 acres	
Coconut-dominant land	2224 acres	69.4
Breadfruit-dominant land	277 acres	8.6
Fresh-water swamp (taro)	6.6 acres	0.2
Scrub forest	566.3 acres	14.5
Secondary forest	74.9 acres	2.3
Saline flats	29.6 acres	0.9
Mangrove "swamp"	26.8 acres	0.8
Rainfall per year	160 in.	

* From Hatheway (1953).

the narrow marginal fringe of scrub forest not separated from the coconut-dominant category, all the land was utilized for major food plants. At Arno about one-fifth of the land is covered by vegetation other than the major food plants, although some Pandanus and scattered coconut palms would be found in the scrub forest and the secondary forest. The smaller emphasis on taro and Cyrtosperma cultivation on Arno also indicates a significant difference in population pressure on food resources. Some 9 per cent of the land on Kapingamarangi is devoted to this arduous culture, as compared with less than 0.2 per cent of the land area of Arno.

This last difference reflects in two atolls the same respective difference in "swamp taro" (mostly Cyrtosperma) cultivation in the Carolines and in the Marshalls as a whole. That is, this culture not only never has been as important in the Marshalls as in the Carolines, but has shown a high degree of abandonment in the Marshalls during recent decades (Fosberg, 1956, p. 184), whereas it still is actively carried on in the rest of Micronesia (Plate 76) and Polynesia southwest and southeast of the Marshalls, including the Gilberts and Ellices, Lines and Phoenixes, and parts of the Tuamotus (Catala, 1957, p. 67). However, Danielsson (1955, p. 102) found that on Raroia and other Tuamotu atolls the 1903 typhoon had filled in taro pits to such an extent that the people tended to abandon them rather than re-excavate them. In such areas the land probably has been used for coconut plantings. Since Cyrtosperma and taro are very sensitive to salinity, they generally can be planted only in small areas in the middle of islands and they do not account for much of the land use. The percentage on such atolls as Kapingamarangi probably is large compared to that on most atolls, although other small atolls of the Carolines, such as Nukuoro and Mokil, may have a relatively high percentage of the land in such use.

Vegetation associations under the various categories shown in the two tables and with respect to geographic position on an island deserve some attention, and these are described below.

1. Sandy lobes: On some of the larger sandy lobes building lagoonward where new land has been added at a rapid rate, a successional trend may become evident in the understory. In one such situation on Kapingamarangi, typical marginal species—Scaevola, Messerschmidia (Plate 56), and Guettarda (Plate 72)—were found to persist inland, where they formed an open, sporadic understory. On these relatively unaltered sands the ground cover was sparse, with only scattered patches of Lepturus and occasional seedlings and saplings of Morinda and Premna. At 100 feet from the margin this pioneer undergrowth gave way to a Premna-Morinda understory typical of the interior regions, where Stenotaphrum, Asplenium, and Nephrolepis (Plates 74 and 75) formed a continuous ground cover. According to Niering (1956) these areas indicate a successional trend in the undergrowth from the early beach pioneers to a Premna-Morinda type. The situation here was not unlike what the writer observed in the northern section of Kili Island on the southern Marshalls.

2. Marginal vegetation: The outermost seaward and channel-side zone of most islets forms a scrub zone, chiefly of *Scaevola frutescens* (Plate 59). [This is the Atlantic species of Scaevola, whereas, according to Niering (1956), the Pacific variety should be called *S. sericea*.] The outer zone is mixed on its inner edges with *Cordia subcordata* and *Soulamea amara*. On very narrow islets and spits between islets this may extend the full width of the

islet. In sandy soil *Suriana maritima* may be an important component (Fosberg, 1949, p. 90). There are variations in this outer zone, however. In parts of the Marshalls the Pemphis (Plates 78 and 79) or Suriana at times forms the outermost zone for stretches of the shore. Leaning coconut palms may characterize the beach ridge on many atoll islets. Originally they probably were planted a few meters inward from the shore, but subsequent erosion may bring mature trees to the high-tide line. The inclined angle also may result from overcrowding and competition for sunlight (Plate 71). Under these palms Scaevola and Guettarda often form a two-layered border and understory. The Scaevola grows in front of or under the Guettarda as a narrow and often discontinuous shrub layer 5 to 12 feet high in a band 15 to 30 feet wide. According to Niering (1956, p. 12) on Kapingamarangi the Scaevola tends to increase in importance where erosion is least severe, whereas Guettarda is common in the more severely eroded sectors.

In addition to these plants on the seaward and channel-side margins, several other marginal species are represented. According to their relative importance they include *Pandanus tectorius, Messerschmidia argentea, Cordia subcordata, Terminalia samoensis, Clerodendrum inerme,* and *Barringtonia asiatica* (Niering, 1956, p. 13).

The value of this marginal zone of salt-tolerant shrubs and trees in protecting coconut and breadfruit plantations from salt spray appears to be recognized by the atoll inhabitants, who most often do not clear this strip of 15 to 30 or more feet for coconut plantings (Plate 64).

On leeward reefs, lagoon shores face the wind and have salt-spray problems somewhat less than, but similar to, seaward situations. Here Scaevola and Guettarda may be prominent shelter-belt vegetation on sandy beach ridges and sand dunes, as on Elizabeth Island of Jaluit or on Imejwa or Likiep Atoll. The leafless strangler vine *Cassytha filiformis* may often be seen covering shrubs in such situations (Plate 72) (Wiens, 1956, p. 16).

On windward reefs, the leeward lagoon shores are protected from salt spray. Protective shelter belts formed by marginal shrubs are unnecessary, so that, normally, where plantations are kept in good condition, coconut trees are planted or seed themselves to the lagoon shore ridge, with little understory shrubs but generally with a ground cover of herbs and grasses. Elsewhere, less-rigorous care permits seedlings and even large trees to form a lagoon-margin vegetation. Drift seedlings are common all along the lagoon beach. Niering (1956, p. 14) made detailed observations regarding the frequency and abundance of seedlings on the backshore of seven islets. The list that follows includes the most important species he observed, arranged according to their relative abundance: *Scaevola sericea, Guettarda speciosa, Pandanus tectorius, Messerschmidia argentea, Barringtonia asiatica, Hibis-*

*cus tiliaceus, Morinda citrifolia, Calophyllum inophyllum, Premna obtu-
sifolia,* and *Hernandia sonora.*

Seldom found on seaward shores, but favoring sandy lagoon shore ridges, is the beautiful, glossy, dark-green-leaved *Calophyllum inophyllum,* probably the preferred lagoon-shore shade tree of all islanders. These trees grow to large size, with trunks and branches several feet in diameter, branching low and often tilted lagoonward because of wave erosion of the sand shore in which they have their roots. They often form landmarks locating lagoonside houses, since the residents refrain from cutting this fine shade tree near their dwellings.

Coconut plantations

Coconut trees are more numerous and cover more forest area on coral atolls than any other trees. Among palm forests, however, there are great differences in conditions, depending upon the amount of rainfall, the size and soil of islets, and the manipulation of man in clearing the forest of undercover and ground cover. It has been pointed out that palm forests on the drier atolls are more open and have trees set farther apart. On very recent sands the lack of humus and accompanying nitrogen and other plant foods result in yellowed chlorotic fronds and poor nut production, if any (Wiens, 1956, pp. 3, 19). Very small islets which lack a fresh-water lens or those with a low-lying soil surface may be similar in this regard.

Hatheway (1953, p. 8) noted that the coconut thrives over an extremely wide range of environmental conditions (Plates 70 and 80). On Arno he found that "It was productive over a 1,000-fold range of ground-water salinity and over at least a 50-fold range of concentration of available phosphorus. It was found on all habitats from fresh-water swamps to dry, windswept dunes, on organic mucks, fine- or coarse-textured sands, or among fragments of coral rock. Except on those few areas in which it was not productive, the coconut was utterly worthless as an indicator of environmental differences." In the writer's field notes from the Marshalls (Wiens, 1956) is an example of the palm's adaptiveness: "The amazing ability of coconut trees to gain a footing in the most barren situations is revealed by the five adult palms, plus a small Pandanus and one young coconut tree growing on Nakor Islet [on] a small sand patch 10 feet by 20 feet on top of bare rock washed by salt water at high tide [Plate 81]. Apparently the sand cover of 1 to 2 feet depth plus pockets holding fresh water in the rock after rainfall supplies the moisture needed by the plants." The extremely extensive root system of the coconut palm absorbs much rainwater draining downward through the soil (Plate 80).

Overcrowding of coconut trees may be the result of neglect and self-propagation. In the latter event, even relatively dry islands may develop an almost impenetrable jungle of coconut sprouts (Catala, 1957, p. 22; Wiens, 1956, p. 17). On wet islands this is a very common condition (Wiens, 1956, pp. 5, 6, 11, 17, 20). However, too-dense plantings of palms occur in many places. On Arno Atoll coconut trees average about 95 per acre (Hatheway, 1953, p. 14). On Kapingamarangi the average number of coconut palms per acre in coconut-dominant zones was about 116. The spacing between palm trunks averaged about 21 feet, but many were much closer together, others farther apart. Early German row plantings in the Marshalls at Kili were at the rate of 78 per acre and in the drier zone at Likiep at 69 per acre (Wiens, 1956, p. 34). This compares with British plantings in Malaya of 40 trees to the acre. On the basis of requirements of tree crowns for sunshine, trees planted 30 feet apart at the corners of an equilateral triangle would be considered adequately spaced in wet areas. This would provide 56 trees to the acre. Pieris (1955, p. 29) recommends 55 trees to the acre with trees 28 feet apart when planted in squares. It is obvious that for best results coral-island plantings should be more widely spaced than they normally are. Fosberg (1956, p. 192) comments that the better and more regularly spaced plantings of the Germans in the Marshalls produce nuts uniformly larger than the irregular or helter-skelter plantings done by many Marshallese.

It seems appropriate to interject a note of caution here concerning statistical counts of the number of coconut palms in the various islands of the Pacific and figures on the areas in which they are planted. Most of the figures on atoll land area are derived from extremely crude methods based upon inaccurate maps and/or maps of too small a scale, so that the percentage of error is high. The atoll of Kapingamarangi may serve as an apt illustration. Table 26 gives the figures furnished the writer in 1954 compared with figures derived from his own sample counts and estimates done with Niering (see Wiens, 1956):

TABLE 26

Palm Trees on Kapingamarangi Atoll, 1956

	Existing figures	New estimates
Total area, acres	332.8	276.4
Area in palm forests, acres	320	233.4
Number of bearing palms	44,752	22,174
Number of immature palms	22,213	(few—several thousand)

The marked discrepancy is evident. The existing figures showed a 20 per cent larger land area, 37 per cent larger acreage planted to coconut palms, and 126 per cent larger number of palms-bearing nuts, not to mention a several hundred per cent larger number of immature palms. It is evident that since the existing statistics were utilized by the administrations over the island areas to calculate the needs and population pressure in terms of land and food, a much higher degree of accuracy is demanded than has been accepted if the writer's estimates are close to being correct. The differences in accuracy may be judged from the different bases of calculation. For the existing figures, land area was based upon tracings of the islets on a hydrographic chart with a scale of 1:50,340 derived from a crude Japanese hydrographic chart. On this the largest islet was only $\frac{1}{4}$ inch wide and the islet contours were generalized and rounded off. The shape and dimensions of the atoll reef itself were distorted and out of scale. For the new estimates, a map of each islet on the scale of 1 inch to 100 feet was made from a ground survey on a plane table with a sight alidade, the distances being averaged from the pacings of two persons, with the high-tide line taken as the island border.

The area in palm forest in the existing figures was derived from subtracting a rough and wholly inaccurate estimate of Cyrtosperma pits from the gross land area. The new estimates were made from the ground-survey map and the demarcation of zones of plant dominance were roughly marked by pacing in at intervals at right angles from the shore line.

The estimates of bearing palms and immature palms in the existing figures were based upon the questioning by District Administration officials of landowners as to their so-called "count" of the number of palms on their land. The following census note for the Gilberts and Ellices also is pertinent for other areas, including Kapingamarangi: "Very few native landowners have even an approximate idea of the number of trees on their land, and when the Census Commissioner was briefing the enumerators, grave doubts were expressed as to their ability to get an accurate figure" (Pusinelli, 1947, p. 13).

In the new estimate at Kapingamarangi, representative sample plots were measured by tape and Niering and the writer with the aid of native assistants made actual counts. Average distances between palm trunks were ascertained also. These were checked by counting the palm crowns of a scaled area on aerial photographs of a dense plantation on Mokil Atoll. Observation established the relative scarcity of immature palms on the land. The writer feels, therefore, that the new estimates are likely to have a relatively high degree of accuracy for 1954 and that the existing figures were completely unreliable.

It is realized, of course, that such detailed ground surveys as was done on Kapingamarangi would not be feasible on many atolls. Many atolls still are known only by rough and unreliable nearly century old maps. Aerial photography since World War II has enabled relatively accurate maps to be drawn of many atolls in Micronesia now under the U. S. Trust Territory Ad-

ministration, although most of the land areas are still on a small scale. However, the guesses of native owners of coconut land cannot serve as a reliable
method of estimating the number of trees. It is doubtful that any native
proprietor has actually counted all the palms on his land, and he has little
idea of land areas and dimensions.

Most of the plantations are of trees of more-or-less-uniform height. In
Micronesia the greater part of the plantations were made during the German
period 60 to 75 years ago, and most plantations are 50 to 80 feet tall. On
wetter islands and older plantations, trees may reach a maximum of 90
to 100 feet. In areas where replantings have been done since the destruction
of World War II, relatively low stands of palms may be seen. For the northern Marshalls, Fosberg (1956, p. 193) found few whole plantations where
the trees average less than 50 feet. Catala (1957, p. 22) wrote that in the
Gilberts most of the palms were between 60 and 70 feet tall and that few
were higher. In the Gilberts, where there were reportedly 2,200,000 coconut
palms (Lefort, 1956, p. 9), the most frequent picture is that of palms of all
ages, which resulted from irregular planting and unrestricted self-seeding
in many places. Most plantations in Micronesia are growing rather old and
are badly in need of replacement. Those planted during the Japanese period, however, are in the full-bearing stage. At Kapingamarangi the people
are aware that their palm plantations are 10 years past their productive
prime. Catala equates the life span of the coconut palm with that of man
and states that in the rather mediocre growing conditions of the Gilberts,
a 50 to 60 year old palm is old and its yield is on the decline. Lefort (1956,
p. 7) asserted that not only in Tahiti but also in "the other groups" of French
Oceania, presumably including the atolls, "coconut plantations are too old,
overcrowded, and neglected." In seeming contradiction Garcia-Palacios (1955,
p. 38) wrote that the Tuamotuan plantations are relatively young and are
in full production. On the whole, however, coconut plantations are in need
of rehabilitation and replacement on most Pacific atolls.

The mature coconut plantation leaves ample room under its canopy for
the growth of understory and ground-cover herbs.

Left to itself, a plantation tends to become choked by a tangled mass
of vines and shrubs and, later, by a thicket of tall shrubs and trees laced
and tied together by lianas. Actually, one finds every stage from bare
ground just after burning to the thickets mentioned above; a sparse or
dense turf of grasses and sedges, a blanket up to a yard deep of vinelike
resinous-smelling Wedelia, mixed tangles of the latter with shrubs of various kinds and Ipomoea (morning-glory) vines, and impenetrable growths
of young coconut plants sprouted from fallen nuts (Fosberg, 1956, p. 193).

In the drier atolls, relatively little effort is needed to keep the plantation
clear beneath the trees. On the wetter atolls much more active growth makes

the work of keeping the plantation clear an arduous task. Clearing is done once a year or oftener, depending upon the wetness of climate and the industriousness of the people concerned. Usually a machete must be used for shrubs; herbs and grasses may or may not be pulled up. The burning of dried, cleared debris often results in the harming of coconut and Pandanus trees through burning of their trunks.

Examples of typical understory and ground-cover plants in coconut plantations on wet atolls as represented by Arno are given by Hatheway (1953, p. 8):

Subtype 1. Lagoon shores and dunes:

Undercover: *Pemphis acidula, Scaevola frutescens, Hernandia sonora, Calophyllum inophyllum, Barringtonia asiatica, Suriana maritima, Pandanus tectorius, Sophora tomentosa, Canavalia microcarpa, Ipomoea tuba*

Ground cover: *Lepturus repens, Fimbristylis atollensis, Thuarea involuta, Cassytha filiformis, Triumfetta procumbens, Vigna marina, Tacca leontopetaloides, Polypodium scolopendria, Euphorbia chamissonis, Canavalia sericea*

Subtype 2. Low interiors:

Undercover: *Morinda citrifolia, Pandanus tectorius,* and other trees of the scrub-forest type

Ground cover: The same as subtype 1 except for the absence or insignificance of Canavalia and the addition of *Wedelia biflora, Boerhavia diffusa,* and the two ferns *Asplenium nidus* and Nephrolepis sp.

Fimbristylis and the grasses grow taller in the interior low places, and Pandanus with sprouts of Morinda, Guettarda, and other scrub-forest trees may form jungles in poorly tended groves. Epiphytic mosses and ferns appear on stumps, fallen logs, and rocks. The habitat appears more moist and wind velocity and hence evaporation are much reduced.

Subtype 3. Boulder ramparts and stony land:

Undercover: Scrub-forest trees, with Scaevola most prominent on the ramparts, *Messerschmidia argentea (Tournefortia),* Guettarda, *Terminalia samoensis, Ochrosia oppositifolia, Pemphis acidula, Cordia subcordata, Intsia bijuga, Pisonia grandis,* and *Allophylus timorensis*

Ground cover: The two ferns listed above and weeds and grasses including Wedelia, Polypodium, Fimbristylis, Lepturus, Triumfetta, Vigna, and Thuarea

That different situations may occur elsewhere is revealed by Stone (1959), who stated that on Nomwin in the central Carolines Glochidion sp. forms at least 50 per cent of the shrub ground cover in the palm and breadfruit groves, unlike what has been observed in the Marshalls. *Piper fragile*(?) also was very prevalent as a ground cover there.

Breadfruit distribution and characteristics

The distribution of breadfruit trees (*Artocarpus altilis*) on atoll islands is governed by the factors of climate, ground-water level and salinity, exposure to salt-water spray, soil fertility, and the location of human settlements. The average temperature suitable for breadfruit is over 71°F., so that all coral atolls have adequate temperatures. It does not have to have high rainfall, although in the atoll realm it does best in wet islands. Thus breadfruit is found in such northern Marshalls atolls as Ailuk, Likiep, Utirik, Meijit (Wiens, 1956), and Ujelang (Tobin, 1955), although north of Ailuk (Plate 77) breadfruit groves are not notable features of the vegetation (Fosberg, 1956, p. 195). On dry atolls in the equatorial belt—the southern Gilberts, for instance—the breadfruit trees are sometimes killed by the periodical droughts affecting these regions (Massal and Barrau, 1956, p. 19). Thus in 1951, after 2 years of drought, an estimated 60 per cent of the Artocarpus had died on Abaiang Atoll and on most of the atolls of the southern Gilberts (Catala, 1957, pp. 61–2).

Most varieties of Artocarpus do not tolerate salinity well, whether in the ground water, soil, or in salt spray. Certain varieties are more salt-tolerant than others. In the Gilberts there is a variety called by the natives *Te maitarika* (*Te mai,* breadfruit; *tarika,* brackish water) which is more tolerant to brackish ground water (Catala, 1957). To avoid salinity and spray damage as well as to take advantage of greater soil fertility, breadfruit trees generally are planted lagoonward of the central part of the islands, and their foliage may overshade areas on wet islands all the way to the lagoon shore. In fact, they are most prevalent close to and in village areas, around scattered houses and in residential yards, providing shade for the occupants and facilitating the picking of fruit when needed. Thus the presence of human habitations generally can be spotted on aerial photographs when breadfruit groves are observed. Catala (1957, p. 64) asserted that in the Gilbert Islands these trees are grown only in the village, and the number of trees often can roughly be correlated with the number of inhabitants. In the Carolines and Marshalls, the Cyrtosperma pits and swamps often have breadfruit trees planted on the rubble piled up around the pits from the excavations.

Breadfruit trees in drier atolls such as the Gilberts and the northern Marshalls may grow to heights of 30 to 65 feet, depending upon age, moisture, and soil conditions. Some trees in the Gilberts reach 65 feet, have trunks 6 to 7 feet in circumference 3 feet from the ground, and generally are over 60 years of age. In less-favorable conditions here, breadfruit trees 8 to 10 years of age may be 26 to 33 feet high with trunk diameters 3 feet in circumference at the same distance from the ground (Catala, 1957, p. 64). These are comparable to tree sizes observed by the writer in the dry northern Marshalls. In the wetter atolls, trees grow much larger. One at Namu was estimated to be over 90 feet tall with a trunk diameter of about 5 feet waist high from the ground (a circumference of almost 16 feet). On Nukuoro, Puluwat, and Kapingamarangi, the writer saw even larger and taller trees. One tree at Kapingamarangi had a trunk diameter of 77 inches measured 3 feet from the ground and an estimated height of 115 feet (Niering, 1956, p. 15). Characteristic of breadfruit are large flaring buttress roots above ground surface.

Few figures are available for sample tree counts per unit area on atoll land. It is believed useful, therefore, to present in Table 27 the representative sample counts made by Niering and the writer on Kapingamarangi (Wiens, 1956, p. 30), although it is realized that breadfruit density varies not only from atoll to atoll but also according to the needs and desires of the inhabitants. The Pandanus association also depends to a large extent upon the needs or clearing activities of the land proprietors.

TABLE 27

Breadfruit, Coconut, Pandanus Association

Plot no.	Breadfruit	Bearing coconut	Immature coconut	Mature Pandanus	Young Pandanus
		Mixed breadfruit-coconut zone			
		(10,812-sq.-ft. plots)			
1	5	16	2	25	14
2	5	11		18	8
3	4	8		8	
		Breadfruit-dominant zone			
		(10,816-sq.-ft. plots)			
1	11	1		125	27
2	13	13	6	130	54

Translated on a per acre basis, the figures are as given in Table 28:

TABLE 28

Number of Breadfruit, Coconut, Pandanus per Acre

Zone	No. of palms (bearing and immature)		No. of breadfruit	No. of Pandanus (old and young)	
Breadfruit-coconut	47.15	6	18.9	63	28
Breadfruit-dominant	28.2	12	50.37	530	180

Under the pure breadfruit stands, the canopy of foliage is often so dense and complete that little light gets through and few forest plants can survive. According to Fosberg (1953, pp. 13–14), seedlings of *Morinda citrifolia* occasionally maintain themselves where conditions are not too extreme, and in the Carolines an as-yet-undetermined species of Piper may form a mat on the ground. Several ferns also occur occasionally in such situations. Seedlings of the seeded breadfruit may be abundant where the light is not too scanty. In openings between breadfruit crowns, occasional coconut palms or Pandanus may grow.

In the more-open breadfruit-coconut association, a great variety of mixed forest plants may occur. At Arno, what Hatheway (1953, p. 18) designated as a breadfruit type of forest has some 15 to 30 breadfruit trees intermixed with from 10 to 15 coconut trees per acre. Other secondary trees are Pandanus, Premna, Allophylus, Pipturus, Guettarda, and Morinda. A ground layer in such areas includes *Wedelia biflora, Tacca leotopetaloides, Lepturus repens, Thuarea involuta, Fleurya ruderalis, Fibristylis atollensis, Polypodium scolopendria, Asplenium nidus,* Nephrolepis sp., *Stenotaphrum subulatum, Vigna marina, Centella asiatica, Ipomoea tuba, Ipomoea littoralis,* Oplismenus sp., *Triumfetta procumbens, Hedyotis biflora, Alocasia macrorrhiza,* and *Crinum asiaticum.*

At Ine Island on Arno, Hatheway found that breadfruit trees grew in widely scattered fashion, 50 to 70 feet tall, with spreading crowns 25 to 75 feet in diameter. Coconuts were common but occupied only a small part of the canopy. Sprouts of Allophylus, Premna, Guettarda, and Morinda were usually abundant along with small breadfruit seedlings. Openings here as at Kapingamarangi permitted rank growths of Wedelia, often interlaced by the purple-flowered morning glory, *Ipomoea littoralis.* In more completely shaded places the grasses Oplismenus, Thuarea, or Stenotaphrum covered the ground. "In fact, the nearly complete ground cover in both breadfruit and coconut types—except where the latter occurred on stony land near the ocean— was characteristic of these artificial forests not shared by types in which wild native trees were predominant" (Hatheway, 1953).

Cyrtosperma and taro plantations

The requirements of the giant taro Cyrtosperma for periodic fresh-water inundation of its root area has made it necessary for atoll inhabitants growing this plant to dig through the hard substratum of atoll land to reach the level of the ground water. This has always been an arduous task, and the large pits developed in some areas represent enormous amounts of work, mostly done with very primitive digging tools. Pits vary in size from a mere hole of a few feet in diameter to areas several acres in extent as on Mokil, Nukuoro, and Kapingamarangi. A muck soil eventually develops, the upper 6 inches of which consist of a fibrous network of roots with an algal covering over the surface layer (Niering, 1956, pp. 11–12). On the taro pits of Onotoa the blue-green algae Phacus and Rhizoclonium were common (Moul, 1957, p. 5). Since the soil is usually saturated, narrow elevated earth paths traverse the pits. Methods of cultivation differ from region to region. At Kapingamarangi Cyrtosperma is planted 8 to 12 inches apart and it varies in height with stage of maturity from 2 to 6 feet or over. In more-shaded situations the plants are taller and more vigorous. Those in the center of the larger patches are frequently smaller and the leaves are yellowish brown, which may be caused by the intense insolation. Intermediate light intensity appears to be most favorable, which may account in part for the planting of breadfruit trees on the banks of the pits. Niering found banana (Musa sp.) and ornamental Hibiscus scattered throughout the patches.

In the Gilberts the cultivation system is unique and can be described as growing the plants in floating pots of fiber (Catala, 1957, pp. 69–70). When a Cyrtosperma shoot is first planted, a mixture of humus gathered from under certain trees in the bush and selected leaves are spread around the plant. As it grows, a basket of pandanus leaves and stakes keeps this debris in place and supports the plant. As more humus is added, the increasing weight anchors the whole basket more firmly to the bottom. According to Catala, the plant would die if the roots grew down into the deep mud instead of spreading within the supporting mass, because it will grow only "because it is rooted in an artificial and aerated medium." Unless this is a special strain of Cyrtosperma, it is doubtful that the last statement is correct, since the plant grows in muck successfully elsewhere without this practice. Catala also asserted, perhaps more correctly, that "contrary to the views of some authors, the water of babai pits is not brackish. Indeed, it is often fresher than that of wells used for drinking or cooking. During prolonged droughts, if water becomes brackish the babai plants are said to wilt rapidly. Brackish water is definitely noxious whatever the age of a plant. Long immersion due to rain water may be fatal, too, but only to young plants."

Weeds found most troublesome in Cyrtosperma pits at Kapingamarangi (Niering, 1956) "were *Jussiaea suffruticosa,* which grows 2 to 3 feet in height. Other herbs occasionally found include *Angelonia angustifolia, Lindernia antipoda, Ipomoea littoralis, Cyperus brevifolius, Hedychium coronarium,* and *Fimbristylis miliacea.* Along the paths one finds *Alternanthera sessilis, Digitaria microbachne,* and *Paspalum vaginatum* . . . Weeding of the above species, especially Jussiaea, is one of the major jobs." At Onotoa common flowering plants found in the taro pits were *Eleocharis geniculata* and *Cyperus laevigatus* (Moul, 1957, p. 5).

In abandoned pits which had become fresh-water swamps the predomi-

nant tree at Arno was the wild variety of *Pandanus tectorius*. Its prop
roots (Plate 73) are well adapted to such situations in contrast to the coconut palm, which finds somewhat unsure footing here, although growing
also where debris has filled the pits to make the peat and muck drier. Pandanus in such situations were found to be about 35 feet tall. In one swamp
described by Hatheway (1953, pp. 44–5) dense stands of Pandanus in dark
mucks contained as many as 250 trees per acre. In the more-open stands of
about half this density the soil was a fibrous peat which smelled strongly
of hydrogen sulfide. Other secondary species included Hibiscus, Intsia,
Morinda, and Allophylus. The ground-layer plants were Eleocharis sp.,
Dryopteris goggilodus, and *Polypodium scolopendria.* Nephrolepis and
Asplenium also were prevalent in abandoned taro pits. On Washington Island the first invader into the peat bog there was reported to be Cyrtosperma, which mixed in the drier places with Polypodium but also formed
pure stands (Christophersen, 1931, p. 50). However, it is more likely that
the Cyrtosperma was a survivor or descendant of earlier plantings rather
than an invader.

Mixed secondary forests and scrub forests

Many areas on atolls are not significantly productive of the major food
plants. Such areas may either be in secondary forests or in scrub forests.
Scrub forests are generally found on smaller islets in drier zones, on stony
ramparts and interior areas of larger islands, or on sterile sands. Scrub and
weeds may take over an area that has suffered war destruction. Secondary
forests grow either under a dominant coconut-palm forest or a breadfruit-
coconut forest. Where food trees have been neglected or areas abandoned
because of food-tree failures or for other reasons, a mixed forest of secondary trees may take over. Abandonment of certain interior areas of large
islands occurred at Arno, apparently owing to a decline in the population
or to certain incidents of native political succession. In some interior areas
coconut plantings apparently failed after a few productive years from some
malady or deficiency. In such areas a secondary forest of small trees in 1952
had taken hold in which *Allophylus timorensis* was the most abundant.
With it and at times predominant were Guettarda, Ochrosia, Premna, and
Pandanus, forming a closed canopy 25 to 35 feet high, scattered among
which were breadfruit trees and coconut palms 10 to 15 feet taller. In the
scrub layer *Randia cochinchinensis* was common. In the ground cover Tacca,
Crinum, and *Allophylus* seedlings were conspicuous (Hatheway, 1953, pp.
47–52).

Hatheway (1953, p. 23) thought that a hundred years ago, before the
development of the copra trade and the planting of large coconut planta-

tions, only about 15 per cent of the land of Arno Atoll was appropriated for agriculture. A similar picture perhaps prevailed on most atolls when an almost entirely self-sufficient economy was the rule, since there was no purpose in covering the islands with coconut palms, and many breadfruit trees—which are seasonal in production—also were not needed.

Hatheway found no evidence on Arno that the indigenous plants were distributed in such a fashion as to suggest that any of the species might be mutually dependent and thus lead to the formation of integrated plant communities the composition and appearance of which were relatively uniform from place to place.

In describing the mixed forest, Fosberg (1956, p. 199) stated that one of the most outstanding features is its diversity. No two stands are exactly alike, the species occurring in varying proportion.

Briefly, the mixed forest may be characterized as an evergreen or partially dry-season-deciduous, broad-leaved, medium-leaf-sized forest of low to medium stature, dense to broken canopy, open to densely tangled beneath, and of characteristically mixed and variable composition . . . It is the most widely distributed and commonly encountered indigenous forest type in the region [northern Marshalls] and covers the greatest area, next to that of the coconut groves, of any vegetation type found there . . . It is also, apparently, the type that most commonly develops on cleared or denuded areas if these are given time to become covered again by forest. It is, further, the type that is approximated when a coconut plantation is allowed to grow up to forest, without any clearing out of undergrowth for a long period of time.

Such forests appear to be especially prevalent in the drier atolls and in the more sparsely populated wet atolls. Garcia-Palacios (1955, p. 38) asserted that several atolls in the Tuamotus that might "easily accommodate new plantations" have not yet been planted to coconut palms. If these are indeed mesophytic atolls suitable for plantations, a field study of these atolls would provide a good idea of the "natural forest" of the coral atoll and should provide a check for speculative reconstructions of the original forest in presently heavily planted islands, as well as of mesophytic forest ecology little manipulated by man.

Hatheway (1953, p. 25) stated that the forest and scrub as it existed at Arno in 1952 was commonly characterized by the presence of small stands consisting of a single species of tree, and, hence, that it would seem unrealistic to attempt to distinguish within the broad scrub-forest-type plant communities based on floristic composition. Fosberg (1956) also wrote that it should be borne in mind that as one or another species assumes dominance locally, the characteristics of the mixed forest vary in the direction of those of pure stands locally. These include Messerschmidia, Cordia, Pisonia, Ochrosia, Pemphis, Pandanus, and Bruguiera. The characteristics of these stands are discussed here largely from Fosberg's descriptions except as other-wise noted. In the northern Marshalls Fosberg (1956, p. 191) found that pure stands of Barringtonia and Pandanus were of limited extent. The writer observed only one pure stand of Barringtonia on brief visits to about 20 atolls and reef islands in Micronesia, and this occurred on Airik Island at Maloelap (Wiens, 1956, p. 18). The most extensive pure stand of Pandanus was observed by the writer on Elizabeth Island of Jaluit. More limited pure stands were seen on Ailinglaplap and on Kapingamarangi. Catala (1957, Plate X) has presented a picture of a pure Pandanus stand in the Gilberts. Before the copra trade began when Pandanus was an important food on many Pacific atolls, pure stands of the tree probably were numerous (Catala, 1957, pp. 49–50).

Mangrove swamps and depressions

The characteristics of mangrove peats and mucks have been described in the chapter on atoll soils. Fosberg and Hatheway both distinguished be-tween vegetation character of mangrove in relatively firm-bottomed de-pressions and mangrove in interior saline swamps. Fosberg (1953, p. 17) wrote that "mangrove of a number of kinds may be found in shallow lagoon margins, in tidal ponds or swamps with outlets, and in depressions with no outlets. In open lagoons Sonneratia or Rhizophora are found, rarely *Bruguiera conjugata*. The latter is much more common in the depressions (Plate 82), either mud-bottomed or rock-bottomed, where it may be ac-companied by Lumnitzera, Intsia, or Pemphis. The latter two are usually found on rock bottoms. In the ponds with outlets Rhizophora is commonest. In the Marshalls, where the depressions without outlets are commonest, there is some evidence that Bruguiera may have been deliberately placed there by man. This is certainly true in some cases. . . . The fruits were used in making a dye."

Hatheway (1953, pp. 38–44) described several mangrove stands on Arno. In several cases shallow embayments or tidal flats opened on the lagoon. In one instance drifting sand had closed off such an embayment. In these places the mangrove trees formed merely a bordering ring around the interior flat, which at high tide was shallowly flooded with salt water.

Scattered, mostly prostrate trees of *Sonneratia caseolaris* . . . bordered the central flats of sand or mud; their erect, conical pneumatophores ex-tended 20 feet or more beyond the main boles of the trees toward the cen-ter of the embayment. Behind the Sonneratia trees and tending to fill the gaps between them occurred the more erect *Bruguiera conjugata*, perched upon which were aerial baskets of Nephrolepis and Asplenium . . . Form-ing a zone around the Bruguiera were thickets of *Pemphis acidula*, the sprawling main trunks of which sent up erect branches 15 to 20 feet in height and over 6 inches in diameter. Behind the Pemphis occurred trees of the scrub forest (especially Intsia and Allophylus), impenetrable thickets of *Clerodendrum Inerme,* or coconut plantations.

Mangrove swamps of the interiors of islands were strikingly different in appearance. Instead of a mere ring of trees bordering a barren embayment or flat, a complete cover of trees occupied the inland swamps. Most of these stands contained only a single species of tree, *Bruguiera conjugata.*

On Onotoa Atoll at the north end of North Island was a large fish pond which ended in extensive sand flats, partially flooded at high tide. "The greatest concentration of mangrove, *Rhizophora mucronata,* bordered the fish ponds and grew on the part of the sand flats flooded by the tides" (Moul, 1957, p. 5).

On Ailinglaplap Atoll in 1956 the writer (Wiens, 1956, p. 3) observed a tidal inlet near Airik in which three types of mangrove were found, Sonneratia, Bruguiera, and Rhizophora, including a very large patch of Rhizophora (Plate 83). Catala (1957, p. 80) also mentions that in the Gilberts Rhizophora may often cover large areas which are submerged at high tide. A Bruguiera depression, swampy in spots, occurs on Bikajla Islet of Ailinglaplap and was described by the writer as follows (Wiens, 1956):

Bikajla Islet across from Buoj shows an extraordinary development of coral boulders lying loosely, and apparently permeable to salt water for about 250 feet inland from the oceanside. In the outer parts dense growths of *Morinda citrifolia* and Guettarda lie in almost rainforest gloom, with liana-like vines of a Wedelia-type weed [it was Wedelia] falling from their crowns and hanging leafless in the perpetual shadows. Farther inland *Bruguiera conjugata* provides dense shade, intermingled with some Pandanus, its gnarled, humped-up roots covered with a hairy green coat of algae or lichen. The land forms a low trough here. *Asplenium nidus* and *Nephrolepis acuta* grow on the trunks and old stumps of coconut and other trees. Throughout the seaward 200 feet or so Pandanus jungle predominates. Few coconut trees occur until, toward the interior, a rise on the lagoonside of the trough and fresh-water holding soil have allowed a dense growth of young coconut sprouts among older trees.

The fact that Pandanus was observed here to be intermingled with Bruguiera appears to indicate that either Bruguiera likes fresh ground water or that Pandanus tolerates some measure of salinity in ground water. Possibly there is a degree of truth in both. Hatheway (1953, pp. 42–4) found Bruguiera in a fresh-water swamp in which the chloride concentration was 15 ppm. or less than 0.1 per cent that of local sea water, and a Bruguiera-Lumnitzera swamp was found to have 640 ppm., about 3 per cent of that of the local sea water. He concluded that the common impression that mangrove swamps are invariably saline or brackish is not correct. It is obvious that Bruguiera is capable of tolerating a wide range of salinity, and it should never be assumed that the presence of Bruguiera is a positive indication of high ground-water salinity.

Mangrove may not occur on all atolls, but it is a very common feature of atoll vegetation, although usually it is found in small stands. Bomb craters from World War II (Plate 84) undoubtedly have added numerous small depressions on Micronesian atolls that form saline, brackish, or freshwater swamps, some of which are suitable habitats for mangrove.

Messerschmidia (Tournefortia) forest and scrub

This tree commonly forms narrow belts just inshore of the seaward Scaevola fringe of islets and is found on almost all atolls. Less often it may form pure stands. Except on rather dry islands, it does not form important pure stands in inland areas. However, on the atoll of Taongi in the most northern Marshalls, it covers most of the land area (Fosberg, 1956, p. 199), but mainly as a scrub 10 to 20 feet high, and it varies from a closed forest, through which a machete is needed to cut a trail, to widely scattered trees with grass or bare rock between. The writer also visited a reef island in the middle Carolines, Gaferut, on which it formed the entire forest except for two scrubby coconut trees. Here the trees grew 30 to 40 feet high and had trunks over a foot in diameter. On dry Christmas Atoll, Christophersen (1931, p. 14) said, "Considering the coconut groves as artificially planted, there is only one natural forest association, namely, the *Sida fallax–Tournefortia argentea* forest." Bryan (1903) found this tree at heights up to 35 feet forming an "impenetrable jungle" on Marcus Island. On Jemo Island Fosberg found the trees reaching as high as 60 feet with trunks several feet in diameter. Similar large trees were seen by the writer on the shore fringes of Kapingamarangi islets but not in pure stands. In the taller pure stands the ground cover may include tangles of *Ipomoea tuba,* and such plants as *Portulaca lutea,* Boerhavia, and Lepturus (Fosberg, 1956; Christophersen, 1931, p. 44).

Cordia forest and scrub

Another forest or scrub type that occurs in pure stands locally is Cordia, found mainly in drier atolls such as the northern Marshalls or the Phoenix group. The trees are usually low, but they attain enormous spread and trunk diameter. The lower limbs often drag on the ground, where they form twisted impenetrable masses, inhibiting the growth of ground cover. A vivid description of this forest type on Canton Atoll is given by Hatheway (1955, p. 3):

The two groves of vigorous trees consist of pure stands of Cordia averaging about 19 feet in height; the tallest tree observed was 24 feet tall. Both forests are in reality nearly impenetrable thickets. Since Cordia on

Canton Island reproduces chiefly by ground layering, the numerous shoots arising from recumbent branches make walking through the groove in a straight line impossible . . . Light reaching the ground level in Cordia forest is rather diffuse; intensities . . . were only 5 to 10 per cent of those obtained outside. The ground is littered with dead branches, fruits, and a few leaves. Reproduction from seed within the grove is practically non-existent. . . .

Pisonia forest

This most widely distributed type of atoll forest at one time may have covered the greatest area of any pure tree stands, and it is still found in small patches on all the northern Marshalls and probably on most other atolls. Fosberg (1956, p. 200) wrote that it occupied not only many small islets, but also the richest land of the interior and is the most easily cleared for plantations. Although growing to immense size, the wood is so soft that a single blow of a machete will cut off a large branch. The stems of these trees have the ability to take root when they touch the ground, so that a blown-over tree not only continues to grow but generates roots at many new points. However, they may die when they fall, without generating new plants.

On the wetter atolls the Pisonia may grow to over 100 feet tall, and a pure stand forms a canopy so complete and thick that the interior is densely shaded. During very dry seasons on drier atolls, however, the Pisonia may lose most of its leaves. "The trunks are a dull cream color with smooth surface, but twisted and variously compound, and reaching elephantine proportions. This pale, grotesque form and almost glowing surface give, in the twilight of these dense forests, an eerie, ghostlike appearance" (Fosberg, 1956). Concerning this tree, Hatheway (1955, p. 61) wrote that "Like many of the native trees of the southern Marshalls, *Pisonia grandis* tends to occur in groves—that is, in pure stands less than 10 acres in size. Present local deposits of phosphatic rock may well coincide with former Pisonia groves." In the Hall Islands Stone (1949) found that while there were pure stands of Pisonia, another tree not found in the Marshalls is a codominant in Pisonia groves.

According to Shaw (1952), *Pisonia grandis* is a species apparently almost entirely confined, in the wild state, to small, often uninhabited islands from the Indian Ocean through the tropical Pacific as far east as the Marquesas, Mangareva, and Pitcairn. He felt that the widespread distribution and the prevalence of these trees, especially on uninhabited islands, must depend upon some unusual and peculiar factors. It is well known, of course, that the Pisonia seeds are sticky and are readily carried by birds from one island to another.

In the chapter on soils, Fosberg's thesis was presented concerning the apparently required presence of Pisonia peat or humus for the formation of phosphate rock. Hatheway (1955) pointed out that the sea birds appeared to "prefer" the branches of the Pisonia to those of any other trees and that the droppings of these myriads of birds would eventually result in the formation of phosphatic rock. Shaw, on the other hand, suggested that *Pisonia grandis* in its turn requires, at least for its germination and early development, an abundant supply of bird guano associated with coral or other limestone as the basic rock. He made note of Christophersen's observation that the root system of the Pisonia is very shallow and has a great horizontal development. Moreover, this is largely confined to the shallow layer of acid phosphatic soil, a remarkable feature of a calcareous base such as coral rock and soil.

However, there is no study indicating that Pisonia takes root more readily in guano areas than in other areas of coral sand or soil. Fosberg (1954, p. 107) said that "Where no humus has accumulated, the guano falling on the limesand or gravel would not become soluble, as neither its own reaction of pH 6 nor that of rain water is sufficiently acid to dissolve it, and the environment is alkaline." Thus, an acid soil does not come into being until the Pisonia becomes mature and creates the acidity with its deposit of dead leaves and branches and its own root system. It would appear to follow that seedlings of Pisonia do not require guano to germinate and to take root on atoll soils. Niering reported scattered Pisonia as a secondary-forest associate of other trees in coconut plantations and also as planted trees on Touhou, an islet entirely devoted to village residences for half a century. Hatheway thought that two islets that have been reforming after the destruction of their land and soil in the typhoons of 1905 and 1918 would be suitable habitats for *Pisonia grandis*. These islets obviously have very young calcareous and relatively sterile soils. It is likely, of course, that Pisonia, as most other atoll trees, do best in fertile moist soils, so bird droppings no doubt stimulate its growth. Also, since it creates acid soil conditions around its roots, it must do best in an acid soil; but the tree would not appear to be dependent upon the birds for the germination of its seeds and early stages of seedling growth.

On Palmyra, Rock (1916, p. 49) found that Eastern Islet and Papala Islet consisted mainly of Pisonia under which the ground cover was the fern *Polypodium phymatodes*.

Where population pressure has been heavy on atoll food sources, Pisonia, except on small islands here and there, has been cleared for coconut plantation or for other more useful trees. Speaking of the Gilberts, Catala (1957, p. 103) said that the tree was not over 10 meters tall and that "Like many other species with useful wood, this tree must have been much more common formerly, it has been much cut because of its soft wood and replaced with the coconut palm . . . The soft wood is useful only to make outrigger floats." On Onotoa two long narrow groves of these trees were found on a ridge of indurated phosphatized soil (Moul, 1957, p. 13).

Niering (1956, p. 29) noted about the vegetation on Kapingamarangi that "There is little evidence of a continuous aspect comparable to the present coconut and breadfruit except on Pumatahati [islet]. Here, as formerly mentioned, a large Pisonia forest dominated until around 1920 when it was cut in order to expand the coconut plantations. Today all that remain are their stump sprouts. The presence of a similar understory occurring locally on other islets would suggest the former importance of Pisonia."

In 1953 Hatheway reported that *Pisonia grandis* was considered a major pest and had been eradicated as an important species from all islands of Arno Atoll except six, although on a seventh, lone Pisonia trees were found. Only a few trees, undoubtedly of seedling origin, were found, although sprouts and suckers were abundant. "Once established, however, the tree seemed to be almost immortal. The virtual indestructibility of the older trees—fire is the only effective means of clearing Pisonia forest—combined with their great powers of vegetative reproduction seem to be sufficient to account for the former predominance of Pisonia on parts of Takleb and Namwi. It is possible that these trees were members of clones resulting from the chance long-distance dispersal and establishment of single seeds."

Undamaged Pisonia woods in the northern Marshalls on such atolls as Rongelap, Rongerik, Bikini, and Eniwetok are seldom met with except on smaller, less accessible, and, usually, western reef islets (Taylor, 1950, p. 178).

Ochrosia forest

A tall slender umbrella-like tree and another pure-stand forest tree, the Ochrosia formerly was probably present only in the mesophytic and wetter atolls; at least it does not occur in pure stands in the drier atolls of the northern Marshalls. *Ochrosia oppositifolia* makes a shade so deep that only its seedlings appear able to grow under its canopy, which varies from 50 to 70 feet high. In places exposed to strong wind it may be lower. In the stands observed, the trees were of uniform height with trunks seldom over a foot in diameter. Fosberg (1956, p. 202) described this tree as follows:

The leaves are large, commonly 8 or 10 inches long, glossy, and dark green. When broken, the branches and leaves exude quantities of a sticky white sap. The flowers are small, white, very fragrant, and borne in clusters. They are followed by pairs of large fruits the size of an egg, covered by a thin flesh, yellow when ripe. This soon rots off after they fall, leaving a surface covered by numerous stiff bristles. The ground under this type of forest is characteristically covered by a layer of these fruits, and by a solid growth of seedlings from a few inches to a couple of feet in height.

Hatheway noted, however, that although Ochrosia seedlings and saplings were conspicuously vigorous when growing in heavy shade, a high proportion of the large fruits of this species failed to germinate among the stones and cobbles of the forest floor. Its occurrence in small stands rather than more intermixed with other trees would appear to be not only because of the tolerance for its own dense shade, but also because its seeds are too large to be carried far from the parent tree except by storm waves sweeping over the land, or by man's transport.

The best areas of Ochrosia dominance observed by Fosberg (1953, p. 7) were on Wotho, but he also found it common on Lae, Ujae, Kwajelein, and Erikub.

Niering did not mention Ochrosia as a significant tree at Kapingamarangi. It was observed on only two of the 33 islets. Although the tree occurs in the Gilberts and Ellices, Catala has not included the tree in his list of Gilbertese plants, so it apparently is not important here either. Rock (1916, p. 20) said that Ochrosia is widely distributed over the islands of the south Pacific, but on Palmyra it occurred only on one islet, growing to heights of 50 feet with trunk diameters of 2 feet and forming a dense forest in company with huge *Pisonia grandis*. Taylor (1950, p. 193) found it uncommon on Rongelap, Bikini, and Eniwetock, but when found it usually formed small groves in the heavily wooded central parts of the larger islands. This relative scarcity seems strange if, as Fosberg asserted, "There seems little question that, at least under conditions of moderate rainfall, such as in the central Marshalls, *Ochrosia oppositifolia* may eventually dominate mixed forest once it gets started, and often will take over completely, forming extensive pure stands . . . There is good evidence that it will eventually crowd out even Pisonia. Pure stands of Ochrosia are relatively permanent and stable. . . ." The explanation must be either that man has cleared the land of the tree or that some disease or soil deficiency eventually results in other trees taking over. Fosberg mentioned noticing small areas in Ochrosia stands suffering from some type of malady resulting in yellowing apparently leading to eventual death.

Barringtonia forest

Barringtonia tree occurs rarely as a pure stand. Fosberg (1953, p. 16) observed only one area of this type, on Lae in the Marshalls, but said that it is such a striking type that it is worth looking for elsewhere. The writer, too, has seen only one such stand, in an area about 150 feet in diameter on Maloelap near the village on Airik Islet. Although the Maloelap stand in 1956 was relatively young, with trunks about 1 or 2 feet in diameter at most, the Lae stand was described as composed of trees "of enormous diameter, massive, 20 to 25 m. tall, canopy complete and dense, nothing on the ground except a colony of Peperomia. The ground in this forest had been covered subsequent to the trees reaching a large size, by a deposit of large boulders to a depth of up to a meter." The Maloelap stand also had a dense, closed canopy with little if anything growing beneath.

Pemphis forest and shrub

Pemphis acidula (Plate 24) is a plant with a marvelous ability to thrive on bare rock and even on rock covered by salt water at high tide (Fosberg, 1953, p. 16). It occurs where no other plant save algae appears able to grow, so tolerant is it of salinity and of drought. Trunks rarely reach a foot thick, and most generally are only a few inches in diameter; the height seldom exceeds 18 to 20 feet (Plates 58 and 78). However, in the dry northern Marshalls they form the thickest of all forest types. Because the wood is so hard, even when the lower brushlike branches die from overshading, they form an intermeshed tangle that usually is much easier to walk around than through. Its peculiar habitat marks it as a sharply distinctive type, and its dull, bluish-green color makes it resemble a conifer, so that it is easily identified from a distance. The writer has often seen it forming a narrow but dense band of forest between mangrove stands and coconut or Pandanus plantations (see also Moul, 1957, p. 18). It may compete with Scaevola for space. It also grows on bare rocky areas of reefs briefly covered by salt water at high tide and on small rock pedestals that may always be surrounded by salt water. In such situations, however, it generally is a scrub. At Jaluit, 3 months after a typhoon in 1958 had stripped all vegetation from some areas and where Pemphis trees had all their leaves and most of their bark stripped off or loosened from the trunks, the writer saw 2-to-3-inch diameter Pemphis growing on bare rock sprouting new leaves and budding new branches from these trunks and their larger limbs.

Suriana maritima scrub

In some sandy depressions behind the beach crest or on elevated ridges on sand flats above the reach of high tide at dry Christmas Atoll, Christophersen (1927, p. 18) found that Suriana forms pure stands, often very dense thickets about 7 feet high. It appeared on a fine yellowish-white sand with very little organic matter.

Heliotropium anomalum dwarf scrub

Christophersen (1927, pp. 18–26) found Heliotropium to be the only dwarf-scrub association on Washington, thriving in the driest and most exposed localities on the coral flats and sand dunes. It was extensively distributed in low areas along the coast between the Suriana and the interior. In many places it occurred in pure stands but in other areas it is associated with Sida, Suriana, *Kadua romanzoffiensis,* and/or such herbs as Lepturus, Boerhaavia, and Portulaca.

Sida scrub

On dry atolls such as Taongi, Christmas, and Canton, a thin scrubby cover of *Sida fallax* may cover extensive areas (Fosberg, 1953, p. 17). It is a sun-loving shrub, growing preferably in good sandy soil in association with any plants that do not subject it to shade. Occasional thick tangles of Sida on Canton provide nesting sites under them for the red-tailed tropic bird (Degener and Gillaspy, 1955, pp. 32, 49). Small areas in openings of scrub forest on dry small islets of other atolls may be covered with this plant. It is usually 2 or 3 feet tall, although where well developed it may grow to 6 feet. Generally, it does not grow so densely as to interfere seriously with walking (Fosberg, 1956, p. 206). Sida is often found together with such ground covers as Lepturus, Portulaca, and Boerhavia as on Christmas Island (Christophersen, 1927, pp. 14–18) and Canton (Hatheway, 1955, p. 6). Similar associations occur in the Tuamotus, but little is known of them. Niering does not include Sida in his list of Kapingamarangi plants, but Catala (1957, p. 107) found it very common all over the mesophytic Gilberts, especially on open or burned areas, where it may get very dense and tall. Here the people use the leaves of the shrub in fertilizing taro plants. In some irregular clearings of North Island, Onotoa, the ground cover consisted of clumps of *Sida fallax, Lepturus, Portulaca,* and *Euphorbia chamissonis.* In many places these patches were of one species only. The bare areas of white sand between them had a broken crust of blue-green algae (Scytonema spp.) with mosses growing on it (Moul, 1957, p. 3). It is interesting to note that on the apparently very dry Chesterfield Islands west of New Caledonia, with only 20 species of plants, *Sida fallax* does not occur (Cohic, 1959), but in the north Pacific it is commonly found on the dry atolls all the way up to and including Wake. Probably it does not do well on wet atolls simply because it cannot tolerate the shade of other plants that may crowd it out, for it is not mentioned by Hatheway for Arno, by Gressitt for Ngaruangl and Kayangel (1952), or by Anderson (1949) for numerous atolls in the Carolines on which he collected plants.

Herbaceous stands

Various herbaceous plants and grasses which occur both in wet and dry atolls may form dominant or pure stands locally. Fosberg (1956) found the largest areas of Lepturus grassland on arid Taongi, where it forms a bunch grass, at times so thick that it may form a rough cover, or at other times widely separated, with open ground between clumps. On such northern Marshalls atolls as Meijit and Likiep (Wiens, 1956) the writer saw extensive stands of this grass parasitized by mats of *Cassytha filiformis,* as mentioned by Fosberg. Most such stands appear on sandy ground. Sand bars and other bare sandy areas may have pure 6 to 8 inch stands of *Portulaca lutea,* a small extremely fleshy plant having bright yellow flowers. Fosberg noted that on Christmas Atoll Christophersen (1927, p. 20) had seen pure stands of Boerhavia which appeared to have grown over and killed the other plants. "On highly saline flats, usually near the lagoon, at practically high-tide level, the vegetation is of scattered mats of *Sesuvium portulacastrum.* This vegetation has been noted on Wake Island, Canton Island, and Christmas Island, and probably occurs more widely, at least in the dry Pacific Equatorial and Phoenix groups" (Fosberg, 1953, p. 18). Moul (1957, p. 13) reported that on coral gravel at places on Onotoa it forms dense stands and that it occurred on all the islands there. Christophersen (1927, p. 33) also reported patches of both Boerhavia and Sesuvium forming dense carpets on arid Jarvis Atoll.

During World War II large areas on various atolls in the Marshalls, Carolines, and Gilberts and probably some of the Melanesian groups were denuded of their vegetation, whether through bombing, shelling and land fighting, or through clearing for use as airfields and other military installations. Where not replanted to coconut palm and other trees and kept weeded, such areas often have become overrun by aggressive weeds and grasses. Large areas of the several islets north of Kwajelein air base in 1956 were seen by the writer to be covered with *Wedelia biflora* and *Vigna marina,* which smothered other growth. *Ipomoea pes-caprae* also formed a creeper mat over parts of southern Ebeje Islet. These herbs also were observed to occupy a similar role in the narrow land strips north and south of Jabwor on Jaluit Atoll, where the abandoned blasted gun emplacements of the Japanese were completely mantled with these weeds. On Lae Atoll Fosberg (1953, p. 19) saw a patch of Wedelia occupying an open meadowlike place of unknown origin in the forest, which had dominated the open place relatively unchanged for 8 years. In flying over Maloelap in 1956 the writer observed large areas more-or-less completely covered by these weeds, including concrete bunkers and the concrete shells of former buildings.

Fosberg (1953, p. 19) reports:

On abandoned compacted coral air strips, *Fimbristylis cymosa* (or *atollensis*) may get started as a pure stand and persist for some time, as on Bikej Islet, Kwajelein.

In 1945 an attempt was made to revegetate Kwajelein Islet and some others that were being used as active military establishments, by planting *Cynodon dactylon.* This has persisted in some places, but soon became invaded by other species, especially *Paspalum vaginatum,* a similar sod-forming grass. The latter is now the commonest grass on Kwajelein Islet. Heavy traffic tends to discourage such plants as Wedelia and to favor such temporary weeds as the obnoxious *Cenchrus echinatus* [sandburs], *Eragrostis amabilis, Eleusine indica,* and several species of Euphorbia. The weedy vegetation around such establishments is complicated by the great influx of new weeds brought in accidentally. *Pluchea odorata* and *P. indica* have become very abundant around most military bases, and for a while there seemed a probability that they would dominate the vegetation. However, where left reasonably undisturbed, Wedelia seems very able to smother them out.

Algal crust on coral sand

Fosberg (1956, p. 210) discusses a mixed group of microscopic blue-green algae which must be universally found on coral atolls over certain sandy locations. They grow in the first few millimeters of sand, which they bind together with their gelatinous cells into a crust. The crust generally is black when dry but greenish when moist, and the sand crust may crack into pieces which curl up their edges when dry. Three filamentous Myxophycae, *Hassallia byssoidea, Scytonema ocellatum,* and *Porphyrosiphon fuscus,* and a gelatinous form, *Gloeocapsa alpicola,* are the chief constituents of this sand crust as identified by Taylor (1950, pp. 103–8). *Hassallia byssoidea* constituted the most important element of this notable flora found on the surface soil inland. While this crust serves an important function in fixing the sand to stop drift, an equally or more important function possibly performed, but relatively unstudied, is its believed role in nitrogen fixation from the atmosphere (Fosberg, 1956; and Newhouse, 1954, pp. 53–4).

At Onotoa according to Moul (1957, p. 26),

The surface of the road that parallels the lagoon from North Island to Tabuarorae was covered by a "skin" of blue-green algae. This was also true of the well-worn paths and the soil where it was bare of vascular plants and remained undisturbed. Two species of Schizothrix and *Scytonema hofmannii* were very common and formed the bulk of this association. . . . The dune sands of the seaward rampart and the lagoon shore had *Microcoleus chthonoplastes* and *Scytonema hofmannii* as the dominant algae . . . These terrestrial blue-greens were present as a soil covering on the bare areas all over the atoll, both in sun and shade.

Moss coatings

In certain bare ground of wet regions constantly shaded by a tree canopy, stands of velvety mosses may form, possibly intermixed with blue-green algae. Thus, on Nukuoro, in the eastern Carolines, the writer observed that sections of the smooth, 6 to 10 foot wide path around the islet on which the residential village stood was covered by a bright light-green turf of moss. Mosses and liverworts often cover piles of coconut husks as well as coconut and other tree trunks (Plate 85). The distribution of mosses and other Bryophytes over the atolls of the Pacific still is little known (Miller and Doty, 1953, pp. 7–8; see also Miller, 1955). They are, most common, of course, on the wet islands and scarce on the dry islands with irregular rainfall (Moul, 1957, p. 23). The difference between drier and wetter atolls is reflected in the "remarkable fact that the trunks of the coconut trees on Christmas Island are free from lichens, while the trees on Fanning, Washington, and Palmyra islands are more or less densely covered" (Christophersen, 1927, p. 14).

CHAPTER 18

ATOLL TERRESTRIAL FAUNA

It is not surprising that an atoll, depauperate as it is in vegetation species, should also be poor in land fauna. Before the arrival of man on atolls, there were no mammals inhabiting them, except for perhaps a few fruit bats in those atolls near the larger "continental" volcanic islands. It is significant that none of the domestic animals now present in the Polynesian atolls—dogs, cats, pigs, and fowl—were there before the coming of the Europeans. Until the coconut palm was established in quantity (not until Europeans arrived), there was little food available to these animals (Buck, 1938, p. 310). In the pre-European period, the only mammal with man on an atoll was brought there most probably by man. This was the Polynesian rat, a gray-brown animal known as *Rattus (Mus) exulans*, distinguished by being smaller and less destructive than his more recently arrived cousin *Rattus rattus*, the common gray house rat of Europe and America. While the dog, cat, pig, and fowl might die of thirst on an atoll, especially on one in a dry climate, *Rattus exulans* can get all or most of its water supply from plant sources such as the enlarged fleshy, fruiting calyces of *Ipomoea tuba*, abundant on many atolls (Fosberg, 1956, p. 222 quoting Schultz).

However, it is not only in the higher forms of fauna that an atoll is depauperate but in all forms of land and fresh-water fauna such as birds, reptiles, and insects. H. F. Moore of the Albatross Expedition (Townsend and Wetmore, 1919, p. 162) found that in the Ellice, Gilbert, and Marshall Islands, land birds were extremely uncommon and of only a few species. They were even poorer than in the Tuamotus, which had been observed to be very poor in this respect compared with volcanic islands such as Tahiti.

The same thing is true of the insects. Gressitt (1954, p. 139) wrote:

404

The atolls and reef islands of the Marshalls, Gilberts, and Carolines present a poor and rather uniform [insect] fauna. Endemism appears to be limited and is often general; that is, with a species being common to many atolls, rather than peculiar to a single atoll. Perhaps most of these supposed endemics will be found on the nearest high islands. An interesting case in point is that of a cicindelid beetle of presumed Philippine origin on Nukuoro Atoll. It is the only cicindelid known from Micronesia, and how it reached Nukuoro is a subject for speculation. The total fauna of these low islands is probably under 2,000 species.

It is not unnatural, of course, that atolls should be poor in fauna. They suffer with other island areas under the principle enunciated by Hesse, Allee, and Schmidt (1937, pp. 522–4) that "Other conditions being equal, an insular area must accordingly have a smaller fauna than an equal area on the mainland." Moreover, the uniform lack of significant elevation of atolls and the general similarity of temperature conditions greatly reduce the variations of habitat as compared with high islands, leaving chiefly moisture, the corresponding vegetation, and soils as differentiators of atoll land habitats.

One of the characteristics of atoll faunas that has resulted from the limited variety in habitat is what Baur, quoted by Hedley (1896, p. 393), called a "disharmonic fauna," in which certain groups will be disproportionate in relation to the whole. This contrasts with the general "harmonic" proportion of various faunal groups on continental areas of the same size. Elaborating on this, Gulick (1932, pp. 407, 413) wrote that mature groups of islands may attain this harmony, but it will reflect the descent from quite a limited number of original importations, which at the beginning will be distinctly miscellaneous and disharmonic.

The isolation suffered by many atolls leads to a certain increase in endemism in speciation. The amount of endemism is inversely proportioned to the accessibility of the island from other more thickly populated areas, usually the nearest mainland or, perhaps, large island. This depends not only on nearness, but also on the ease or the means of transport and locomotion. According to Hesse, Allee, and Schmidt (1937, p. 87),

Endemic species are thus sometimes more numerous among mollusks and reptiles than among insects and more numerous in the latter group than among bats and birds. On the other hand, where lizards traveled readily from atoll to atoll via the canoes of man, as in parts of Polynesia, there may be identical species of lizards from island to island, whereas landbirds restricted to short range flights may be found in endemic species. In any case, the amount of endemism on an island is little influenced by the mode of its origin, whether by the breaking up of a former continental connection or by independent development as in a volcanic island or a coral atoll.

In the development of specialized faunas on oceanic islands an important factor is the isolation of the islands. Gressitt (1954, p. 127) stated that

Starting with, say, a small group of colonists, the fauna of an island is the result of isolation, plus time, plus ecological opportunity. The latter involves the size, topographic, and vegetational diversity, and suitability of climate of the island. Thus a tropical high island offers much greater ecological opportunity and greater chance of initial survival than does a low island. Degree of isolation, again, determines to a considerable extent the numbers of potentially successful colonists and thus determines the degree of competition, which is important. Well-isolated islands which receive few immigrants may have successful colonists which develop great divergence from the ancestors, to the extent of new genera developing and filling empty ecologic niches.

Because of greater isolation, one would expect to find greater speciation in such an area as southeastern Polynesia than in Micronesia. However, the extent or geographical area covered by such a term as Micronesia or Polynesia is much greater than their separations from neighboring areas such as the Philippines or the Melanesian high islands. One must think of the isolation of smaller groups of islands or single islands within the area both in terms of separation from other parts of the larger areas and from neighboring "continental" areas. However, Gressitt (1954, pp. 127–30) found that in spite of the fact that Micronesia neighbors on various zoogeographical regions outside its area, the insect fauna is not as diverse as might be assumed from this situation. "This, again, suggests that the insect fauna is highly selected and that its ancestry consists largely of types of insects prone to be transported by air or water and from certain sources in particular. It also suggests that the insects brought by pre-European man came from limited sources."

The isolation of atolls affords any particular species of fauna protection against the entrance of competitors. With the relatively smaller number of forms on a single island, the struggle for existence is less severe. This applies not only to an atoll as a whole but also to each islet on a reef isolated by a water channel from other islets. Any animal requires a certain space to enable it to develop and live freely, and this space varies with the size, activity, and mode of feeding of the animal. The limitation of available space in the smaller islands is reflected in the composition and development of their faunas. In the case of insects on islands "There tends to be a dominance of small-sized forms, dull coloring, obscure habitats, erratic distributions with absence of many families, superfamilies, and entire orders, and a sparse representation of fresh water forms" (Hesse, op. cit., 522). The last characteristic is especially applicable to atolls with its general absence of open fresh water.

Hesse, Allee, and Schmidt (1937, p. 524) also pointed out that the effect of the high relative humidity together with the great extent of coast line favors the land crustaceans on islands, especially the amphipods and decapods. It is not surprising, therefore, that the atoll islands have great numbers of hermit and land crabs, many of which range far inland from the coast. Hermit crabs may even adopt the shells of land snails. Hesse, Allee, and Schmidt noted that on Cocos Keeling Atoll there are no less than 16 species of land crabs and 7 of hermit crabs adapted to land life. The variety of land crabs found on Pacific coral islands is described and listed by Holthuis (1953). The giant coconut crab *Birgus latro* is very widespread among the Pacific atolls.

One peculiarity of island fauna, which is probably referable to their spatial limitations, is the dwarfing of both birds and mammals, in contrast with the converse phenomenon of giantism also found in insular birds. Degeneration in size of mammals on islands seems to be well established (Hesse, Allee, and Schmidt, 1937, p. 523). Whether these peculiarities occur from atoll habitation remains to be demonstrated, since so few mammals and land birds occur on atolls. Although atoll pigs are a small breed, their smallness is due in part to the inadequate food available and in part to the fact that the breed may have been small originally. Data are not available concerning the Polynesian rat, which has been a resident on most atolls long enough to demonstrate any characteristic reduction in size, if this has occurred.

A final peculiarity of insular forms which must be considered is their liability to extinction. Hesse, Allee, and Schmidt (1937, p. 524) recalled that the Lord Howe Islands were made a bird reservation in 1879 but that a plague of house rats defeated the hope of preserving the endemic birds. In attempting to explain why island birds are so vulnerable to extinction, Mayr (1945, p. 279) pointed out that these island animals live in an unusually uniform environment with little variety of climate and food and few or no natural enemies. Thus they become adapted to a situation that requires very little "struggle for existence." Because of the smallness of the total populations on an island, a species tends to become genetically rather uniform and, therefore, less capable of coping with new conditions. Introduction of new enemies or changes in the habitat may doom them to quick extinction.

The extermination of the Wake Island rail is a classic example. A number of phenomena and practices on atolls bring disruptive conditions to the life of land birds and affect their distribution. The practice of clearing underbrush, especially by fire, destroys cover and insect and other foods such as lizards. Tidal waves and marine inundation from hurricanes wash away vegetation and even the land itself, and the fury of the wind and waves may damage or even exterminate populations of land birds (Asplonis, Acrocephalus, and others). World War II, with its mass shelling and bombing, the subsequent "recreational shooting" of birds by garrison troops, and the use of DDT and other insecticides had extremely serious effects on the land birds and their food supply on atolls (Baker, 1951, p. 59).

The possible dispossession of the Polynesian rat by the more noxious house rat was indicated by Waite (1897, p. 174). He wrote that in Funafuti "The native rat is described to me as having been driven from the village, and indeed almost exterminated upon the main islet by the foreign rat. Upon the other islet it exists and in some cases swarms. . . ." On the other hand, Hedley (1896, p. 59) noted that the cat had been introduced to Funafuti and had "proved of great service in destroying the brown rat," so it is not definitely shown in this instance that the introduced rat displaced the native rat; cats may well have been responsible. However, the missionary Gill (1876, p. 316) also asserted that "In many of the islands the indigenous breed has been exterminated by the imported rat."

Domestic animals

On atolls the dependency of domestic animals upon the coconut for a large part of their food has generally greatly restricted their number. Larger livestock, such as horses and cattle, usually are completely excluded, especially where fresh water is a problem. The only exception known to the writer, even among wetter atolls, is the herd of 15 cattle observed in 1947 on Niulakita in the Ellice Islands. It is said that the cattle were introduced many years ago when the island was worked as a commercial copra plantation. During World War II the herd survived in a semi-wild state (Pusinelli, 1947, pp. 13, 20, 102).

Goats normally are too destructive to vegetation in the limited habitat-space of atolls to be tolerated. However, several goats are kept on Tarawa to provide milk for the Europeans there (Pusinelli, 1947, p. 13). The domestic animals that are acceptable are the pig, the dog, the cat, and fowl, all in limited numbers and all regarded as luxuries. None are eaten as a regular food even today when coconut plantations may cover most of the land on many atolls. There seems no doubt that prior to the coming of the Europeans, domestic animals were extremely scarce on atolls because of the scarcity of coconut palms.

The scarcity of coconut palms, at least in eastern Polynesia, has been clearly shown by Danielsson (1955, pp. 57–65). Palms existed in the Tuamotus only in limited numbers even as late as the 1870's. At Amanu Atoll in 1842 Lucett (quoted by Danielsson) saw only "a few groves of cocoa-nut trees . . . The cocoa-nut is not abundant and the fruit is only partaken of on rare occasions." In 1844, "Two cocoa-nut trees were all that could be seen above the low intricate scrub" on Akiaki. At Ravahere, "We noted a solitary cluster of cocoa-nut trees" and on Tikahau there were "a few cocoa-nut trees on its northwest side." Only Anaa was "densely covered with cocoa-nut trees." Danielsson pointed out that the exceptional situation of this was shown by the remark that the Anaa natives "are alive to the advantage the cocoa-nut tree gives them over their neighbors."

The reasons for this scarcity were superstition and warfare. When a man died, his possessions were burnt, "his plantations destroyed, and his coco-nut palms mercilessly cut down in order to offer their core to his manes." During raids and warfare among the islands, the enemy's palms were de-liberately cut down to diminish his food supply (Danielsson, 1955). Under such conditions, the hog could not be supported, and it should occasion no surprise that Lucett found on Hao Atoll that "They have no quadrupeds, save a few wretched dogs which they kept for eating, and a small species of rat which infests the islands in myriads" (Danielsson, 1955).

This scarcity of pigs on atolls was not restricted to the isolated Tuamotus in eastern Polynesia. Eilers (1934, p. 230) stated that pigs appeared unknown on Nukuoro in the eastern Carolines before the middle of the nineteenth century. At Kapingamarangi, 178 miles south of Nukuoro, there were only eight pigs for the estimated 150 inhabitants in 1910 (Eilers, 1934, p. 70). In both places the animal was called by the rough phonetic equivalent of the English term "pig," indicating the absence of knowledge of such an animal before the arrival of an Englishman (Eilers, 1934, pp. 14, 192). In the Mar-shalls the pigs and chickens were first introduced by the Germans and mis-sionaries (Stone, 1951, p. 32).

The scarcity of pigs on atolls prevails today, although in exceptional in-stances pigs may be found in comparatively large numbers. Speaking of Onotoa in the Gilberts, Moul (1954, p. 3) stated that pigs were not common but that in each village there were a few stockades built of logs to confine one or two. He was informed that pigs were used for food only on special feast days. The same thing is true of Arno where the population in 1951 was 800 to 1,000 and there were an estimated 100 to 150 pigs. However, they had been greatly reduced in number during World War II. The entire Mar-shalls group, with an estimated 10,400 people in 1946, had only an esti-mated 500 pigs, or one for each 20 people (U. S. Navy, 1948, pp. 77, 92). Moreover, wrote Stone of Arno, it appears that both animal numbers and attempts to improve the breed will be restricted by the nature and amount of food available. In the same year in Raroia, which had a population of 109, there were a total of only 12 pigs (Danielsson, 1955, pp. 108, 178).

The 1947 census in the Gilberts revealed that there were 6,326 pigs for the whole group of atolls, or 0.23 pig per person. The Ellice Islands group in 1947 had 3,201 pigs. The number of pigs per head of population in the Ellices, however, was three times as large as in the Gilberts (Pusinelli, 1947,

p. 13) and no doubt is a reflection of the greater abundance of copra in the wetter Ellice Atolls. At Ifalik Atoll Burrows and Spiro (1953, p. 32) wrote:

Hogs are few. The little pigs are treated as pets, occasionally even suckled by the women. When they grow bigger their feeding seems to be rather haphazard. Indeed, except for coconuts and taro—of which they get the left-overs—there is not much food to spare for them. Some reach a good size and look well fed. But pork is so highly prized and meat of any kind so scarce, that they are a constant temptation. There seems to be little prospect of their number increasing greatly.

The keeping of small pigs as pets is prevalent on many atolls but does not prevent their being eaten when they grow to the right size. At Ifalik the appearance of the pigs, which were not present in 1909, indicated their recent introduction. Most of them looked like Berkshires. There were only 33 pigs for the 260 people (Bates and Abbott, 1958, p. 78).

Kapingamarangi is an example of an island where today the pigs are raised in comparatively large numbers. In 1946 an estimate placed the number of pigs at 288 in a population of about 527 (Wiens, 1956, pp. 7, 27). However, in 1954 they were not quite so numerous, and the population also had dropped by about 100 through emigration. This large number amounted to about one pig for each 2 people in contrast to the one to 20 people in the Marshalls generally. Swain's Island, which in 1941 had 111 persons, had a reported 200 pigs. But Coulter (1941, p. 44) thought this was a "liberal" estimate.

Because of the damage that pigs do to herbaceous vegetation especially, they usually are not permitted to run free. Often they are tethered by ropes or penned in enclosures of logs or scrap metal such as the perforated steel sheets used to surface temporary airplane runways during World War II. In some areas, the Gilberts, for example, pigs must be confined or tethered, according to the edict of the magistrate. On Arno and some other atolls, stone-walled enclosures keep the pigs restricted to certain areas for the most part, but some pigs run wild. Because coconut meat is not fed in quantity to pigs except to fatten them for lard, the pigs fare better in richly vege-tated islands if left to run at large. However, they soon wipe out the plants that supply their feed, and also prevent the growing of tacca, bananas, taro, sugar cane, etc. Portulaca, Boerhavia, Thuarea, and leaves of Messerschmidia and *Ficus tinctoria* are fed to tethered pigs, which in the Gilberts may also get an average of two coconuts per day (Catala, 1947, p. 142).

Another problem that restricts the number of pigs on some atolls is the seminomadic character of the islanders' existence. When distant land sectors across the lagoon have to be worked, families having pigs must leave some-one behind to take care of them. Usually this is an old relative, if one is available, who is also staying behind with the school children (Danielsson, 1955, pp. 177–8).

Chickens apparently were introduced to most atolls after the arrival of Europeans. Chamisso (1821, p. 157) found them already in a wild state in the Marshalls. Old men of Raroia informed Danielsson (1955, p. 54) that in their parents' time there were neither pigs nor chickens. However, the atoll inhabitant today pays as little attention to fowl as to pigs. The 109 Raroians had only 76 hens in 1951 (Danielsson, 1955, p. 178). Catala (1957, p. 143) said that the Gilbertese seldom eat their chickens. Occasionally, fowl become wild where there is dense vegetation. In one village of 115 persons, Catala counted 205 chickens, an average of 1.78 chickens per person. For the Gilberts as a whole in 1947 there were 15,131 domestic fowl, or 0.54 per person. The Ellice group had 7,332 but only 1.63 per person (Pusinelli, 1947, p. 102), a comparative proportion for these two archipelagos similar to that for pigs and probably reflecting the greater pressure on food supplies in the Gilberts.

On Ifalik, where 260 people raised only 50 chickens, fowl were eaten as a delicacy and their eggs rarely were eaten (Burrows and Spiro, 1953; Bates and Abbott, 1958). Marshall (1951, p. 13) said that at Arno Atoll chickens are eaten only on special occasions and that the Arnoese do not like eggs. As a result, he found a great excess of chickens over those actually needed for food. On Kapingamarangi chickens were similarly regarded. There were some 946 chickens, or more than 2 per person in 1946, but few if any eggs were eaten. Three or four ducks were observed here in 1954, but appeared to be curiosities (Wiens, 1956). Most of the eggs observed by the writer in the Marshalls were of the size of pullet eggs in the United States. In all of the Marshalls in 1946 there were only an estimated 2,500 fowl for over 10,000 people (U. S. Navy, 1948). Turkeys were formerly common in the dry northern Marshalls but were all eaten by the Japanese during World War II. Ducks and geese were recommended for places with fresh-water swamps, such as Kili (Hatheway, 1957, p. 8).

The chickens are fed scraps of coconut meat and household scraps but generally forage at large as well, eating plant and grass seeds, ants, maggots, beetles, grass, and leaf hoppers and skinks. Marshall (1951, p. 13) thought that Arnoese fowl allowed to roam had plenty to eat. This probably would not be true of the drier atolls. Catala (1957) wrote that at each low tide the fowl go on the uncovered flats both on the ocean and lagoon sides and eat animals (copepods) and seaweed, although in small quantities. Marshall noticed that parasites were abundant on the fowl at Arno, including such nematodes as Ascaridia, Capillaria, Acuaria, and tapeworms, and such Protozoa as Trichomonas and Entamoeba. However, the fowl that were allowed to roam freely appeared healthy and robust (Marshall, 1951).

Dogs appear to have been the earliest domestic animals of the atoll dwellers. It already has been indicated that dogs were eaten by the early Polynesian aborigines (see also Forster, 1777, pp. 42, 45). They still are eaten in many places (Burrows and Spiro, 1953; Danielsson, 1955, p. 179). Danielsson wrote:

Of all the domesticated animals the dogs alone can accompany the islanders on their trips to other parts of the atoll, which is certainly the main reason for their continued popularity. Dogs seem primarily to be appreciated for their food value and only in a very secondary way for their companionship. As no dogs are regularly fed, only young dogs are tender enough to be eaten. Many dogs are, however, saved for reproductive reasons, and most of the 44 dogs found at the time of my survey were of a fairly advanced age, many of them actually too old, which is not so surprising, as the Raroians never kill a dog except when they intend to eat him. There is a tax imposed in order to keep down the number of dogs, but as it is extremely small it does not have the desired effect.

At Ifalik dogs are not raised for food but are eaten on occasion. However, there were only five dogs in 1953 and three of them were killed that year because they had bitten human beings (Burrows and Spiro, 1953; Bates and Abbott, 1958).

Dogs are not wanted on all atolls. At Kapingamarangi they became a nuisance and were all exterminated in the late 1940's. Hedley recounted a tale related by Moss (1889, p. 187) concerning the extermination of dogs on Funafuti. The dogs apparently interfered with the watch on the morality of the people undertaken by leaders among the newly converted Christians. "At Funafuti the Turimen march round the village during the night, and quietly steal into the houses to see if all is right. It was found that the house dogs barked and gave notice of their approach, so they forthwith decreed the destruction of all dogs on the island and again became masters of the situation."

One reason for the disinterest in dogs is that they have to be fed coconut meat and do not catch much of their own food. It was reported on Majuro that some dogs roamed in packs along the beach and cornered and cooperatively caught fish from the tide pools (Marshall, 1951, p. 23).

Cats are the only other domestic animals on atolls, except for occasional tamed frigate birds or other sea birds sometimes kept as pets. That cats are recent introductions is indicated by the fact that they are called by their European names. On Funafuti, although Hedley (1896, p. 59) said they had been long in residence, they were known as "pussy" and were valued for having destroyed many of the brown rats, a great pest. At Kapingamarangi, the cats were introduced after 1910, but with the destruction of all the dogs there, they multiplied greatly and on the two residential islands of Werua

and Touhou had virtually exterminated the rat (Emory, 1954). Marshall
(1951, p. 22) found that cats on Arno (here called Kuj) were common pets
and appeared to be of great use because they caught house rats. They appeared to be on friendly terms with the chickens, dogs, and pigs and did not
seem to have gone wild. All were rather thin and scrawny, so that it would
appear that their foraging did not bring them much food. They also ate
breadfruit and coconut meat. Cats introduced to uninhabited Enderbury
Island were found to have gone wild and burrowed for homes, living off the
birdlife of the island (Luke, 1945, p. 229).

Rats and mice

There probably is no atoll wet or dry which the rat has not penetrated
(Hedley, 1956, p. 169). It is the most destructive pest on an atoll, and a
number of different kinds are known. The commonest and of ancient origin
is the indigenous Polynesian rat, *Rattus exulans,* sometimes called a mouse
by certain German writers (Fosberg, 1956, pp. 222–3). Although it enters
houses in search of food, it apparently nests outdoors away from human
habitation.

There is no doubt of the ancient origin of this rat. "At Mangaia they
were mythically regarded as the progeny of Echo, the ironical goddess 'who
talks out of the rocks.' The rat figures again and again in their ancient songs
and myths" (Gill, 1876, p. 317). Mayor (1924, p. 75) stated that the Polynesians "esteemed them for food and took much delight in hunting them for
sport." They certainly were found in enormous numbers on inhabited atolls
by early European explorers. Wilkes (1845, p. 75) wrote that "Mr. Peale
found no quadrupeds except rats [in the northern Gilberts] which were in
great plenty, and running in all directions. . . ." Paulding, 14 years earlier
(1831, p. 167), said of Mili in the southern Marshalls that "The islands were
swarming with a species of small rats. . . ." On Nukuoro Robertson (1877)
found the "number of rats on the group almost beyond belief; they are so
tame that they come to where people are eating and sit around waiting for
any morsels that fall. Houses are built without sides, being merely roofed,
and supports carefully smoothed down to prevent rats from climbing up
and eating the provisions stored on shelves." Quantitative figures for rats
on some islands inhabited by sea birds have been described in Chapter 13.
The great numbers that may occur is seen by the report that on Wake Island
at the end of World War II, "in one single day an all-out run on rats netted
40,000 which were killed and eaten" by starving Japanese soldiers (Howard,
1951, p. 944).

Fortunately, the Polynesian rat is not as destructive as the more recently
introduced European or Asiatic house rat, *Rattus rattus,* nor are they always

so numerous. Moul (1954, p. 2) said that the rodents at Onotoa were not numerous and that he heard no complaints from the natives about them, but that they certainly were kept from becoming pests by the number of dogs, cats, and pigs around the village. They suffered little damage to their supplies and found that the rat there was not destructive to food. Catala (1957, p. 43) thought that the number of coconuts destroyed by rats on Tarawa probably was not large enough to be significant. On Kapingamarangi Niering (1956, p. 21) wrote that although the Polynesian rat was locally abundant on some of the larger islets, he observed no damaged coconuts. Marshall (1951, p. 25) concluded that the main food of the rats on Arno was fallen coconuts, but that in spite of the abundance of *Rattus exulans,* they have little influence on the copra production, "for only a small part of the available nuts are ever harvested."

Contrasted with these reports concerning the general innocuous character of the Polynesian rats on atolls are reports of important damage done by rats. Coulter (1941) reported that on Swain's Island, before barium carbonate poisoning greatly reduced the rat population, it was estimated that 20 per cent of the coconut crop was damaged by rats. Ranson (1952, p. 59) wrote that it is not a new discovery that rats eat coconuts and that as a result copra production in the Tuamotus was decreasing. Rat-catching dogs were said to have been introduced with visible effect on the rat population, and a chemical was to be tried also.

Students of rat ecology believe that the real damage is not done by the Polynesian rat but by *Rattus rattus,* the larger animal that has been brought into many atolls by trading vessels. Marshall (1951, pp. 23–6) found young, green coconuts cut into and eaten on Arno only where he found *Rattus rattus* in evidence. In the rest of the islands, where *R. exulans* was abundant, no green nuts were eaten by rats. He felt that this was just another line of evidence supporting others to acquit the daintier animal of this economic offense. He believed that *R. exulans* only ate fallen nuts. The house rat also did considerable damage to stored copra at the warehouse on Arno. The house rat was found to stick very close to human dwellings, none being found in a transect area half a mile from a village. By contrast, *R. exulans* generally were distributed even on some of the smallest islets of Arno. *R. exulans,* however, was found to eat coconut blossoms and was often seen at night climbing in the flowering coconut stalks. Other food includes the seeds of grasses and other plants, such as *Triumfetta procumbens.* Hedley (1896, p. 169) wrote that the Polynesian rat is usually said to feed only on vegetable substances. He cited Pandanus fruits among other vegetative matter eaten by this rat. There appears to be no evidence that it eats the hermit or other crabs that are so prevalent on land. However, Fosberg (1956) said that it has been seen eating newly hatched turtles and that it no doubt eats birds and birds' eggs. He thought, however, that it was not terribly destructive to birds, since the rat is abundant on Taongi, where there are an enormous number of birds.

Parasites found by Marshall on *Rattus rattus* at Arno included mites and lice but no fleas. There were abundant tapeworms and stomach nematodes and flagellates in the caecum. Similar infestations were found on *R. exulans*, and some whipworms threaded in the stomach lining of a specimen examined. No biting "true bugs" were associated with them.

Rat nests often are found in the crowns of coconut trees, near the base of the fronds. Marshall found globular masses of soft dead leaves about 5 inches in diameter inside rotten logs, stumps, and among the hanging leaves of Pandanus. He even found them inside empty coconut husks.

In addition to the rat, the mouse, *Mus musculus,* also has spread to many atolls, from the Marshalls and Carolines to the Tuamotus (Sachet and Fosberg, 1955), and, as elsewhere, is often a house animal. It does not appear to be very important as a nuisance, however. Farrell (1928, pp. 397–8) reported "myriads of mice" on Lisiansky but the mice may have been the small Polynesian rat.

Concerning the problem of elimination and control of the rat in the Pacific Islands, MacMillan (1946, pp. 40–1) wrote that the structure of the native houses, the sheds for cooking, the accumulation of debris, and the bush areas all provide easy hiding places from which it would be difficult to exclude the rat. He thought that the animal could be controlled by a vigorous and sustained program of trapping and by the careful use of poison so as not to harm other animals and children. These measures might diminish the rodent population but would not exterminate the entire population of rats, so that any relaxation of controls might quickly restore the rat population to the maximum limit.

It has been noted earlier that the larger house rat may war on *Rattus exulans*. At Funafuti the Polynesian rat was described as having been driven from the village and almost exterminated on the main island by the more-destructive pest *Rattus rattus* (Waite, 1897, p. 174). However, the latter may not be able to compete effectively for food in the bush with *R. exulans*.

Other mammals on atolls

In rare instances other animals, such as rabbits and guinea pigs, have been introduced to atoll habitats. A guano-company manager introduced domestic rabbits and Belgian and English hares to Laysan Island in the Hawaiian group with the intention of starting a rabbit-canning business. While the business apparently did not materialize, the rabbits and hares multiplied and in 1911 swarmed in thousands over the islets of Laysan. Dill and Bryan

(1912, p. 28) reported that "The amount of damage done by them can better be imagined than told. They are exterminating first one species of plant, then another." Some guinea pigs also were introduced, but apparently they were unimportant in numbers. It is not known what has happened to the rabbit population since 1912.

Phoenix Atoll also teems with rabbits introduced by guano-company people. They share the atoll with the even more numerous sea birds and some feral cats (Luke, 1945). The feral cats may help to keep down the numbers of rabbits here.

A little-known species of seal, *Monachus schauinslandi,* is reported to visit Laysan Island (Dill and Bryan, 1912, p. 9).

On Ulithi Atoll in the western Carolines, Fosberg (1946, p. 78) observed fruit-eating bats eating the seedy variety of breadfruit. It is possible that they may be found also on other atolls in this area or on atolls in the vicinity of the Bismarck Archipelago, New Guinea, and other large high islands of Melanesia.

Atoll land and fresh-water birds

The origins of the shore birds of the Pacific atolls were discussed together with the sea birds in Chapter 13. Land birds and fresh-water birds are in a somewhat different category because of their different requirements and the more-stringent limitations of the atoll habitat for them. Mayr (1941, p. 192) grouped the Pacific island birds under a Polynesian subregion which he defined as "all the tropical and subtropical islands of the Pacific Basin which indicate by their impoverished fauna that they have had no recent continental connection (after early Tertiary) and which derived the major part of their fauna directly or indirectly from the Papuan Region or jointly from Australia and the Papuan Region." This region is divided into Melanesian, southern Melanesian, Micronesian, central Polynesian, eastern Polynesian, and Hawaiian subdivisions. However, as far as land and fresh-water birds are concerned, Baker (1951, p. 43) considers the Marshall Islands and the Gilbert group more closely related to the central Polynesian subdivision than to the other Micronesian subdivisions.

Most of the discussion concerning Pacific islands land and fresh-water birds pertains to high islands and thus is little concerned with atolls except as these birds may have used atolls as stepping stones of migration or arrival. The Marshall Islands, for instance, have received no avian components from Melanesia, although the high islands of the Carolines, Palaus, and Marianas have. According to Baker (1951, pp. 45, 54), "The absence of 'high' islands in the Marshalls and the possible inability of birds accustomed to life on the luxuriant islands of Melanesia to become established on relatively barren atolls are logical reasons for this." For the same reason, there appear to be no land birds from the Moluccan and Celebesian components in the Marshalls. However, one species of bird from the Philippean component actually has been recorded at Bikini. Baker's analysis showed that Micronesia, with the exception of the Marshall Islands and the Gilberts, has little affinity to Polynesia and greater affinity with Melanesia.

The atolls present great difficulties to land birds, as they do to all mammals except the rat and, in rare instances, the rabbit. The long east-west line of the Carolines, for instance, presents a "broad front" to bird wanderers from Melanesia, a scant 500 miles to their south. One might conclude that the Carolines would be well populated with a large variety of birds from Melanesia. Actually there are only a few widely spaced volcanic islands in this vast archipelago which possess the proper vegetation, fresh water, and other qualities to make them capable of supporting immigrant land and fresh-water birds. The other islands are low coral atolls with little open fresh water and a meager variety of fruits, insects, and other suitable foods (Baker, 1951).

The isolation of scattered Pacific islands is conducive to speciation and endemism among birds and other animals. Although most of this occurs on "high" islands, even the coral atoll, if left undisturbed by man and the predators which he introduces, can develop unique species, as illustrated by the Wake Island flightless rail, a shore bird.

Although faunas of oceanic islands are often believed to undergo "adaptive radiation," so that a few basic types come to fill unduly large proportions of the population as compared with the population on neighboring continents, the latter can occur without the former. In the Carolines, the starling (*Aplonis apacus*) dominates much of the available habitat on some of the atolls, and even on high islands, where other land birds are present. Yet, "There appears to be no tendency towards selective adaptations occurring, or towards ecologic isolation" (Baker, 1951, p. 57).

Land birds are rather scarce on atolls. One of the most widespread is the long-tailed New Zealand cuckoo (*Eudynamis taitensis*). This bird is very widespread and is often the *only* land bird on many atolls in Polynesia and Micronesia and possibly in parts of eastern Melanesia (Morrison, 1954, p. 25; Baker, 1951, pp. 214–5; Mayr, 1945, p. 71). Niering (1956, p. 19) found it at Kapingamarangi, and Fosberg (1956, p. 223) says that it is a rare visitor in the northern Marshalls. Marshall (1951, p. 20) observed single cuckoos of this species 13 times at Arno, always in dense forest. He found it an agile bird, leaping around in trees, and extremely secretive as well. A specimen he obtained had eaten a 4- or 5-inch brown emoia, five green katydids, and a roach. He believed that they roam over great distances in feeding. The Marshallese called it "udrej."

Another widespread land bird on atolls of the Marshalls and Carolines is the Micronesian pigeon (*Ducula oceanica*) (Baker, 1951, pp. 194–7; Marshall, 1951, p. 19). On Arno Atoll, Marshall found it localized on Arno, Ine, and the islets of the eastern horn of the atoll. It is called "mule" by the natives here. Some individuals were observed here breeding during the summer. Breadfruit was one of their chief foods and they also were observed eating Allophyllus fruit and papaya blossoms. The people keep some of these birds as pets and recognize that they make good eating. Bennett (1840, pp. 365–77) noted that Caroline Atoll in the central south Pacific had large numbers of "small pigeons, with white head and neck, and the rest of their plumage a rich brown color." This description differs from that of Baker for the Micronesian pigeon.

The Micronesian starling (*Aplonis apacus angus*) is found on many atolls of the Caroline chain, both east and west (Baker, 1951, p. 290), and was observed by Niering in Kapingamarangi. On only recently inhabited (since 1954) Oroluk Atoll, Marshall (1957, p. 5) estimated some 400 starlings on the 15 acres of land in the single islet. Marshall does not mention its presence on Arno, and Fosberg (1946) only mentions a related bird, the Indian mynah (*Acridotheres tristis*), as having been introduced and become common on Kwajelein in the central Marshalls.

The nightingale reed-warbler (*Acrophalus luscinia*) is a year-round resident on atolls in the Carolines such as Woleai, Lamotrek, Kukunor, and Nukuoro. It has been observed as far east as Nauru, but no mention is made of its occurrence in the Marshalls, where it seemingly is absent (Baker, 1951, pp. 254–60). The five or six warblers on Wolauna Islet of Ant Atoll near Ponape were considered a large population for such a small islet (Marshall, 1957, p. 3).

The only other land bird at Raroia aside from the warbler was the migrant New Zealand cuckoo (Morrison, 1954, pp. 20, 26).

The white-collared kingfisher (*Halcyon chloris*) has been observed on Kayangel Atoll in the western Carolines (Baker, 1951, p. 233), but this atoll is only about 18 miles from Babelthuop in the Palaus, so that this may be regarded as a stray wanderer from the large volcanic island, rather than as a regular atoll resident or visitor. The only other land bird, aside from the shore birds mentioned by Baker (1951, p. 184), is the crimson-crowned fruit dove (*Ptilinopus phorphyraceus*), one of which was once observed at Ebon, but which may have become extinct since the observation. Burnett (1910, pp. 14–21) mentions that on Fanning there was "a very small, brightly colored paraquette," the origin of which at such an isolated island he considered a mystery, and "a small grey insect-eating bird."

The most frequently observed foods of the starling were berries and papaya. Fruits, berries, and green plantstuffs also form the chief food of the Micronesian pigeon. The cuckoo feeds chiefly upon caterpillars, skinks and geckos, and other insects, and the nightingale reed-warbler is chiefly an insect feeder. Neither the food or nesting habits of the land birds are significantly destructive of economic plants.

By contrast, some of the sea birds which nest in large numbers on bread-fruit trees may harm the trees. Niering (1956, p. 19) wrote that at Kapinga-marangi,

The gregarious nesting habit of the white-capped tern may have con-siderable influence on the breadfruit. The natives report that these birds have actually killed their trees in the past. In one, 90 feet in height and 2 ft. in diameter, 80 nests were estimated, all of which were concentrated in the upper 30 ft. of the crown. On one branch 6″ in diameter and 15 ft. in length, 12 nests 1–2 ft. apart were recorded. Where the nests are this abundant, at least 75% of the branches are white with fecal matter. Below these nests no branches occur. Previously existing branches were probably severely injured or killed as a result of the birds, thus necessitating removal.

Lizards

Geckos and skinks are common lizards on most atolls from which re-ports are available. In the northern Marshalls, Fosberg (1946, p. 225) said there were at least two kinds of geckos and three kinds of skinks. Marshall (1957, 2–11) expressed amazement that lizards obtained from Bikini were different from those found on Arno. At Arno, he found four species of geckos and four of skinks. These are the rock gecko (*Gymnodactylus pela-gicus*), the small house gecko (*Lepidocactylus lugubris*), the big tree gecko (*Gehyra oceanica*), the four-fingered gecko (*Hemiphyllodactulus typus*), the skinks (*Dasia smaragdina*) (two forms, black and green), the blue-tailed skink (*Emoia cyanura*), and the ground Emoia (the brown *E. boettgeri* and the black *E. arnoensis*). A giant skink called by the Marshallese "mennuel," or "terrible lizard," was unidentified but was said by Marshall to be certainly harmless in spite of its formidable appearance. The small house gecko, an-other gecko, *Peropus mutilatus,* the blue-tailed skink, and another skink, *Cryptoblepharus boutonii,* have been recorded from Wake Island (Bryan, 1959, pp. 14–15). On Marcus Island, Bryan (1903) said that the gecko *Pe-rochirus articulatus* was found in abundance all over the island, especially in hollow trees or under loose bark, coming out at nightfall and commonly observed all about the thatched huts and the trees but rarely on the ground. He found the skink *Ablepharus boutonii* more abundant than the gecko, often on the ground and under stones and clumps of grass. At Onotoa Atoll, Moul (1954, pp. 7–8) found the rock gecko, the big tree gecko, and the blue-tailed skink. The small house gecko, the blue-tailed skink, and the glossy black *Dasia smaragdina* were prevalent at Ifalik (Bates and Abbott, 1958,

p. 198). Doane (1861) reported five species of lizards on Ebon Atoll, four of the Lacertinidae and one of the Geckotidae.

On the other hand, some atolls may have few species of lizards. Montrouzier (1876, p. 645) reported that a small gecko with adhesive toe disks, and two species of turtles, were the only reptiles on the Huon and Surprise Islands in the Coral Sea. At arid Canton Atoll, Degener and Gillaspy (1955, p. 48) tell of an adhesive-toed gecko climbing about in the shrubbery and driftwood, and a skink darting about the sand and rocks. Surprisingly, Bennett (1840, pp. 365–77) wrote that on Caroline Atoll north of the Tuamotus his party observed no lizards or other land amphibia.

Characterizing atoll fauna, Usinger and La Rivers (1953, p. 18) wrote:

It is noteworthy that most of the food chains end with lizards. This is a partial explanation for Marshall's statement that lizards (the blue-tailed skink in particular) are the most numerous land vertebrates on the atoll. This does not mean that the skinks have no enemies for they were eaten on occasion by cuckoos, herons, chickens, and even by a land crab, *Geograpsus*. However, none of these predators is generally distributed and none depends primarily on lizards for food. Therefore, the lizards are relatively free from predators. They do have numerous endo-parasites, including stomach nematodes and rectal flagellates.

The nocturnal rock gecko lacks the adhesive disks on the toes for climbing and is the only gecko on Arno that stays on the ground. It lives among rocks and eats centipedes, weavils, spiders, sand fleas, beach crickets, and other small insects.

The house gecko is a small species often found in houses. Although nocturnal, they are active for a longer period than other geckos. Marshall (1957) also found them on Arno in Pandanus and Pipturus trees, hopping from leaf to leaf in their foraging. At Onotoa, Moul (1957) found this gecko on almost every Scaevola and Guettarda flower cluster waiting for night-flying insects. Their habitat is not restricted and they are found everywhere. Among their few natural enemies is the Huntsmans spider (Heteropodidae), which sometimes catches the lizard in its web.

The big tree gecko can most regularly be seen on tall coconut trunks that have crevices for hiding, but they are found also in thatched houses and Pandanus trees. Marshall (1957) thought they tended to avoid dense groves of breadfruit trees, and they are almost never on the ground. They are active only at night. Their adhesive toe disks give them a remarkable clinging power, for instance, to coconut leaves, from which they cannot be shaken by hand or wind. They like to roost high in coconut trees. They are about 6 inches long on Onotoa, where Moul found them to be the largest lizard on the atoll. The four-fingered gecko is very similar but has a tail like that of the house gecko.

Dasia is a strictly arboreal skink and is the daytime counterpart of the big tree gecko, sleeping at night on the tree wherever they happen to be at day's end and seldom roosting at the same spot. Although usually a bright green color, they may be olive, olive-green, brownish, or even black, or black with yellow edging on their scales. A variety of insects form their diet: beetles, winged and nonwinged ants, maggots, sow bugs, cockroaches, moths (Marshall, 1957).

The blue-tailed skink was found to be the most numerous and common on both Arno and Onotoa and is found everywhere on or near the ground on piles of coconuts or husks, fallen fronds, Scaevola thickets, the lower matted dead leaves of Pandanus, thatched houses, and rocks and gravel. Marshall said that they rarely attempt to climb smooth overhanging trunks and seldom climb up trees other than Pandanus. They are active from 7:30 A.M. to 5 P.M. and like sunshine, but they hide under rocks or in crevices at night. They eat insects and fruits such as that of Scaevola and are preyed upon by birds, chickens, and the land crab (Marshall, 1957).

Of the two ground Emoias, Marshall (1957) wrote that he considered them to be races or variants of the same species, but that he was surprised to find that the two forms had mutually exclusive distribution on Arno. Brown and Marshall (1953) considered the black form, which they named *Emoia arnoensis,* a variant and subspecies of *E. boettgeri.* They thought it likely that the two forms compete with each other for food, habitations, and forage areas to the extent that one drives out the other. Both are found in houses and in piles of coconut husks. *E. boettgeri* is more apt to be found in open interior areas; *E. arnoensis* likes to stay among the rocks at the edge of vegetation and in more direct sunshine. It was not obvious to them, however, why one form of Emoia should establish itself on some islets and the other form on other islets, when atolls seem to have such a uniform and monotonous environment. Both of them coexist with *Emoia cyanura.* The hypothesis was raised that selective forces might operate differentially upon the two species, thus determining which will "win out" in a given islet environment. Supporting this suggestion was the predominance of certain color phases of *Dasia smaragdina* correlated with the dominant color phase of the two ground Emoias. The observations indicated that the proportion of light-colored Dasia individuals on those islets occupied by the brown *E. boettgeri* is higher than should be expected and that the dark phases of Dasia individuals predominate on those islets occupied by the black *E. arnoensis.*

In a few atolls of Micronesia during the Japanese administration, big gray-green monitor lizards (*Varanus indicus*) were introduced to control the rat population. These are huge lizards, some of them 5 feet long. They are known to have been found on Kayangel Atoll (Gressitt, 1952, p. 3), Woleai

Atoll (Kaneshiro, 1950), Ifalik Atoll (Bates and Abbott, 1958, p. 197), Japtan Islet of Eniwetok Atoll (Fosberg, 1956, p. 225), and Aur Atoll (Fulbeck, 1947, pp. 122–4). They may be on other atolls to which man has brought them, but it is not likely that they would be found naturally.

Monitors at Ifalik were thought by older men to have done a good job in reducing the rat population from their earlier huge numbers. However, the monitors do not confine themselves to rats but also snap up land crabs, hermit crabs, the smaller coconut crabs, and other lizards. They were said to have caught and eaten birds also (Bates and Abbott, 1958). On Woleai in 1950 it had become a pest; it ate chickens, so that poultry could not be raised in the open. The Japanese were said to have eaten both the lizard and its eggs, but the Micronesians abhorred the thought of eating them. They wished to exterminate the lizard and had thought of bringing in poisonous toads (*Bufo marinus*) from the Palaus. However, chickens and ducks also eat young toads and would have been poisoned. Toads had been introduced on Kayangel, but Gressitt (1952) thought this unfortunate because he said that the monitor lizards are predators upon the coconut beetle, which had at that time been introduced to the atoll. He felt that coconut palms were more important than chickens to the atoll people here and that the toads polluted the scarce well-water supply by dying in the wells or in crevices among the rocks lining the wells.

Turtles

The only other reptile found on coral atolls is the turtle, found throughout Polynesia, Micronesia, and Melanesia. Smith (1946, p. 59) said that both the hawksbill (*Chelonia imbricata*) and the green turtle (*Chelonia mydas,* or *japonica*) are found throughout Micronesia but are more abundant in the Carolines and less abundant in the Marshalls and Marianas. Hedley (1896, p. 409) said that the green turtle was the only one found at Funafuti in the Ellice Islands and probably was to be "traced to the uttermost limits of Polynesia." Other members of this group of powerful swimmers are widely spread in the South Seas. Gill said that "Several species of turtle—loggerhead, hawksbill, green turtle, etc.—are very plentiful on Rakahanga in the breeding season." Danielsson (1955, p. 190) found that the people on Raroia Atoll had names for eight different varieties of turtle. Seurat (1904, p. 8) wrote that the Pukapuka natives catch the green turtle, but that the hawksbill turtle, although occurring also in the Tuamotus, is rare. Marine turtles have been abundant in some of the Tuamotus: Napuka, Fagatu(?), Fakahina(?), Tatakoto, Pukaruha, Reao, Vahitahi(?), Tikei, Tepoto, and Matahiva, among others (Donat and Seurat, 1904, pp. 926–31). On Huon and Surprise Islands in the Coral Sea the only two species of turtle recorded were *Testudo maculosa* and *Testudo lacrymata* (Montrouzier, 1876, p. 645).

Fosberg (1956, p. 225) stated that the green turtle was formerly an important source of food in the Marshalls but that it is rare now on most atolls because it is hunted incessantly and its eggs are dug up whenever found. According to Japanese reports (Smith, 1946), about 200 hawksbill turtles were taken annually during the Japanese period of administration in Micronesia, mostly from the Palaus, Truk, and Ponape. This small number was due to strict Japanese conservation regulations. The hawksbill is carnivorous, so it is not highly regarded as food, but it has 13 overlapping large plates on its back, which are the "tortoise shell" of commercial importance. Smith mentions that a few hawksbill turtles were taken on Nukuoro and Likiep Atolls. The turtle shells taken at Likiep seldom exceeded 18 inches in maximum length. The green turtle does not have the overlapping plates and has no commercial value but they are tasty to eat because they are herbivorous.

Marine turtles vary in abundance from atoll to atoll. Emory (1954) said that on Kapingamarangi the turtle was quite rare and that it was forbidden to kill it. However, the writer saw the 30-inch-long shell of a recently killed turtle on one of the islets of the atoll in 1956. This was the only one observed in 2 months. In a 3-month summer stay on Arno, Marshall (1957) saw a marine turtle only three times—in the lagoon. The writer observed a few small green turtles in fish pens on Mokil and Pingelap in 1956. They are most abundant on uninhabited atolls that are relatively inaccessible, and these usually are the drier atolls with little economic value. Fosberg found them most prevalent on arid Bikar Atoll and the single islet of Jemo, both uninhabited reef isands in the northern Marshalls. Turtles were said to abound on Fanning Atoll half a century ago (Burnett, 1910, p. 21). Tresilian (1838, p. 245) told of numerous green turtles 50 to 300 pounds in weight at Christmas Atoll. Billings (1856, p. 116), the master of a sailing vessel lost on D'Entrecasteaux Reefs (Surprise Island) near New Caledonia, told of catching a turtle weighing over 600 pounds. After the party had been on the island several weeks, turtles

began to come on shore in great numbers. Two large pens were built, and upwards of eighty, weighing on an average 5 cwt., were put in them. The pens being full, they commenced drying the flesh of others to provide against the time they would desert these shores; which they do during the months of November and December, after depositing their eggs, and return early in July, increasing daily from this period. They were so numerous in September that the Master turned twenty-seven one morning without wetting his feet, and he counted eighteen more asleep in about six inches of water.

Sachet (1954, p. 20) quotes from Graeffe (1873) the following account of turtles on Rose Atoll: "On the sand island, in the months of August and September, a great number of sea turtles came to lay their eggs. Most of them were the common sea turtle (*Chelonia mydas L.*). More seldom came the caret (*Chelonia imbricata I.*). When the time came for the young to hatch, the surrounding sea was full of sharks who avidly snapped up the little turtles as fast as they arrived in deeper water."

The most prized of all animal foods at Ifalik Atoll is the meat of the sea turtle. Although not uncommonly seen in the lagoon here, they were not often caught. Burrows and Spiro (1953, pp. 39, 102) knew of four being caught at Ifalik in 6 months, three of them at one time. The people here reported that these turtles are commoner on some of the other atolls of the Carolines, notably Lamotrek and Elato, and especially on the uninhabited atolls. The writer can confirm this for Gaferut, a single small reef islet in the western Carolines, on the sandy beaches of which in September of 1954 were innumerable holes apparently marking places where turtles had deposited eggs. Many turtles also were seen here swimming in the waters over the leeward reef. Oroluk Atoll, with its one small 15-acre islet, also was said to abound with turtles. Three Kapingamarangi men returned to Ponape on June 6, 1956, with 27 adult female green turtles which they had caught on the beach laying eggs. Others were seen at Oroluk in the lagoon (Marshall, 1957, p. 5). On Raroia in the Tuamotus, which is a much larger atoll than Ifalik, the total number of turtles caught in 1950 was 17 and the average number per season generally has been between 15 and 20. As on Ifalik and most other atolls, turtle flesh is highly prized on Raroia, and the men are ready to abandon all other occupations when a turtle is sighted (Danielsson, 1955, p. 193).

The season at Raroia lasts from June to September, during which months a small number of turtles appear in the sea immediately west of Raroia fairly close to shore. At the beginning of the season both male and female turtles are caught when they breed in the water. At the end of the season, most of the turtles caught are females that have crawled onto the sand beaches to lay their eggs. Seurat (1904b) said that at Pukapuka the green turtle comes near the shores to mate and lay eggs starting in October when the Pleiades rise in the east. According to Danielsson, the Raroians are firmly convinced that they can predict the day when a female turtle returns after a first visit by counting the number of eggs laid. "If a turtle has laid let us say 84 eggs the first time, she will return in 4 days, if there are 85 eggs in 5 days, and so on."

This type of prediction appears to be less trustworthy than the predictions of the Marshallese of Ujelang (Tobin, 1955), who say the usual egg-laying cycle is every 12 days for three to six times and who lie in wait for expected returns of turtles on this basis. Tobin tells of being on Ujeland when a nest of 100 turtle eggs was uncovered and the prized delicacies were distributed to all the villagers in proportion to the size of the families. The eggs are round and about the size and appearance of ping-pong balls, according to

Fosberg (1956). The turtle carefully covers up the eggs with sand to let the sun hatch them. Smith (1946) wrote that females may lay up to 150 eggs and that the young hatch at the end of 60 days, the laying season being during late spring and early summer. When the young emerge, they instinctively head directly for the sea. At this stage they are soft and many are caught and eaten by hermit crabs and rats, so few may survive the journey. More get eaten by marine predators after they reach the water. The relatively small number that become adult and of significant size are hunted so relentlessly on many atolls that they are likely to become extinct if conservation practices are not carried out.

Powell (1957) confirms the 12-day interval between egg laying for the green turtles which are plentiful on Palmerston Atoll. He wrote that eggs may number between from around 70 to over 200 eggs in each hole or nest. Men locate these nests by probing in the sand with a sharp stick. When the stick comes up smeared with egg remains, the nest is dug out for the remaining eggs. An experiment conducted by Ioapa Marsters at Palmerston gave encouraging results for the raising of green turtles in captivity. Dug-up eggs were buried in the sand near the village and surrounded by wire-mesh netting. When the turtles hatched, they were put in a wire-netting covered wooden box floating in the lagoon. They were fed kitchen scraps, fish, and shell fish. At 10 months each had a carapace about 5 to 6 inches wide and 6 to 8 inches long. Powell thought that in 2 or 3 years these turtles could find a ready sale in Rarotonga and possibly New Zealand.

The food of the green turtle is mostly seaweed (Smith, 1946; Sachet, 1954, p. 20), but Powell said that they were omnivorous feeders, and that they did not seem to require any special food to gain weight. They fed on almost anything he gave them, from fresh fish to tinned beef and rice. Their ecology in the lagoon and reef areas is little known. On the outer reef at Palmerston there were several deep surge channels where turtles are known to sleep in caves. The islanders here regard night fishing for turtles in these channels as great sport. Slipping quietly into a channel, they swim under water and grab a sleeping turtle from a deep cave. Many an islander searching for turtles in coral caves has suffered the vicious bite of a moray eel lurking nearby.

The land aspects of the ecology of the green turtle are more readily ascertained than the sea or reef aspects. A detailed field study of this reptile done by Hendrickson (1958) provides well-documented information on the terrestrial habits and the characteristics of *Chelonia mydas*. Hendrickson follows Carr (1952) in considering that there is a single world-wide species *mydas*, although he points out that there are several recognizable forms in the Indo-Pacific which may be considered subspecies. These several recognizable forms may account for the Raroian names for eight different varieties of turtles. Although Hendrickson studied *Chelonia mydas* in Malaya and

Sarawak in southeast Asia, its ecology in the coral atolls probably is very similar, so that it will be useful here to give an abstract of Hendrickson's information. The study treats the breeding, nesting, and hatching processes, the characteristics of the environment, the characteristics of the turtles observed and their habits, and recommendations for their conservation (which might well be applied to the coral atolls on which they are becoming scarce). The following information on the green turtle is taken entirely from Hendrickson (1958).

The mating of *Chelonia mydas* is believed to occur only close to breeding beaches and occurs mostly in shallow surface water, rarely less than one-half mile from shore. The male turtle is distinguished from the female by its long tail, compared with the short stublike tail of the female. Except when stranded on the beach by a rapidly receding tide during the mating process, the male turtle is almost never found out of water. The female only goes on land to nest.

Beaches used by the turtle for nesting must have suitable sand areas. The limited number of suitable breeding beaches available imposes a limiting factor on the potential increase in turtle populations. Because of this limitation, *Chelonia mydas* tends to build up large breeding concentrations around a small number of beaches. In the record of tagged turtles, it was found that 96 per cent of the individuals tagged returned repeatedly to nest in the island previously used. The return of numbers of tagged turtles to the same beaches 3 years after tagging indicated a probable 3-year breeding cycle for Sarawak green turtles.

In Sarawak the Chelonia have a definite peak season of nesting activity in July and August which appears to coincide with the low rainfall period of maximum insolation of the monsoon season. (At this period Sarawak is in the rainshadow of the Borneo Mountains, and the rain-bearing winds are from the south-southeast. It is not known whether Chelonia that may be present along the southeast coastlands and waters of Borneo, which at this season have a rainfall maximum, have a different peak of nesting activity.) During the rainy season the sand on the "high beach" becomes too hard-packed to provide ideal stimuli to nesting instincts, according to Hendrickson. Moreover, during long rainy periods, the loss of heat at the surface of the sand and the increased heat conductivity of the wetter sand may significantly increase the heat loss from the egg chamber and lead to hatching failures.

Females ascend the beaches at twilight, when the horizon has become blurred. They spend a variable amount of time in shallow water a few centimeters deep inspecting their surroundings and are easily alarmed and flee to deep water if frightened. The turtle's vision appears roughly equal to that of the human being under the same light conditions. There is a flight response to strange objects, and this occurred when a turtle reached as close to a motionless human observer as 10 to 12 feet.

The adult turtle ascends the beach in a series of short lurches, using all four limbs like oars in unison to move the body forward and resting the plastron on the sand between strokes. The young Chelonia, by contrast, characteristically move by alternate movements of the limbs. By the direction in which the sand is pushed, it is easy to distinguish incoming from outgoing turtle tracks.

It takes most individuals up to 25 minutes to reach the "high beach" or beach area behind the beach ridge, the movement being from as little as 2 feet per minute to as much as 10 feet per minute. Once on the "high-beach" platform there may be a period of random wandering on the sand before nest digging of from 2 minutes to as much as $3\frac{1}{2}$ hours. Breathing is difficult for the turtle while out of water and limbs and head must be extended for this. Walking or digging activity thus interrupts breathing, and activity alternates with rest periods. The average time of wandering on the "high beach" is about 14 minutes.

Digging starts only after a short period of complete freedom from alarm stimuli, but digging turtles were observed to abandon their hole if disturbed by vibrations of the sand caused by other turtles or other sources too near by, even if no visual disturbances were observable. Loose sand continuing to slip into the hole dug also tended to cause abandonment. "There would appear to be adaptive advantage in this intolerance toward other turtles digging nearby in that it would induce a nightly spacing of nests over all the suitable beach area" (Hendrickson, 1958, p. 475). Contact with hard objects, rocks, driftwood, roots, or clay tended to reinforce the inclination to wander about.

In digging, the turtle throws its flippers up and back, so that a depression gradually forms in front of the turtle. During this process the turtle stops to breathe every 20 to 45 seconds for 15 to 60 seconds. Within 10 to 30 minutes it will have dug a hole 16 to 32 inches deep. In the last 5 to 15 minutes only the hind flippers are active, pushing the sand back and packing it against the rear wall of the hole. At this stage the turtle is resting horizontally in the bottom of the hole in moist sand. It now uses its hind flippers laterally to scoop out the egg cavity in the moist sand, shifting its posterior end from side to side to bring left and right flippers to median position in the egg cavity and then to scoop the sand to alternate sides.

The size and depth of the egg cavity depend upon the size of the female. It may be from 12 to 18 inches in diameter and 8 to 28 inches below the beach surface. In egg laying, both rear flippers are arranged on either side of the tail to shield the opening of the egg hole and may rest on the rim of the hole or dangle into the cavity.

Once the egg laying starts, sensitivity to external stimuli appears to be completely lost. An observer may even sit on the turtle's back without causing cessation of the egg-laying process. When the last egg is laid the turtle begins using hind flippers to push sand in sweeping arcs into the hole to cover the eggs with 5 to 8 inches of the moist sand removed in the digging process. The sand is compacted into a slight mound over the egg hole, the whole process taking about 7 to 10 minutes. Still another 15 to 60 minutes or more may be spent "swimming through" the sand and flipping sand back and forth to cover the original depression excavated. In effect, the depression of the egg pit "is moved horizontally away from the spot where the eggs were laid, leaving behind an extensive area of disturbed sand built up to a level which is often slightly above the general beach level" (Hendrickson, 1958, p. 479).

The return to the beach takes place at an average rate of about 6.5 feet per minute on the loose sand but about twice as fast on the packed beach.

The turtles nest more than once during the nesting season. Those on Sarawak averaged six to seven clutches in a breeding season, and these were laid between 9 and 12 days apart, but the intervals may be anywhere from 0 to 118 days. The number of eggs laid was found to vary from 3 to 184, the mean number being 105. Freshly laid eggs varied in weight from 28 to 48 grams and some eggs were deformed into a variety of shapes, although they normally are round. Turtles often nest in previously nested sites and thus destroy previous clutches of eggs, often scattering partially developed eggs in the surrounding area.

The eggs occupy a moist sand level and are covered by moist sand. The air in the interstices between the eggs is presumably at a continually high relative humidity, kept thus by the moist sand. In no cases were the nests found at levels where it was clear they would be constantly inundated by salt water under the sand surface. Usually the egg nest was above spring high-tide level. Although the surface beach-sand temperatures vary considerably, as much as 23°C. or 41°F., the fluctuations become gradually modified with depth. At a depth where the eggs were deposited, the measured temperatures never fluctuated more than about 2°C. or 3.6°F. The metabolic heat from the developing eggs in their insulated egg nest, however, rose much above the prevailing temperature of the sand around them, reaching temperatures as high as 35°C. or 95°F. by the time of hatching. This heat differential appears to be important in successful hatching, which is correlated with the largeness of egg clutches. Too small a clutch resulted in a proportionately too rapid heat loss to the surrounding sand, with resulting hatching failures. This heat loss also may be significantly increased during long rainy spells because of greater heat conductivity of the wet sand, and this, too, may lead to hatching failures.

Hatching after egg laying took an average time of 51.4 days, but there was a period of at least 4 to 5 days between hatching of the eggs and the struggle to the surface, as the sand capping the egg chamber gradually is eroded away by the struggle of the young turtles. A protective instinct appears to prevent their emergence during the heat of the day, when the surface temperatures would kill them in a few minutes. They emerge at night, but not all of them emerge the same night. Succeeding nights may see other batches of turtles working up to the surface from the same nest.

Upon emergence the young appear to be guided toward the lighter sea area and breaker zone by a geotrophic response which avoids the darker vegetated zone inland from the beach. This geotrophic response was confirmed by the tendency of the hatched turtles to follow the beam of an electric torch or flashlight, and they can be led in any direction by such a light. The young turtles meet a tremendous obstacle course in climbing up and down the pitted surface of the sand to reach the sea. Upon reaching the sea water they always swim against the water movement and from the time of entering the water will shy away from any large solid mass.

In a study of eight nests left undisturbed, it was found that the number of hatchlings emerging from the nests varied from 3 to 90 per cent, averaging 46.7 per cent for all the nests. Among predators of newly hatched turtles are ghost crabs (Ocypoda sp.), which also burrow into the nests. Others on Sarawak are rats, lizards (*Varanus salvator*), and snakes. The latter, however, are not normally found on atolls. In the water, sharks eat many young turtles, and also the larger turtles up to adult size. "It seems reasonable to assume that predation pressure on *Chelonia mydas* is most extreme during the first few weeks of life in the water. After this original period has passed the young turtles have not only grown somewhat and become more vigorous and better-coordinated swimmers, but they have lost the disadvantageous buoyancy which had originally prevented any effective diving, thereby severely limiting their escape activities" (Hendrickson, 1958, p. 522). The mortality rate is undoubtedly exceedingly high, even without man on the scene. How many reach the adult or mature stage and continue to live out a normal life span is not known. In estimating the necessary survival rate at various stages of existence to achieve a stable green turtle population, Hendrickson assumed an average of 100 eggs laid at a time, with six to seven clutches in a breeding season. He thought that the average female experienced at least three and possibly double this number of laying seasons, so that the total egg output during a lifetime would reach at least 1,800 eggs and possibly 3,600 eggs. On this basis he estimated that the population would remain stable if only slightly more than $\frac{1}{10}$ of 1 per cent of the turtles lived out complete lives.

The Asian green turtle appears not to mature in less than 4 years and probably in 4 to 6 years. The nesting turtles observed on Sarawak and on the Great Barrier Reef appeared to have carapaces measuring between 35 and 43 inches in length. The weights of turtles between 35 and 40 inches in length were from 200 to 250 pounds.

External parasites noted on turtles included mosquitoes, which were observed biting nesting turtles on the relatively soft skin of the upper eyelid. The encrusting barnacle *Chelonibia testudinaria* occurred commonly on about one-third of the turtles studied. These appeared to cause little inconvenience to the turtles as a rule, although the rare burrowing barnacle *Stephanolepas muricata* erodes "tumorous" cavities through the carapace, in which it has been found imbedded.

Because of the high rate of decimation of Chelonia during various stages of development, the addition of man to its list of predators may easily jeopardize the survival of turtle populations in a particular region. In many parts of the world governing authorities have regulated or restricted the taking of turtles. In the Pacific atolls and islands during the past, native taboos have restricted the eating of turtle by the common people or by women and have restricted this delicacy to chiefs or priests. These measures were a form of conservation for the privileged few. In Sarawak and Malaya Muslim custom includes an apparent prejudice against the eating of turtle flesh, but there seems to be no aversion to the eating of turtle eggs, which are much sought after here. In most other parts of the *Chelonia mydas* areas the meat is sought after avidly, and both practices if pursued too far may reduce the turtle population to below maintenance level.

Hendrickson analyzed the differences in the supply of food obtained from the slaughter of the mature female turtle and that from gathering its eggs and concluded that in three breeding seasons the average female would produce food in the form of eggs equal to the weight of food obtained from slaughtering the turtle. He believed, however, that the average adult female had more than three breeding seasons in a lifetime and thus that the weight of high-protein food which could be gathered from eggs would be greater than the weight of flesh and fat of the turtle if eaten. He had no doubt that the exploitation for wild green turtle eggs is more profitable in terms of quality and quantity of nutrition than is the exploitation for flesh and fat.

In view of the high rate of decimation of newly hatched turtles, it seems apparent that artificial hatching, providing protection from predators for the initial few days or weeks of growth, alone would aid in greatly increasing turtle supply on coral atolls. Aiding the released young turtles get distributed in deep water after their initial period of a week or more of growth would result in a large saving of turtles from predators. In considering the situation of a breeding beach in Sarawak, Hendrickson wrote:

If the beach concerned here produced a total of one million eggs per year, the annual release in deep water of 17,000 week-old baby turtles in good condition (1.7 per cent) would be inadequate [sic; probably should be *adequate*] replenishment for maintenance of a stable population. If hatchlings were not kept for a week, but were dumped into the sea on the same day they hatched, 140,000 individuals (14 per cent) would have to be produced annually; by merely scattering the day's production of hatchlings widely at sea in deep water after dark, this number could be cut to 70,000 (7 per cent), etc.

Experimental hatching from transplanted nests indicated that an average of about 47 per cent of the eggs produced hatchlings, a much higher percentage than natural production. Eggs moved on the morning after laying seemed to suffer little from relatively rough handling. However, when the embryonic disk and overlying albumen had become adherent to the shell, concussion and rotation of the developing eggs were uniformly damaging. "Hatchlings may be kept in tanks of clean sea water for about a week before they exhaust the yolk supply which is incorporated from the egg; there is no indication at present that any feeding is necessary during the first week in a nursery tank" (Hendrickson, 1958, p. 527).

The harvesting of eggs rather than the slaughter of grown turtles represents "exploitation at that stage of the life cycle where the species is adapted to sustain high losses in the natural course of events. A very large portion of the eggs collected represent, not new losses to the population, but diversion of losses which would have occurred even if there had been no intervention by man." In the slaughter of the mature female turtle, however, there "is a direct threat to the dynamic equilibrium of the population, and it would appear that the species is ill-adapted to sustain such losses" (Hendrickson, 1958, p. 525).

Hendrickson (1958, p. 528) concluded that "In a properly managed industry, up to 96 per cent or more of the average turtle's productivity may be utilized for human consumption, without removal of the producing units from the population and with the possible expectation of bonus productivity during all breeding seasons after the first three. In exploitation for flesh and fat, 100 per cent of the turtle's productivity is utilized once and for all, and that particular unit ceases to confer any benefits." In view of the poor condition of green turtle populations on Pacific atolls compared with what they once were and compared with their potential if properly conserved, it seems imperative that the administrations concerned institute measures to control exploitation and, equally important, educate the atoll peoples to the advantages to them of conservation practices and of artificial breeding for local dispersal of young turtles.

Terrestrial crabs

"The dominant note in the life of a coral atoll," wrote Hedley (1896, pp. 127–8), ". . . struck me as the abundance and ubiquity of Crustacea. . . . Not an inch of the atoll world is secure from them."

Three types of crabs are found on most coral atoll islets: the so-called land crab (Plate 86), the coconut crab (Plate 87), and the hermit crab (Plate 88). All are important scavengers and the first two do a great amount of burrowing, some of which is helpful in moving surface organic matter underground, where it may be utilized by plant roots.

The habits of the coconut crab (*Birgus latro*) have been the subject of much controversy in the literature. Its giant size among land crabs, as well as its tasty flesh, have focussed special attention upon it both by the people who eat it and by those who study it. A map of its distribution by Reyne (1939, p. 315) shows that it is found throughout the tropical Pacific Islands except for the Hawaiian group, Wake, and Midway, and it is found in the west Pacific from Timor to the Ryukyus. Among the Indian Ocean islands, it also is found in the islands south of the equator. Although it has this great geographic spread, it probably does not occur on all atolls, since on the very dry atolls it does not find enough suitable food. In the northern Marshalls, for instance, Fosberg (1956, p. 232) wrote that it was found on possibly all the atolls except Bikar and Pokak (Taongi). Coconut crabs are common only on the smaller and less-inhabited atolls, where they have not been subject to as intensive hunting by the inhabitants. Degener and Gillaspy (1955) do not mention it among the crustacea of arid Canton Atoll. On the other hand, wetter Gardner Atoll in the same group was said to have a large number of coconut crabs (Ellis, 1936). In the moderately moist Ellice Islands some 80 years ago Gill (1876, p. 275) found that "These crabs are so plentiful as to constitute an important article of diet amongst the natives." Streets (1877, p. 72) described Washington Atoll as "the home of the gigantic *Birgus latro* . . . ," but he says nothing of its occurrence on Fanning, which he also described. However, Hermes (1926, p. 254) revealed 50 years later that "Coconut crabs, while still to be found on Washington Island, are almost extinct on Fanning Island. . . ." On Palmyra Atoll, Rock (1916, p. 16) found "the much talked of coconut crab (*Birgus latro*) which abounds in great numbers . . . some of enormous size. . . ." Friederici (1910) wrote that "In addition to rats on Maria [in the Tuamotus] we saw a considerable number of coconut crabs." Bates and Abbott (1958, pp. 114–15) found the coconut crab a rarity on Ifalik, apparently surviving only on the uninhabited little islet of Ella. However, on Oroluk Atoll this crab was reported to have carried off rat traps set by Marshall (1957, p. 5). Neither Danielsson (1955) nor Morrison (1954) mention the coconut crab among the land animals of Raroia, so it must be scarce or absent here. At Anaa Atoll, however, Cuzent 75 years ago (1884) attributed much damage of young coconuts to these crabs, which he said climbed to the top of the palms and cut the young nuts off, then climbed down and broke them open to eat the meat. One such specimen was said to have been more than 60 centimeters long, surely a giant even among coconut crabs. Dana (1849, p. 69) saw great numbers of coconut crabs burrowing over Swain's Island, some of them 6 inches in breadth (of carapace). On Kapingamarangi the writer accompanied some young men and boys at night in the catching of several medium- and large-sized coconut crabs in 1954. By day some were observed in burrows under breadfruit tree roots. Here, too, as pointed out by Niering (1956, p. 18) the pressure on this delicacy keeps the population at a minimum. The coconut crab is rare also on Onotoa in the Gilberts, apparently for the same reason (Moul, 1957, p. 10).

Some writers (Cuzent, 1884; MacGinitie and MacGinitie, 1949; Verrill, 1940; Gill, 1876; Farrell, 1928), although unable to cite instances of actual observation of *Birgus latro* climbing coconut trees to cut down nuts, nevertheless claim that this occurs. Reyne (1939, p. 314) asserted, on the other hand, that no naturalist has witnessed the crab opening a coconut, although coconuts broken by their fall might very well be opened by the crab.

According to Gibson-Hill (1949), a considerable portion of the writing on the crab claims that it feeds only or largely on coconuts and that it climbs the palms to fetch them. Most of these descriptions were based on accounts of Rumphius, Darwin, and Forbes, who in turn got the information from natives. Gibson-Hill thought that there is no doubt that the crab feeds readily on coconut flesh, and does climb trees, and can open cracked nuts; "But I believe that it is unable to break into an undamaged one, and that it certainly does not ascend the palms in search of them."

That the coconut crab can climb trees is verified by Seurat (1905, p. 147), who said that he placed one of these animals at the foot of a coconut tree and observed that he could easily climb this tree, using the pincers and the fourth pair of legs. Hedley (1896, p. 128) wrote that "As everybody knows, Birgus is as much at home on a palm bole as a squirrel on an oak."

Bates and Abbott (1958, p. 115) cited two natives of Ifalik who asserted that the crabs very definitely did open intact nuts that had fallen to the ground. These men showed them the evidence in the form of strips torn off the nut and pieces of the hard shell. They claimed that the crabs used one of their claws to scratch the husk to enable them to pull off strips of fiber. Thereafter, the crabs would use one finger of the claw to pierce the soft eye and break open the shell. Both men claimed to have watched the process. Although they often had seen the crabs in the tops of the palms eating young leaves, they had not seen a crab actually cut down a nut. The authors pointed out that, of course, the coconut crab is not confined to a pure coconut diet but scavenges for all kinds of food.

There is no doubt of the strength of this crab, although some of the feats it performs are probably only done by the larger animals. Cuzent (1884) collected a specimen more than 60 centimeters long, while Gibson-Hill (1949) claimed that a fully mature adult weighs between 5 and 6 pounds, with a width across the carapace of over 6 inches and an extreme span from the tips of the first pair of walking legs of nearly 3 feet. They have been known to rip open a strong biscuit tin with the lid bound down with wire and to escape from a box made with ½-inch planking. A snap of their pincer can cause an ugly wound, but they may be handled safely if care is taken (Plate 87).

The animal appears to be omnivorous, like the allied genus Cöenobita (hermit crab), but it is attracted to coconut meat. No reports condemn it as a pest to coconut culture. There probably are too few large crabs around to do much damage. It has been seen in Pandanus trees eating the fruit (Reyne, 1939). This appeared to be one of its chief foods on Maria Atoll when visited by Friederici in 1910, for there were no coconut palms here, although Pandanus were plentiful. It also will eat dead fish, dead rats, or dead crabs, including its own kind (Reyne, 1939). The flavor of coconut-crab meat is affected by its diet, and the meat may be bitter after it has been feeding on certain fruits (Gibson-Hill, 1949). Whether it is for this or other reasons is not known, but Jungmichel (1862) reported that the people of Mapia Atoll north of western New Guinea did not eat the coconut crab, the only report of this aversion noted by the writer.

According to Gill (1876), the *Birgus latro* hibernates about the beginning of July and emerges from its seclusion at the end of October. During its period of seclusion it is in a quiescent state in its burrow deep at the end of a passage blocked with soil and debris. This is the period when it molts its old shell and acquires a new and larger one. This also is the period when its tail is fat, and the natives eagerly seek it at this stage. After November and December, which are the spawning months, they are not valued for eating. At this season the female goes down to the sea and dips her tail in the water, "causing thousands of eggs to hatch the moment they were moistened" (Schultz, 1948, p. 301).

Hermit crabs (*Coenobita* sp.) swarm over the land areas of all atolls in huge numbers. They are active day and night, dragging their adopted shell home with them wherever they go. However, during the day, especially where larger animals or man are moving about them, they tend to withdraw into their shells and lie still on the ground as though they were just other pebbles among the coral debris. They tend to be somewhat nocturnal in that they are most active after dark. Seurat (1904) stated that "*Cenobita perlata* is extremely abundant on all the low islands (motus) of the Gambier and Tuamotu Archipelagoes. In many uninhabited islands it is the main part of the terrestrial fauna together with birds. Natives use them as bait for fishing, breaking the shell and sticking the soft abdomen on the hook; most fish are very fond of this bait." Fosberg (1956, p. 231) thought that this practice not only makes them scarcer around inhabited islets but also may be responsible for the abundance of flies on inhabited islets. In describing the crustacea of Canton, Degener and Gillaspy (1955, p. 46) wrote:

The crabs that are really best adapted to terrestrial life, arouse interest and cause worry are the countless small pale hermit crabs *Coenobita perlatus*. Every small dead spiral mollusk shell—there must be hundreds of thousands available about Canton—houses one of these lopsided, soft-abdomened animals. They are particularly numerous feeding on the jetsam along the beach facing the lagoon, and also penetrate inland. Here they may be found seeking protection from the heat of the day under branches, fallen leaves and coral slabs, and in shaded crevices. As these crabs increase in size their housing shortage, for lack of an abundant supply of large mollusk shells, must be so acute as to cause a catastrophe eventually among them. Only those that can find the comparatively rare, cats-eye shell (Turbo), measuring up to about three inches in diameter, survive. Even so, these mature hermit crabs, now red like boiled lobsters, are numerous enough to over-run the island.

Atoll hermit crabs come in only a few species, which are very widespread. *Coenobita perlatus* appears to be most common. Bryan (1903) listed *C. olivieri* and *C. compressa* for Marcus Island but did not include *C. perlatus*. On Palmyra *C. olivieri* is the only species mentioned by Rock (1916, p. 14). Neither of the two species mentioned by Bryan is included by Holthuis (1953, pp. 36–41) (collections from the Marshalls in 1950–1952, Onotoa in 1951, Raroia in 1952). However, Holthuis, in addition to *C. perlatus*, names *C. brevimanus, C. carnescens, C. rugosus,* and *C. spinosus. C. perlatus* and *C. brevimanus* were present on Kapingamarangi (Niering, 1956, pp. 16–17).

Fosberg (1956, p. 231) pointed out that these crabs are not only completely harmless but are very useful animals, eating dead organic matter of the sort that would normally decay and produce bad odors as well as breeding places for flies. However, they can be a nuisance. Any food placed within their reach may attract them in large numbers, and, since they are adept at climbing all kinds of obstacles, care must be taken in storing food. Rock (1916) found that the Palmyra hermit crabs attacked his bags of rice and other victuals, the contents of which he found on the ground after his first night ashore. Seurat (1904) said that they have a strong sense of smell. "If we ate several times in the same place, at first there would be a few of them, later droves." Some of them climbed onto his table, eating anything. The hermit crabs also are partial to certain plant flowers and fruits. Rock saw them feeding on the flowers of Messerschmidia trees. On Jaluit Schnee (1902, p. 138) caught half a dozen crabs which had dragged their shells up the smooth stem of the native lily (spider lily?) and had eaten off the flowers.

On the arid atolls, their search for food may have a serious effect on vegetation. Degener and Gillaspy (1955, p. 47) wrote that the hermit crabs on Canton Atoll living far from the rookeries were per force mainly vegetarian.

They seem to browse among the vegetation, and even climb *kou* [*Cordia subcordata*] trunks and branches as high as four and a half feet in search of food. They eat the bark along the upper side, most *kou* trees showing long scars, the result of past injury. A common habit, especially of the less heavy individuals, is to cleverly tear off and eat only the ovary and stamens of the flowers of *Portulaca lutea* and of the local Sesuvium. In the latter, I also observed them boring out of the ovary the ripening seeds for food. These are certainly not isolated acts, but ones perfected by practice and perhaps instinct. They probably decimate the flora, feeding particularly on tender seedlings of certain species, which ones have not yet been determined. I believe these hermit crabs are largely responsible for the paucity of different kinds of plants on Canton, any seeds of new kinds of plants washing to its shores being subject to their inspection on germination and, if palatable, sacrificed to their appetite. The foreign plants now being introduced as seeds and seedlings to Canton likewise must not only surmount the drastic conditions of drought and salinity, but must surmount the hurdle of voracious hermitcrabs.

It has not been reported whether Coenobita injures germinating coconuts, but in some areas, for example, Kapingamarangi, the natives tie nuts to branches or put them on roof tops until the sprouts are well formed, after which crabs apparently do not harm them. Niering (1956) observed the crabs chewing the tips of the twigs of Barringtonia and damaging petioles of Guettarda. Terminal portions of seedlings of breadfruit, Calophyllum, and Hibiscus were nipped off by crabs, he thought.

Seurat (1904) has described some of the habits of hermit crabs which he studied in the Tuamotus. He stated that the youngest stage of Coenobita must be looked for on the outer reef or lagoon shore under stones left dry at low tide. At this stage the animals are aquatic in life and inhabit small shells of *Nerita maxima*, *N. plicata*, *Cerithium rugosum*, *Littorina obesa*, etc., usually selecting shells that are in a good state of preservation. The adults like shells of *Turbo setosus,* which were abundant on the outer reef and in the lagoon. Medium-sized animals take the most common shells of the right size. At South Marutea they chose first *Echinella coronaria,* which were very common on the dead reef flat, then shells of *Littornia obesa.* Larger, but not yet adult, hermit crabs chose shells of Natices, Cassidaires, Murex, or young *Turbo.*

The hermit crab has too little hooks at the end of his tail, with which he grips the interior of the shell so tightly that he seems to be cemented to it. The animal will let itself be pulled in two rather than to be pulled straight out, but it may be extracted by twisting his cephalothorax in the opposite direction to that of the shells' twist, pulling at the same time. The animal also comes out if the shell is held over a flame.

Seurat said that the shell always contains some sea water, which is retained normally to keep the gills wet. Every evening at sundown the hermit crabs go to the lagoon shore to let the waves wet them and renew their supply of water. This often may involve a strenuous trip of as much as 200 meters. After a few minutes, they climb back to the interior of the islets. This necessity would appear to be an important reason for their greater scarcity in the central part of large islets.

According to Seurat, the animal gets out of his shell to defecate. Its eggs develop inside the shell and are attached to the abdominal legs. At an advanced stage the female goes to the sea or lagoon and drops the eggs into the water. He found that in September at South Marutea the hermit crabs had not yet laid their eggs. They appear to molt their skins in October about the same time as the coconut crab, and females were found with well-developed eggs in December.

Hermit crabs are not usually eaten by the atoll people, but Seurat said that in some of the Tuamotu atolls, especially at Tureia Atoll, the natives do eat hermit crabs.

In the interior of some of the islets of Palmyra where the undergrowth is not so dense, Rock (1916) found that the ground was undermined and when walking along one was likely to sink a foot or more into the ground. These excavations, he found, were made by a large land crab a foot or so in diameter, which he identified as a species of *Cardisoma* that might be identical with *C. obesum,* collected by Streets on Fanning Atoll. In all, Holthuis (1953) recorded some 15 land-crab species from collections made between 1950 and 1952 in the Marshalls, at Onotoa in the Gilberts, and at Raroia in the Tuamotus, not including *C. obesum* but including two other Cardisoma, *C. carnifex* and *C. rotundum.* At Raroia on the dry rock flats of many windward islets covered with low but very dense growths of Suriana and Pemphis, there were many individuals of *C. carnifex.* Their burrows were all over the lower ground of some islands, but at night, when they are most active, these crabs may range all over the higher ground a considerable distance from water (Morrison, 1954).

Among the more abundant forms of land crabs at Kapingamarangi, Niering (1956) found *Cardisoma rotundum* and *Gecarcoidea lalandei*. Of lesser importance were such forms as *Metasesarma aubryi, Sesarma rotundatum, Geograpsus crinipes,* and *G. grayi*. They were found on all islets but were most numerous on the larger ones, occurring both above and below ground. The numerous holes in the scattered porous rock offered a natural habitat, while in sandy areas the land crabs dug holes at least 18 inches deep. Niering observed areas in the loose rubble where within a 10-by-10-foot square he counted up to fifteen holes. "The banks surrounding the puraka [Cyrtosperma] pits are undermined with holes which occur in a layer-like fashion among the breadfruit roots. The amount of constant sloughing of the banks indicates considerable activity."

In a strip transect 40,560 square feet in area, Niering counted a total of 316 hermit, 205 land, and 5 coconut crabs. In a single square 52 by 52 feet the maximum number was 72 hermit and 38 land crabs. The maximum number of crabs were observed under the older coconut palms, where they utilized piles of coconut husks for hiding places. On the other hand, the sandy, loose rubble lagoonward contained numerous burrows, with few crabs visible. Crabs and burrows along the transect were most numerous near shore and less numerous in the center of the island.

At Ifalik Abbott found that the land crabs burrowed in the ground almost everywhere, but the large Cardisoma apparently did not burrow in the mud near the edges of the Cyrtosperma fields, where other smaller land crabs made their holes. In rough transect counts he found that there was an average of some 22 Cardisoma holes per 100 square feet, about half of which appeared currently occupied (Bates and Abbott, 1958, pp. 241–2).

According to the Ifalikians, the land crabs come out in great numbers on three nights of full moon each month during the summer months of May, June, and July, going down to the beach to spawn. Probably the basic spawning rhythm wherein eggs are matured once a year is physiological, but "the trigger for spawning, whereby the crabs went down to the water on only a few particular nights, might have been a response to either the tide or the light. The crab holes on the land probably went down to water level, so that water in the holes would rise and fall with the tides; and the crabs, coming out to forage every night, might also easily react to the changing intensity of moonlight" (Bates and Abbott, 1958, pp. 99–100).

During this spawning period the Ifalik people caught them in great numbers; they prize them for food, especially the egg masses. Bates thought the flavor not unlike that of shad roe. There is a considerable amount of very tasty flesh, not only in the claws and legs but also in the body. In a dissection of four specimens, he found that the aggregate weight of the flesh was about 9 ounces out of the total body weight of 1 pound, $7\frac{1}{2}$ ounces, or a total of about 2 ounces of food per crab (Bates and Abbott, 1958, pp. 101–3).

Terrestrial mollusks

Only a few brief notes are available on the land mollusks of coral atolls. Hedley (1896, p. 397) remarked that land shells of the Ellice Islands procured by Graefte have been described by Mousson (1873). "The distinction between the marine and terrestrial mollusca, so sharply drawn in temperate zones," said Hedley, "fades away in the tropics. At a distance from the sea, in close association with such forms as Stenogyra and Endodonta, occur Littorina, Nerita, Truncatella, and Melampus." The latter forms, however, are shore-zone mollusks. Farther inland, on the higher sandier ground and in the leafmold of the coconut groves, Morrison (1954, p. 3) on Raroia and Moul (1954, pp. 9–10) on Onotoa found that a few species of small land snails occur. On Raroia, according to Morrison,

These include the ubiquitous, tiny white *Gastrocopta pediculus* Shuttleworth, a tiny reddish species of Nesopupa, *Lamellidea serrata* Pease, *Lamellidea oblonga* Pease, and two species of Opeas. It seems likely that this helicinid snail and both the species of Lamellidea were carried to Raroia with the plants brought there by the Polynesian natives. Around one of the brackish (or fresh?) groundwater ponds was found another landoperculate, a species of Syncera (or Omphalotropis?), white in color, that seems distinct from its gold-colored relative found along the salty lagoon shores in certain places. All of these small land snails are facultatively xerophytic; that is, they can withstand considerable heat and drought between rains and during the dry season.

The terrestrial mollusks found on Onotoa included *Opeas gracilis junceus*, *Lamellidea peponum*, and three forms of Gastrocopta—*G. pedicula, G. pedicula nacca,* and *G. lyonsiana.* One fresh-water snail was found in a mass of green algae in a well. This closely resembled a *Melanoides* sp. found on Niaofou (Moul, 1957).

Worms

Aside from parasitic worms in human beings and other animals, atolls also have some earthworms, such as *Pheretima upoluensis, P. bincincta,* and Dichogaster sp., found on Kapingamarangi by Niering (1956, p. 16). *Pheretima upoluensis* and *P. montana* were found on Raroia by Morrison (1954), who said that they undoubtedly came to Raroia in soil on the roots of plants brought by the Polynesians generations ago. In Raroia the earthworms were found only in the deeper leafmold layers of lower, more-moist ground and in the denser stands of Guettarda and other trees, away from the presently cleared coconut groves. He found them extremely active and "jumpy" when disturbed. Although Niering did not find them common, he said that they were locally abundant wherever there is considerable moisture and organic matter in the process of decomposition, especially in such areas as the moist humus under piles of coconut husks. In one such area, in a sample plot ½ by ½ meter square and 15 centimeters deep that had been treated with mercuric chloride, he sifted out 101 specimens. One new species was found from this atoll by G. E. Gates, who determined the annelids.

Moul (1957) said that a number of Nematode worms were found in algal material taken from brackish pools and Cyrtosperma pits on Onotoa, but the identification was not given.

Referring to the northern Marshalls, Fosberg (1956, p. 230) wrote that earthworms exist here as elsewhere; the greatest number are found in rotting coconut logs and other concentrations of decomposing organic matter as well as in old taro pits.

Spiders, scorpions, and centipedes

Among the animals recorded by the Funafuti expedition were 27 arachnids and 5 myriopods. These species appear to be well represented for such a barren habitat as a coral atoll (Hedley, 1896, p. 391). Spiders and scorpions have been noted by many atoll students. Spiders are the most numerous.

A number of different spiders are found on atolls, and most of them are very useful in preying on mosquitoes and flies. Only one harmful species, the "false black widow," *Latrodectus geometricus,* was found in one atoll of the northern Marshalls; this one was introduced on Kwajelein, probably by military equipment. A parasitic wasp, *Eurytoma* sp., was introduced in 1950 to control it, and it is not known whether the spider persists.

On Onotoa a large black-and-yellow species of orb weaver was ubiquitous, according to Moul (1957, pp. 10–11). Its webs stretched between branches of low shrubs or across the paths in Scaevola, Guettarda, and Pandanus thickets. Most of the webs were found to be empty, but their very number indicated a fairly abundant food supply for the weavers. Large crab spiders with legs up to 2½ inches long occurred quite commonly. These were provisionally identified as belonging to the family Heteropodidae (Sparassidae). In the web of one a gecko was completely covered with silk, and the spider spent most of two days feeding upon it. Other spiders at Onotoa included a "jumping spider" found in the litter under trees and on the leaves of trees.

Usinger and La Rivers (1953, p. 6) were impressed with the great number of crab spiders hunting on the rocks and vegetation bordering the lagoon sand on Arno. By directing a flashlight at night at eye level, they could see the light reflected in myriads of diamond-bright points which proved to be the eye shine of hunting spiders.

On Marcus, Bryan (1903) found that the only spider that had established itself was "the widely distributed web-spinning species, *Epeira nautica* Koch." He found their stout webs quite a nuisance as he walked through the forest. The writer has had to brush spider webs from his path through the forests and plantations of many atolls in the Marshalls.

Centipedes and scorpions also are found on most atolls, according to Sachet (1953), and they often inspire unwarranted fears. Although scorpions in some parts of the world can be deadly, Sachet asserted that the scorpions that occur on atolls are rather small and relatively harmless. Their sting is painful, but the pain vanishes after some hours, leaving no after effects.

Two of the six families of scorpions have been recorded from atolls. In the family Scorpionidae is the species *Hormurus australasiae*. It has been found under sticks and stones, in coconut trash, and under the bark of dead logs. At Onotoa one was found in a box of food and clothing (Moul, 1957, p. 11). This scorpion also has been found on Ailuk, Ailinglaplap, Arno, and Bikini in the Marshalls; Ulithi, Kapingamarangi, and Nukuoro in the western and eastern Carolines respectively; at Raroia in the Tuamotus; Funafuti in the Ellices; and at Duizend Eilanden in Indonesia. This would appear to justify the statement that it is found on atolls throughout the Pacific. In the family Buthidae three and possibly more species are found on atolls. *Isometrus maculatus* is found on Jemo and other Marshalls islands, on Canton Atoll, on Pratas in the South China Sea, and on a number of atolls in the Indian ocean. Two species of Lychas have been recorded on atolls, *L. scutatus* on Cocos-Keeling and *L. mucronatus* in the Duizend Eilanden but none in the oceanic atolls of the Pacific (Sachet, 1953).

Fosberg (1956, p. 230) wrote of the northern Marshalls that a few small centipedes (*Scolopendra* sp.) were found on some of the atolls, but that nothing is known of their habits or the extent of occurrence, although probably they are capable of biting rather painfully. It is likely that their distribution extends to the Carolines and other atoll groups farther south.

Usinger and La Rivers (1953, p. 14) said that the Arno Atoll Marshallese very much feared scorpions and centipedes. Although admitting no personal experience, they asserted that the bite of a centipede or the sting of a scorpion usually are of the order of severity of a bad bee sting, and they thought that the native fears were exaggerated. However, it is known that in the case of a bee sting, different people have various reactions. Some people show such an extreme allergy to a bee sting that it may be fatal to them; others shrug it off easily. It is possible that severe reactions among some individuals of the Marshallese to scorpion or centipede bites have aroused exaggerated fears.

Origin and dispersal of atoll insects

Since the vast space of the eastern Pacific is as great an obstacle to westward migration of fauna from the Americas as it is to plants, we may look for a parallel pattern in floral and faunal dispersion in general among the Pacific islands and atolls. Moreover, most of the forces that disseminate plants and insects to oceanic islands are the same (Gressitt, 1954, p. 20). It is not surprising, therefore, that we find among certain animals the same kind of attenuation of species with progression eastward as is found among the flora (Hedley, 1896, p. 397). Until recently there has been, furthermore, no sign of an American emigration of fauna to Polynesia.

Garrett's tabulation of the range of three families of marine Mollusca indicates this eastward deterioration in fauna for some marine forms from Fiji and Tonga to the Carolines, Cooks, Tuamotus, and the distant groups of Hawaii and the Marquesas. A similar listing for insects (Gressitt, 1954, p. 135) indicates that in total number the Fiji Islands have an estimated 25,000, Micronesia some 10,000, Samoa some 7,000, and the Society Islands some 1,000. This certainly appears to support the picture of eastward deterioration. On the other hand, Hawaii has an estimated 12,000 species, while the Marquesas have an estimated 2,000. These figures, of course, are very rough estimates based on a variety of criteria, such as the numbers actually collected (from only an eighth to almost half of the numbers estimated), the length of time for any one collector, the number of collectors, the habitat coverage, and so on. Not enough is known about the insects to make reliable pictures of the areas of origin in detail, but it appears clear that the origins of most of the insects in the Pacific Islands are in the west.

According to Gressitt (1954, p. 133),

Essentially, Micronesia has an insect fauna of small species, the ancestors of many of which might have been brought by air or by objects floating on the sea, plus a considerable number brought by man. Possible sources include all the neighboring areas, such as Japan, the Ryukyu Islands, Formosa, the Philippines, the Moluccas, New Guinea, the Bismarck Archipelago, and islands of eastern Melanesia and central and southeastern

Polynesia. The fact that there is much in common with central and southern Polynesia does not, perhaps, any more mean migration from that direction than a more or less common origin relating to the type of insects transported, or than a more or less common source of origin, which probably centered in eastern Melanesia. On the other hand, there is much evidence, particularly in western Micronesia, of Asian origins of insect types scarce or lacking in Polynesia . . . The Melanesian influence is also strong in the west.

Gressitt (1954, p. 8) wrote that the early Polynesian and Micronesian migrants moving eastward in the Pacific and carrying various foods and plants in their canoes inevitably brought with them such insects as ants, cockroaches, flies, and other household pests. The latter include beetles and moths which attack dried foods, insects associated with their plants, and body parasites. He thought, however, that the number of species the early immigrants brought with them was small compared with those brought by more recent voyagers and traders. It would appear that even mosquitoes were relatively recent immigrants to some atolls. Hedley (1896, p. 411) noted that Gill stated in 1885 that mosquitoes were accidentally conveyed in water casks to Penryhn and Rakahanga Atolls in 1859 and to Manihiki in 1862.

Hedley pointed out that it is known to most collectors of insects that numbers of small invertebrates attach, either as ova, larva, or adult, to fallen leaves and that a gust of typhoon wind easily might launch these leaves and propel them to islands a hundred miles distant or more. Thus a dozen species of insects, spiders, and snails might fall at once on an island where no life was before. He was quite satisfied that herein lies the explanation of the wide distribution of Helicina, Endodonta, and Tornatellina in the south Pacific. Gressitt (1954, p. 130) thought that possibly most of the natural infiltration of insects to oceanic islands is to be attributed to movements in the atmosphere.

Among the Micronesian islands and atolls, Gressitt gave importance to the southern component of cyclonic vortices, whether or not they developed into hurricanes. These components are west winds, which accompany the northwestward progress of the vortices and lie roughly between 0 and 5°N. According to Gressitt (1954, p. 131),

Thus during the so-called wet season, west winds may extend for several weeks at a time along the equator from Asia across the Carolines to the southern Marshalls, and may attain speeds as high as 28 km/hr (15 knots), even in the absence of typhoons. Frequent temporary changes, therefore, must not be overlooked in assessing transport of insects by air currents in terms of average wind directions, or in terms of sources and directions of storms. Above the surface winds are high air currents (jet streams) of great velocity and of different directions from surface winds. Though largely above probable survival levels for most insects, they may have some role in dissemination. The proximity of the Mariana and western Caroline islands to Formosa, the Philippines, the Moluccas and New Guinea would suggest possibilities of transfer of insects in the winds circulating around vortices; that is, in directions opposite to the trade winds.

Buoyant insects such as the plentiful small moths and the dragonflies and damselflies are most apt to have arrived at isolated atolls airborne. The more compact or heavy-bodied insects, such as weevils and other beetles, are more likely to have come via floating logs or other objects or by hitch-hiking rides in man-invented transport. Ants may be carried to distant isles during their mating flights aloft. Many insects carried by air currents, according to Gressitt, are small species, and may even be wingless. He mentions a high-altitude record of 9,140 meters for spiders cited by Glick (1939). Oddly enough, species of the relatively stronger flying butterfly are less numerous than those of small moths. However, the sphinx moths and certain nymphalid butterflies like Hypolimnas and Precis are strong fliers and probably arrived on isolated islands partially under their own power rather than by being carried passively by air currents, as was probably the case for a large part of the small-winged or nonwinged species of insects, and arachnids were undoubtedly carried by air currents (Gressitt, 1954, p. 132).

The monarch butterfly, though absent when the milkweed, its host, is wanting, arrives soon after the accidental or deliberate establishment of the milkweed (Asclepias curassavica).

Many recent introductions by man have occurred on atolls because of the great amount of communications and transport, especially during and after World War II. Some of these are seriously detrimental to the atoll economy or to the people's health and comfort. Among these that have been introduced to such atolls as Kwajelein, Eniwetok, and Majuro are the infamous migratory locust and a second, slightly smaller grasshopper, the night mosquito, the Odynerus wasp, and a tick (Usinger and La Rivers, 1953, p. 21).

Insect numbers

Earlier it was noted that the total insect fauna for the atolls of Micronesia was estimated at only 2,000 species—relatively few compared with the number for high volcanic islands and continental areas of similar size. Nevertheless, even this smaller number is so large in the consideration of insect ecology that the subject of atoll insects and ecology is quite immense. Gressitt (1954, p. 144) has pointed out that atoll insect ecology has received very little attention and that the accumulation of ecological data has been limited and generally incidental to other studies.

The numbers of insects on atolls varies considerably, depending upon their geographical position with respect to rainfall zones, to distance from other atolls and especially from "high islands" or continental areas, and to position upwind or downwind of other land areas.

However, in order to have comparative figures on the number of insect species on different atolls, each atoll should have been covered with as much intensity as was necessary to obtain the identities of nearly all the insects present. Few atolls have had this intensive coverage. Gressitt compared the insect species for three atolls: Ngaiangle (Kayangel), a small humid atoll close to a large high island (Babelthuap); Arno, a fairly large, humid atoll in the southern Marshalls; and Onotoa, about the same size but relatively dry. The numbers of insect species recorded from the three atolls are 273, 296, and 96, respectively. However, only about 24 hours was spent in collecting on Ngaiangle. The collection from Arno, on the other hand, represents a thorough searching for several months and presumably is closer to the total fauna present. The collection from Onotoa represents a season's part-time work by a botanist, who was concerned chiefly with plants.

In a prediction as to insect numbers to be expected on different kinds of atolls Townes (1946) estimated that a large, humid atoll like Ulithi, relatively close to high islands and continental areas, might possess an insect fauna of 1,200 species, whereas a rich, isolated, large atoll might have 800 species and a large, dry atoll like Eniwetok and others in the northern Marshalls might have 500 species. Gressitt (1954, p. 135) thought that these might be somewhat too high estimates. He estimated the likely total fauna for Ngaiangle at 1,100, for Arno 500, and for Onotoa 170. On Funafuti, which is three times as wet as Onotoa and which Hedley (1896, p. 391) claimed was the most fully surveyed zoologically of any central Pacific island up to his time, only 42 insects were collected. Arid Canton Atoll, a "well-collected atoll," was reported to have 108 arthropods, 93 of them insects and 15 belonging to related orders (Van Zwaluwenburg, 1955, p. 11). If Onotoa actually may be credited with 170 insect species, and if arid Canton actually has a total of 93 species, then Funafuti might reasonably be expected to have over 200 species, and Funafuti may not be as depauperate in insects as Hedley's 42 species would appear to make it out to be.

Insect ecology

Studies of insect ecology on atolls are limited. One of the most complete is that concerning wet Arno Atoll by Usinger and La Rivers (1953). Another important study is that of Moul on dry Onotoa Atoll. Other more incidental notes are found in Fosberg (1956, pp. 226–9), Catala (1957), and Niering (1956).

The considerable variety of distinct plant and animal associations that exist in the practically level land of similar origin and relatively uniform composition comes as a surprise to atoll observers, according to Usinger and La Rivers. They find that at Arno there are at least four distinct terrestrial communities and numerous distinct but interrelated strata within each. These are in addition to the marine habitat, which includes tide pools and the open ocean inhabited by water striders. They list these four as the strand community, the inner beach community, the open woodland community, and the canopy woodland community. They also add a fifth entitled the human community.

In these communities (which are listed in Appendix D) the authors have attempted to show some of the food chains as they exist on Arno Atoll in the southern Marshalls. Although quantitative data are lacking, it may be accepted as a basic premise that the herbivores of small size were most numerous. In the earlier discussions about atoll reptiles, the authors' comment was noted that most of the atoll food chains end with lizards, even though lizards form the sporadic food of cuckoos, herons, chickens, and even land crabs. The significance of the data presented, according to Usinger and La Rivers (1953, p. 18), is "that the majority of the food chains are independent of man. Only in the immediate vicinity of villages is the picture significantly altered and in such places man enters the basic food chains mainly via chickens and pigs. Aside from this, man has moved into the atoll biota and made his own niche."

Some special and noteworthy aspects of the ecological communities are described in the following sections, principally from Usinger and La Rivers (1953).

The strand. The strand supports few insects except robber flies, capturing mostly flies. At night, however, great numbers of a small white cricket were observed to be ranging all over the beaches, especially at low tide, when the greatest expanse of beach was exposed. They appeared quite agile at catching small flying ants and seemed to be omnivorous, even attacking their own wounded fellows. However, their large numbers and the small numbers of prey available to them indicated that they probably fed on plant matter and were thus an important agent in reducing plant materials. They themselves were preyed upon by the ghost crabs and probably by the crab spiders, which roamed the beaches as well.

In the intertidal zone insects are virtually absent. However, numerous flies, usually absent from this zone, are attracted to the human feces deposited here for tidal flushing.

The inner beach. Each of the strand plants, Scaevola, Messerschmidia, Guettarda, Pipturus, and Cordia, harbors a distinct fauna. A leaf-mining agromyzid fly makes conspicuous serpentine burrows in the thick Scaevola leaves. Caterpillars of the Achaea moth associate with Cordia; the day-flying moth, Utetheisa, with red and black spots on a white background, is found on Messerschmidia; and the beautiful blue Hypolimnas butterfly associates with Sida.

The rich habitat in the dying or dead limbs and leaves of Scaevola and Messerschmidia, burned by the natives to provide space for coconut palms, attract two Scolytid beetles, a round-headed borer, and several predaceous rove beetles. Other beetles here included two predaceous bugs of the family Anthocoridae and a little predator called Ceratocombus. Scaevola supports a small endemic bug, Campylomma, with distinctive spots on its hind legs. Pemphis was the only strand plant here that appeared to be inhospitable to insects, for none was found on this unusually hard-wooded tree. However, on Jaluit, not far to the southwest, Schnee found many lace-wing flies (*Chrysopa jaluitiana*) on the leaves of *Pemphis acidula*. Some small red coccidae were also seen apparently attacking the Pemphis leaves, thickening and deforming them. The Chrysopa larvae probably were feeding on the coccidae (Kempny, 1904, p. 355).

The open woodland. The coconut-pandanus forest is an open type of forest allowing sunlight to reach the ground much of the day. Although many other parts of the tropics have coconut-palm pests, Arno appeared singularly free of them. The most conspicuous pest on fronds and green husks was the Micronesian coconut scale, an oval, reddish scale nearly a quarter of an inch in diameter. However, insect life teemed on the trunk and base of the tree. A whole community is gathered here for the protection afforded by the tree. These include several kinds of cockroach, small bark lice, earwigs, ants, and the like, all of which fall prey to the roving skinks of the same habitat.

The Pandanus does not provide as good protection as the coconut palm and only at the bases of the fronds is there a microhabitat. Enough rain-water accumulates to sustain dragonfly naiads and mosquitoes, although on Arno only earwigs and small beetles were found, because moisture was insufficient during the period of observation. Decaying Pandanus fruits on the ground, however, have enough sugar content to harbor vinegar flies (Drosophila), fruit beetles (Nitidulidae), and many predators such as Staphylinidae, Antocoridae, and Ceratocombidae. A small and active white predaceous mite is found here also.

Under the coconut and Pandanus and in the openings between them there is a considerable and sometimes dense growth of ground-cover plants that is rich in insect life. The undersides of Vigna are heavily infested with the Micronesian red spider mite (Tetranychus). A hopping bug, Halticus, causes Vigna and Fleurya to become spotted and withered. The grasses act as hosts for the green plant bug Trigonotylus. The sedge, Fimbristylis, shelters a community of true bugs, including the herbivorous sedge bugs Ninus and Orthotyllelus and *Nysius picipes, Pachybrachius nigriceps,* and *P. pacificus.* Also present here is the predaceous *Nabis capsiformis,* but it does not appear to check the large numbers of its prey.

Usinger and La Rivers point out that *Nysius picipes* is of particular interest because it is found only on the islands remote from air bases in the Marshalls, whereas *Nysius pulchellus,* from Guam, is found exclusively on Majuro and Kwajelein.

The canopy woodland. This is the richest zone of Arno. The buttressed trunks of breadfruit support epiphytic bird's-nest ferns, a moss, *Calymperes tenerum,* the thick low undergrowth of Polypodium fern, and numerous decaying logs with Polyporus and Schizophyllum fungi. In this moist habitat of decaying logs are wire-worm larvae, stag beetle adults and larvae, termites, ants, Machilis and a large red Collumbolan, wood roaches, earwigs, predaceous rove beetles, and many other invertebrates, including several species of land snails, scorpions, pseudoscorpions, centipedes, earthworms, isopods, and millipedes. Fungus beetles (Ciidae and Endomychidae) and fungus gnats (Mycetophilidae) are found on the fungi growing on the logs. Tree holes often provide water to breed the endemic Marshallese mosquito, *Aedes marshallensis,* the larvae feeding on the organic matter at the bottom of their tiny pools.

Also in the canopy woodland zone are the taro pits. Strangely enough, they appear almost devoid of insects. A fresh-water snail may be seen, while closer inspection may reveal blood worms in the mud. From the latter a few midges emerge, the remainder forming the basic diet of the dragonfly naiades. Adult dragonflies are seen in the open forest, but the slower damselflies generally were seen in the vicinity of the taro pits.

Although not conspicuous in the canopy forest, the herbivorous insects are abundant. A large red corizid bug occurs on Allophyllus and the bird's-nest fern, *Asplenium nidus.* A small but spry spider mite is found on breadfruit leaves, and a large number of saprophytic and parasitic insects make their habitat in fallen rotting breadfruit. "The productivity of one rotten breadfruit in terms of individual Dropsophila flies is enormous" (Moul, 1957, p. 11).

These representative habitats for Arno, a wet atoll, are not necessarily present on drier atolls, and quite different situations are found on such atolls as Canton, Enderbury, Bikar, and Taongi. Moul's characterization for Onotoa (1957, p. 11), an atoll with average annual rainfall of about 45 inches compared with Arno's more than 120 inches, applies to the drier atolls generally: "The abundance and variety of insect life usually evident to an entomologist was lacking on this dry atoll. The house-fly, one species of dragon fly, and three species of Lepidoptera (two butterflies and a moth) were common. Other insects were generally uncommon, and it was necessary to search for them. The clouds of insects so typical of any grass field in eastern United States were never seen."

Insect destruction and agricultural pests

The very fewness in number of species of insects for any atoll, representing an "unharmonic balance," leads to some dangers in the introduction of new species that might be without local biotic controls. Speaking of Canton, Degener and Gillaspy (1955) wrote: "The number of native species of insects are few, as expected, considering the difficulty for these small terrestrial creatures, crossing extensive wastes of ocean to Canton and, when once there, finding suitable fare with such a limited flora. There is some injury to native plants by native insects, but in the main, this is not serious. They have always been exposed to such depredations and survived." This type of damage to strand plants and other indigenous plants was described for Kapingamarangi by Niering (1956, p. 18):

Certain trees and shrubs show considerable insect damage. The leaves of Scaevola are frequently attacked by a leaf miner. New shoots and buds of Calophyllum and *Barringtonia asiatica* are often infested to the point of disrupting the normal growth pattern, especially in the latter. The scalloped foliage of Premna and other species is indicative of leaf feeding or cutting forms. The smaller Pandanus trees are sometimes parasitized by mealy bugs to the point that they are cut down and burned.

However, more serious to the plant ecology, according to Degener and Gillaspy (1955),

is the habit of amateur plant lovers, introducing plants of their choice by boat and plane from Fiji, Hawaii, and elsewhere without fumigation against insect pests. As a result Canton Island is a safe, enemy-free Paradise for some foreign insects such as mealy bugs that harass native and introduced grasses, scale insects that weaken coconut palms about the hotel grounds, crater scale on the single remaining Plumeria, etc. This unnecessary introduction of insect pests not only adds one more hurdle for plants to surmount for survival, it likewise makes Canton a very dangerous stepping stone for the passage of injurious pests to and from all regions touched by planes using the atoll for refueling or otherwise.

Fortunately, so far, the invasion of most atolls by undesirable insect pests has not reached serious proportions. Niering wrote of Kapingamarangi that although insects are common, there are no major pests.

Usinger and La Rivers (1953, pp. 12–13) also found that there were no agricultural pests of any significance on Arno. It was free of such notorious scourges of the tropics as the coconut moth, the coconut beetle, the Oriental fruit fly, and the locust. Even the ubiquitous copra beetle was not seen, although it is likely to be present, because it is difficult to transport copra bags to an atoll without introducing the beetle. On many atolls they swarm in the copra sheds. Catala (1957, p. 27) stated that with some named exceptions, the coconut palms in the Gilberts are at present free of the worst pests, such as Brontispa and the rhinoceros beetle.

Not all atolls are so free of plant pests and on some they may be seriously destructive to plants valued by man. Fosberg wrote of the northern Marshalls (1956, p. 228) that the red coconut scale is widespread in plantations and doubtless does some harm, although it was difficult to estimate the amount. The large mealy bug is common locally on a number of plants and sometimes infests breadfruit trees, where it may do some damage. Both of these insects are carried around and placed on their host plants by ants which tend them and eat a sweet secretion produced by them. So the ants also may be considered an agricultural pest. On Kili, Drucker (1950) reported little insect damage. A few trees had ragged fronds partly eaten to the midrib. There also was an infestation of red scale (*Furcaspis oceanica*), but these pests appeared to have done little harm. On Majuro, according to Usinger and La Rivers, hopping plant bugs (Halticus) and mealy bugs are very numerous and are destructive to the beans and sweet potatoes that are grown there.

In the Gilberts, the locust *Graeffea cocophaga* has caused much damage to palms on Abemama and posed a serious threat to the rest of the atolls. This insect eats the leaflets of the palm and in bad infestations leaves nothing but the stiff veins of the fronds. Eggs are deposited in the trough formed by the main vein and the stems of the leaflets, falling either on the ground in different directions or rolling to the base of the stem, where control measures are extremely difficult. Graeffea is said to have been introduced to the Gilberts from Hawaii or from the high island of Kusae. On Abemama, the infestation and destruction were localized in the extreme northwestern and extreme southwestern sections of the atoll land in 1941. Ten years later they had spread to most of the land areas between. Catala (1957) cited an account by Wyatt Gill of the invasion of this pest on the Hervey Islands in the Cook group: "An invasion of these voracious insects is almost as much dreaded by the Islanders as a plague of locusts in the East. I have seen immense groves of coconut palms destroyed in a few months by this species of phasma."

Catala said that although the Abemama infestation was not as much of a catastrophe as that described above, the damage was enough to reduce nut yields. The great fear was that it would spread to other atolls in the Gilberts from Abemama.

Other insects damaging to the coconut palm in the Gilberts include a moth of the Decadarchis species, which is common, but the damage has not been cause for worry. A weevil, *Diocalandra frumenti,* is fairly widely distributed in the Gilberts but does not create the spectacular damage caused by the closely related species *D. tahitiensis* in other parts of the Pacific. Herms (1926, pp. 258–60) said this beetle was rather widely distributed among the islands of the South Seas. He believed it was undoubtedly the most important coconut-palm pest on Fanning. It also was on Washington Atoll but had up to then caused little damage. Small nuts that have failed to set and have fallen to the ground often contain them. Both adult and the pupae and larvae are found under the bark of the tree trunk. A beetle of the Papuana species is said to attack young coconut plants near the base of the stem. There is also a tiny psychid that causes a little damage and an undetermined borer which burrows in the blade of the leaflets and pupates there. None of these cause serious damage, however (Catala, 1957).

The *Brontispa chalyeipennis,* or blue coconut beetle, occurs on Likiep, laying its eggs on the palm leaves, upon which the larvae feed when they hatch. In sufficient numbers they kill the leaf. A tiny parasitic wasp, *Tetrastichus brontispae,* was introduced from Java and apparently has done good work destroying the beetle (Feeney, 1952, pp. 238–40). Still another coconut pest that is serious on Raroia and possibly other Tuamotu atolls is *Aspidiotus destructor.* This pest first appeared after the cyclone of 1906 and probably was brought in by the storm winds. It has gradually spread over the atoll. The insect attaches itself to the leaves and sucks out the sap, impeding the growth of nuts and in serious cases killing the tree. The most serious damage occurs on seaward plots, where the soil and ground-water resources are poor. The natives appear not to be fully aware of the threat and the only action taken to exterminate the insect is to burn the husks and other refuse at the foot of palm trees, which also damages the tree (Danielsson, 1955, p. 155).

On Danger Atoll the natives were reported to have become much concerned at the large number of palms falling because of termite injury. On Pukapuka Islet it was reported that the coconut trees had been almost completely destroyed (Kelsey, 1945, p. 69). At Funafuti half a century ago (Hedley, 1896, p. 100) the termite *Calotermes marginipennis* was said to confine its attention to the coconut palm. The termite attacked the tree about 3 to 6 feet from the ground, tunneling through and weakening it, so that the trees are snapped by strong winds. Although Usinger and La Rivers (1953, p. 12) do not cite damage to coconut trees on Arno from termites, they found four species of termites, each belonging to a separate genus. Each harbored distinctive Protozoa in its gut. Without these Protozoa, the termites would be incapable of utilizing the dry cellulose of dead wood as nutritive material.

Herms (1926, p. 254) also reported that the scale *Hemichionaspis aspi-distrae* signoret, "which occurs in all parts of Fanning Island and is abundant in places," attacks all parts of the coconut tree both young and old, except for the roots. Ripe nuts in husk in certain badly infested trees were sometimes almost white, owing to the presence of countless numbers of the white male scales. He found some caterpillars damaging trees and killing the very young trees by feeding on the tender cabbage or sprout.

The Pandanus, too, has some important enemies. Catala (1957, p. 60) told of a caterpillar in the Gilberts that damages the plant by burrowing between the upper and lower surface of the leaves, forming a blister. This, of course, ruins the leaves for use in mat weaving. A far worse Pandanus pest is a white scale which, according to Cumberland (1956, p. 268), has resulted in the disappearance of the Pandanus on Rarotonga in the Cook Islands. Whether this pest has spread to nearby atolls is not reported.

There are several types of pests and diseases that hit breadfruit trees. One of these is *Sphaerostilbe repens,* which attacks the roots of the tree. In 1954 this had not been reported from the Marshalls according to a report by Boyd Mackenzie to the District Administrator of the Marshall Islands. Another pest is *Phytophora* sp., which attacks the fruit. In 1956 the writer observed a variety of black rot on breadfruit on several trees at Likiep Atoll which was worrying the local landowners. This had been recently observed, but it is not known whether this resulted from the Phytophora. The fluted scale *Icerya aegyptiaca* attacks the leaves, and this insect is found in parts of the Marshalls, including Likiep. It causes the leaves to turn black and finally drop off. Fortunately, two parasites feed on the scale to prevent it from getting too much out of hand. These are the lace wing fly (Chrysopa) and the lady bird beetle (Feeney, 1952). Although Catala (1957, p. 66) noted a fruit fly in the Gilberts, he said that the breadfruit seemed free of insect pests.

Two pests of taro which had not developed into a serious threat in the Gilberts are a scarabaeid beetle, *Pentodon* or *Papuana* sp. The larvae bore galleries in the older tubers. It also attacks the banana plants grown in the pits. The other pest is a lepidopteron, *Prodenia litura,* whose caterpillars sometimes cause serious damage to the Cyrtosperma leaves (Catala, 1957, pp. 71–2).

Fortunately, the great scourges of the Pacific Islands, the rhinoceros beetle, which causes havoc to coconut plantations, and the giant African snail, have not been introduced to coral atolls, so far as reports are available, although both are found on high islands of the Palaus and the Philippines. The snail is found also on Guam and Ponape. It is possible that the large populations of hermit crabs on atolls create an obstacle for the giant

African snail, as the crabs apparently destroy the snails, and fewer snails are present where hermit crabs are abundant (Westerman, 1956). However, the interior parts of the larger atoll islets have few hermit crabs and would present ideal conditions for the snail were it to gain a foothold.

CHAPTER 19

MAN IN ATOLL ECOLOGY

The title of this chapter is not intended to convey the idea of a survey of the scope that would be covered by such a title as "Human ecology on coral atolls." That would demand a treatment at least as long as this entire volume. In this chapter the writer only wishes to relate briefly some of the ways in which man affects and is affected by his atoll environment and ecology. Many aspects of the marine ecology, such as the ecosystems of the live reef and even of the land ecology of coral atolls, may be little affected by man's presence and can be considered separately. Other aspects, particularly those concerned with vegetative land use and the accompanying soil changes and certain aspects of land and marine bird life and the food fishes, are intimately related to human ecology.

Many of the effects of man's activities have been described in preceding chapters as parts of plant or animal ecology. It hardly need be emphasized that man's ecology on the coral atoll cannot be considered without regard to his physical and biological environment. The latter also set certain limits to the support of human life beyond which further numbers of human beings can be sustained only with great difficulty or only through subsidy from outside the atoll.

Man's effect upon the reef and land morphology

The effects that man exerts upon the reef morphology generally are slight and the effects occasioned are more likely the results of the activities of outsiders rather than of the inhabitants of the atolls. The chief form that these effects take is the killing of exposed marine biota through the deposit at low tide of films of petroleum and waste oils discharged from passing ships or from shipwrecks. World War II activities in the Pacific atoll realm appear to have brought the killing of certain stretches of reef corals and algae, as on the seaward side of Uliga Islet on Majuro in the Marshalls.

Man's activities have a more widespread effect upon the morphology of the land areas. Here several differing processes and effects are observable. One is the protection from erosion of certain stretches of seaward beaches through the building of sea walls, as was done by the Japanese military forces on Aineman and Jabwor Islets of Jaluit in the Marshalls (Wiens, 1956, p. 9). That such efforts are not always successful was shown by the effects of Typhoon Ophelia in 1958, when the writer observed that the violence of the storm had overturned or torn out stretches of the sea walls and scoured out parts of the land behind the walls. However, the walls prevented more severe destruction of the land and during lesser storms were effective in protecting the shores. A second method of preventing shore-line erosion was observed by the writer in 1954 at Nukuoro Atoll in the eastern Carolines. Here groins of coral boulders were built outward from the shore at intervals on the seaward reef near the lagoon pass. No information was obtained on the effects of such groins, however.

At Kapingamarangi Atoll small extensions of the chief residential area on overcrowded Touhou Islet was obtained through the building of groin-like platforms adjoining the land on the seaward reef. Sea walls of coral boulders also had been built along parts of the seaward and channel sides of this islet to prevent erosion by wave scour.

In earlier chapters the writer has commented on the building up of islet surfaces through the trapping of sediments behind walls of boulders constructed on the higher central parts of the dead reef flat. In this manner two islets were originated and enlarged at Kapingamarangi within a few decades. Moreover, the natural extension of the land area lagoonward may result when causeways are built to connect two adjoining islets, also observed at Kapingamarangi, or through the trapping of beach sand by coral block jetties, as in the sheltered anchorage on Likiep Islet of Likiep Atoll (Wiens, 1956, p. 13). Some minor effects in slowing down the rush of tidal currents on the reef flat between islets and the trapping of sediments may occur because of the construction by the inhabitants of adjoining islets of long lines of rock to form fish traps. However, the writer did not study the extent of such effects.

Within the islets the most significant morphological changes are those caused by the digging of taro or Cyrtosperma pits and the deposit of the debris from such diggings near the pit rims to form elevated mounds or ridges. The pits in time form artificial fresh-water peat swamps. Minor topographic irregularities have resulted from man's burial mounds or from the sacred moraes or ritual platforms. Low platforms also are built for house floors or foundations.

Man's effect upon the vegetation pattern and soil

The substitution of coconut plantations for natural forest growth over much or most of the land surface on atolls with sufficient moisture has been man's most outstanding effect upon atoll and reef island vegetation patterns. Accompanying this process was the introduction of such other exotic food plants as the breadfruit, taro, certain edible forms of Pandanus, the banana, and minor food plants such as papaya, limes, sugar cane, pumpkin, and possibly arrowroot. The encouragement or introduction of certain useful or decorative plant species at the expense of other indigenous plants are other effects of man's activities, as are the introduction of weed species abhored by man.

It has been pointed out that the development of the export trade in copra has also led to soil depletion of potash and other elements in coconut plantations, which are not replaced, while other practices of man, such as the disposal of dead vegetative debris through burning or through dumping into the lagoon, also result in losses of organic fertilization from the soils. The long-term disposal of personal body wastes through excretion in lagoons or on tide-washed reef flats also results in the removal of fertility from the soils. The returns of fertility that man provides are small in proportion to the losses.

Man's effect upon the composition of land and bird fauna

In addition to the domestic animals introduced and raised by man on coral atolls, man significantly affects the composition of the natural fauna mainly by frightening marine and shore birds away from reef islands inhabited or frequently visited and worked by man, by the introduction of various insects and other lower orders of fauna, and by the introduction of such other pests as the rat and the mouse. By eating certain indigenous land animals such as the land crab man may greatly reduce their numbers from the "normal" state.

Man's effect upon marine fauna

The most obvious other activities of man that affect marine and reef ecology are those concerned with fishing from reefs and lagoons and the gathering of mollusks, snails, clams, oysters, and palolo worms for food;

the harvesting of trochus and pearl oysters for industrial shells and pearls; and the collection of a great variety of sea shells for curios. The former trade in bêche-de-mer—dried, edible sea cucumber—no longer is so active, but there still is some collecting. The hunting of marine turtles for shell or flesh and the digging up of their eggs from the sand beaches are other ways in which man is involved in marine ecology. All these activities reduce certain species populations, which reduces the competition for food among the survivors. This may lead to increases among their natural prey and at the same time reduce the food of their predators and cause the predators to seek other prey as food. The interrelations have wide ramifications, so the ecological effects may be considered to be far reaching. In the event of extreme overfishing, gathering, or capture of certain marine forms, the reduction may be so drastic as to lead to near extinction on some atolls, as in the cases of the green turtle and the hawksbill (tortoiseshell) turtle and the pearl oyster and trochus snail.

Not only do man's activities on an atoll reduce the total number of certain marine fauna and change the natural proportion of the various existing species, but the changes most often also are localized on those sections of the reef and adjoining sea or lagoon sectors most conveniently accessible to man. Reef, sea, and lagoon areas near residential villages are most likely to undergo the greatest degree of ecological disturbance as a result of man's activities. Such areas may be depleted of their faunal stocks while other parts of the atoll far from the villages or inconveniently located with respect to outrigger canoes or access on foot may have a relative abundance of the same species. The greater the isolation, the less the natural ecology is disturbed. The greatest abundance of green and hawksbill turtles and other forms of marine life desired by man occurs on the most isolated atolls.

Changes in man's utilization of resources affecting atoll ecology

The greatest point of change that has occurred in man's use of atoll resources came with the beginning of the demand for copra, which resulted in the conversion of the natural forest of the humid and semihumid atolls into coconut-palm plantations. Prior to this, the Pacific atoll inhabitants often depended as much on Pandanus as on coconuts for food. There were larger breadfruit forests, and more attention was paid to Cyrtosperma, taro, and marine foods. The coconut is the sole food plant adapted to atoll conditions that has furnished a cash crop which commands a significant world market. This change to coconut plantations has had both good and bad effects upon the atoll inhabitants, but it cannot be denied that copra brought greater security in food supplies, opened up new cultural worlds to the atoll dweller, brought him new and improved tools, and eased his labor in many respects. Steel axes and pickaxes, saws, and adzes made it easier for him to fell and shape trees for canoes and house timbers. Sail-cloth and loincloths reduced his dependence upon leaf-woven matting for sails and wrap-arounds. The use of banana-leaf or hibiscus-bark fiber for weaving cloth has been abandoned in favor of imported flowered prints.

The development of concrete tanks for catching rain water undoubtedly has reduced the use of and dependence upon green coconuts as a source of drinking liquid on many atolls. Wooden-frame houses with corrugated galvanized tin roofs today also substitute for the use of coconut and Pandanus leaf thatching and mat house walls.

In the matter of food, also, there is less dependence upon the natural supply of reef and lagoon, although these still retain a high place in filling dietary needs. However, changes in the diet—generally for the worse—have reduced the toll exacted from the marine fauna, as less effort is necessary in making and selling copra and buying rice, flour, tinned meats, and even tinned fish than in acquiring a steady supply of fresh fish and other marine foods from the atoll.

Population pressure upon atoll resources

From historical accounts it appears that at an earlier time, when Europeans first made contact with the atoll dwellers, most of the Pacific atolls supported larger populations than they do today. This is not to say that their earlier living standards were higher than those of the present-day inhabitants, or that it is desirable to crowd the atolls with as high a population as they had in the past. In fact, the early accounts often indicated a miserable existence for the inhabitants of many of the atolls visited. Social taboos and restrictions applied also to the use of many resources which today are in less-restricted use. However, satisfactory analyses have not been made of the problem of population pressure on the food and other resources of human livelihood on coral atolls.

This is partly because quantitative evaluations of the resources available, required, or used are extremely difficult to make, especially those of marine food animals. It is not known how intensively these may be exploited and depleted before the margin of safety is reached beyond which species reproduction may be endangered. Robert Rofen, an ichthyologist who has spent much time studying Pacific atoll fish ecology and collecting atoll fish species, stated to the writer in 1954 that in his estimation the current intensive scale of fishing activity at Kapingamarangi Atoll, for instance, was such as to maintain equilibrium in the fish ecology, but that additional commercial fishing for outside sale very likely would endanger the reproductive stock of fish required to maintain the equilibrium. In other words, heavy overfishing to support a large expansion of population would endanger the future supply of the edible fishes. But at what point this actually would occur is not known.

The estimation of the amount of land area necessary per capita for population support on an atoll depends upon the wetness of the atoll as well as upon the extent to which the person's needs are met from marine food supplies. However, it is easier to estimate the amount of land that will supply any given amount of plant food required per capita than to estimate the amount of reef and marine habitat required to supply a given per capita amount of food.

To obtain a reliable approximation of the areas of land, reef, and lagoon required for the satisfaction of minimum subsistence standards for man, one must know a great many facts not now available. One must know the average amount of plant and/or animal food consumed by the atoll inhabitant and what proportion of the food comes from the land and what from the sea, reef, and lagoon. Since to a certain extent the lack of land area may be compensated for by greater reliance upon marine foods, and the lack of access to marine foods also may be compensated for by an increase in productive land area, one needs to arrive at a suitable formula for equating in terms of food production a certain unit of productive land with a certain area of reef, lagoon, and fringing sea. Because of the variance in the productivity of land with differing rainfall and also with soil and ground-water conditions, and because the productivity of different reefs and atolls also may show significant variance, such a formula would have to be based upon specific data from specific atolls and reefs. Such data are not now available.

Lacking such data, the evaluation of population pressure on different atolls can be approached only qualitatively. Qualitative evaluations of population pressures on atolls may be facilitated by comparisons of per capita areas of land, reef, and lagoon for different atolls. As an illustration of the method and also of its limitations, Table 29 has been compiled for four atolls of differing sizes, populations, and rainfall.

From Table 29, it is seen that the Pingelap people get along with the minimum per capita areas of land, reef, and lagoon. It is clear that the wetter atoll of Arno has many more times the minimum land requirements to supply needed human food from vegetable sources and from animals supported by terrestrial plant foods. Arno has been considered by observers to be underexploited in its food resources, and population pressure here is low compared with such areas as either Pingelap or Kapingamarangi. Stone (1951, p. 5) estimated that Arno's average annual production of about 600 tons of copra could at least be doubled, for instance, even though he considered only about five-eighths of its 3,200 acres of land suitable for coco-nut plantations, and he pointed out that less than this is actually in planta-tions, which are poorly tended.

It also would appear that Arno's reef and lagoon resources are far superior to those of Pingelap, although its per capita reef resources are not as good as those of Kapingamarangi. Moreover, Arno also has a larger and more reliable rainfall than any of the others.

TABLE 29

Statistics for Four Pacific Atolls

	Arno *	Pingelap	Kapingamarangi	Raroia †
Total population	1,005	596	426	200 (1956)
Total atoll area, square miles	147.00	1.77 ‡	31.70	154.40
Average annual rainfall, inches	120+	100+	80+	46+
Land acres per person	3.2	0.48	0.65	25.59
Reef acres per person	7.0	1.05	12.25	50.31
Lagoon acres per person	83.8	0.36	35.30	415.00

* From Wells (1951, p. 2).

† From Newell (1956). The writer has added an estimated 1.5 square miles for the more than 2,000 lagoon patch reefs to the total reef area (the reef area less the land surface on the reef).

‡ Calculated from Japanese charts by the writer (adjusted for Kapingamarangi through the use of aerial photographs and ground surveys).

Pingelap has been cited to the writer by the Trust Territory District Administrator at Ponape as having the greatest population support prob-lems among the atolls in Ponape District, and it is followed closely in this respect by Kapingamarangi. Both atolls are considered overpopulated on a minimum subsistence basis. Both have sent surplus population to settle on Ponape. Superficially, Kapingamarangi appears to have much less popu-lation pressure than Pingelap. However, if we might assume that both are supporting the maximum number of people on similar standards of living, we must conclude that the sum of the productivities of land, reef, and lagoon areas in Pingelap for human support roughly equals that for Kapingamarangi. Since in each of these categories the per capita surface for Kapingamarangi surpasses that for Pingelap, there must be some other element at Pingelap that is superior to the same element at Kapingama-rangi. This could be either superior land productivity or superior reef productivity or both. If it were assumed that, in general, per unit areas of reefs at conditions of biological equilibrium (neither depleting nor increasing total biomass) were equally productive on different atolls, then it follows that Pingelap must have superior land productivity. Better soils or higher rainfall can account for superior land productivity. Since Kapingamarangi has been found to have relatively high quality soils for an atoll, the chief difference would most likely be in rainfall. Pingelap does lie in a higher rainfall zone than Kapingamarangi, although no actual annual records are known to the writer that gives quantitative comparisons.

Harry (1953, p. 184) pointed out that at Raroia the reefs and their vicinity support about three-fourths of the fish population of the atoll although the lagoon area is eight times the reef area. Thus we may conclude that the reef area of an atoll is by far the most significant marine food factor. Actually, aside from fish, the reef areas support other forms of marine life used for food by people, such as clams, snails, and crustacea, so that the relative population-support-capacity of reefs over that of lagoon waters is even higher.

Now if we assume from the Raroia example that the fish-support-capacity of an area of reef is three fish, it would require about eight times such an area of lagoon to support one fish, or 24 times such an area of lagoon water to support the same number. We may conclude, therefore, that a unit of area of the atoll reef may be considered 24 times as productive of fish as a unit area of lagoon, calculated on the basis of the rough estimate of comparative capacity at Raroia by Harry. If this equivalence were to be granted, the per capita reef-area-equivalence of Pingelap's lagoon is only 0.015 acres. Pingelap thus has a total productive reef and reef-equivalence of 1.065 acres per capita.

Kapingamarangi, by contrast, has 13.72 acres of reef and reef-equivalence per capita, or more than twelve times as much as Pingelap.

The figures for all categories of per-capita area for Raroia shown in Table 29 are high and, superficially, it might appear that Raroia is the most underpopulated of all. It must be noted, however, that Raroia has only about half the rainfall of Pingelap and possibly of that of Kapingamarangi, so that its land productivity might be much lower per unit of area. On the other hand, Danielsson (1955, p. 165) estimated that almost three times as much copra could be produced on Raroia as was being produced. He indicated that only 587 hectares of 1,450 acres of atoll land actually were covered by coconut plantations, however, so that only 7.25 acres of coconut plantations per capita are found. This is less than a third of the total land area listed. The copra production per acre on Raroia is shown to be about 0.37 tons per acre, which appears to be about equal to that at Arno. Stone (1951, p. 5) lists a minimum of 0.3 and a maximum of 0.5 tons per acre for Arno. It seems justifiable to state, therefore, that Raroia's 7.25 acres per capita of coconut land normally has about the same productivity as a similar area of land on any of the other three atolls listed in the table. Since Raroia also claims adjoining Takume atoll as its territory, the population density for Raroia district seems very low for its potential capacity for population support, given the average subsistence standard of the Pacific atoll inhabitant.

The qualitative comparisons of population support capacities among these atolls can go little beyond what has been said above on the basis of the limited quantitative data. Although the preceding type of analyses may provide a very rough qualitative idea of comparative population-support capacities of different Pacific atolls, there are many doubtful assumptions in the analyses, and it is obvious that the analyses ignore some important facts. Much of the land-area estimates, such as in the case of Raroia, include islet surfaces that support no vegetation, and much of the vegetation on other parts of the land is not food-producing. Well-groomed plantations cannot be compared in productivity with coconut forest interspersed with other forest trees and dense undergrowth. In the estimation of reef areas, dead reef flats of low productivity are not distinguished from live reefs of high productivity.

It is obvious that the determination of the intensity of the effects of man on atoll ecology through the comparisons of population pressures on individual atolls becomes extremely complex and difficult. The mere comparison of the densities of population per unit of land or unit of land-and-reef-and-marine area on different atolls is relatively meaningless.

Statistical uncertainties

Moreover, there is considerable uncertainty about the reliability of the statistics available. The U. S. Navy handbook (1948, pp. 8–9) has two tables, attributed to E. H. Bryan, Jr., listing lagoon and dry land areas for the Marshall and Caroline Islands. These tables are also reproduced in Freeman (1951). The U. S. Navy report (1948, p. 3) asserts that these statistics are "based on precise measurements from the best available maps, and in some cases checked closely with measurements made of air photographs." In these figures, Majuro is given an area of 3.54 square miles of land and Kwajelein 6.33 square miles of land. However, in an earlier estimate by Bryan (1944), based on aerial photographs, a figure of 8,726,400 square feet, or 0.31 square miles, was listed for the total land area of Majuro, and Kwajelein was given an area of 5.8 square miles. A presumably more recent estimate of land areas for atolls in the northern Marshalls by the U. S. Army Engineers (Fosberg, 1956, p. 34) gives a figure of 5.63 square miles for the land area of Kwajelein. For such small areas as are represented by atoll islets, the percentages of divergence among these figures are large.

Bryan's list (Freeman, 1951) gives Kapingamarangi in the eastern Carolines a land area of 0.521 square miles and a lagoon area of 22.01 square miles. The writer's own estimate of the lagoon area, based upon uncontrolled aerial-photograph mosaics, is 23.8 square miles. For the land areas the writer made estimates based upon his own ground mapping of each of the islets on a scale of 1 inch to 100 feet. The total land area thus estimated came to only 276.4 acres, or 0.422 square miles.

It is obvious that many of the available statistics on the areas of atolls and/or atoll land must be viewed with caution if they are to be used to evaluate pressure on atoll food resources. Published maps and charts of atolls generally are on such small scales that the margin of error, especially in estimating the tiny bits of land on the reef, is bound to be large. For many areas where corrected charts based upon new surveys and aerial photography have not been made, estimates may be far from true values. Available information on the Tuamotus is meager. Official French statistics concerning land area and population in the Tuamotu atolls and reef islands may not apply to individual atolls and generally list only the 35 atolls that form the administrative districts. The figures for a particular district may include combined the areas or populations of more than one atoll and thus are not comparable to statistics for individual atolls elsewhere. Danielsson (1955, p. 107) wrote of the Tuamotus that "It is impossible with available data to compute the exact population for each inhabited atoll."

In cautioning the reader of the 1947 Census for the Gilbert and Ellice Islands colony, the Census Commissioner had this to say, as reported by Pusinelli (1947, p. 7):

The only island in the Colony for which a comprehensive land survey has been made is Ocean Island. For the other 36 islands no maps have ever been made. Before the war the only cartography which had been undertaken was a series of charts by both the Admiralty and the United States Hydrographic office . . . The bases of these insets [charts] were sketches by various naval officers or ships' Masters mostly in the nineteenth century, in particular for most of the Gilbert Islands sketches by the United States Exploring Expedition 1841 to scales of about 1 to 145,000. During the war the United States Navy made new chart insets for Butaritari, based on a Japanese chart, and for Tarawa, South Nonouti, Nanumea, Niutao, Vaitupu, Nukufetau, and Funafuti. These are all accurate, being in most cases based on aerial surveys and are to scales of between 1 to 26,000 and 1 to 140,000. In pre-war Government publications figures are given for the land area of each island, but comparison of these with the recent United States charts showed serious discrepancy, and the basis of these estimates is not now known . . . Apart from the reliability of the charts the method of producing the estimated area is liable to up to 10 per cent error due to the most irregular nature of the land and the small scale of several of the insets. In all but the recent United States charts, it is considered that this error is small compared to the probable error in the charts themselves.

Changes in atoll population densities

Population figures for the various Pacific atolls are improving in reliability and completeness but also suffer from many deficiencies and uncertainties. The U. S. Navy handbook (1948, p. 52) pointed these out in the following comment:

It must be understood, however, that population changes for any given island are affected not only by vital trends, but also by the extensive inter-island migrations and displacements of modern times. The earlier statistics, too, are often of even more dubious accuracy than those of the Japanese and American periods. Those made before 1900 are usually counts or estimates made by voyagers, missionaries, or early scientific visitors, while the later ones are official censuses or estimates. A number of small islands have been devastated by storms, and their populations moved partly or wholly elsewhere; this explains some of the extreme shifts.

According to the 1958 report, "The first thorough census of the Trust Territory using uniform census schedules and trained census teams was conducted in the year under review . . . Much of the statistical data comes from municipal officials. The data furnished by local authorities are checked against previous reports, but there are sources of error which cannot be controlled."

TABLE 30

Total Populations of Atolls Groups in Various Periods

	1935	*1945*	*1948*	*1958*
Marshall atolls	10,383	9,593	10,553	13,728
Caroline atolls	9,954		9,496	8,137
Ellice atolls	3,994 (1931)		4,487 (1947)	
Tokelau atolls	1,102 (1931)		1,416 (1947)	1,571 (1951)
Phoenix atolls	31 (1931)		984 (1947) (Migrants from Gilberts)	
Gilbert atolls	26,416 (1931)		27,824 (1947)	28,675 (1950)
Tuamotu atolls	4,668 (1936)	6,143 (1946)	6,733 (1951)	7,615 (1956)

The following discussion is limited to population changes in the major atoll groups for which statistics were obtained (Table 30). On the basis of the data, it is seen that the total population in each of the Marshall, Ellice, Gilbert, Tokelau, and Tuamotu atoll groups have increased between 1930 and 1958, whereas that in the Caroline atolls has shown a steady decline.

The decline in the Carolines appears to be a continuing one from the last century, although it doesn't apply to all parts of the archipelago. This decline is the result of many factors, among them epidemics, poor sanitation, and poor nutrition (especially the lack of vitamin E, which led to low fertility as well as to low survival rates) (Burrows and Spiro, 1953, pp. 4–6). Other influences leading to the declines on the atolls are natural calamities, the shifting about of groups of people by the Germans and Japanese, and migration to and resettlement on the high volcanic islands, such as Ponape, Truk, and the Palaus. The net results in terms of effect upon the atoll ecology on most atolls has been a reduction in the population pressure upon the atoll resources. Only the populations of Nama, Ifalik, Pulusuk, Mokil, Ngatik, Nukuoro, and Kapingamarangi show an increase in 1958 over the 1935 figures and thus an increasing pressure upon the atoll food plants and animals.

Rough estimates of the population in the Marshalls before the German occupation of the islands were between 15,000 and 16,000, but these may have been far from reliable. At the time of the German occupation, the figure had fallen to between 12,000 and 13,000. The official German figure in 1909 was 9,267 and in 1913, 9,546 (Yanaihara, 1939). By 1939 it was fairly clear that the decline in population in the Marshalls had come to an end. In 1958 the only reef islands and atolls in the Marshalls not showing a larger population than in 1935 were Lib, Jaluit, Aur, Wotje, Mili, and the two atolls involved in the nuclear bomb tests, Bikini and Eniwetok. From the latter two the population has been removed permanently or for an indefinite period. The total increase in the Marshalls population over that of 1935 was over 32 per cent, or an average of about 1.4 per cent per year.

Early figures for the population of the Gilberts may have been exaggerated, but Gulick (1862, p. 410) cited Captain Randall's estimate of over 50,000 people for the different atolls here. Twenty years later Finsch (1882) estimated the group to have some 37,000 people. If these estimates are reliable, the Gilberts, with only 28,675 people in 1950, had a much-decreased population pressure, although the concentration in villages localized the pressure on the land and marine resources much more than in the pre-European times. The 1931 census showed that the population of seven southern Gilbert atolls had changed little in three decades but that the northern(?) ones and the Ellice atolls had increased substantially (Maude, 1952). The 1947 census gave an average annual increase of 8.28 per thousand, or 0.8 per cent per year, for the Micronesians and Polynesians in the two groups over the 16 years since the 1931 census (Turbott, 1949, p. 37). The much smaller Micronesian rate of only 5 per thousand per year compared with the Polynesian rate of 15.5 per thousand per year, or only one-third the Polynesian rate (Pusinelli, 1947, p. 21) probably is related to the greater population density and demand on food in the Micronesian Gilberts. In the more-isolated Tokelau atolls, the increase between 1931 and 1951 amounted to 2.8 per cent per year. Because of drought conditions in the Gilberts, the British in 1938–1939 encouraged the resettlement of over 1,000 Gilbertese on Sydney, Hull, and Gardner Atolls in the Phoenix group to relieve the pressure on food resources (Laxton, 1951). This would seem to belie the large estimates for the early populations.

According to available statistics (Danielsson, 1955, p. 113), the Tuamotu population dropped from 6,588 in 1863 to a low of 4,294 in 1902. The earlier figure was not surpassed until 1951. In 1958 the population of this group had reached 7,615, or over 1,000 more than that of the 1863 figure, according to a letter to the writer from the Secretary General of French Polynesia (November 6, 1959). The atoll totals probably would have been a good deal larger were it not for emigration of atoll dwellers to Tahiti and especially to the capital, Papeete. Thus the atoll population figures do not show the real natural increase in the Tuamotu group, which actually is larger than the figure showing the resident population.

Conclusion

In general, the conclusion is inescapable that with the improved medical supplies, education, and sanitation in recent decades, the population pressure upon the atoll food resources gradually is increasing—in some atolls at rapid rates. Man's effects upon atoll land and marine ecology will further increase as rising population numbers compel an intensified effort to extract more food from the land, the reef, and the waters around them. Conservation practices to prevent destructive exploitation and to preserve a maximum sustained yield becomes all the more essential and must command the vigilant attention of local and higher authorities alike.

PERCENTAGE FREQUENCY OF WINDS OF EACH BEAUFORT FORCE IN THE TROPICAL NORTH PACIFIC

Beaufort force	2	3	4	5	6	7	8	9
JOHNSTON ISLAND								
January	5	17	35	23	14	2		0
February	5	15	38	29	11	1		0
March	2	11	31	36	17	1		0
April	1	11	37	36	13	1	0	0
May	2	8	43	37	9		0	0
June	1	6	48	39	6	0	0	0
July	1	8	47	38	5	0	0	0
August		6	53	35	5		0	0
September	2	13	51	28	5		0	0
October	3	11	41	34	10		0	0
November	2	8	36	38	13	1		0
December	2	13	32	31	17	3		0
WAKE ISLAND								
January	9	18	25	20	14	7	2	0
February	12	17	26	19	12	6	1	
March	9	26	38	18	4	1		0
April	8	29	38	18	4	1	0	0
May	14	27	33	16	4		0	0
June	15	38	34	6	1		0	0
July	12	36	38	9	1		0	0
August	10	36	39	10	1		0	0
September	14	30	37	0			0	0
October	9	29	37	16	4	1		0
November	9	24	41	17	4		0	0
December	9	26	38	16	5	1		0

Beaufort force	2	3	4	5	6	7	8	9
KWAJELEIN ATOLL								
January	2	13	34	34	13	2		0
February	1	11	49	31	6	1	0	0
March	3	19	46	24	7		0	0
April	3	17	50	25	5		0	0
May	3	24	49	20	3		0	0
June	4	23	54	16	2		0	0
July	13	36	36	8	1		0	0
August	22	38	24	5	1		0	0
September	24	35	20	4	1		0	0
October	23	40	23	5			0	0
November	11	31	42	11	2		0	0
December	3	17	44	26	8	1	0	0
OROLUK ATOLL								
January		4	24	30	26	15	1	0
February	1	10	42	28	16	3		0
March	0	15	60	17	7	1		0
April	2	18	44	29	7		0	0
May	4	25	43	17	11		0	0
June		13	68	16	2	1	0	0
July	16	39	29	7	1		0	0
August	24	36	30	3	1	0	0	0
September	23	26	24	7	3			
October	19	28	29	10	3	1		0
November	5	14	41	24	10	3		
December		3	20	45	25	7	0	0
PALMYRA ATOLL								
January	7	18	42	26	6	0	0	0
February	11	20	36	21	8	0	0	0
March	8	24	30	29	5	0	0	0
April	1	19	37	34	7	1	0	0
May	5	18	44	28	5		0	0
June	7	16	46	27	3	0	0	0

Beaufort force	2	3	4	5	6	7	8	9

PALMYRA ATOLL (*cont.*)

	2	3	4	5	6	7	8	9
July	7	17	44	27	5	0	0	0
August	16	21	44	14	1	0	0	0
September	15	34	28	14	2	0	0	0
October	15	23	39	18	0	0	0	0
November	10	19	32	25	12	1	0	0
December	5	15	33	27	17	1	0	0

CHRISTMAS ATOLL

	2	3	4	5	6	7	8	9
January	17	43	32	4		0	0	0
February	20	41	29	5		0	0	0
March	16	38	33	8		0	0	0
April	20	43	27	3		0	0	0
May	26	40	20	1		0	0	0
June	31	38	19	1		0	0	0
July	29	43	20	1	0	0	0	0
August	24	44	21	4			0	0
September	29	40	19	3		0		0
October	26	47	16	1		0	0	0
November	24	44	23	2		0	0	0
December	22	41	29	3		0	0	0

NAMONUITO VICINITY

	2	3	4	5	6	7	8	9
January	7	18	37	23	9	1	1	0
February	7	15	43	26	5		0	0
March	7	24	35	24	1	1	1	0
April	14	22	37	21	3	1	0	0
May	8	29	42	14	4	0		0
June	18	27	36	11	2	0	0	
July	22	31	29	7	2		0	0
August	25	27	25	7	5	1	1	
September	26	20	26	11		0	0	0
October	20	34	24	6	4	2	0	0
November	10	23	32	19	6	1	1	1
December	10	17	26	26	10	4	2	0

Beaufort force	2	3	4	5	6	7	8	9
OCEAN AREA EAST OF THE PHILIPPINES								
January	5	23	31	21	13	5		0
February	13	21	37	17	7	2	0	0
March	13	29	26	19	12	1		0
April	18	37	22	8	3		0	0
May	29	36	22	3		1	0	0
June	27	31	25	3	2	2		0
July	26	30	17	9	4	2	1	
August	20	27	21	14	3	2	1	0
September	27	26	14	7	4	5	3	1
October	23	27	26	10	2	2	1	
November	11	21	33	19	8	4		0
December	9	17	31	17	14	5	2	1

APPENDIX B

RAINFALL RECORDS

ISLANDS	AVERAGE ANNUAL RAINFALL, INCHES	YEARS OF RECORD	SOURCE
Marshall Islands:			
Eniwetok	53	5	1
Ujelang	77	16	1
Wotje	78.2	4	2
Kwajelein	107	8	1
Arno	120(?)		3
Jaluit	157	25	2
Caroline Islands:			
Mokil	100(?)		4
Kapingamarangi	80–100(?)		5
Lamotrek	104		6
Kayangel	150(?)		7
Ulithi	114.21	2	8
Line Islands:			
Palmyra	149.72	1	8
Johnston	32.90	2	8
Washington	122.00	7	9
Fanning	81.00	41	9
Christmas	58.00	12	9
Malden	28.00	33	9
Flint	(56.00)	3	9
Penryhn	70.98	14	10
Northern Cook Islands:			
Manihiki	94.74	14	10
Pukapuka (Danger)	109.42	14	10
Palmerston	82.82	11	9
Tokelau Islands:			
Atafu	114.70	24	11
Phoenix Islands:			
Canton	17.32	14	8
Sydney	41.41	3	12
Gardner	46.06	4	12
Hull	32.68	3	12
Raised atoll:			
Ocean	82.34	2	12

ISLANDS	AVERAGE ANNUAL RAINFALL, INCHES	YEARS OF RECORD	SOURCE
Gilbert Islands:			
Little Makin	100.23	16	13
Butaritari	121.50	16	13
Marakei	71.17	16	13
Abaiang	73.58	16	13
Tarawa	64.02	15	13
Maiana	57.32	16	13
Abemama	53.04	15	13
Kurea	48.57	11	13
Aranuka	49.72	12	13
Nonouti	43.18	13	13
Tabiteuea	40.98	16	13
Beru	45.29	14	13
Nikunau	42.10	14	13
Onotoa	45.83	18	13
Tamana	50.39	13	13
Arorae	52.30	13	13
Ellice Islands:			
Nanumea	121	4	12
Niutao	119	5	12
Nanumanga	92	1	12
Nui	123	5	12
Vaitupu	124	5	12
Nukufetau	117	1	12
Funafuti	133	5	12
Nikulaelae	145	2	12
Nurakita	141	1	12
Tuamotu Islands:			
Hikueru	55	4	14
Takaroa	59	4	14
Mopilia	73	4	14
Raroia	46	1	15
Makatea (raised atoll)	58	4	14

SOURCE:

1. Fosberg (1956).
2. U. S. Navy (1944).
3. Stone (1951).

4. Murphy (1950, p. 61).
5. U. S. Navy (1952).
6. U. S. Navy (1943).
7. Gressitt (1952).
8. U. S. Weather Bureau (1955; 1956).
9. New Zealand Meteorological Service (1956).
10. New Zealand Meteorological Service (1955).
11. New Zealand Meteorological Service (1957).
12. New Zealand Meteorological Service, Annual Meteorological Summary, Suva, Fiji, 1950–1955.
13. Sachet (1957).
14. Service Meterorologique No. 22/MET, as contained in a letter to the author from J. Huber, Secretary General to the Governor of French Polynesia, January 22, 1960.
15. Danielsson (1955).

APPENDIX C

RECORDS OF DESTRUCTIVE TYPHOON EFFECTS

Ellice Islands [1]:

Feb. 18, 1891—entire Ellice Islands devastated.

Marcus Island [2]:

Oct. 1901—a sea 20 feet high above ordinary water line added a new beach 40 feet wide and 12 feet high.

Tokelau group [1] (*Atafu Atoll*):

Jan. 7, 1914—devastated island.

Palmerston Atoll [3]:

Dec. 1883—waves swamped even 20-feet-high elevation. A second typhoon also washed over atoll.

Hervey Island [1]:

Dec. 24, 1848—no details.

Suvarrov [4]:

1942—the occupants of a small yacht at anchor in the lagoon barely saved themselves by tying themselves to the top of the highest trees. A New Zealand official present on Suvarrov during the typhoon wrote: "We escaped by a very narrow margin, being all tied into the tops of some tamanu trees, which were one of the few things left on Anchorage Islet, the sea sweeping right over the atoll and the tops of the seas being some 26 feet above normal high water . . . I had a grandstand seat to watch the tremendous power of the sea as it washed automobile-size boulders over the land and saw conditions which either raise the level of an islet or completely wash it out to reef level." [6]

Tuamotu group:

1825 [5]—trees torn up and seas rose over the land; many lives lost.

Jan. 4–9, 1875 [1]—no details.

Jan. 18–19, 1877 [1]—hurricane between Tuamotus and Society Islands.

Sept. 2, 1877 [1]—severely devastated Manihiki, Kaukura, Fakarava, Anaa, and Nihiru. (No records are available concerning the intervening atolls, but they also must have suffered similar destruction.)

Feb. 5–8, 1878 [6]—the reports state that all the plantations, buildings, and canoes were virtually wiped out and more than 200 people perished, including 117 people at Kaukura alone; a total of 112,000 coconut trees were uprooted or snapped. Anaa was swept by a huge wave; other atolls severely hit included Raroia, Apataki, and Fakarava. (Other adjacent atolls from which no word is available probably suffered serious damage.)

Jan. 14–15, 1903 [7]—in all, some 517 people were killed, mostly from a sudden wave inundation. These include some 373 on Hikueru and 95 on Marokau; taro pits were filled with gravel, whole islets disappeared and three-fourths of all the palms were destroyed; some new islets developed from storm debris. The other atolls of the group especially affected included Napuka, Amanu, Makemo, Ravahere, Takume, Raroia, Reitoru, and Hao.

March 25, 1905 (Visher dates it March 12) [8]—storm traveling NNE to SSW, with its center passing near Manihiki, Apataki, Kaukura, and to the east of Tahiti; the storm diameter was 120 miles and it traveled at a speed of 15 to 18 kilometers per hour. Winds did most of the damage; storm tide was not too serious.

Feb. 7–8, 1906 [9]—western atolls of group suffered especially with immense damage being done by waves reaching a height of 28 feet at Anaa. The mean velocity was about 5.5 miles per hour between Flint and Tikahau Islands and 22 miles per hour between Anaa and the Gambier Islands. Over 150 people perished, mostly from drowning; Haraiki underwent great changes; Reitoru suffered terribly and 4 years later was described still as "looking like a winter landscape"—white sand with gray leafless trees.

The Caroline group:

Ifalik [10]—six severe storms remembered by middle-aged men, only one severe enough to cause inundation by the sea, lasting about 2 hours.

Tobi [11]—1833—inundation of land and filling in of taro.

Woleai and Ulithi—March 1906 [12]—"almost destroyed" by typhoon.

Pingelap, Mokil, Ngatik, and Ant Atolls, April 20–22, 1905. [1]

Dec. 16, 1920 [1]—followed a destructive path through the Carolines running from the Ngatik vicinity past Satawan and Woleai and Yap.

March 22–27, 1923 [1]—moved northward in vicinity of Namomito, Pulap and Pulusuk.

Kapingamarangi:

1858 [13]—destroyed Matukerekere islet.

1886—much damage to palms and breadfruit trees.

1896—inundation of eastern islets by tidal waves (perhaps not typhoon-caused).

1947—worst storm recalled by islanders; washed away most of remainder of Matukerekere that had been rebuilt: 67 breadfruit trees, 10 palms, and 30 houses blown down on other islets.

The Marshall group [14]:

At Eniwetok the inhabitants stated that about the middle of the nineteenth century typhoon waves washed over the island and drowned all the inhabitants.

Typhoon:

June 30, 1905—center passed through Jaluit and Mili atolls and affected many other atolls; barometer fell to 27.6 inches and storm waves rose to 46 feet at Mille, where entire southern islands were inundated. Knox islands adjoining southern Mili were completely washed away—in their place only a sandbank with a few tree stumps remaining. Only 2 of 70 inhabitants survived after being washed to Mili on a breadfruit tree. Arno was equally hard hit with loss of 8 lives; three-fourths of the land in the southeast was swept away by waves reported to reach to tops of coconut palms. At Majuro two stretches totaling 3 miles of narrow land were swept away. Three women lost their lives here. At Jaluit an enormous sea wave swept across much of the land, but fortunately occurred during low-tide stage; the eastern islets were almost entirely swept away and 73 people lost their lives. The storm reached Ujelang between July 1 and 2 and tore away the southwestern part of the main islet in a patch 1,300 feet wide and 2,600 feet long.

Typhoon Georgia:

March 21–25, 1951 [15]—winds of 100-knot velocity near the eye. The path indicated that the following atolls were within the area of severe winds: Aur, Maloelap, Ailuk, Wotje, Taka, and Rongelap. However, damage also occurred on Namu, Arno, Majuro, Kwajelein, and Utirik. Estimated damage totaled $1 million. At least seven lives were lost. On Aur over 4,000 coconut palms were destroyed as well as many breadfruit and other trees; houses and canoes were smashed or damaged and 12 tons of copra ruined. On Arno some 200 coconut palms, 500 breadfruit trees, and 250 Pandanus trees were destroyed; on Ailuk about 200 coconut palms and 50 breadfruit trees and a few houses were blown down. Maloelap lost 2,000 coconut and breadfruit trees. Namu lost 272 trees. Utirik was severely damaged, but no breakdown of damage is available. Majuro lost some 200 palms.

Typhoon Lola [16]:

November 10–12, 1957—this caused severe damage on Pingelap and minor damage on Mokil. During the latter part of the storm the winds reached their highest speeds and washed a wave of sea water over the lowest parts of Pingelap and inundated the large taro field. What taro was not immediately dug up and dried was unfit for consumption. The soil in the field would require 6 months of normal rainfall to be washed free of salts. All bearing breadfruit trees were badly damaged or blown down, while Pandanus and banana trees were badly affected. About 30 per cent of the coconut palms were blown down or otherwise badly damaged, and survivors had their crowns badly mauled. As a result of the storm the year's production of copra was expected to be only half of normal. About 25 per cent of homes and canoes were destroyed or damaged.

Typhoon Ophelia [17]:

Jan. 7, 1958—the chief damage was to Jaluit and Namorik Islands, with minor damage to Kili and Mili Atolls. Jaluit, over which the eye of the typhoon traveled, was very severely damaged. Winds up to 125 knots caused inundation over most of the islets along the eastern and southeastern reefs, washing away vegetation, buildings, and soil and piling up coral debris in places. In the islets along the west or leeward reefs damage was mostly caused by wind, with limited innundation a short distance inshore. The summary of damage of the islets along the eastern half of the reef as reported by the Majuro District Administration is as follows:

"1. Coconut trees 80% destroyed.
2. All coconuts knocked down, including flowers.
3. All subsistence plants destroyed by wind and salt water.
4. All houses not built of concrete destroyed.
5. Water cisterns on all islands but Jabor not potable.
6. Most of the foodstuff on these islands destroyed or swept to sea.
7. Most of people's personal belongings lost in the typhoon.
8. Many injured—four seriously injured cases known.
9. 16 people missing or dead. 2 died after the storm from exhaustion. Balance of 14 swept out to sea.
10. All but two small lagoon sail boats were destroyed. Catholic 50-footer lost during storm. MORNING STAR saved (but beached). Many canoes destroyed."

In the islets of the western half, most of the houses were blown down. From 40 to 75 per cent of the coconut palms and a proportionately larger percentage of Pandanus palms suffered. All breadfruit trees suffered severe damage, ranging from breakage of most of the branches to uprooting. Without outside aid, Jaluit islanders (about 1200) would have suffered famine.

The effect of the typhoon on coconut palms in Namorik was disastrous
—more than 80 per cent of all palms being overturned, probably between 90 and 95 per cent. Although most of the nuts already on the
tree that were mature could be harvested, since there was virtually no
inundation, future supplies required almost 100 per cent replanting.

SOURCE:

1. Visher (1925).
2. Bryan (1903).
3. Cumberland (1956, p. 261).
4. Pacific Islands Yearbook (1959); Powell (1959).
5. Danielsson (1955).
6. Danielsson (1955); Giovanelli (1940); Visher (1925, p. 153).
7. Danielsson (1955); Giovanelli (1940); Gibbings (1948, pp. 244–8).
8. Giovanelli (1940); Visher (1925).
9. Danielsson (1955); Giovanelli (1940); Gibbings (1948); Friederici (1910, pp. 121, 138–40); Cuzent (1884).
10. Burrows and Spiro (1953, p. 25).
11. Seidel (1905).
12. Krämer (1908).
13. Wiens (1956, pp. 19–20).
14. Jeschke (1906); U. S. House of Representatives (1945, p. 1114).
15. Arbuckle (1951); Dodd (1951); U. S. Trust Territory Pacific (1951a; 1951b; 1951c).
16. U. S. Trust Territory Pacific (1957; 1958b).
17. U. S. Trust Territory Pacific (1958c; 1958d; 1958e; 1958f).

APPENDIX D

TERRESTRIAL ECOLOGICAL COMMUNITIES

In the tables below, reproduced from Usinger and La Rivers (1953), the role of each species listed is indicated by appropriate letters as follows: herbivores (H), predators (Pred), parasites (Par), saprophytes (Sapr), and scavengers (Scav). The list starts with herbivores and, in order, proceeds to scavengers and successive groups of predators, members of each group preying on members of preceding groups, with the exception of the human community, the scheme of which is self-explanatory.

TABLE D–1

Strand Community

A. Open-beach stratum—mostly nocturnal
   Sand crickets—H
   Sand fleas—Scav
   House flies—(human feces)—Sapr (daylight)
   Robber flies—Pred (daylight)
   Marine water striders (blown onto beach)—Pred
   Crab spiders—Pred
   Ghost crabs—Pred

   Rock geckoes—Pred

   Plover—Pred
   Curlew—Pred
   Tattler—Pred

Marine Insect "Community"

A. Surface stratum
   Pelagic plankters—Pred, H
     (large—open ocean)
   Marine water striders
     (large—tide-pool species) Pred
     (small—protected coves)

TABLE D–2

Inner Beach Community

A. Foliage stratum
   Leaf-mining fly—H—Scaevola
   Plant bugs—H—Scaevola

Caterpillars—H—Cordia, Messerschmidia, Sida
Leaf-cutting bee—H
Aphis—H

Ants—Scav

Ladybird beetles—Pred
Green lacewings—Pred
Syrphid flies—Pred
Spiders—Pred

Geckoes—Pred
Skinks—Pred
B. Bark and dead-wood stratum
Bark beetles—wood borers
Round-headed borers—wood borers

Rove beetles—Pred
Predaceous bugs—Pred
Spiders—Pred

Geckoes—Pred
Skinks—Pred
C. Ground stratum
Sand crickets—H
Crab spiders—Pred
Ghost crabs—Pred

Golden plover—Pred
Heron—Pred

TABLE D–3

Open Woodland Community

A. Coconut—Pandanus stratum
Coconut scale—H
Sugar-cane weevil—H
Bark lice—Scav
Ants—Scav
Cockroaches—Scav

Earwigs—Pred
Luteva—Pred
Spiders—Pred

      Geckoes—Pred (night)

      Skinks—Pred (day and night)

B. Ground cover—Vigna, Wedelia, Fleurya, Fimbristylis, Lepturus, Cassytha

      Red spider mite—H—Vigna leaves

      Hopping plant bug—H—Vigna and Fleurya

      Green grass bug—H—grasses

      Leafhoppers—H

      Sedge bugs—H—Fimbristylis

      False chinch bugs—H—Fimbristylis

      Thrips—H

      Bees—H

      Caterpillars—H

      Mealybugs—H

      Aphids—H

      Ants—Scav

      Damsel bugs, Nabis—Pred

      Spiders—Pred

      Thrips—Pred

      Stink bugs—Pred

      Ladybird beetles—Pred

      Green katydids—Pred

      Geckoes—Pred (night)

      Skinks—Pred (day and night)

C. Fallen green coconuts

      Rats—H

      Coconut crabs—H

      Mosquitoes—larvae, detritus

D. Rotten Pandanus fruit stratum

      Vinegar flies—Sapr

      Fruit beetles—Sapr

      Rove beetles—Pred

      Spiders—Pred

      Predaceous bugs—Pred

      Predaceous mites—Pred

      Geckoes—Pred

      Skinks—Pred

E. Soil stratum

      Earthworms—Sapr

      Millipedes—Sapr

      Sowbugs—Sapr

TABLE D–3 *(continued)*

Garden centipedes—Sapr, H
Silverfish—Scav

Ants—Scav

Hermit crabs—Pred, Scav
Rock geckoes—Pred (night)
Ground skinks—Pred

TABLE D–4

Canopy Woodland Community

A. Breadfruit stratum
    Corizid bug—H—bird's-nest fern
    Leafhoppers—H
    Spider mite—H—breadfruit leaves

    Mosquito larvae—detritus, tree holes

    Ants—Scav

    Spiders—Pred

    Geckoes—Pred (night)
    Skinks—Pred (day and night)
B. Underbrush stratum—Alophyllus, Pipturus, Terminalia, Pisonia, Cordia
    Aphids—H
    Mealybugs—H
    Leafhoppers—H
    Corizid bugs—H
    Fruit flies—H

    Ants—Scav

    Spiders—Pred
    Ladybird beetles—Pred
    Syrphid flies—Pred

    Geckoes—Pred (night)
    Skinks—Pred (day and night)
C. Fallen log stratum
    Fungous flies—Sapr
    Fungous beetles—Sapr

    Weevils—wood borers
    Termites—wood feeders

    Wireworms—Sapr
    False wireworms—Sapr
    Stag beetles—Sapr

    Ants—Scav

    Earwigs—Pred
    Spiders—Pred
    Pseudoscorpions—Pred
    Scorpions—Pred

D. Rotten breadfruit stratum
    Vinegar flies—Sapr
    Fruit beetles—Sapr

    Rove beetles—Pred
    Spiders—Pred
    Predaceous bugs—Pred
    Predaceous mites—Pred

    Geckoes—Pred
    Skinks—Pred

E. Soil stratum
    Earthworms—Sapr
    Millipedes—Sapr
    Sowbugs—Sapr
    Garden centipedes—Sapr, H
    Silverfish—Scav
    Springtails—Sapr
    Ants—Scav

    Rock geckoes—Pred
    Ground skinks—Pred

F. Taro-pit aquatic stratum
    Midge larvae—detritus
    Shrimp—Pred
    Snails—H
    Dragonfly naiades—Pred

TABLE D–5

Human Community

Man—omnivorous—fish, coconut, breadfruit, taro, pandanus, bananas, papaya, and various imported foods
    Ectoparasites—lice, bedbugs
    Endoparasites—amoebae, hookworms, etc.

TABLE D–5 (*continued*)

Domesticated animals
    Dogs—scavenger—copra, garbage
    Pigs—scavenger—soil insects, roots
    Chickens—omnivorous—copra, ground insects, skinks
    Cats—omnivorous—rats
Household vermin
    Rats—eaten by cats
      Ectoparasites—mites and lice
    Cockroaches—Evania parasites
    Termites
    Mosquitoes—cisterns—dragonfly naiad predators
    Houseflies—Hermetia parasites—privies
    House gecko—eats all household insects

BIBLIOGRAPHY

Agassiz, Alexander, 1903, "The Coral Reefs of the Tropical Pacific," *Mem. of the Museum of Com. Zool. at Harvard College* (Cambridge), *28*, 1–409.

Alldredge, L. R.; Keller, Fred, Jr.; and Dichtel, W. J., 1954, "Magnetic Structure of Bikini Atoll," *U.S. Geol. Surv. Prof. Pap. 260-L*, pp. 529–35.

Anderson, Donald, 1951, "The Plants of Arno Atoll," *Atoll Research Bull.*, no. 7, Nov. 15.

Antevs, Ernst, 1928, *The Last Glaciation* (New York, Amer. Geograph. Soc.).

Arbuckle, B. J., 1951, Account of Typhoon Georgia Forwarded by Civil Administrator Marshalls to CincPac, April 21.

Arnow, Ted, 1954, "The Hydrology of the Northern Marshall Islands," *Atoll Research Bull.*, no. 30, May 31.

———— 1955, "The Hydrology of Ifalik Atoll, Western Caroline Islands," *Atoll Research Bull.*, no. 8, Aug. 15.

Arundel, J. T., 1890, "The Phoenix Group and Other Islands of the Pacific" (San Francisco, Geograph. Soc. of the Pacific). *New Zealand Herald*, July.

Asano, K., 1942, "Coral Reefs of the South Sea Islands," *Contributions, Inst. of Geol.* (Tohoku University), *39*, 1–19.

Bach, L. E., 1950, Letter from Chief Administrator, Field Headquarters, Trust Territory, to the High Commissioner, Trust Territory, July 12.

Baden-Powell, D. F. W., 1953, "Correlation of Pliocene and Pleistocene Marine Beds," *Nature*, Oct. 24, pp. 762–3.

Baker, R. H., 1951, "The Avifauna of Micronesia," *Univ. of Kansas Museum of Nat. Hist. Bull., 3*, no. 1.

Banner, A. H., 1952, "Preliminary Report on Marine Biology Study of Onotoa Atoll, Gilbert Islands, I," *Atoll Research Bull.*, no. 13, Dec. 15.

Barnes, C. A.; Bumpus, D. R.; and Lyman, J., 1948, "Ocean Circulation in the Marshall Islands Area," *Trans. of the Amer. Geophys. Union, 29*, 871–6.

Barrau, Jacques, 1958, "Plant Introduction and Exploration in the South Pacific," *South Pacific Commission Quart.*, January.

Barrell, J., 1917, "Rhythms and Measurements of Geologic Time," *Bull. of the Geol. Soc. of Amer., 28*, 776–85.

Bartsch, Paul, 1921, "Ocean Currents in Relation to Organisms," *Proc. of the First Pan-Pacific Scientific Conf.* (Honolulu), pp. 504–9.

Bates, Marston, 1956, "Man as an Agent in the Spread of Organisms," in W. L. Thomas (ed.), *Man's Role in Changing the Face of the Earth* (Chicago, Univ. of Chicago Press), pp. 788–804.

———— and Abbott, Donald, 1958, *Coral Island, Portrait of an Atoll* (New York, Scribner).

Beechey, F. W., 1831, *Narrative of a Voyage to the Pacific and Bering's Strait* (London), vol. 1.

Bennett, F. D., 1840, *Narrative of a Whaling Voyage Round the Globe, 1833–1836* (London).

Benson, George, 1838, "Sketch on Christmas Island, with a Chart of the Island," *Hawaiian Spectator, 1* (2), 64–8.

Bernstein, Joseph, 1954, "Tsunamis," *Sci. Amer., 191,* 60–4.

Bigelow, H. B., and Edmondson, W. T., 1947, "Wind, Waves at Sea, Breakers, and Surf," *Hydrographic Office Pub. 602* (Washington, U. S. Navy).

Billings, William, 1856, "Narrative of the Loss of the Chinese Junk 'Ningpo' on D'Entrecasteaux Reefs near New Caledonia with an Account of the Reefs," *Nautical Magazine, 25.*

Blair, T. A., 1942, *Climatology, General and Regional* (Englewood Cliffs, N.J., Prentice-Hall).

Blumenstock, D. I., 1958, "Typhoon Effects at Jaluit Atoll in the Marshall Islands," *Nature, 182,* 1267–9.

———— (ed.), 1961, "A Report on Typhoon Effects upon Jaluit," *Atoll Research Bull.,* no. 75, April 15.

British Colonial Office, 1950, *Report on the Gilbert and Ellice Islands Colony for the Year 1949,* London.

Brooks, C. E. P., 1921, "The Clash of the Trades in the Pacific," *Quart. J. of the Royal Meteorol. Soc., 47,* 3–9.

Brown, W., and Marshall, J., 1953, "New Scinooid Lizards from the Marshall Islands, with Notes on Their Distribution," *Copeia,* no. 4.

Bryan, E. H., Jr., 1944, Revegetation of Certain Marshall Islands, Memo. to Commanding Gen. Central Pacific Base Command, Oct. 10.

———— 1953, "Check List of Atolls," *Atoll Research Bull.,* no. 19, Sept. 30.

———— 1959, "Notes on the Geography and Natural History of Wake Island," *Atoll Research Bull.,* no. 66, May 15.

Bryan, W. A., 1903, "A Monograph of Marcus Island," *Bernice P. Bishop Museum Occas. Pap.* (Honolulu), 2, 77–139.

Buck, P. H., 1938, *Vikings of the Sunrise* (Philadelphia, J. B. Lippincott).

———— 1950, "Material Culture of Kapingamarangi," *Bernice P. Bishop Museum Pub. 200* (Honolulu).

Burnett, Frank, 1910, *Through Tropic Seas* (London, F. Griffiths).

Burrows, E. G., and Spiro, M. E., 1953, *An Atoll Culture; Ethnography of Ifaluk in the Central Carolines* (New Haven, Human Relations Area Files).

Byrne, J. V., 1956, "The Sediments," in N. D. Newell (ed.), "Geological Reconnaissance of Raroia (Kon Tiki) Atoll, Tuamotu Archipelago," *Amer. Museum of Nat. Hist. Bull., 109,* article 3.

Carr, Archie, 1952, *Handbook of Turtles* (Ithaca, N.Y., Comstock).

Carson, Rachel, 1951, *The Sea Around Us* (New York, Oxford Univ. Press).

Catala, R. L. A., 1957, "Report on the Gilbert Islands: Some Aspects of Human Ecology," *Atoll Research Bull.,* no. 59, Oct. 31.

Chamisso, A. von, 1821, "Remarks and Opinions . . . of the Naturalist of the Expedition," in O. von Kotzebue, *A Voyage of Discovery into the South Seas and Bering's Straits,* 3 vols. (London).

Christophersen, E., 1927, "Vegetation of Pacific Equatorial Island," *Bernice P. Bishop Museum Bull., 44,* 1–79.

———— 1931, "Vascular Plants of Johnston and Wake Islands," *Bernice P. Bishop Museum Occas. Pap.* (Honolulu), *9* (13), 1–20.

Cloud, P. E., 1952, "Preliminary Report on the Geology and Marine Environments of Onotoa Atoll, Gilbert Islands," *Atoll Research Bull.,* no. 12, Dec. 15.

Cohic, F., 1959, "Report on a Visit to the Chesterfield Islands, September 1957," *Atoll Research Bull.,* no. 63, May 15.

Collombet, E., 1926, "En Oceanie Française: Un Voyage aux Tuamotu," *Bull. Agence Gale, 19,* 691–706.

Cotton, C. A., 1948, "The Present-Day Status of Coral Reef Theories," *New Zealand Sci. Rev.,* 6 (6), 111–13.

Coulter, J. W., 1941, "Land Utilization in American Samoa," *Bernice P. Bishop Museum Bull., 170,* 14–16, 43.

Couthouy, J. P., 1843–44, "Remarks upon Coral Formations in the Pacific," *Boston J. of Nat. Hist., 4,* 137–44, 152–5.

Cox, D. C., 1951, "The Hydrology of Arno Atoll, Marshall Islands," *Atoll Research Bull.,* no. 8, Dec. 15.

Cromwell, Townsend, 1953, "Circulation in a Meridional Plane in the Central Equatorial Pacific," *J. of Marine Research, 12.*

Crossland, Cyril, 1927, "Marine Ecology and Coral Formations in the Panama Region, the Galápagos and Marquesas Islands and the Atoll of Napuka," *Trans. of the Royal Soc. of Edinburgh, 55,* 552–4.

Cullis, C. G., 1904, "The Mineralogical Changes Observed in the Cores of the Funafuti Borings," in W. J. Sollas et al., *The Atoll of Funafuti,* Rept. of the Coral Reef Committee of the Royal Soc. (London), pp. 392–420.

Cumberland, K. B., 1956, *Southwest Pacific; a Geography of Australia, New Zealand, and Their Pacific Island Neighbors* (New York, McGraw-Hill).

Cushman, J. A.; Todd, Ruth; and Post, Rita, 1954, "Recent Foraminifera of the Marshall Islands, Bikini and Nearby Atolls; II, Oceanography (Biologic)," *U.S. Geol. Surv. Prof. Pap. 260-H,* pp. 319–84.

Cuzent, G., 1884, "Archipel des Pomotu," *Bull. de la Société Academique de Brest, II, 9,* 49–90.

Daly, R. A., 1910, "Pleistocene Glaciation and the Coral Reef Problem," *Amer. J. of Sci., 30,* 297–308.

Dana, J. D., 1849, "Geology," *United States Exploring Expedition* (New York, Putnam), *10,* 1–756.

———— 1851, "Forms and Special Features of Coral Islands," *Amer. J. of Sci., 12.*

Danielsson, Bengt, 1955, *Work and Life on Raroia Atoll* (Uppsala, Almquist and Wiksells Boktrykeriab).

Darwin, Charles, 1889, *The Structure and Distribution of Coral Reefs*, 3rd ed. (New York, Appleton-Century-Crofts).

Davis, W. M., 1928, "The Coral Reef Problem," *Amer. Geograph. Soc. Spec. Pub. 9.*

Degener, Otto, and Gillaspy, Edwin, 1955, "Canton Island, South Pacific," *Atoll Research Bull.*, no. 41, Aug. 15.

DeLaubenfels, M. W., 1955, "Sponges of Onotoa," *Pacific Sci., 9* (2).

Dietrich, Günter, and Kalle, Kurt, 1957, *Allgemeine Meereskund* (Berlin, Gebrüder Borntraeger).

Dietz, R. S., and Menard, H. W., 1951, "Origin of Abrupt Change in Slope at the Continental Shelf Margin," *Bull. of the Amer. Assoc. of Petr. Geol., 35,* 1994–2016.

Dill, H. R., 1913, "The Albatross of Laysan," *Amer. Museum J., 13,* 185–92.

—— and Bryan, W. A., 1912, "Report of an Expedition to Laysan Island in 1911," *U.S. Dept. of Agriculture, Biol. Surv. Bull., 42,* 1–30.

Doane, E. T., 1861, "Remarks upon the Atoll of Ebon in Micronesia," *Amer. J. of Sci. and Arts, 2* (31), 318–25.

Dobrin, M. B., and Perkins, B., Jr., 1954, "Seismic Studies of Bikini Atoll," *U.S. Geol. Surv. Prof. Pap. 260-J.*

Dodd, W. S., Jr., 1951, Report to Civil Administrator of the Marshalls on Field Trip to Examine Typhoon Damage, April 1.

Donat and Seurat, L. G., 1904, "Sur Quelques Similitudes des langues et des coutumes des indigènes de Funafuti (Ellice Group) et des indigènes des îles de la Société de l'Archipel des Tuamotu, etc.," *Proc. of the Linnean Soc. of New South Wales, 28,* 926–31. (Communicated by C. Hedley.)

Doty, Maxwell, 1954, "Distribution of the Algal Genera Phiphilia and Sargassum in the Central Pacific," *Pacific Sci., 8* (3).

—— and Morrison, J. P. E., 1954, "Interrelationships of the Organisms on Raroia Aside from Man," *Atoll Research Bull.*, no. 35, Nov. 30.

——; Newhouse, Jan; Miller, H. A.; and Wilson, Kenneth, 1954, "Floristic and Plant Ecology of Raroia Atoll," *Atoll Research Bull.*, no. 33, Nov. 30.

Drews, R. A., 1944, "Gilbert Island Horticulture," *Amer. Anthrop., 46.*

Drucker, Philip, 1950, Report on the Ex-Bikini Occupants of Kili Islands, Letter from the Chief Administrator, Field Headquarters, Trust Territory Pacific Islands, to High Commissioner, Trust Territory, July 12.

DuMont, P. A., and Neff, J. A., 1955, Report on Midway Islands—Albatross Study, Memo. to Lt. Gen. Joseph Smith, Military Air Transport Service, U.S. Air Force, Jan. 4.

Edgeworth, David T. W. E., and Sweet, G., 1904, "The Geology of Funafuti," in W. J. Sollas et. al., *The Atoll of Funafuti,* Rept. of the Coral Reef Committee of the Royal Soc. (London), pp. 61–124.

Eilers, Anneliese, 1934, *Inseln um Ponape, Ergebnisse der Südsee Expedition, 1908–1910* (Hamburg, Friederichsen, De Gruyter).

Ekman, Sven, 1953, *Zoogeography of the Sea* (London, Sidgwick and Jackson).

Ellis, Albert, 1936, *Adventuring in Coral Seas* (Sydney, Angus and Robertson).

Elsehner, C., 1915, "The Leeward Islands of the Hawaiian Group," *Honolulu Advertiser*, reprint, 1–68.

Emery, K. O., 1946, "Marine Solution Basins," *J. of Geol.*, *54*, 209–28.

——— 1956, "Marine Geology of Johnston Island and Its Surrounding Shallows, Central Pacific Ocean," *Bull. of the Geol. Soc. of Amer.*, *67*, 1505–20.

——— 1958, "Shallow Submerged Marine Terraces of Southern California," *Bull. of the Geol. Soc. of Amer.*, *69*, 39–60.

——— and Cox, Doak, 1956, "Beachrock in the Hawaiian Islands," *Pacific Sci.*, *10*, October, 382–402.

———; Tracey, J. I.; and Ladd, H. S., 1949, "Submarine Geology and Topography in the Northern Marshalls," *Trans. of the Amer. Geophys. Union*, *30*, no. 1, 55–58.

———; ———; ——— 1954, "Geology of Bikini and Nearby Atolls," *U.S. Geol. Surv. Prof. Pap. 260-A.*

Emiliani, Cesare, 1954, "Temperatures of Pacific Bottom Waters and Polar Superficial Waters during the Tertiary," *Science*, *119*.

——— 1955, "Pleistocene Temperatures," *J. of Geol.*, *63*, 538–78.

Emory, K. P., 1939, "Archeology of Mangareva and Neighboring Atolls," *Bernice P. Bishop Museum Bull.*, *163*.

——— 1954, The People of Kapingamarangi, unpublished manuscript.

Fairbridge, R. W., 1947, "A Contemporary Eustatic Rise in Sea-Level?" *Geograph. J.*, *109*, July, 157 (correspondence).

——— 1948, "The Low Isles of the Great Barrier Reef: A New Analysis," *Geograph. J.*, *111* (1–3), January–March, 67–88.

——— 1950, "Landslide Patterns on Oceanic Volcanoes and Atolls," *Geograph. J.*, *115*, 84–8.

——— 1952a, "Marine Erosion," *Proc. of the Seventh Pacific Sci. Congr.*, *3*.

——— 1952b, "Multiple Stands of the Sea in Post-Glacial Times," *Proc. of the Seventh Pacific Sci. Congr.*, *3*.

——— 1958, personal communication, January, enclosing manuscript of a paper entitled "Radio-Carbon Dates of Late Quaternary Sea-Level Changes," prepared for the Commission for Study of the Coastline, International Association of Quaternary Research, V, Madrid-Barcelona. Much of the substance of this paper was presented in a talk before the Yale University Geology Club, April 1958.

——— and Teichert, Curt, 1948, "Some Coral Reefs of the Sahul Shelf," *Geograph. Rev.*, *38*, no. 2, 222–49.

Farrell, Andrew, 1928, *John Cameron's Odyssey* (New York, Macmillan).

Feeney, T. J., 1952, *Letters from Likiep* (New York, Pandick).

Finsch, O., 1882, "Über den Jahren 1879–1882 unternomenen Reisen in die Südsee," *Verhandlungen der Gesellschaft für Erdkunde zu Berlin, 9,* 553–64.

Fisk, H. N., 1944, Geological Investigation of the Alluvial Valley of the Lower Mississippi River, U. S. Army, Corps of Engineers.

Flint, Richard, 1947, *Glacial Geology and the Pleistocene Epoch* (New York, John Wiley).

———— 1957, *Glacial and Pleistocene Geology* (New York, John Wiley).

Ford, W. L., "Radiological and Salinity Relationships in the Water at Bikini Atoll," *Trans. of the Amer. Geophys. Union, 30* (1), 49–54.

Forster, G., 1777, *A Voyage Around the World* (Cook's Second Voyage), *1* (London, B. White).

Fosberg, F. R., 1946, Botany of Micronesia, unpublished report.

———— 1949, "Atoll Vegetation and Salinity," *Pacific Sci., 3,* 89–92.

———— 1953, "Vegetation of Central Pacific Atolls," *Atoll Research Bull.,* no. 23, Sept. 30.

————, 1954, "Soils of the Northern Marshall Atolls with Special Reference to the Jemo Series," *Soil Sci., 78* (2).

———— 1956, Military Geography of the Northern Marshalls, prepared under the direction of the Chief of Engineers, U. S. Army, and the U. S. Geological Survey.

———— 1957a, "Description and Occurrence of Atoll Phosphate Rock," *Amer. J. of Sci., 255,* 584–92.

———— 1957b, "Some Geological Processes at Work on Coral Atolls," *N.Y. Acad. of Sci.* [II], *19.*

———— 1959, "Vegetation and Flora of Wake Island," *Atoll Research Bull.,* no. 67, May 15.

———— and MacNeil, F. S., 1954, The Geography of the Northern Marshalls, unpublished manuscript.

Freeman, O. T. (ed.), 1951, *Geography of the Pacific* (New York, John Wiley).

Friederici, George, 1910, "Ein Beitrag zur Kentniss der Tuamotu Inseln," *Mitteilungen der Gesellschaft für Erdkunde zu Leipzig, 7,* 97–176.

Frings, Hubert, and Frings, Mable, 1959, *Studies on the Albatrosses of Midway Islands—A Preliminary Report,* Penn. State Univ. Dept. of Zoology and Entomology.

Fulbeck, Jack, 1947, "Monitors in the Marshalls," *Fauna, 9* (4).

Gabites, J. F., 1956, "A Survey of Tropical Cyclones in the South Pacific," *Proc. of the Tropical Cyclone Symposium, Brisbane, December 1956* (Melbourne, Bureau of Meteorology).

Garcia-Palacios, Carlos, 1955, "Plant Introduction in Tahiti," *South Pacific Commission Quart. Bull.,* October.

Gardiner, J. S., 1903, *Fauna and Geography of the Maldive and Laccadive Archipelagoes* (London, Cambridge Univ. Press), vol. 1.

———— 1931, *Coral Reefs and Atolls* (New York, Macmillan).

Gibbings, Robert, 1948, *Over the Reefs* (London, J. M. Dent).

Gibson-Hill, C. A., 1949, "The Robber Crab," *Zoo Life, 4,* 58–60.

Gill, William, 1876, *Life in the Southern Isles* (London, Religious Tract Society).

Ginsberg, R. N., 1953, "Intertidal Erosion on the Florida Keys," *Bull. of Marine Sci. of the Gulf and Caribbean, Center Marine Laboratory, Univ. of Miami,* no. 98, 55–8.

Giovanelli, J. L., 1940, "Les Cyclones en Oceanie Française," *Bull. de la Société d'Études Oceaniennes* (Papeete), *6,* 250–67.

Glick, P. A., 1939, "The Distribution of Insects, Spiders and Mites in the Air," *U.S. Dept. of Agriculture Tech. Bull. 673.*

Gosline, W. A., 1955, "The Inshore Fish Fauna of Johnston Island, A Central Pacific Atoll," *Pacific Sci., 9,* no. 4, October.

Gräffe, E., 1873, "Samoa oder die Schifferinseln," *J. des Museums Godeffroy* (Hamburg), *1,* 1–32.

Graham, Michael, 1956, "Harvest of the Seas," in W. L. Thomas (ed.), *Symposium: Man's Role in Changing the Face of the Earth* (Chicago, Univ. of Chicago Press), 487–503.

Gressitt, J. L., 1952, "Description of Kayangel Atoll, Palau Islands," *Atoll Research Bull.,* no. 14, Dec. 15.

———— 1954, *Insects of Micronesia,* Bernice P. Bishop Museum (Honolulu), *1,* 144–57.

Griggs, D., 1939, "A Theory of Mountain Building," *Amer. J. of Sci., 237,* 611–50.

Groves, K. E., 1951, Report of an Expedition to Polynesia for the Purpose of Collecting Fishes, Epidemiological and Ecological Data Relative to Ichthyotoxism, Loma Linda, California, pp. 1–24 (mimeographed).

Gulick, A., 1932, "Biological Peculiarities of Oceanic Islands," *Quart. Rev. of Biol., 7,* 405–27.

Gulick, L. H., 1862, "Micronesia," *Nautical Magazine and Navy Chronicle, 31,* 169–82, 237–45, 298–308, 358–63, 408–17.

Gunn, R., 1943, "Quantitative Aspects of Juxtaposed Ocean Deeps, Mountain Chains, and Volcanic Ranges," *Geophysics, 12,* 238–55.

Guppy, H. B., 1906, *Observations of a Naturalist in the Pacific between 1896 and 1899; II, Plant Dispersal* (London, Macmillan).

Hague, James, 1868, "Some Coral Islands and Islanders," *Atlantic Monthly, 22.*

Hamilton, E. L., 1956, "Sunken Islands of the Mid-Pacific Mountains," *Geol. Soc. of Amer. Mem. 64.*

———— 1957, "Marine Geology of the Southern Hawaiian Ridge," *Bull. of the Geol. Soc. of Amer., 68,* 1011–26.

Hammet, L. U., 1854, "Narrative of the Voyage of H.M.S. Serpent," *Nautical Magazine, 23.*

Harry, R. R. [Rofen, R. R.], 1953, "Ichthyological Field Data of Raroia Atoll, Tuamotu Archipelago," *Atoll Research Bull.,* no. 18, July 31.

Hartman, Olga, 1954, "Marine Annelida from the Northern Marshall Islands, Bikini and Nearby Atolls, Marshall Islands," *U.S. Geol. Surv. Prof. Pap. 260-Q,* pp. 619–44.

Hatheway, W. H., 1953, "The Land Vegetation of Arno Atoll, Marshall Islands," *Atoll Research Bull.,* no. 16, April 30.

———— 1955, "The Natural Vegetation of Canton Island, an Equatorial Pacific Atoll," *Atoll Research Bull.,* no. 43, Aug. 15.

Hawkes, Alex, and Degener, Otto, 1950, "The Screwpine," *Gardener's Chron. of Amer., 4,* 97.

Hedges, H. M., 1958, Letter from the Ponape District Administrator to Herold Wiens, Feb. 27, on typhoon damage.

Hedley, Charles, 1896, "General Account of the Atoll of Funafuti," *Australian Museum Memoir III* (Sydney), 1896–1900.

Hendrickson, J. R., 1958, "The Green Sea Turtle *Chelonia mydas* in Malaya and Sarawak," *Proc. of the Zool. Soc.* (London), *130,* 455–535.

Hercouet, C., 1895, "Note sur un archipel peu connu de la micronesie" (Iles Francis, Gilbert ou Kingsmill), *Bull. de Geographie Historique et Descriptive, 1896* (Paris).

Herms, W. B., 1926, "*Diocalandra taitensis* (Guerin) and Other Coconut Pests of Fanning and Washington Islands," *Philippine J. of Sci., 30,* 243–71.

Hess, H. H., 1946, "Drowned Ancient Islands of the Pacific Basin," *Amer. J. of Sci., 244,* 772–91.

Hesse, Richard; Allee, W. C.; and Schmidt, K. P., 1937, *Ecological Animal Geography* (London, John Wiley).

Hiatt, R. W., 1951, "Marine Zoology Study of Arno Atoll, Marshall Islands," *Atoll Research Bull.,* no. 4, Oct. 15.

———— 1958, Marine Life at Arno, unpublished manuscript.

Hidaka, Koji, 1955, "A Theoretical Study on the General Circulation of the Pacific Ocean," *Pacific Sci., 9* (2).

Hiyama, Yoshio (ed.), 1943, Report of the Investigations on Poisonous Fishes of the South Seas (in Japanese), Nissan Fisheries Research Laboratory, Tokyo.

Hinde, G. J., 1904, "Report on Funafuti Atoll Boring," in W. J. Sollas et al., *The Atoll of Funafuti,* Rept. of the Coral Reef Committee of the Royal Soc. (London).

Hoffmeister, J. E., and Ladd, H. S., 1935, "The Foundations of Atolls," *J. of Geol., 43,* 653–65.

————, ———— 1944, "The Antecedent Platform Theory," *J. of Geol., 52,* 388–502.

Holthuis, L. B., 1953, "Enumeration of the Decapod and Stomatopod Crustacea from Pacific Coral Islands," *Atoll Research Bull.,* no. 24, Nov. 15.

Howard, W. S., 1951, "Life on a By-passed Atoll," *U.S. Naval Inst. Proc., 77,* 943–5.

Houon, G. S., "Deep Diving by Bathyscape off Japan," *Nat. Geog., 117* (1), 138–50.

Howland, Llewellyn, 1955, "Howland Island, Its Birds and Rats as Observed by a Certain Mr. Stetson in 1854," *Pacific Sci., 9* (2).

Hutchings, J. W., 1953, "Southwest Pacific Tropical Cyclones," *New Zealand Geographer, 9,* 42–6.

Hutchinson, G. E., 1950, "The Biochemistry of Vertebrate Excretion," *Bull. of the Amer. Museum of Nat. Hist., 96.*

—— 1952, "The Biogeochemistry of Phosphorous," in *The Biology of Phosphorous* (Lansing, Michigan State Univ. Press).

Illing, L. V., 1954, "Bahamian Calcareous Sands," *Bull. of the Amer. Assoc. of Petr. Geol., 38,* 1–95.

Island Development Officer, Majuro, 1958, Jaluit Notes, January 7–31, February 8, Memo. to Dist. Admin., Marshalls.

Jeschke, C., 1905, "Bericht über den Orkan in den Marshall Inseln, an 30 Juni 1905," *Petermann's Mitteilungen, 51* (11), 248–9.

—— 1906, "Bericht über den Marshall Inseln," *Petermann's Meitteilungen, 52, 270–7.*

Johnson, Martin W., 1949, "Zooplankton as an Index of Water Exchange between Bikini Lagoon and the Open Sea," *Trans. of the Amer. Geophys. Union, 30* (2), 238–44.

—— 1954, "Plankton of the Northern Marshall Islands," *U.S. Geol. Surv. Prof. Pap. 260-F,* pp. 301–14.

Johnston, W. B., 1953, "Land, People and Progress in the Cook Islands," *Econ. Geography, 29,* 107–24.

Jungmichel, 1862, "De St. Davids- of Mapia-eilanden, benoorden Nieuw-Guinea," *Tijdschrift voor Indische Taal-Land-en Volkenkunde* (Batavia, The Hague), *11* (ser. 4, Vol. 2), 155–6.

Kaneshiro, Shigeru, 1950, Anthropological Report on Woleai-Lamotrek Field Trip, Report to Chief Admin., Field Headquarters, Trust Territory of the Pacific Islands.

Kelsey, J. M., 1945, "Termite Damaging Coconut-Palms on Suwarro Island: Calotermes (*Neotermes rainbowi* Hill)," *New Zealand J. of Sci. and Tech., 27,* 69–75.

Kempny, P., 1904, "Habit of Chrysopa Jalutiana," *Verhandlungen der Kaiserlichköniglichen Zoologisch-Botanischen Gesellschaft in Wien, 54,* 355.

Koidzume, Gen-i-ti, 1917, "Plants of Jaluit Islands," *Rigakukai* (Science World), *15* (1–2); translated by the U. S. Army, 1956.

Kotzebue, Otto von, 1821, *A Voyage of Discovery into the South Seas, 3* vols. (London, Longman, Hurst, Rees, Orme, and Brown).

Krämer, Augustin, 1905, "Die Gewinnung und die Zubereitung der Nahrung auf die Ralik-Ratakinseln (Marshallinseln)," *Globus, 88,* 140–6.

—— 1908, "Studienreise nach den Zentral und Westerkarolinen," *Mitteilungen aus die deutschen Schutzgebieten, 21,* 169–86.

———— 1928, "Der Taro und die Nasskultur," *Petermann's Mitteilungen, 74.*

Krempf, Armand, 1929, "About the Shape of the Coral Reefs and the System of the Alternating Winds," *Proc. of the Fourth Pacific Sci. Cong., 3a,* 477–80.

Kuenen, P. H., 1947, "Two Problems of Marine Geology: Atolls and Canyons," *Verhandelingen de Koninklijke Nederlandse Akademie van Wetenschappen, Afdeling Natuurkunde, 43.*

———— 1950, *Marine Geology* (New York, John Wiley).

Ladd, H. S., and Tracey, J. I., Jr., 1949, "The Problem of Coral Reefs," *Sci. Monthly, 69* (5), 1–8.

————; ————; Wells, J. W., and Emery, K. O., 1950, "Organic Growth and Sedimentation on an Atoll," *J. of Geol., 58* (4), 421–2.

Laxton, P. B., 1951, "Nikumaroro," *J. of the Polynesian Soc., 60,* 134–60.

LeBlanc, R. J., and Bernard, H. A., 1954, "Résumé of Recent Geological History of the Gulf Coast," *Geologie en Mijnbouw* (The Hague), *16,* 185–94.

Lefort, E. J. E., 1956, "Economic Aspects of the Coconut Industry in the South Pacific," *South Pacific Commission Tech. Pap. 92.*

Littlehales, G. W., 1921, "Hydrographic Aspects of Ocean Currents," *Proc. of the First Pan-Pacific Scientific Conf., 1921* (Honolulu), 498–500.

Loison, Guy, 1955, "Poisonous Fishes of the South Pacific," *South Pacific Commission Quart. Bull., 5* (4), 28–31.

Lucett, Edward, 1851, *Rovings in the Pacific* (London), vols. 1 and 2.

Luke, Harry, 1945, *From a South Seas Diary, 1938–1942* (London, Nicholson and Watson).

McCurdy, P. G., 1947, "Manual of Coastal Delineation from Aerial Photographs," *Hydrographic Office Pub. 592* (Washington, U. S. Navy).

McEwen, George, 1921, "The Status of the Oceanographic Studies of the Pacific," *Proc. of the First Pan-Pacific Scientific Conf.* (Honolulu), 487–97.

MacGinitie, G. E., and MacGinitie, N., 1949, *Natural History of Marine Animals* (New York, McGraw-Hill).

McKee, E. D., 1956, "Geology of Kapingamarangi Atoll, Caroline Islands," *Atoll Research Bull.,* no. 50, June 30. Also published in 1958 under same title in *Bull. of the Geol. Soc. of Amer., 69,* 241–78.

————; Chronic, John; and Leopold, Estella B., 1959, "Sedimentary Belts in the Lagoon of Kapingamarangi Atoll," *Bull. of the Amer. Assoc. of Petr. Geol., 43,* no. 3, 501–62.

MacMillan, H. G., 1946, "Agriculture and Soils; I, Agriculture," *General Economic Survey of Micronesia,* compiled for U. S. Navy, Library of Congress Microfilms, *10.*

MacNeil, F. S., 1954, "The Shape of Atolls: An Inheritance from Subaerial Erosion Forms," *Amer. J. of Sci., 252,* 402–27.

Mao, Han-Lee, and Yoshida, Kozo, 1955, "Physical Oceanography in the

Marshall Islands Area, Bikini and Nearby Atolls, Marshall Islands," *U.S. Geol. Surv. Prof. Pap. 260-R,* pp. 645–84.

Marshall, J. T., 1951, "Vertebrate Ecology of Arno Atoll, Marshall Islands," *Atoll Research Bull.,* no. 3, Oct. 15.

Marshall, Sheina, 1932, "Notes on Oxygen Production in Coral Planulae," *The Great Barrier Reef Expedition 1928–1929,* Sci. Reps. of the British Museum of Nat. Hist. (London), *1,* no. 9.

Mason, Leonard, 1957, An Introduction of Plants and Ornamentals to Arno, unpublished manuscript.

Massal, Émile, and Barrau, Jacques, 1956, "A Survey of Subsistence Problems in the South Pacific," *South Pacific Commission Quart. Bull., 35.*

Maude, H. E., 1952, "The Colonization of the Phoenix Islands," *J. of the Polynesian Soc., 61,* 62–89.

Mayor, A. G., 1921, "Rose Atoll, American Samoa," *Proc. of the Amer. Phil. Soc., 60,* 62–70.

—— 1924, "Growth Rate of Samoan Corals," *Carnegie Inst., Dept. of Marine Biol., 19.*

Mayr, Ernst, 1945a, "Bird Conservation Problems in the Southwest Pacific," *Audubon Magazine, 47,* September–October, 279–82.

—— 1945b, *Birds of the Southwest Pacific* (New York, Macmillan).

Menard, H. W., 1952, "Deep Ripple Marks in the Sea," *J. of Sedimentary Petrology, 22,* no. 1, 3–9.

—— 1955, "Deformation of the Northeastern Pacific Basin and the West Coast of North America," *Bull. of the Geol. Soc. of Amer., 66,* 1149–98.

—— and Dietz, R. S., 1951, "Submarine Geology of the Gulf and Alaska," *Bull. of the Geol. Soc. of Amer., 62,* 1263–86.

Merrill, E. D., 1945, *Plant Life of the Pacific World* (New York, Macmillan).

—— 1954, "The Botany of Cook's Voyages," *Chronica Botanica, 14.*

Merrin, S., 1955, "Beachrock in Northeastern Puerto Rico," *First Caribbean Geol. Congr., Antigua, British West Indies* (mimeographed).

Michael, E. L., 1921, "Effect of the Up-welling Water upon the Organic Fertility of the Sea in the Region of Southern California," *Proc. of the First Pan-Pacific Scientific Conf.* (Honolulu).

Miller, H. A., 1955, "Bryophytes Collected by F. R. Fosberg in the Marshall Islands," *Atoll Research Bull.,* no. 40, May 15.

—— and Doty, M. S., 1954, "Ecological and Floristic Notes on the Bryophyta of Raroia," *Atoll Research Bull.,* no. 33, Nov. 30.

Montrouzier, Rev. Father, 1876, "Natural History of Huon and Surprise Islands," *Bull. de la société geographie de Paris, 6,* 12.

Moore, H. F., 1921, "Influence of Ocean Currents on the Distribution of Fish," *Proc. of the First Pan-Pacific Scientific Conf.* (Honolulu), pp. 527–31.

Moresby, John, 1876, *Islands in the Ellice Group; Discoveries and Surveys of New Guinea and the D'Entrecasteaux Islands* (London, John Murray), **Chap. 6.**

Morrison, J. P. E., 1954, "Ecological Notes on the Mollusks and Other Animals of Raroia," *Atoll Research Bull.*, no. 34, Nov. 30.

Moseley, H. N., 1892, *Notes by a Naturalist; An Account of Observations Made During the Voyage of H.M.S. Challenger* (London, Macmillan).

Moss, F. J., 1889, *Through Atolls and Islands in the South Seas* (London, S. Low, Marston, Searle and Rivington), pp. 1–37.

Moul, E. T., 1954, "Preliminary Report on Land Animals at Onotoa Atoll, Gilbert Islands," *Atoll Research Bull.*, no. 28, May 31.

———— 1957, "Preliminary Report on the Flora of Onotoa Atoll, Gilbert Islands," *Atoll Research Bull.*, no. 57, Sept. 15.

Mousson, A., 1873, "Faune malacologique de quelques îles de l'océan," *J. de Conchyliogie*, *21*, 101–16.

Munk, W. H., and Sargent, M. C., 1954, "Adjustment of Bikini Atoll to Ocean Waves, Bikini and Nearby Atolls, Marshall Islands," *U.S. Geol. Surv. Prof. Pap. 260-C*, pp. 275–80.

Murphy, R. E., 1950, "Economic Geography of a Micronesian Atoll," *Annals of the Amer. Assoc. of Geographers, 40*, March.

Neff, J. A., 1959, Personal letter from a research biologist, U.S. Dept. of the Interior, Fish and Wildlife Service, Denver, to Herold Wiens, Nov. 2.

Newell, N. D., 1954, "Reefs and Sedimentary Processes of Rarioa," *Atoll Research Bull.*, no. 36, Nov. 30.

———— 1955, "Depositional Fabric in Permian Reef Limestones," *J. of Geol.*, *63*, 301–9.

———— 1956, "Geological Reconnaissance of Rarioa (Kon Tiki) Atoll, Tuamotu Archipelago," *Bull. of the Amer. Museum of Nat. Hist.*, *109*, article 3, 311–72.

———— 1960, "Marine Planation of Tropical Limestone Islands" (abstract), *Science, 132*, no. 3420, 144–5.

———— and Imbrie, 1955, "Biological Reconnaissance in the Bimini Area, Great Bahama Bank," *Trans. of the N.Y. Acad. of Sci.* [II], *18* (1), 3–14.

———— and Rigby, J. K., 1957, "Geological Studies on the Great Bahama Bank," in R. J. LeBlanc and Julia Breeding (eds.), "Regional Aspects of Carbonate Deposition," *Amer. Assoc. of Petr. Geol. Spec. Pub.*, 5.

Newhouse, Jan, 1954, "Ecological and Floristic Notes on the Myxophyta of Raroia," *Atoll Research Bull.*, no. 33, Nov. 30.

New York Times, 1956, "Hurricane Study Cites Warm Seas, New York University Researchers Report Water Temperature Affects Direction of Storms," Oct. 2, p. 37.

———— 1957a, "Report on Curious Tidal Changes Recorded at Canton Atoll," July 28.

———— 1957b, "Seismic Waves in the Pacific and Alaska Gulf Trench," Sept. 10.

———— 1958a, "Report on Soviet Oceanographic Research in Equatorial Pacific," June 8.

———— 1958b, "Report on Bathyscaphe Observations off Japanese Coast,"

June 29. See also G. S. Houon, "Deep Diving by Bathyscaphe off Japan," *Nat. Geog., 117* (1), 138–50.

——— 1959, "Albatrosses Face Death on Midway," Oct. 16, p. 16.

——— 1960a, "Tsunami's Power: Earthquakes Produce Tidal Wave by Disturbing Ocean Bottom," May 29, p. E-8.

——— 1960b, "Work on the Shark Research Panel of the American Institute of Biological Research," July 6.

New Zealand Journal of Science and Technology, 1928, "The 'Dana' Expedition," *10,* 371–3.

New Zealand Meteorological Service, 1955, "Cook Islands and Niue," *Meteorol. Notes 3-B* (Wellington).

——— 1956, "Line Islands," *Meteorol. Notes 11-B* (Wellington).

——— 1957, "Tokelau Islands," *Meteorol. Notes 7-B* (Wellington).

Niering, W. A., 1956, "Bioecology of Kapingamarangi, Caroline Islands: Terrestrial Aspects," *Atoll Research Bull.,* no. 49, June 30.

O'Connor, F. W., 1922, "Some Results of Medical Research of the Western Pacific," *Trans. of the Soc. of Tropical Med. Hyg.* (London), *16,* 28–56.

Odum, E. P., and Odum, H. T., 1957, "Zonation of Corals on Japton Reef," *Atoll Research Bull.,* no. 52, Sept. 15.

Odum, H. T., and Odum, E. P., 1955, "Trophic Structure and Productivity of a Windward Coral Reef Community on Eniwetok Atoll," *Ecol. Monographs, 25,* 291–320.

Okabe, M., 1941, "A Botanical Research of the Marshall Islands," *Sangyo no Nanyo* (Industry of the South Seas), *4* (5), 1–10; trans. by Risayoshi Takeda for the U.S. Geol. Surv., U. S. Military Branch, July 1952.

Oliver, Mildred, 1954, "Recent Changes in the Concept of the Broadscale Wind and Pressure Patterns of the Tropics," *J. of Georg., 53,* no. 8, 353–60.

Orr, A. P., 1933, "Physical and Chemical Conditions in the Sea in the Neighbourhood of the Great Barrier Reef," *The Great Barrier Reef Expedition, 1928–1929,* Sci. Repts. of the British Museum of Nat. Hist. (London), *2,* no. 3, 37–86.

Otter, G. W., 1937, "Rock-Destroying Organisms in Relations to Coral Reefs," *The Great Barrier Reef Expedition, 1928–1929,* Sci. Repts. of the British Museum of Nat. Hist. (London), *1,* no. 12.

Pacific Islands Yearbook, 1959 (Sydney, Pacific Publications).

Pacific Science Association, Information Bulletin, 1961, *13,* no. 1, 1–13.

Palmer, C. E., 1952, "Tropical Meteorology," *Quart. J. of the Royal Meteorol. Soc., 78,* 126–64.

Paulding, H., 1831, *Journal of a Cruise of the U. S. Schooner Dolphin* (New York, Carvill).

Pieris, W. V. D., 1955, *Wealth from the Coconut* (Sydney, South Pacific Commission Literature Bureau).

Powell, Ronald, 1957, "Breeding Turtles for Profit," *South Pacific Commission Quart. Bull.*, July, 41–2.
———— 1959, Letter from the Cook Islands Administration, Rarotonga, to Herold Wiens, Jan. 29.
Proudman, J., and Groves, G. W., 1959, *Encyclopaedia Britannica*, vol. 22.
Pusinelli, F. N. M., 1947, *Gilbert and Ellice Islands Colony: A Report on the Results of the Census of Population* (Suva, Fiji, Govt. Press).

Raitt, R. W., 1954, "Seismic Refraction Studies of Bikini and Kwajelein Atolls," *U.S. Geol. Surv. Prof. Pap. 260-K.*
Randall, J. E., 1952, "Preliminary Report on Marine Biology Study of Onotoa Atoll, Gilbert Islands, II," *Atoll Research Bull.*, no. 13, Dec. 15.
———— 1955, "Fishes of the Gilbert Islands," *Atoll Research Bull.*, no. 47, Aug. 31.
Ranson, Gilbert, 1952, *Preliminary Notes for a Report on Pearl Oyster in the E.F.O.* [French Oceania] (mimeographed, Papeete).
———— 1955, "Observations sur les principaux agents de la dissolution du calcaire sous-marine dans la zone cotière des îles corallienes de l'Archipel des Tuamotu," *Comptes rendus de l'académie des sciences, 240,* 806–8.
———— 1955, "La Consolidation des sediments calcaires dans les regions tropicales," *Comptes rendus de l'académie des sciences, 242,* 640–2.
Reid, J. L., Jr., 1960, "Evidence of a South Equatorial Countercurrent in the Pacific," *Scripps Inst. of Oceanography Contributions No. 1112* (La Jolla Univ. of California), 749–50.
Revelle, Roger, and Emery, K. O., 1957, "Chemical Erosion of Beach Rock and Exposed Reef Rock," *U.S. Geol. Surv. Prof. Pap. 260-T*, pp. 699–707.
Reyne, A., 1939, "On the Food Habits of the Coconut Crab with Notes on Its Distribution," *Archives néerlandaises de zoologie, 3,* 283–320.
Rice, D. W., 1959, "Birds and Aircraft on Midway Islands, 1957–1958 Investigations," *Spec. Sci. Rept. Wildlife 44* (Washington, U.S. Dept. of Interior).
Riehl, H., 1954, *Tropical Meteorology* (New York, McGraw-Hill).
Robertson, R., 1877, "The Caroline Islands," *Trans. of the Asiatic Soc. of Japan* (Yokohama), 5, 41–63.
Rock, J. F., 1916, "Palmyra Island, with a Description of Its Flora," *College of Hawaii Pub., Bull.* (Honolulu), 4, 1–53.
———— 1929, "The Voyage of the Luka to Palmyra Island," *Atlantic Monthly, 144.*
Rogers, D. P., 1947, "Fungi of the Marshall Islands, Central Pacific Ocean," *Pacific Sci., 1,* 92–107.
Russell, R. J., 1941, "Climatic Change through the Ages," in *Climate and Man, 1941 Yearbook of Agriculture* (Washington, Dept. of Agriculture), 67–97.
———— 1957, "Instability of Sea Level," *Amer. Scientist, 45,* 414–30.

Sachet, M. H., 1953, "Scorpions on Coral Atolls," *Atoll Research Bull.*, no. 26, Nov. 15.

———— 1954, "A Summary of Information on Rose Atoll," *Atoll Research Bull.*, no. 29, May 31.

———— 1955, "Pumice and Other Extraneous Volcanic Materials on Coral Atolls," *Atoll Research Bull.*, no. 37, May 15.

———— 1957, "Climate and Meteorology of the Gilbert Islands," *Atoll Research Bull.*, no. 60, Oct. 31.

———— and Fosberg, F. R., 1955, "Island Bibliographies," Natl. Acad. of Sci., *Pacific Science Board Pub. 355.*

Safford, W. E., 1921a, "Cultivated Plants and the Migration of the Polynesians," *Bernice P. Bishop Museum Pub. 7.*

———— 1921b, "Dispersal of Plants by Ocean Currents," *Proc. of the First Pan-Pacific Science Conf.* (Honolulu).

Sargent, M. C., and Austin, T. S., 1949, "Organic Productivity of an Atoll," *Trans. of the Amer. Geophys. Union, 30* (2), 245–9.

————, ———— 1954, "Biologic Economy of Coral Reefs, Bikini and Nearby Atolls, II," *U.S. Geol. Surv. Prof. Pap. 260-E,* pp. 293–300.

Sauer, C. C., 1957, "The End of the Ice Age and Its Witnesses," *Geograph. Rev., 47,* 31–2.

Schmidt-Nielsen, K.; Jorgensen, C. B.; and Osaki, J., 1957, "A Report to the Closing Session of the Forty-First Annual Meeting of the Federation of American Societies for Experimental Biology," *New York Times,* April 20.

Schnee, P., 1902, "Beiträge zur Fauna der Marshall-Inseln," *Der Zoologische Garten (Zoologische Beobachter)* (Frankfurt), *43.*

———— 1904, "Land und Leute der Marshallinseln," *Zeitschrift für Kolonialpolitik, Kolonialrecht und Kolonialwirtschaft, 6* (4), 245–65.

Schott, Wolfgang, 1935, *Geographie des Indischen und Stillen Ozeans* (Hamburg, Deutsche Seewarte).

Schuchert, C., 1932, "The Periodicity of Oceanic Spreading, Mountain Making and Paleogeography," *Bull. of the Nat. Research Council,* no. 85, 537–61.

Schultz, L. P., 1948, "The Biology of Bikini Atoll with Special Reference to the Fishes," *Annual Rept. of the Board of Regents of the Smithsonian Institution, 1947.*

———— and collaborators, 1953, "Fishes of the Marshall and Marianas Islands," *U.S. Natl. Museum Bull. 202* (Washington, The Smithsonian).

Seelye, C. J., 1950, "Rainfall and Its Variability over the Central and Southwestern Pacific," *New Zealand J. of Sci. and Tech. [B], 32* (2), 11–24.

Seidel, H., 1902, "Von den Marshall Inseln," *Deutsche Kolonialzeitung, 19,* 193–7.

———— 1905, "Die Bewohner der Tobi-Inseln (Deutsch-Mikronesian)," *Globus, 87,* 113–17.

Seurat, L. G., 1903, *Observations on the Structure, Fauna and Flora of South Marutea Islands (Tuamotus)* (mimeographed, Papeete).

———— 1904a, "Observations biologiques sur les cenobites," *Bull. du Musée d'histoire naturelle* (Paris, Edwards), *10.*

———— 1904b, *Observations sur quelques îles orientales de l'archipel Tuamotu* (mimeographed, Papeete), pp. 1–11.

———— 1905, "Sur le crabe des cocotiers," *Bull. du Musée d'histoire naturelle* (Paris, Edwards), *11.*

Shaw, H. K. A., 1952, "On the Distribution of *Pisonia grandis* R. Br. (Nyctaginaceae), with Special Reference to Malaysia," *KEW Bull.,* pp. 87–97.

Shepard, F. P., 1948, *Submarine Geology* (New York, Harper).

————; MacDonald, G. A.; and Cox, D. C., 1950, "The Tsunami of April 1, 1946," *Bull. of the Scripps Inst. of Oceanography, 5.*

———— and Suess, H. E., 1956, "The Rate of Post-Glacial Rise of Sea-Level," *Science, 123,* 1082–3.

Smith, Robert, 1946, "Fishery Resources," *General Economic Survey of Micronesia,* compiled for U. S. Navy, Library of Congress Microfilms.

Sparrow, F. K., 1948, "Soil Phycomycetes from Bikini, Eniwetok, Rongerik, and Rongelap Atolls," *Mycologia, 11* (4), 445–53.

Stearns, H. T., 1946, "An Integration of Coral-Reef Hypotheses," *Amer. J. of Sci., 244,* 245–62.

Steinbach, E., 1894, "Mitteilungen aus dem Schutzgebiet der Marshall Inseln," *Forschungsreisenden und Gelehrten aus den deutschen Schutzgebieten, 7* (4), 305–18.

Stephenson, T. A., and Stephenson, Anne, 1931, "Comparison of the Ecology of Other Reefs with That of Low Isles," *The Great Barrier Reef Expedition, 1928–1929,* Sci. Repts. of the British Museum of Nat. Hist. (London), *3,* no. 2.

Stevenson, L., 1953, "Microbiological Examination of Soils of Arno Atoll," *Soil Sci., 75,* 225–331.

Stone, Benjamin, 1959, "Flora of the Hall Islands," *Pacific Sci., 13,* 88–104.

Stone, L. E., Jr., 1951, "The Soils and Agriculture of Arno Atoll, Marshall Islands," *Atoll Research Bull.,* nos. 5, 6, Nov. 15.

———— 1953, "Summary of Information on Atoll Soils," *Atoll Research Bull.,* no. 22, Sept. 30.

Strasburg, D. W., 1955, "North-South Differentiation of Blenniid Fishes in the Central Pacific," *Pacific Sci., 9* (3).

Streets, Thomas, 1877, "Some Account of the Natural History of the Fanning Group of Islands," *Amer. Naturalist, 11.*

Sverdrup, H. U., 1942, *Oceanography for Meteorologists* (New York, Prentice-Hall).

————; Johnson, M. W.; and Fleming, R. H., 1954, *The Oceans, Their Physics, Chemistry, and General Biology* (New York, Prentice-Hall).

Tayama, Risaburo, 1935, "Table Reefs, a Particular Type of Coral Reef," *Proc. of the Imperial Acad. of Japan, 11,* 268–70.

Taylor, W. R., 1950, "Plants of Bikini and Other Northern Marshall Islands," *Univ. of Michigan Studies, Sci. Ser.* (Ann Arbor), *18.*

Tobin, Jack, 1955, Special Field Study Ujilan Atoll, 2/17/55–3/29/55, Report of the Dist. Anthropologist, Marshall Islands, to the Deputy High Commissioner, Trust Territory, Majuro, April 15.

Townes, H. K., 1946, "Results of an Entomological Inspection Tour of Micronesia," *General Economic Survey of Micronesia*, compiled for the U. S. Navy, Library of Congress Microfilms.

Townsend, C. H., and Wetmore, Alexander, 1919, "Reports on the Scientific Results of the Expedition on 'Albatross': The Birds," *Bull. of the Museum of Comp. Zool. at Harvard College* (Cambridge), *63*, 149–225.

Tracey, J. I., Jr.; Cloud, P. E.; and Emery, K. O., 1955, "Conspicuous Features of Organic Reefs," *Atoll Research Bull.*, no. 46, Aug. 15.

———; Ladd, H. S.; and Hoffmeister, J. E., 1948, "Reefs of Bikini, Marshall Islands," *Geol. Soc. of Amer. Bull.*, *59*, 861–78.

Tresilian, F. H., 1838, "Remarks on Christian Island," *Hawaiian Spectator, 1*.

Turbott, I. G., 1949, "Diets, Gilbert, and Ellice Islands Colony," *J. of the Polynesian Soc.*, *58*, 36–46.

U. S. Coast Pilot, Pacific Islands, 1950.

U. S. Department of State, 1955, "Trust Territory of the Pacific Islands, 1954," *Publication 5735*.

U. S. House of Representatives, 1945, "Study of Pacific Bases," A Report on Pacific Bases of the Sub-Committee on Naval Affairs, House of Representatives, 79th Congress, 1st Session, *H. Res. 154*, 1015–19.

U. S. Navy, 1920, "Australian Pilot" (Washington, Hydrographic Office), *1*, no. 167.

——— 1943, "Weather Summary for H. O. Publication 273," *Naval Air Pilot, West Pacific, Caroline and Marshall Islands Area* (Washington, Hydrographic Office).

——— 1944, "A Brief Climatic Summary of the Marshall Islands," *Navaer* 50-IR-78 (Washington, Chief of Naval Operations, Aerology Section).

——— 1946, *Marine Atlas of the World; Vol. 2, North Pacific* (Washington, Chief of Naval Operations, Aerology Section).

——— 1948a, *Handbook on the Trust Territory of the Pacific Islands*.

——— 1948b, "Trust Territory of the Pacific Islands," *OPNAV-P22-100E*.

——— 1952, *Sailing Directions for the Pacific Islands* (Washington, Hydrographic Office), *1*, no. 165A, and *3*, no. 166.

——— 1953, Annual Typhoon Rept.

——— 1954, Annual Typhoon Rept.

——— 1955, Annual Typhoon Rept.

——— 1956, Annual Typhoon Rept.

——— 1957, Annual Typhoon Rept.

U. S. Trust Territory Pacific, 1951a, Civil Admin. Rep., Kwajelein, Memo. to Governor, Marshall Islands, March 30.

——— 1951b, Civil Admin. Rep., Kwajelein, Letter to Dist. Admin., Majuro, April 5.

———— 1951c, Civil Admin., Marshalls, Rept. to High Commissioner, Trust Territory of the Pacific Islands, April 6.

———— 1957, Extension Agriculturist, Ponape, Memo. to Acting Dist. Admin., Ponape Dist., on Typhoon Lola Damage to Pingelap, Dec. 29.

———— 1958a, Annual Rept.

———— 1958b, Director of Coconut Operations, Rept. to High Commissioner, Trust Territory of the Pacific Islands, on Post-Typhoon Situation at Mokil and Pingelap Atolls, Jan. 3.

————, 1958c, Director of Coconut Operations, Rept. to High Commissioner, Trust Territory of the Pacific Islands, on Typhoon Damage to Namrik and Jaluit Coconut Groves, Jan. 30.

———— 1958d, Island Development Officer, Rept. to Dist. Admin., Marshalls, on Typhoon Damage to Jaluit, Jan. 31.

———— 1958e, M. N. Sproat, Director, Agriculture and Fisheries, Memo. to High Commissioner, Trust Territory of the Pacific Islands, on Effects of Typhoon Ophelia, Jan. 31.

———— 1958f, Extension Agriculturist Trainee, Memo. to Dist. Admin., Marshalls, on Typhoon Damage to Mili, Feb. 26.

U. S. Weather Bureau, 1938, *Atlas of Climatic Charts of the Oceans, Pacific Ocean.*

———— 1956, *Climatological Data, Hawaii, Annual Summary, 1955.*

———— 1957, *Climatological Data, Hawaii, Annual Summary, 1956.*

Usinger, R. L., and La Rivers, Ira, 1953, "The Insect Life of Arno," *Atoll Research Bull.,* no. 15, April 30.

Van Zwaluwenburg, R. H., 1941, "Canton Island," *Hawaiian Planters' Record* (Honolulu), *14* (1).

———— 1942, "Notes on the Temporary Establishment of Insect and Plant Species on Canton Island," *Hawaiian Planters' Record* (Honolulu), *46* (2).

———— 1955, "The Insects and Certain Other Arthropods of Canton Island," *Atoll Research Bull.,* no. 42, Aug. 15.

Vaughan, T. W., 1911, "Studies of the Geology of the Madreporaria of the Bahamas and of Southern Florida," *Carnegie Inst. Yearbook* (Washington), no. 11, 153–62.

———— 1913, "Physical Conditions under Which Paleozoic Coral Reefs Were Formed," *Geol. Soc. of Amer. Bull.,* 22, 238–52.

———— 1915, "The Geologic Significance of the Growth-Rate of the Floridian and Bahaman Shoal-Water Corals," *Washington Acad. of Sci. J.,* 5, 591–600.

———— 1916, "The Results of Investigations of the Ecology of the Floridian and Bahamas Shoal-Water Corals," *Proc. of the Natl. Acad. of Sci.,* 2, 95–100.

———— 1919, "Corals and the Formation of Coral Reefs," *Annual Rept. to the Board of Regents of the Smithsonian Institution, 1917* (Washington), 189–276.

Verrill, A. H., 1940, *Wonder Creatures of the Sea* (New York, Appleton-Century).

Vening Meinesz, F. A., 1944, "De verdeling van continenten en oceanen over het aardoppervlak," *Verslagen en Mededeelingen Koninklhijke Akadamie Van Wetenschappen, 5* (53), 151–9.

—— 1948, "Major Tectonic Phenomena and the Hypothesis of Convection Currents in the Earth," *Quart. J. of the Geol. Soc.* (London), *103,* 191–207.

Visher, S. S., 1925, "Tropical Cyclones of the Pacific," *Bernice P. Bishop Museum Bull., 20.*

Von Arx, W. S., 1954, "Circulation Systems of Bikini and Rongelap Lagoons, Bikini and Nearby Atolls, Marshall Islands," *U.S. Geol. Surv. Prof. Pap. 260-B,* pp. 265–73.

Waesche, H. A., 1938, "An Equatorial Cruise," *Volcano Letter, 461.*

Waite, E. R., 1897, "The Mammals, Reptiles, and Fishes of Funafuti," *Australian Museum Memoir III* (Sydney), 1896–1900.

Wells, J. W., 1951, "The Coral Reefs of Arno Atoll, Marshall Islands," *Atoll Research Bull.,* no. 9, Dec. 15.

—— 1954, "Recent Corals of the Marshall Islands, Bikini and Nearby Atolls, II, Oceanography (Biologic)," *U.S. Geol. Surv. Prof. Pap. 260-I,* pp. 385–486.

Wentworth, C., 1925, "A Tropical Peat Bog," *Bull. of the Geol. Soc. of Amer., 36,* 137.

Westerman, William, 1956, Dist. Agriculturist, Palau, undated mimeographed rept. received 1956.

Wharton, A. J. L., 1897, "Foundations of Coral Atolls," *Nature, 55,* 390–3.

Whitmee, S. J., 1871, *A Missionary Cruise in the South Pacific,* 2nd ed. (Sydney, J. Cook).

Wiens, H. J., 1956, "The Geography of Kapingamarangi Atoll in the Eastern Carolines," *Atoll Research Bull.,* no. 48, June 30.

—— 1957, "Field Notes on Atolls Visited in the Marshalls," *Atoll Research Bull.,* no. 54, Sept. 15.

—— 1959, "Atoll Development and Morphology," *Annals of the Assoc. of Amer. Geographers, 49,* 31–54.

Wilkes, Charles, 1845, *Narrative of the U.S. Exploring Expedition.*

Wood-Jones, F., 1912, *Coral and Atolls* (reissue) (London, Lovell-Reeve).

Yabe, Hisakatsu, 1942, "Problems of the Coral Reefs," *Univ. Geol. and Paleontology Inst. Rept.* (Tohoku), *39,* 1–6 (in Japanese).

—— and Tayama, Risaburo, 1937, "Depth of Atoll-Lagoons in the South Sea Islands," *Proc. of the Imperial Acad. of Japan, 13.*

Yanaihara, Tadao, 1939, *Pacific Islands under Japanese Mandate* (Shanghai, Kelly and Walsh).

Yonge, C. M., 1940, "The Biology of Reef-building Corals," *The Great Bar-*

rier Reef Expedition, 1928–1929, Sci. Repts. of the British Museum of Nat. Hist. (London) *1,* no. 13, 353–91.

————— and Nicholls, A. G., 1931, "Studies on the Physiology of Corals," *The Great Barrier Reef Expedition, 1928–1929,* Sci. Repts. of the British Museum of Nat. Hist. (London), *1,* no. 4.

Yoshida, K.; Mao, Han-lee; and Horrer, P., 1953, "Circulation in the Upper Mixed Layer of the Equatorial North Pacific," *J. of Marine Research, 12,* 99–120.

Zeuner, F. E., 1945, *The Pleistocene Period, Its Climate, Chronology and Faunal Succession* (London, Bernard Quaritch).

————— 1952, *Dating the Past: An Introduction to Geochronology,* 3rd ed. (London, Methuen).

PLATE 1. A parallelogram-shaped atoll 15 miles in circumference, Hull Atoll lies in the semiarid Phoenix group. It has no navigable pass into the deep lagoon except a channel that has been blasted to provide passage for small boats.

PLATE 2. Enderbury Atoll in the Phoenix group is a small, dry island with only sedges and scrub bushes for vegetation. It is only about 3 miles long and 2½ miles wide, and it has a very small lagoon.

PLATE 3. Reef spurs growing out into the lagoon from the peripheral reef of Namorik Atoll, southern Marshall Islands. In some instances such reef arms may enclose small secondary lagoons. Namorik has a very wet climate and dense plantations and forests.

PLATE 4. Secondary lagoons and pools on the lagoon reef off Matamat Islet, Namorik Atoll, southern Marshall Islands, February 1952. The inlet, or small channel, leads to a mangrove swamp in the interior of the islet (right background). The curious pattern of reef pools enclosed by strips of reef probably derives from subaerial solution during an emergent period of the reef, and the mangrove depression no doubt has the same origin. Compare these pools with those in Plate 5. Many of the trees on this islet were destroyed during the January 1958 typhoon.

PLATE 5. Small, shallow, secondary lagoon basins comparable to those in Plate 4 are seen here adjoining Ebon Islet, Ebon Atoll, southern Marshall Islands. Two semicircular fish traps of coral stone are visible at the upper right end of the central basin. Village residences stand between the lagoon shore and the path through the densely planted coconut-breadfruit forest. Ebon has a high rainfall.

PLATE 6. The northeastern quadrant of Kapingamarangi Atoll, showing the numerous large patch reefs in the deep parts of the lagoon. Werua, the largest (but not the longest) islet of the atoll, is at the lower left. On Werua there is a large excavated Cyrtosperma field surrounded by numerous breadfruit trees, which are surrounded in turn by coconut plantations. The islet covers 41 acres and is about 1,850 feet long and 1,200 feet wide (see Figs. 14, 30, and 93).

PLATE 7. Jabwor Islet, on the southern and near side of Southeast Pass, Jaluit Atoll, southern Marshall Islands, is the chief anchorage for Jaluit and was the administrative center for the Marshalls under the Germans and the Japanese. As seen here in June 1952, 8 years after warfare had destroyed the village that once occupied most of the visible land, the area was largely overgrown with vines, brush, and forest. Its trees were blown down and much of the area was inundated during the January 1958 typhoon. Enybor lies across the channel.

PLATE 8. Bock Pass, adjoining Bock Islet, is over 100 feet deep and lies on the leeward western reef of Namu Atoll in the central Marshall Islands. The clear water permits a view of the bottom almost to mid-channel. Although small coral clumps are visible, none apparently rises much above the floor of the channel. Namu is a wet atoll. Only a small part of the dense vegetation on Bock Islet consists of food trees.

PLATE 9. Enybor Islet in 1952, with the deep Southeast Pass of Jaluit Atoll, southern Marshall Islands, in the foreground. An interesting feature here is the long reef arm extending lagoonward for over three-quarters of a mile parallel to the pass; it may have been derived from sediment bars formed by storms and currents. A horseshoe-shaped stone fish trap is visible near the base of the reef arm. Enybor was ravaged of much of its vegetation during World War II bombings, and the January 1958 typhoon destroyed the rest. The white beach areas are comprised of foraminiferous sand.

PLATE 10. The southeastern quadrant of oval-shaped Kapingamaringa Atoll, eastern Caroline Islands. The lagoon diameter along the right edge of the photograph is about 8 miles. Elongated Hare Islet (in the foreground) is about 1 mile long and 300 to 400 feet wide. The sole deep ship's pass has several channels through the pass-mouth reef patches. Foam streaks toward the pass from the left foreground indicate that the surface current is driven by prevailing easterly winds. Breadfruit trees in the central part of Hare Islet tower over the coconut plantations (see Fig. 14).

PLATE 11. The sole deep pass into Ebon Atoll Lagoon, shown here in October 1951, is divided into two channels by a patch reef at its lagoon mouth. The marked resemblance to delta deposits at the marine mouth of a river may be as real as they are apparent. A ground view of this pass area is shown in Plate 18.

PLATE 12. Mili Islet, the largest land area of Mili Atoll in the southern Marshall Islands, seen here in October 1951, was used by the Japanese during World War II for an air base. The outlines of the criss-cross of runways still were visible 7 years later, although shrubs, weeds, and grass had begun to overgrow the area. Few trees grow in the hard-packed surface of the old runways, and such areas present difficulties in the re-establishment of coconut plantations. Moreover, buried shells and undetonated bombs created risks that frightened the islanders from attempting to dig and clear the area. The scalloped reef configuration shows the significance of the reef bends in creating wide land areas.

PLATE 13. The seaward reef margin off Arbor Islet on the south reef of Rongelap Atoll, northern Marshall Islands, showing the probable effect of hydraulic breakage from storm waves. The serration of this reef margin is of a different character from that on the windward eastern and northeastern reef margins, where exposure to wave attack is constant. Boulders spotting this reef flat undoubtedly derive from the reef margin breakage. Arbor Islet is striking for the absence of coconut plantations, although a few scattered clumps indicate the unused potential of this semihumid atoll in December 1951. The light patches about 150 feet seaward from the breaker zone may mark the sedimentary deposits on the "10-fathom terrace."

PLATE 14. Characteristic serrated reef margin with surge channels and Porolithon-veneered buttresses forming the rough cavernous front on the seaward, windward side of an atoll. These rocks at Majuro Atoll in the Marshall Islands had a purplish-pink hue.

PLATE 15. A remarkable lagoon reef flat, as smooth as a concrete floor and the size of a football field, sprinkled with a few loose coral and conglomerate cobblestones at Ebon Islet, Ebon Atoll, 1956.

PLATE 16. Burok Islet and the southwestern reef of Rongelap Atoll, northern Marshall Islands, October 1951. This provides a dramatic illustration of the change in reef character with a change in exposure to wave attack from the broken and serrated reef margin at the right to the smooth reef margin at the left. Although both sections are in leeward situations, the more-protected western reef is at the left, the less-protected southwestern reef at the right.

PLATE 17. The exposed northern seaward reef of Arno Atoll, southern Marshall Islands, showing the well-developed groove-and-buttress system of the reef margin as well as the surge channels extending shoreward beyond the breaker zone. There appears to be a relationship between the shallow grooves of the reef flat and the deeper grooves of the reef margin. The origin of the surge channels has not been established definitely. They may have been caused by solution processes during an exposed stage or by the erosive abrasion of sediment moved by tidal currents.

PLATE 18. The rough, boulder-strewn reef flat adjoining the pass at Ebon Atoll. The pass runs between two vegetated islets.

PLATE 19. Two blocks of reef rock torn from the reef margin and tossed shoreward some 150 feet from the breaker zone in the background off Aineman Islet, Jaluit Atoll, seen 1956. The size of the blocks may be judged by comparison with the bag, which is 18 inches long.

PLATE 20. Indentions and outwash fans resulting from inundations from the sea and headward erosion on the lagoon reef side of Kamome Islet, Taongi Atoll, June 1954. Note the prolific coral heads growing in the lagoon. Their light-colored centers probably indicate that the parts have reached the surface and died from exposure. Semiarid Taongi Atoll supports a vegetation of xerophilous scrub and sedges.

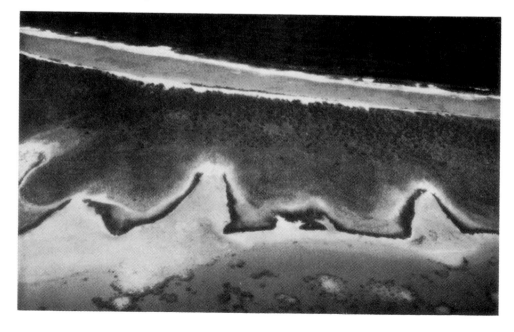

PLATE 21. Overlapping sheets of beach rock on Bird Islet, Jaluit Atoll, April 1958.

PLATE 22. The violent force of typhoon-driven waves is indicated by this view of three concentric semicircular cobble ramparts formed on coral and coralline debris 8 or more feet above the level of the seaward reef flat (in the background) at the northeastern end of Utirik Islet, which lies on the southeastern tip of Utirik Atoll. This patch of rubble was observed by the writer to extend for about ¼ mile, with an inshore width up to 100 yards. See also Plate 59.

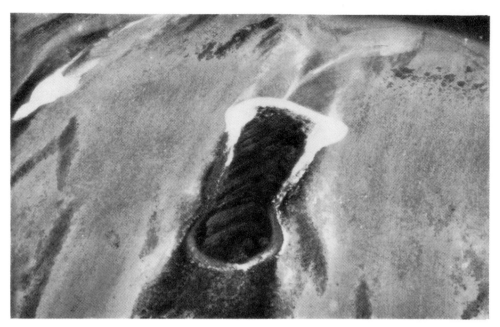

PLATE 23. Even salt-tolerant shrubs and trees show the effects of salt-spray planing. This October 1951 view of Boggelinenlapp Islet, Ujelang Atoll, also shows the effect of the prevailing wind and spray in aligning the pattern of foliage. It can be deduced that the prevailing easterly winds move across the area shown from lower left to upper right. Waves and currents from the seaward side have built a horeshoe-shaped gravel rampart in the foreground and a white beach of foraminifera tests on the lagoon end.

PLATE 24. An old reef of conglomerate rock pedestal, 80 to 90 feet long, which may represent part of an earlier island area, supports a grove of *Pemphis acidula* shrubs 10 to 12 feet tall. The surface nature of the rock is shown in Plate 25; the undercut face of the rock in Plate 26. There is no soil on the surface. The scene was photographed at Ebon Atoll in 1956.

PLATE 25. The surface of rock created by rainwater solution and known as "makatea" (from the name of a raised reef island in the Tuamotu group). After showers, the pools and cavities on this surface hold fresh water that is partly soaked up by the porous rock and utilized by the xerophytic Pemphis bushes. This is the surface of the rock shown in Plate 24.

PLATE 26. The tidal nick or undercutting so common on limestone coasts of Pacific islands is shown here on the shoreward side of an elevated pedestal rock at Ebon Atoll, seen also in Plates 24 and 25.

PLATE 27. Three different rock layers or reef layers on the lagoon reef flat off Aineman Islet, Jaluit Atoll, December 1951, which may have been exposed by the hydraulic wave motion of lagoon waves. On the seaward reef stands a large boulder 10 to 12 feet long. It was probably torn off the reef margin and washed ashore.

PLATE 28. Imejwa (foreground) and Maat (upper right), Likiep Atoll, and smaller islets—a striking picture of island fractioning and destruction on coral atolls. The dark rock strips evidently are the remnants of old island rock formerly underlying a single large island that was part of present Imejwa. Their elongation in an ocean-lagoonward orientation appears to indicate causal factors relating to the advance and retreat of tidal waters, although the initial destruction of their overlying forest and sediments may have been from storm inundation. Sediment abrasion also has played a role in shaping the pattern. Almost the entire land area, shown here in June 1952, supports coconut plantations. The trees are relatively widely spaced because of the low rainfall.

PLATE 29. Conglomerate island rock exposed by typhoon water scour at Jaluit Atoll in January 1958 (photographed in April). The upper layer (2 feet thick), against which the board leans at the right, appeared less cemented than the older, darker (algae-blackened) conglomerate beneath and was cut through by the inundation.

PLATE 30. A sedimentary fan, Kamome Islet, Taongi Atoll, northern Marshall Islands, June 1954. The fan obviously resulted from storm-pushed sea water pouring across the islet and scouring away the overlying sediment in the channel it made. The islet vegetation reveals the semiarid climate of the northernmost Marshalls.

PLATE 31. Another example of reef-islet fractioning caused by storm-driven marine inundation and accompanying erosion. A channel has cut off the left end of the islet but did not complete the cut at the center to the lagoon. As viewed here in June 1952, Aliet Islet of Ailuk Atoll stands at the right.

PLATE 32. Storm-initiated marine inundation and current scour probably led to the separation of a former, larger reef island into three islets, now called Naen, Piganyaroyaro, and Yugui, on the northwestern reef of Rongelap Atoll, northern Marshall Islands. This view in December 1951 shows the channels cut through the old island rock and the tidal fans on the lagoon side at the left. The scattering of coconut palms planted near the channel indicates the potential for more-productive economic use of the land.

PLATE 33. What was once called Sydney Pier in the lagoon about a mile south of Jabwor, Jaluit Atoll, December 1951. The bomb craters on the reef form pools, some of which contain a lining of coral. A dense tangle of Pandanus, Wedelia, and other creeping vines cover the former military installation and oil depot. Compare with Plate 34.

PLATE 34. The site of Sydney Pier and the Japanese oil-storage depot shown in Plate 33 as it appeared after the typhoon of January 1958. That marine inundation, from both ocean and lagoon, swept the land at different times during the typhoon is evident from the seaward shift of the heavy oil tanks off their circular concrete foundations near the lagoon, and from the 8-foot-high gravel bar, which created a moat between the bar and the old land area. The bar contains mostly freshly broken bits of the reef margin and reef flat. For a ground view of the bar see Plate 35.

PLATE 35. A view of the typhoon-wave-created bar of coral debris standing 8 feet above the old reef flat on the seaward reef south of Jabwor, Jaluit Atoll, April 1958, 3 months after the typhoon. The dark algal-stained lower half shows the level of high tide on the bar.

PLATE 36. Coconut-palm logs and stumps washed out and torn out by the roots were strewn over the lagoon and lagoon flat off the islet of Medjato, the most devastated of the islets on the windward reef of Jaluit, seen here in April 1958, 3 months after the typhoon.

PLATE 37. At Jaluit Atoll the January 1958 typhoon at places washed out trees and the land on which the trees grew; at other places it spread a veneer of coral and coralline rubble, as shown in this view 2 miles south of Jabwor. Dead tree trunks of Pemphis, Guettarda, and Pandanus surround a few surviving coconut palms, which by April had grown a few fronds.

PLATE 38. A 2-to-3-foot-deep layer of coral and coralline debris that was spread over some parts of the inundated islets on the eastern reef of Jaluit Atoll during the January 1958 typhoon.

PLATE 39. A view of the dense vegetation on the narrow strip of Jaluit Islet about 2 miles south of Jabwor, Jaluit Atoll, summer 1956. The vegetation was destroyed by the January 1958 typhoon.

PLATE 40. In a wet atoll such as Jaluit, a dense and flourishing forest of trees and coconut plantations existed prior to January 1958. Typhoon Ophelia toppled 85 to 100 per cent of the palms and Pandanus trees in various parts of the atoll, leaving this scene in April 1958.

PLATE 41. The barren landscape left by Typhoon Ophelia in January 1958 on the eastern reef islands of Jaluit Atoll, as seen 3 months later.

PLATE 42. Surge channels in the tide-pool zone of the seaward reef are the habitats of small fish hunted by the atoll dweller with rubber-band zip-spear and goggles. Uliga, Majuro Atoll, 1956.

PLATE 43. A Trochus (bottom center), several black-spined sting urchins, and a large, harmless slate-pencil urchin (*Heterocentrotus trigonarius*). The latter was overturned to show its rasping mouth. These were observed on the windward, seaward reef flat at low tide in the areas with an inch or two of standing water.

PLATE 44. The tide-pool surface is plastered with a veneer of coralline algae, which also line the surge channels. Crevices such as this one at Uliga, Majuro Atoll, run for 50 to 100 feet or more inward from the reef margin and may be 5 to 10 or more feet deep.

PLATE 45. The cavernous structure of some of the reef flats in the tide-pool zone is shown in this view of Uliga, Majuro Atoll, southern Marshall Islands. Although the massive coralline surface provides a strong framework, the walker must watch his step on such a reef.

PLATE 46. A beautiful display of coral colonies (*Acropora sp.*) on the windward, seaward reef flat adjacent to Ebeje, Kwajelein Atoll, 1956. Although these corals cannot withstand long emergence, their partial exposure at low tide indicates upward growth during high-tide stages.

PLATE 47. The tide-pool zone of the windward, seaward reef displays a varied assemblage of reef fauna and flora. Seen in this view at Ebeje reef, Kwajelein Atoll, is a loaf-shaped holothurian (sea cucumber), numerous black-spined sting urchins (*Diodema setosum*), a patch of colonial anemone at the upper left, and various corals at the right.

PLATE 48. Coral forms right and left and what appeared to be a coralline algal mantle at the center, photographed at the leeward reef of Meijit Island, northern Marshall Islands. The central corallinelike object appeared like leather in color and texture and seemed to have grown over irregularities in a way that resembles a flexible mantle dropped over the objects beneath. However, the sheet was about 1 centimeter thick and was rigid and rocklike.

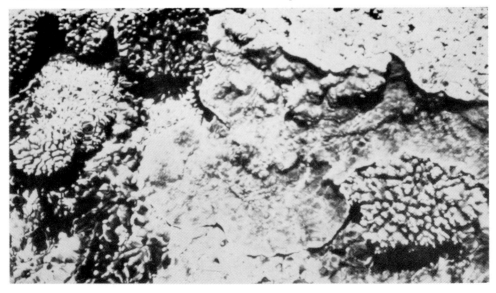

PLATE 49. A fan coral and other coral species on the leeward reef of Meijit Island, northern Marshall Islands.

PLATE 50. An assemblage of shallow-water lagoon reef corals photographed off Ebon Islet, Ebon Atoll, near the raised pedestal seen in Plates 24 and 26. The handlike coral at the left is a blue coral, some pieces of which have been broken off. The coral with the numerous round cells at the right was pink, and the fragile coral at the center was creamy in color.

PLATE 51. An expanding colony of Heliopora coral in the shallow inter-islet channel west of Ebon Islet, Ebon Atoll. The surface became exposed at low tide and is dead coral covered with a film of foraminiferous sand on which grew an assortment of algae. The massive lavender or pinkish peripheral parts of the circular block comprises the live, outward-growing coral animals.

PLATE 52. A long period of growth of numerous Heliopora corals on an undisturbed lagoon reef flat may result in the merging of the colonies into a single sheet through expansion and mutual annihilation. The colonies shown were photographed on the lagoon reef on the eastern end of Ebon Islet, Ebon Atoll, 1956.

PLATE 53. Harmless small sand sharks frequently prowl the shallow lagoon and reef waters looking for anchovies and other small food items. This specimen was caught on the reef at Kapingamarangi Atoll after it had been disabled by a stone that was thrown at it.

PLATE 54. A specimen of the spiny puffer fish (Tetraodon sp.) photographed at Kapingamarangi Atoll. The flesh of this common inhabitant of coral reefs is poisonous to eat.

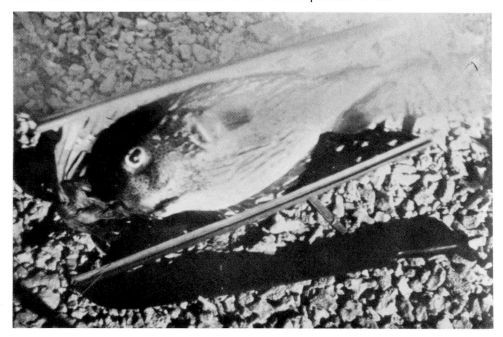

PLATE 55. Sea birds are common on all atolls but are numerous chiefly on uninhabited dry atolls and reef islands. The photograph, taken in 1939, shows part of the colony of hundreds of thousands of birds on Enderbury Atoll in the dry Phoenix Islands. The low rainfall supports only low grasses, sedges, and xerophytic shrubs.

PLATE 56. Characteristic branch structure and foliage of *Messerschmidia argentea*, the sole tree species on uninhabited Gaferut reef island except for two stunted coconut trees. This photograph, taken in 1954, also shows a pair of white fairy terns.

PLATE 57. A tame frigate bird, photographed at Kapingamarangi Atoll. Atoll inhabitants often make pets of this avian pirate, whose normal method of securing food appears to be to dive-bomb terns to force them to disgorge their catch of fish, which the frigates catch in mid-air.

PLATE 58. Nesting white-capped noddies, common terns on coral atolls, photographed on Pemphis trees on Bird Islet, Jaluit Atoll, 1958, where they also were nesting thickly on Pisonia trees.

PLATE 59. Scraggly tangles of Scaevola, growing here in algae-blackened beds of cobblestones. Photographed in 1956 in the same area as that shown in Plate 22.

PLATE 60. Ornamental plants at the Capelle residence on Likiep Atoll, northern Marshall Islands, 1956, included Croton bushes, swamp taro, Plumeria, Bougainvillaea, Hibiscus, and a species of cactus.

PLATE 61. Gardner Atoll in the Phoenix group lies in the semiarid area of the central Pacific and has an average annual rainfall of 46 inches. Although occasional drops in annual rainfall to less than 20 inches create critical conditions for people and vegetation, coconut trees will grow and produce nuts here. Between 1938 and 1940, 8,000 coconut trees were planted and a settlement of Gilbertese was established by the British authorities. Much of the island formerly supported chiefly Pisonia trees and scrub forest, as shown here in 1939.

PLATE 62. This view of Rongelap Islet, Rongelap Atoll, 1951, shows the poorly managed plantation areas, which undoubtedly are capable of supporting a much larger number of coconut palms. Rongelap is deficient in rainfall, but human rather than physical factors probably lie behind the low level of exploitation of land.

PLATE 63. An open coconut plantation on a sandy section of Utirik Islet, Utirik Atoll, northern Marshall Islands. A sparse growth of Lepturus, in places intermixed with *Cassytha filiformis* vines, forms a ground cover. The coconut trees, toppled by storm winds but with part of their roots intact, have continued their growth with a right-angle turn upward in their search for sunlight.

PLATE 64. This small islet, about 700 by 700 feet, lies immediately southeast of Enebin Islet, Wotje Atoll. This view in March 1952 shows the well-developed shelter belt of halophytic shrubs and trees, probably mostly Scaevola and Guettarda and some Pemphis, on the windward, seaward, and channel sides. A widely spaced stand of coconut palms occupies the rest of the islet to the lagoon shore. On the sand beach a single outrigger canoe stands near the sole house on the islet.

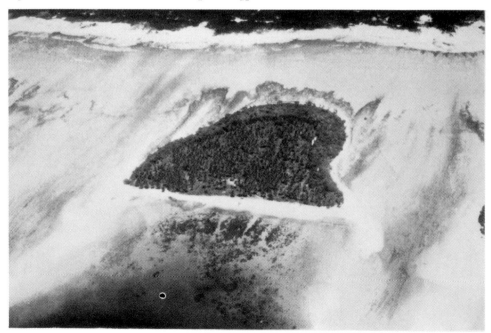

PLATE 65. The mixed coconut forest on Airik Islet, Maloelap Atoll, central Marshall Islands, an open type in a moderate rainfall zone.

PLATE 66. Namorik Atoll lies in the wettest part of the Marshall Islands and may get up to 180 inches of rainfall annually. Its dense tropical forest is largely planted with coconut and breadfruit trees. A large central depression on Matamat Islet, seen in February 1952, had a thick stand of mangrove forest. Many of the plantation trees were destroyed by Typhoon Ophelia in January 1958. The violence of storm waters is shown by the large blocks of reef rock torn up from the seaward reef margin in the right background and strewn on the reef flat.

PLATE 67. Two breadfruit trees on Elizabeth Islet, Jaluit Atoll, April 1958, 3 months after most of their limbs and all their leaves had been stripped by typhoon winds. The tree in the foreground had generated a flourishing new foliage, although the one in the rear had sprouted only a sparse growth of leaves on the trunk and stubs of the branches.

PLATE 68. A dense Pandanus jungle in the midst of a coconut plantation, April 1958, following the damage of Typhoon Ophelia in January. Virtually all the Pandanus trunks were snapped or toppled and the trees killed, whereas a small percentage of the coconut palms survived. From the writer's survey of damage on Jaluit, he concluded that the Pandanus is more vulnerable to wind damage than the coconut palm.

PLATE 69. When Bikini Atoll was selected as the site of nuclear-bomb testing in 1946, the people of Bikini, under 100 in number, were moved to temporary homes elsewhere and finally given the reef island of Kili in the southern Marshall Islands as their permanent new home. Kili, shown here in March 1952, is not an atoll but a single reef island, so there is no lagoon, and fishing must be done in the open sea on the leeward side of the island. The wet climate, however, provides for a far more flourishing and productive coconut and breadfruit plantation than existed at Bikini. The open taro depression was scarcely used by the inhabitants when the writer visited Kili in 1956.

PLATE 70. Matuketuke Islet on the eastern windward reef of Kapingamarangi Atoll in the eastern Caroline Islands, 1954, was 410 feet long (in the direction away from the viewer) and 150 feet wide. The palms were 50 to 75 feet tall on this very low lying patch of rubble and sand. The tidal stage was nearly at high tide when the photograph was taken, so the islet land surface is seen to be no more than 2 to 3 feet above high-tide level. The ability of the coconut palm to grow under such conditions indicates a highly efficient root system that makes use of the percolating rain water before it filters away, as well as of the fresh-water lens underground.

PLATE 71. A flourishing, if superannuated, grove of coconut trees about 60 years old on Kapingamarangi Atoll. Some of the trees are over 100 feet tall. Their peak of productivity was already long passed when photographed here in 1954. Although their natural tendency is to grow vertically, crowded trees along the beaches may seek the sun by growing outward over the reef flat, curving upward when there is room. Undercutting of stumps and roots by tidal wash also may accentuate the downward tilt and in some cases may cause the trees to fall.

PLATE 72. A Guettarda tree being choked by a growth of the leafless *Cassytha filiformis* vine on the seaward beach in the northern part of Enybor Islet, Jaluit Atoll. This yellow-green vine resembles a tangle of millimeter-gauge insulated wire. Other typical strand plants in the view are the Messerschmidia, projecting a branch to the right of the Cassytha, and the Scaevola bush in the left foreground.

PLATE 73. This view of the base of Pandanus trees shows the prop roots that support the top-heavy crown structures of the trees. In swampy environs, these prop roots are especially necessary.

PLATE 74. *Asplenum nidus* forms a ground cover 6 feet tall in the wet coconut forest of Kili Island, 1956.

PLATE 75. Nephrolepsis ferns forming a thick ground cover in the dense, wet coconut forest on Ebon Islet, Ebon Atoll, 1956.

PLATE 76. Cyrtosperma, or swamp taro, is the tuberous, large-leaved plant seen here growing in a depression excavated down to the fresh-water lens on Nukuoro Atoll, eastern Caroline Islands, 1954. Compare the height of the man with the plant heights.

PLATE 77. A flourishing grove of large breadfruit trees backed by coconut plantations surrounds the main village of Ailuk Atoll, seen here in December 1951. The nearness of the breadfruit trees to the lagoon beach shows that an adequate fresh-water lens extends nearly to the lagoon beach. Semicircular stone fish traps appear on the beach, and several outrigger canoes are drawn up near the village pier.

PLATE 78. A clump of *Pemphis acidula*, stripped of branches, leaves, and much bark by typhoon-wind-driven spray in January 1958, had regenerated leaves from the trunks by the end of April.

PLATE 79. A close-up of a typhoon-damaged Pemphis tree, which had regenerated leaves from the trunk even after the windward half of the bark had been stripped off.

PLATE 80. An excellent illustration of how the coconut palm is able to grow in relatively dry atolls and under poor ground-water conditions. The elaborate root structure exposed by typhoon-water wash on Jaluit Atoll acts as a sponge to soak up a great part of the percolating rain water before it gets much below the surface soil cover. These roots are from the single tree standing in the middle.

PLATE 81. The amazing ability of the coconut palm to survive and grow in the most unfavorable environment is shown by this clump of trees on tiny Nakor Islet northeast of Ebon, Ebon Atoll, 1956. This patch of sand was 20 by 30 feet and perched on bare rock. The wet, rainy climate of Ebon and the ability of the palm roots to absorb falling rain rapidly help to explain this situation.

PLATE 82. A mangrove (Bruguiera) swamp on Elizabeth Islet, Jaluit Atoll, April 1958. Slimy greenish algae covered the surface of the foreground.

PLATE 83. A patch of mangrove (Bruguiera) trees growing in a tidal inlet and depression near Airik village, Ailinglaplap Atoll, southern Marshall Islands.

PLATE 84. Atolls that were fortified or used for air bases by the Japanese during World War II suffered heavily in bombing attacks. This view of a part of large Wotje Atoll in March 1952 shows that vegetation has obscured many of the craters on the land. However, numerous new habitats have been created on land and reef for atoll biota. Small, open, fresh-water pools and miniature swamps, some with brackish water and mangrove trees, are now found on the land. On the reef flat new tide pools and deeper holes provide different habitats for corals and other marine fauna.

PLATE 85. Cushion moss (*Leucophanes smaragdinum*) growing on a coconut stump on wet Ebon Atoll, 1956.

PLATE 86. The land crab (Geograpsus sp.), a scavenger on atoll land, is a busy burrower and aerates the soils of reef islets.

PLATE 87. The large coconut crab (*Birgus latro*) is very widespread on coral atolls and is hunted as a delicacy for food. These two specimens were captured at night at Kapingamarangi Atoll, 1954.

PLATE 88. The important and omnipresent scavengers on reef islets (especially prevalent on shore areas near the beach) are the hermit crabs, here shown in small hordes devouring the remaining copra inside the halves of a coconut at Kapingamarangi Atoll.